# PHYSICAL METHODS
## IN
# CHEMICAL ANALYSIS

*Edited by*

WALTER G. BERL

*Applied Physics Laboratory, Johns Hopkins University, Silver Spring, Maryland*

## VOLUME III

1956

ACADEMIC PRESS INC., PUBLISHERS

NEW YORK

## CONTRIBUTORS TO VOLUME III

A. A. BENEDETTI-PICHLER, *Department of Chemistry, Queens College, Flushing, New York*

W. J. BLAEDEL, *Department of Chemistry, University of Wisconsin, Madison, Wisconsin*

GEORGE L. CLARK, *Department of Chemistry, University of Illinois, Urbana, Illinois*

W. DONALD COOKE, *Baker Laboratory, Cornell University, Ithaca, New York*

BENJAMIN P. DAILEY, *Department of Chemistry, Columbia University, New York, New York*

KLAUS DOSE, *Institute of Organic Chemistry, University Frankfurt am Main, West Germany*

KENNETH W. GARDINER, *Central Research and Engineering Division, Continental Can Company, Chicago, Illinois*

H. S. GUTOWSKY, *Noyes Chemical Laboratory, University of Illinois, Urbana, Illinois*

W. W. HAVENS, JR., *Physics Department, Columbia University, New York, New York*

ERWIN W. MÜLLER, *Department of Physics, The Pennsylvania State University, University Park, Pennsylvania*

D. L. PETITJEAN, *Aluminum Company of America, New Kensington, Pennsylvania*

COURTENAY S. G. PHILLIPS, *Inorganic Chemistry Laboratory, Oxford University, England*

WALTER J. PODBIELNIAK, *Podbielniak, Inc., Chicago, Illinois*

SEATON T. PRESTON, *Podbielniak, Inc., Chicago, Illinois*

T. I. TAYLOR, *Chemistry Department, Columbia University, New York, New York*

THEODOR WIELAND, *Institute of Organic Chemistry, University Frankfurt am Main, West Germany*

# PREFACE

Volume III of the "Physical Methods in Chemical Analysis" extends the ground covered in the previous volumes of this series. The adaptation and extension of newly discovered physical techniques to analytical ends continues at a rapid pace and thus strengthens the position and power of the analytical chemist. How rapid the advances are is shown by the fact that when the first two volumes were in preparation the principles of nuclear magnetic resonance had only just been disclosed to the scientific world. In less than ten years the method has become for the analyst a valuable new tool with unique and impressive capabilities. Gas chromatography and several other methods treated in this volume have had a similar history.

The scope of the analyst's functions is changing rapidly and fundamentally. Apart from identifications and quantitative estimations the problems of shape and structure on the molecular and on grosser levels have been added to his province. Much of this expansion is due to the wide adoption of physical methods of separation and measurement. Despite the frequent complexity of the techniques and the attendant expense in first cost and maintenance of the equipment they have become valuable and often indispensable companions to the well established classical methods. No analyst can practice his profession effectively without thorough acquaintance with this modern branch of analysis.

The editor has attempted to maintain the policy laid down previously which is to present a review of the status of physical measurements and their application as analytical tools. The discussion of principles is stressed. The reviews are intended to broaden the horizon of students and practicing chemists, acquainting them with the promising new research tools at their disposal and explaining the scientific basis upon which they are built. They also aim to indicate the areas of usefulness as well as the limitations to which they are subjected.

The chapters in Volume III range over many diverse fields of analytical interest. Gas chromatography represents an extraordinarily useful extension of chromatographic analysis and is rapidly gaining a firm foothold in the quantitative estimation of low-molecular-weight substances. Its capabilities are very wide and its use is so rapidly expanding that no review can hope to remain up to date for long. Electrochromatography is finding its main role in biochemical applications as a worthy companion to paper chromatography. The high precision and convenience of electrical measurements is finding various outlets in electrochemical and polarographic micro-procedures and titrations. Although the range of applicability of the field ion microscope is limited it represents nevertheless one of the most sensitive devices for the detection of adsorbed films and for the study of individual crystal planes. It should find increased application in the analytical laboratory in the future.

No matter how elegant and precise the analytical techniques may be, faulty sampling of inhomogeneous mixtures may lead to incorrect conclusions. The chapter on sampling reviews the principles on which meaningful sampling procedures should be based. The spectroscopic armament of the analyst has received new additions through either the development of older principles or the introduction of quite new physical measurements. Flame photometry and fluorescent X-ray analysis belong to the former group where component developments have led to greatly improved practical utility. Microwave, nuclear resonance, and neutron spectroscopy, on the other hand, are based on quite new principles of physical measurements, now applied to analytical work. Finally, neutron activation opens up regions of versatility and sensitivity of detection unmatched by any other technique.

Without the unselfish cooperation of the authors of the individual chapters this book would be an empty shell. The publisher, as before, has assisted in every possible way.

WALTER G. BERL

*August, 1956*

# CONTENTS

## Field Emission Microscopy

By ERWIN W. MÜLLER, *Department of Physics, The Pennsylvania State University, University Park, Pennsylvania*

## Theory and Principles of Sampling for Chemical Analysis

By A. A. BENEDETTI-PICHLER, *Department of Chemistry, Queens College, Flushing, New York*

## Flame Photometry

By KENNETH W. GARDINER, *Central Research and Engineering Division, Continental Can Company, Chicago, Illinois*

## Microwave Spectroscopy

By BENJAMIN P. DAILEY, *Department of Chemistry, Columbia University, New York, New York*

## Analytical Applications of Nuclear Magnetic Resonance

*By* H. S. GUTOWSKY, *Noyes Chemical Laboratory, University of Illinois, Urbana, Illinois*

## Fluorescent X-Ray Spectrometric Analysis

*By* GEORGE L. CLARK, *Department of Chemistry, University of Illinois, Urbana, Illinois*

## Analytical Distillation

*By* WALTER J. PODBIELNIAK AND SEATON T. PRESTON, *Podbielniak, Inc., Chicago, Illinois*

## Neutron Spectroscopy and Neutron Interactions in Chemical Analysis

*By* T. I. TAYLOR AND W. W. HAVENS, JR., *Chemistry and Physics Departments, Columbia University, New York, New York*

# Gas Chromatography

### By

### COURTENAY S. G. PHILLIPS

*Inorganic Chemistry Laboratory, Oxford University, England*

## 1. GENERAL THEORY

### 1.1. Introduction

The term *gas chromatography* will be used to distinguish those chromatographic techniques in which the traditional moving liquid phase is replaced by a moving gas. The separations achieved in gas chromatography depend therefore upon repeated equilibrations between a moving gas and a fixed (or column) phase.

1

The most important advantage obtained by replacing the moving liquid by a gas is the greater rapidity with which equilibria involving gases are set up. This means that gas chromatographic columns work highly efficiently and can be run at greater speed than the corresponding liquid columns. The limits of the gas chromatographic techniques are not very severe. The substances to be chromatographed must be sufficiently volatile to be detectable in the gas phase at the temperature of operation, and the column materials must be sufficiently involatile to act as a separate phase. Small concentrations of vapor are easily measured in the moving gas by physical methods of general application, and the chromatographic separations can be followed and recorded automatically.

Despite the long history of chromatography and its wide practical applications, it is only relatively recently that the possibilities of gas chromatographic methods have been investigated in any detail. The development of gas chromatography can be traced largely to the fundamental contributions made by Claesson (4) in 1946 with displacement columns and by James and Martin (17) in 1952 with partition columns. In some ways it is curious that gas chromatography should have followed from conventional chromatography, for the behavior of gases is so much simpler and better understood than is the behavior of liquids.

## 1.2. Single Vapors

The word *vapor* will be used throughout to describe the substances which are being chromatographed, although in some cases these substances would be gases at the temperature of the column. The word *gas* will be reserved for the mobile phase.

We begin by considering the behavior of one vapor as it is carried through a long column by the gas until it finally emerges in the gas stream. The distribution of the vapor in this effluent stream is, ideally, directly related to the isotherm for the equilibrium distribution between the vapor and the fixed phase of the column. The distribution is recorded as a peak in the chromatogram. Three basic patterns can be distinguished for this peak (Fig. 1). Symmetrical (Gaussian) peaks result if the isotherm is linear, as is usually the case with partition isotherms (fixed liquid on the column) at low concentrations of vapor in the fixed phase. They are also found for adsorption at very low surface coverages. The detailed theory of these symmetrical peaks has been worked out by Martin and Synge (28) using the concept of the theoretical plate. This is defined as a layer at right angles to the column, the layer being of such thickness that the mean concentration of the substance in the fixed phase in this layer is in equilibrium with its vapor in the gas phase leaving the layer. The smaller the height of this theoretical plate, that is, the more rapidly equilibrium is reached between the moving gas and the fixed phase, the more efficient is the column and the less the spread of the vapor peak. The column efficiency may be expressed in terms of the number of its theoretical plates $r$, which may be calculated from the peak shape. Two methods are given by

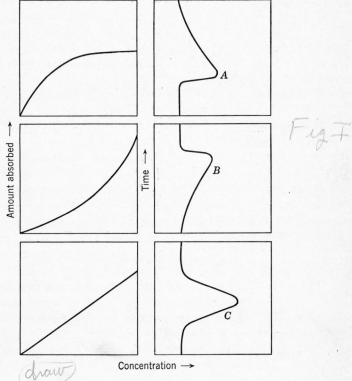

Fig. 1

draw

Concentration →

FIG. 1. Equilibrium isotherms and chromatogram peaks (22).

Martin and James (17). In the first the rate of removal of the vapor from the column is measured at the peak maximum, $S$. Then

$$r = 2\pi \left(\frac{St}{M}\right)^2$$

where $M$ is the total quantity of substance put onto the column and $t$ is the time taken before the peak maximum emerges from the column. In the second method the time $(\tau)$ taken for the center of the peak to leave the column (i.e., between ordinates one standard deviation on either side of the peak, or 68.3% of total quantity of material in the peak) is measured. Then

$$r = 4 \left(\frac{t}{\tau}\right)^2$$

Some values taken from James and Martin (17) for a 4-ft.-long silicone/stearic acid column are given in Table I.

The peak maximum occurs when a certain volume of gas, the retention volume $V_R$, has emerged from the column. If the gas were an incompressible fluid, the retention volume $V_R{}^0$ would be given by the relation

$$V_R{}^0 = l(a + \alpha b)$$

where $l$ is the length of the column, $b$ is the cross-sectional area of the column occupied by the fixed (liquid) phase, $a$ is the cross-sectional area

TABLE I

*Determination of Column Efficiency*
($r$ = number of theoretical peaks)

| Flow rate of gas, ml./min. | r | |
|---|---|---|
| | Method I | Method II |
| 35 | 550 | 400 |
| 18.2 | 718 | 600 |
| 10.3 | 765 | 730 |

of the column occupied by the moving gas, and $\alpha$ is the distribution (or partition) coefficient of the vapor between the fixed and the gas phase.

$$\alpha = \frac{\text{(weight of substance per unit volume of fixed phase at equilibrium)}}{\text{(weight of substance (vapor) per unit volume of gas at equilibrium)}}$$

In practice, as there is always a pressure drop across the column, the gas is compressed at the beginning and there is a gradient of gas velocity along the column. If $p_1$ is the pressure of gas at the column inlet and $p_0$ the pressure at the outlet, then (17)

$$V_R = \frac{2}{3} V_R{}^0 \frac{[(p_1/p_0)^3 - 1]}{[(p_1/p_0)^2 - 1]}$$

As $\alpha$ is a characteristic of the vapor (for a particular fixed phase and at a particular temperature), $V_R{}^0$ can be used to identify a substance being chromatographed. A typical relationship between $V_R{}^0$ and the number of carbon atoms in an homologous series is illustrated in Fig. 2.

Peaks with sharp fronts and diffuse tails result if the isotherm curves toward the vapor-pressure axis, as in Langmuir-type adsorption. In the case of such isotherms (2) high concentrations of vapor will move faster through the column than will low concentrations. The position of the

sharp front, unlike the position of the peak maximum for a linear isotherm, depends not only on the character of the vapor, but also on the
amount. Peaks with diffuse fronts and sharp tails result if the isotherm
curves away from the vapor-pressure axis, as is frequently the case for
partition equilibria with high concentrations of vapor in the fixed liquid

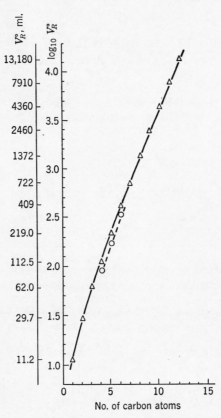

Fig. 2. Relationship between $V_R^0$ and the number of carbon atoms in the
lower fatty acids.

$\Delta$ = $n$-acids      o = $iso$-acids

Data for a 4-ft. silicone–stearic acid column at 137° C. (17).

phase. It is also observed with the adsorption of water vapor on charcoal
at 20° C. (30).

### 1.3. Elution Analysis of Mixtures

If a small quantity of a mixture of volatile substances is brought to the
beginning of the column, each substance will, to the first approximation,

behave independently of the others and produce its characteristic vapor peak in the effluent gas stream. The area (on the record) under each peak will measure the amount of the corresponding substance in the original mixture. In the case of linear isotherms (symmetrical peaks) each component of the mixture can be characterized by its retention volume, $V_R{}^0$.

With partition columns the components of the mixture, except insofar as they make slight modifications in the solvent properties of the fixed phase, interfere relatively little with one another. With adsorption columns, however, the various substances compete for lattice sites on the surface of the adsorbent. An important consequence of this [as has been shown most clearly by Hagdahl, Williams, and Tiselius for the case of Langmuir adsorption (11)] is that the more strongly adsorbed vapor will tend to push a more weakly adsorbed vapor ahead of it along the column. This means that the adsorption column has a "self-sharpening" property not possessed by partition columns. Substances not only separate by virtue of their differing individual rates of movement on an otherwise empty column, but in addition traces of a more weakly adsorbed component are rapidly accelerated out of a zone of a more strongly adsorbed component.

### 1.4. Displacement Analysis

This displacing action of one substance upon another during chromatography on an adsorbent column is the basis of the method of displacement analysis. In this method the mixture is first brought to the column

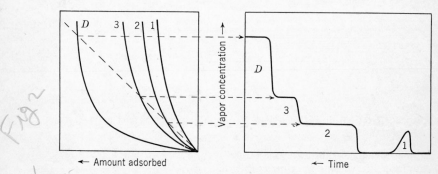

Fig. 3. Adsorption isotherms and displacement analysis.

as in elution analysis, but then a constant concentration of a substance (the displacer) more strongly adsorbed than any of the components of the mixture is fed into the moving gas stream at the beginning of the column. This displacer pushes the mixture ahead of it along the column, so that each component of the mixture acts as a displacer for the next most strongly adsorbed component. The final chromatogram recorded from the effluent gas consists of a series of steps, each step corresponding to one component of the mixture leaving the column at a fixed concentration and finally to the displacer. Each concentration is a characteristic (for a fixed adsorbent, temperature, displacer, and displacer concentration) of the component, as is also its place in the displacement sequence. Qualitative analysis can thus be reduced to a measurement of step heights. The length of the step measures the quantity of the component present in the original mixture. The step heights may be deduced from the corresponding isotherms, as is shown in Fig. 3. In practice, these heights are obtained by calibration, and displacement analysis is used (22) to determine the isotherms rather than the reverse.

## 2. APPARATUS

### 2.1. Introduction

There are thus three basic gas chromatographic methods: (a) gas-liquid partition chromatography (elution analysis only), (b) elution gas-adsorption chromatography, (c) displacement gas-adsorption chroma-

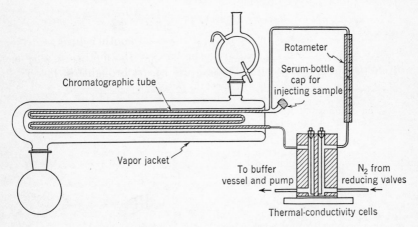

FIG. 4. A complete apparatus for elution (gas-liquid partition) analysis (32).

tography. Of these methods (a) is the simplest in principle and in general the most effective in practice. We shall therefore discuss the apparatus for gas-liquid partition chromatography in some detail and then only mention such modifications of this apparatus as are necessary for its application to the two gas-adsorption methods.

Figure 4 illustrates a typical partition apparatus, described by Ray (32). Nitrogen gas is taken from a cylinder via reducing valves and flows through the column at a rate controlled by the pressure drop across the column and measured by means of the rotameter. The gas flows through the reference side of the thermal-conductivity vapor detector before passing onto the column and through the sensing side of the detector as soon as it leaves the column. The fixed liquid phase (dinonyl-phthalate) supported on an inert macroporous material (kieselguhr) is packed into a glass tube 6 ft. long and 4 mm. in internal diameter. The tube is formed into a $W$ shape to restrict the length of the air jacket which maintains it at the temperature of operation. The air-jacket temperature is controlled by a surrounding vapor jacket. The sample is injected as a liquid into the gas stream through the serum-bottle cap by means of a hypodermic syringe. The component vapors are detected and their concentrations in nitrogen recorded by the sensing side of the detector.

## 2.2. Chromatographic Column

The following procedure has been found satisfactory for the packing of a partition column.

1. The inert solid support (e.g., Celite 545, Johns Manville Company, Ltd.) for the absorbing liquid is first graded by being suspended in water in a tall 3-liter beaker and allowed to settle for 3 min. The supernatant liquid is then decanted off.

2. The precipitate is washed with acid and distilled water and is dried at 100° C.

3. This material is treated with the appropriate amount of the immobile column liquid (e.g., 0.3 to 0.4 g. of liquid to 1 g. of Celite). The two are then thoroughly agitated together for 8 hr. in a cannister attached to a small electric motor. Alternatively the immobile liquid is dissolved in ether and the solution is added to the Celite to form a slurry, which is stirred continuously as the ether is evaporated off in a stream of air (26).

4. The column material is poured carefully into the column while the column is held against the rotating flattened spindle of an electric motor. The vibration of the motor causes the powder to pack in a uniform compact mass.

Very small particles are to be avoided as they cause excessive resistance in the column to passage of gas.

If the column liquid is, for all practical purposes, involatile at the temperature of operation of the column, then it is possible to use the same column repeatedly and reproducibly over long periods of time. However sharper resolution (larger number of theoretical plates) is frequently obtained with low-molecular-weight column fluids because of their greater solvent power and their lower viscosity. The following are examples of column liquids which have already found considerable application: liquid paraffin and silicone fluids (both nonpolar and especially suitable for the separation of saturated hydrocarbons), dinonyl-phthalate and tritolyl-phosphate (polar and therefore producing a selective retardation of polar molecules), benzyl-diphenyl (for selective retardation of aromatics) polyethylene-oxide (Lubrol MO) (H bonding with "active" hydrogen, e.g., primary and secondary amines), glycerol (for selective retardation of alcohols and especially water vapor).

James and Martin (17) employed solutions of stearic acid or orthophosphoric acid (10% by weight) in silicone DC 550 fluid for the separation of fatty acids. The dissolved acid produces a marked increase in the linearity of the absorption isotherm.

### 2.3. Vapor Detectors

Vapor detectors for gas chromatography should be of high sensitivity to all vapors, should respond rapidly to changes in vapor concentration (hence be of small internal volume), and should not react with or adsorb any of the vapors. For quantitative work it is important that the detector signal should be directly proportional to vapor concentration and, if possible, independent of the nature of the vapor.

2.3.1. *Thermal-Conductivity Cell.* So far this has proved to be the most widely used detector in gas chromatography. It can be applied generally, is rapid in response and simple to construct, and with a little care can be made extremely sensitive. It gives a linear response to vapor concentration and, if helium (or hydrogen) be used as the carrier gas, a response which is very nearly proportional to molar concentration for a wide range of vapors of the same general type (13). A full account of the thermal-conductivity cell has been given by Weaver (35).

In the detector a heated wire (e.g., platinum) passes down the center of a tube, through which gas flows from the column. The wire loses heat via the gas to the walls of the tube, and the temperature and hence resistance of the wire are therefore dependent upon gas composition. The cell forms one arm of a Wheatstone bridge, the out of balance of which is fed to a recorder.

Metal tubes produce a slightly faster response than glass tubes do, because of their higher heat conductivity. Rapid temperature fluctuations of the tube walls give rise to unsteadiness in the base line, an effect which is overcome most simply by enclosing the tube in a metal block of high heat capacity. Slow temperature changes produce a drift of base line, which may be overcome by immersing the block in a very good thermostat or by using a second reference cell mounted with the sensing cell in the same block and placed in opposition in the bridge circuit. This latter method also provides a high measure of insensitivity to flow-rate variation and is adopted in most commercial instruments.

A considerable increase of sensitivity (and a reduction in detector volume) can be effected by use of thermistors in place of the heated wire.

Figure 5 illustrates the cell used in the Perkin-Elmer Vapor Fractometer*
(13). Constructional details for a simple twin-thermistor cell have been
given by Ambrose and Collerson (1). Sensitivity may also be increased by
use of a carrier gas of higher thermal conductivity (e.g., by use of either
hydrogen or helium instead of nitrogen) or by an increase in the wire
temperature.

2.3.2. *Other Differential Detectors.* Various other differential vapor
detectors (i.e., detectors which measure vapor concentration in the
effluent gas) have also been used in gas chromatography.

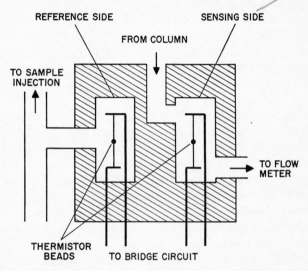

Fig. 5. Thermal conductivity cell employing thermistors. (Courtesy of Perkin-
Elmer Corp.)

The *gas-density balance* of James and Martin (19, 20) measures the
difference between the density of the gaseous effluent from the chromatogram and that from a comparison column through which only nitrogen is
passed. The apparatus consists essentially of a series of tubes bored in a
copper block (held at the same temperature as the column) and connected
in a manner analogous to a Wheatstone bridge, so that a difference of
flow rate of the two gas streams led into the block causes no pressure
difference between two points in the system. Two sets of channels are
connected by a cross channel in such a way that any density difference
between the two gas streams causes a pressure difference and hence a flow
of gas through the cross channel. This channel contains a flow detector,
consisting of a small filament (electrically heated) arranged below and

* A commercial gas chromatographic instrument, manufactured by the Perkin-
Elmer Corporation, Norwalk, Connecticut.

equidistant from two connected thermocouples; any cross flow of gas causes the stream of hot convected gas from the filament to be diverted to one or the other of the thermocouples, so that one is heated and the other cooled. The thermoelectromotive force produced is fed to a commercial D.C. amplifier and recording galvanometer. The galvanometer deflection is linearly related to the density difference of the two gas streams. The instrument is very sensitive, e.g., $\frac{1}{16}$ μg. of amyl alcohol is detectable/ml. of nitrogen.

The use of an *infrared gas analyzer* has been recommended by Martin and Smart (27). Organic vapors are converted to carbon dioxide by passage over copper oxide heated to dull redness, the gases after oxidation being led into an infrared gas analyzer sensitive to carbon dioxide.

The hydrogen-flame detector has been described recently by Scott (34). Hydrogen, which is used as the carrier gas, is burned at the exit of the column at a small vertical jet. A thermocouple (e.g., iron and constantan or platinum and 14% rhodium-platinum for high-temperature columns) is placed slightly above the hydrogen flame. When an organic vapor is present in the gas, the flame lengthens and engulfs the thermocouple. The output from the thermocouple is led through a suitable potentiometric network to a recorder. The detector has a linear response and a small volume and is very easily constructed. It may prove of particular value in connection with columns operated at high temperatures.

The *surface-potential* detector (9, 10, 31) measures changes in the surface-potential difference between two dissimilar metal plates exposed to the gas and vapor leaving the chromatographic column. As the detector is not very rapid in response, it has so far been used largely in conjunction with displacement analysis. Its high sensitivity however has made it possible for one to follow the gas chromatographic separation of substances with vapor pressures as low as $10^{-2}$ mm. at the operation temperature.

Flow impedance and various heat effects have also been investigated (9).

*2.3.3. Integral Detectors.* Quantitative analysis is effected most simply from the recorded chromatogram if the detector automatically integrates the vapor concentrations leaving the column. One detector which achieves this result is the *automatic recording burette*, which was devised by James and Martin (16, 17, 18) and used by them to obtain the first gas-liquid chromatograms. The principle of the device is illustrated in Fig. 6.

The gas stream from the column bubbles up through the titration cell, and the acidic (or basic) vapors alter the pH of the solution, and hence the color of an indicator, in the titration cell. The color change operates the automatic burette and recorder by means of a photocell relay, so that the original pH is at once restored by appropriate addition of standard

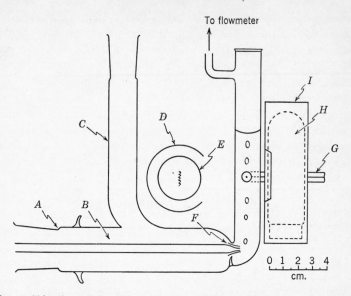

FIG. 6. Side view of titration-cell unit. $A$, vapor jacket; $B$, chromatographic tube; $C$, air-condenser socket; $D$, lamp house; $E$, lamp; $F$, rubber gasket on capillary; $G$, capillary lead from burette; $H$, photoelectric cell; $I$, photoelectric cell housing with adjustable window (17).

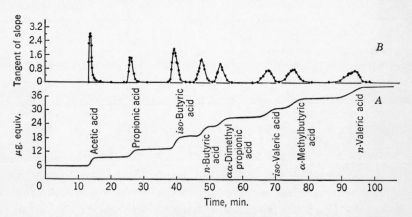

FIG. 7. The separation of acetic, propionic, $n$-butyric, and isobutyric acids and the isomers of valeric acid, showing the complete resolution of all bands and change in shape of the bands as the series ascends. Curve $A$, experimental results; curve $B$, differential of experimental curve.

Column length, 11 ft.; liquid phase, DC 550 silicone containing 10% w/w of stearic acid; temperature, 137° C.; rate of flow of nitrogen, 18.2 ml./min.; pressure of nitrogen, 740 mm. Hg (17).

alkali (or acid). Because of the adsorption of the highly polar vapors onto glass the distance between column and titration cell is reduced to a minimum. Typical records obtained with this burette are given in Figs. 7 and 10. Figure 7 also shows the corresponding derived elution chromatogram. The record consists of a series of steps, each rise resulting from fresh addition of alkali (or acid) to neutralize another vapor which is leaving the column. Full details of the automatic recording burette are given in (17).

Another integrating method has been devised by Janak, in connection with his extended work on elution gas-adsorption chromatography (23).

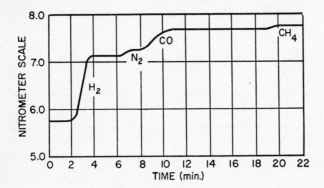

FIG. 8. Analysis by Janak's method (23).

Carbon dioxide, which is used as the carrier gas, is, on leaving the column, passed into a nitrometer containing alkali. All the carrier gas is thus absorbed, and the vapors leaving the column in the carrier-gas stream collect (as gases) above the alkali. A typical chromatogram obtained by Janak is illustrated in Fig. 8.

### 2.4. Gas-Adsorption Chromatography

For elution gas-adsorption chromatography no essential change in the design of apparatus is required, except that the partition-column material is replaced by a suitable adsorbent such as charcoal, silica gel, or alumina. In general better separations are obtained with small particle size, but there seems to be little gained in reducing this below about 50 mesh (29). The adsorbent should be sieved and dried before use.

In displacement gas-adsorption chromatography a device is necessary to produce a constant concentration of displacer vapor in the gas passing onto the column. A simple saturator, in which the gas is passed through the displacer liquid at a controlled temperature, proves quite effective (21). Displacement columns are frequently designed so as to take advantage of the self-sharpening character of gas-adsorption chromatography. Thus a column may be tapered or built in sections, so as to produce good separations with a small over-all column length and hence small resistance to gas flow. The wide portions of the column effect a rough separation, which is then improved by the later narrower sections (30). Activated charcoal* has proved most generally useful as an adsorbent. It may be regenerated after use (i.e., freed from displacer) by being heated to a high temperature in a current of nitrogen. However the charcoal flows very easily, and it is often simpler to repack the column with fresh adsorbent.

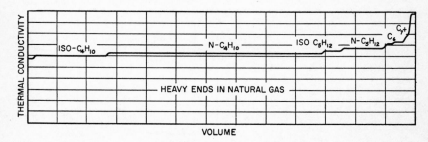

FIG. 9. Analysis by the Fracton. (Courtesy of Burrell Corp.)

Two commercial instruments, the Turner-Burrell adsorption fractionator and the Fracton,† operate on principles very similar to displacement chromatography. In the Adsorption Fractionator the adsorbed vapors are removed from the column by means of an electric heater which moves up the outside of the column while hot mercury vapor moves up the inside of the column to act as stripping agent. The Fracton employs a displacer vapor which is fed onto the column at a controlled rate. An analysis obtained with the Fracton is illustrated in Fig. 9.

## 3. ANALYTICAL APPLICATIONS

### 3.1. Gas-Liquid Partition Chromatography

Examples of chromatograms obtained with gas-liquid partition chromatography are illustrated in Figs. 10 to 15. Figure 10 shows two analyses of amines carried out by use of the automatic recording burette. The chromatograms of Fig. 11 were recorded by Ray using the apparatus which has been described and illustrated (Fig. 4) above. Figures 12 and 13 show chromatograms from a modern commercial instrument (the

* For example, No. 208 C, B.S.S. 30-40, supplied by Sutcliffe and Speakman, Leigh Lancashire, England.

† Burrell Corporation, 2223 Fifth Avenue, Pittsburgh 19, Pennsylvania.

Perkin-Elmer Vapor Fractometer). The chromatogram of Fig. 14 indicates the possibilities of resolution with even a very complex mixture; it was obtained by James and Martin with their gas-density balance. Figure 15 illustrates the use of the method in continuous plant analysis.

### 3.2. Qualitative Analysis

The identification of a vapor peak is performed by measurement of its retention volume or, more conveniently, its retention time at constant gas flow rate. Owing to slight fluctuations of flow rate and column tem-

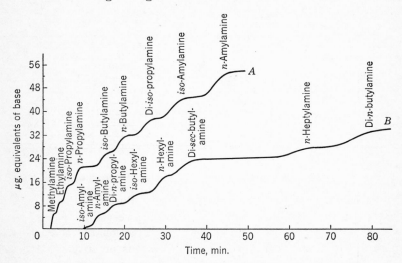

Fig. 10. Separation of aliphatic amines by elution (gas-liquid partition) analysis. Column length, 4 ft.; liquid phase, liquid paraffin; temperature, 100° C.; rate of flow of nitrogen, 5.7 ml./min. (curve A), and 18.7 ml./min. (curve B); pressure of nitrogen, 75 mm. Hg (curve A), and 225 mm. Hg. (curve B) (15).

perature from one analysis to another, greater accuracy [better than 1% (26)] can be secured by use of an internal standard (32) or marker substance in the vapor mixture. Retention times are then expressed relative to the retention time of the internal standard.

Hitherto it has been necessary to calibrate a column with the individual vapors. However a number of simple relationships apply connecting retention volumes with other properties of the vapors, such as vapor pressures, boiling points, or carbon atoms in an homologous series (Fig. 2), and it is now becoming possible to achieve absolute identification. Moreover such identification can be checked readily by rechromatographing on another column containing a different fixed liquid phase (14). Variation of column liquid serves primarily in distinguishing chemi-

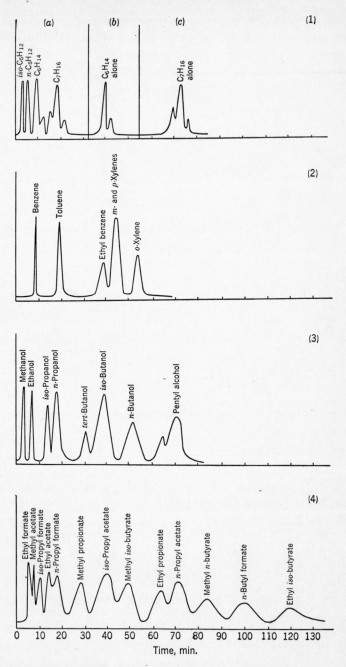

Fig. 11. For descriptive legend see opposite page.

cal type, as is shown by the results plotted in Fig. 16. A good example is also provided by the early work of James and Martin (16), in which they were able to distinguish primary, secondary, and tertiary amines by comparing their behavior on columns of liquid paraffin and of Lubrol

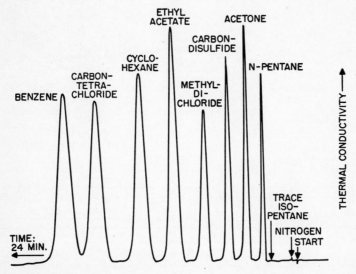

FIG. 12. Analysis of 8-component mixture by use of a Vapor Fractometer (13). (Courtesy of Perkin-Elmer Corp.)

MO. Lubrol MO contains a polyethylene oxide chain, the oxygen atoms of which can form hydrogen bonds with the H-N groups of the primary and secondary amines.

Now that many different laboratories are using gas-liquid partition columns, it would seem highly desirable that the results should not be

FIG. 11. Separation of mixtures by elution (partition) analysis. Column length, 6 ft.; liquid phase, dinonyl phthalate.

(1) Total sample (a) 10 μl.
       (b) 2 μl.
       (c) 2 μl.
    Column temperature, 65° C.; rate of flow of nitrogen, 20 ml./min.; inlet pressure, 740 mm.; outlet pressure, 400 mm.
(2) Total sample, 10 μl.
    Column temperature, 80° C.; rate of flow of nitrogen, 20 ml./min.; inlet pressure, 500 mm.; outlet pressure, 180 mm.
(3) Total sample, 20 μl.
    Conditions as in (2).
(4) Total sample, 50 μl.
    Column temperature, 57° C.; rate of flow of nitrogen, 30 ml./min.; inlet pressure, 740 mm.; outlet pressure, 175 mm. (32).

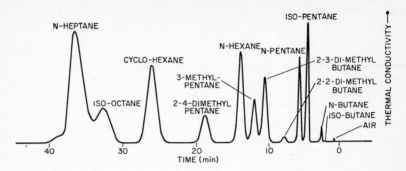

FIG. 13. Analysis of hydrocarbon mixture (total sample 20 liquid microliters) by use of Vapor Fractometer (13).

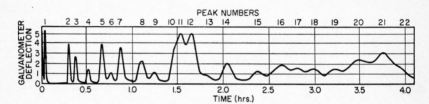

FIG. 14. Separation of aliphatic hydrocarbons by use of an 11-ft. column at 78.6° C. with paraffin wax as the fixed phase (nitrogen pressure 68 cm. Hg, nitrogen flow rate 16.3 ml./min.); peaks in order of appearance: (1) air (oxygen in 0.5 ml.); (2) isopentane; (3) n-pentane; (4) 2,2-dimethylbutane; (5) cyclo-pentane, 2-methylpentane, 2,3-dimethylbutane; (6) 3-methylpentane; (7) n-hexane; (8) 2,2-dimethylpentane, 2,4-dimethylpentane, methylcyclopentane; (9) 2,2,3-trimethylbutane; (10) 3,3-dimethylpentane, 2-methylhexane; (11) cyclohexane; (12) 2,3-dimethylpentane, 3-methylhexane; (13) 3-ethylhexane; (14) n-heptane; (15) 2,2-dimethylhexane; (16) 2,5-dimethylhexane, 2,4-di-methylhexane, methylcyclohexane; (17) ethylcyclopentane; (18) 3,3-dimethyl-hexane; (19) 2,3,4-trimethylpentane; (20) 2,3-dimethylhexane, 2-methyl-heptane, 4-methylheptane; (21) 2-methyl-3-ethylpentane, 3,4-dimethylhexane; (22) 3-methyl-3-ethylpentane, 3-ethylhexane (19).

expressed merely in the form of recorded chromatograms, but that values of fully corrected retention volumes per gram of column liquid [$V_g$ values (26)] should also be determined. These values should be quoted with the exact composition of the fixed phase and if possible plotted as a function of the column temperature. Alternatively results may be expressed in terms of $\alpha$, the partition coefficient.

### 3.3. Quantitative Analysis

Quantitative analysis is performed most simply by measurements of the differential step heights in the chromatograms produced by an

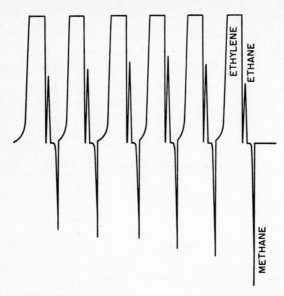

Fig. 15. Ethane ethylene separation (3).

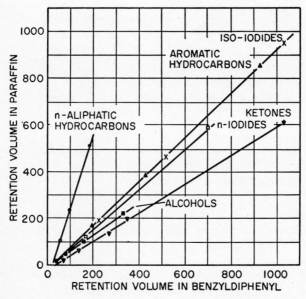

Fig. 16. Graphical representation of relative interaction forces in two types of fixed phase, liquid paraffin and benzyldiphenyl (19).

integrating detector, such as the automatic recording burette. When a differential detector, such as the thermal-conductivity cell, is employed, the quantity of substance may be determined by measuring chromatogram peak areas (e.g., 25). This can be done with a planimeter or by use of the product of peak height and half-band width (13). For many purposes peak heights alone provide a satisfactory measure of vapor quantity (32). Because of the small sample size (order of liquid microliters), it is often difficult to introduce an exactly determined quantity. It is therefore customary to use an internal standard or an internal normalization

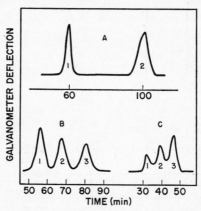

FIG. 17. Separation efficiency.

A. Separation of cis (1) and trans (2) dichloroethylene at 35° C. Fixed phase: silicone 702; separation factor: 1.70; 1500 theoretical plates.

B. Separation of p-xylene (1), o-xylene (2), and isopropyl benzene (3) at 111.4° C. Fixed phase: silicone 702; separation factors: 1.20 (1 and 2) and 1.20 (2 and 3); 1500 theoretical plates.

C. Separation of aniline (1), N-methyl aniline (2), and di-N-methyl aniline (3) at 157° C. Fixed phase: tritolyl phosphate; separation factors: 1.23 (1 and 2) and 1.18 (2 and 3); 650 theoretical plates (26).

technique (in which total vapor determined is equated to 100%). Table II illustrates the accuracy which can be secured. The results were obtained on the Perkin-Elmer Vapor Fractometer, and one of the corresponding chromatograms is reproduced in Fig. 12.

### 3.4. Separation Efficiency

The separation efficiency of a column may be expressed in terms of a *separation factor* and the *number of theoretical plates*. The separation factor is the ratio of two retention volumes; the number of theoretical plates is the measure of the spread or broadening of a vapor peak. Figure 17 illustrates two chromatograms (*A* and *B*) with different separation factors (number of theoretical plates constant) and two chromatograms

## TABLE II

### Quantitative Analyses with Gas-Liquid Partition Chromatography (13)
#### (Internal Normalization)

| Recording No. | 1 | 2 | 3 | 4 | 5 | 6 | 7 | 8 | 9 | 10 | 11 | 12 | Average | Amount present |
|---|---|---|---|---|---|---|---|---|---|---|---|---|---|---|
| Flow-rate (ml. He/min.) | 200 | 200 | 380 | | 100 | | 200 | | 200 | | 200 | | | |
| Temperature (°C.) | 49 | 49 | 49 | | 50 | | 75 | | 100 | | 50 | | | |
| | | | | | Concentrations found (Molar %) | | | | | | | | | |
| Pentane | 4.50 | 4.15 | 4.93 | 4.71 | 5.11 | 4.72 | 4.77 | 4.77 | 4.30 | 4.25 | 4.51 | 4.56 | 4.44 | 4.50 |
| Acetone | 7.82 | 7.65 | 8.25 | 7.87 | 7.87 | 8.27 | 7.71 | 7.69 | 8.23 | 8.26 | 8.13 | 8.11 | 7.99 | 8.00 |
| Carbon disulphide | 8.76 | 8.93 | 9.05 | 8.58 | 8.86 | 8.85 | 8.20 | 8.20 | 8.72 | 8.81 | 8.15 | 8.17 | 8.60 | 8.50 |
| Methylene dichloride | 8.94 | 8.44 | 8.38 | 8.45 | 8.18 | 8.40 | 8.40 | 8.40 | 8.72 | 8.75 | 8.10 | 8.11 | 8.44 | 8.50 |
| Ethyl acetate | 16.28 | 16.80 | 16.00 | 16.60 | 16.05 | 15.90 | 16.41 | 16.32 | 17.19 | 17.02 | 16.70 | 16.57 | 16.49 | 16.50 |
| Cyclohexane | 16.50 | 16.49 | 16.50 | 16.35 | 16.42 | 16.55 | 16.73 | 16.56 | 15.69 | 15.69 | 16.59 | 16.62 | 16.39 | 16.50 |
| Carbon tetrachloride | 16.92 | 17.30 | 16.60 | 17.10 | 17.20 | 16.80 | 17.30 | 17.05 | 16.70 | 16.74 | 16.80 | 17.29 | 16.98 | 17.00 |
| Benzene | 20.20 | 20.19 | 20.40 | 20.30 | 20.30 | 20.70 | 20.41 | 20.92 | 20.30 | 20.40 | 20.90 | 20.50 | 20.46 | 20.50 |

(*B* and *C*) with different numbers of theoretical plates (very similar separation factors).

The separation factor depends upon the nature of the vapor and of the column fixed phase and upon the column temperature. Thus for hydrocarbon vapors and a nonpolar fixed liquid phase, addition of one —CH₂— group means a separation factor about 3.5 at room temperature, falling steadily to about 1.5 at 200° C. With a nonpolar fixed phase, non-polar vapors pass through the column in an order approximately that of their boiling points. In terms of their boiling points polar vapors pass through more rapidly, for in solution in the column liquid they lack the polar-polar attractions present in their own liquid phases. Increase of polarity of the column fluid will selectively retard the more polar vapors. Examples will be found especially in the paper by Keulemans, Kwantes, and Zaal (24). The use of hydrogen bonding between vapor and column fluid has been exploited by a number of workers (e.g., 3, 12, 16). The formation of complexes with metal salts in solution in the column liquid has been suggested by the work of Bradford, Harvey, and Chalkley (3), who have used silver nitrate dissolved in glycol for the selective retardation of ethylenic and acetylenic hydrocarbons.

The number of theoretical plates of a column depends upon details of column design and operation, as well as upon the vapor, fixed liquid, and temperature. As it is a measure of the effective number of equilibrations which take place between the gas and liquid phases along the length of the column, it increases with intimacy of column packing and with the length of the column. It will be high if the liquid is spread as only a thin film of low viscosity (more precisely high vapor diffusivity). At high gas flow rates, slow diffusion in the liquid film is the limiting factor, but at low gas flow rates, diffusion in the gas along the length of the column becomes an important factor, and so an optimum flow rate obtains. Greater solubility of vapor in the column liquid leads to an increase in the number of theoretical plates. The number falls with increase of sample size. The influence of temperature is complicated by the operation of many competing factors. At constant retention time and under conditions where liquid diffusion is the controlling factor, the number of plates has been found (17) to increase with rise of temperature, because of more rapid diffusion in the column liquid. At constant flow rate the vapors pass through the column more rapidly (are less soluble) at higher temperatures, and a decrease of plate number has been found (26).

### 3.5. Range and Operating Conditions

A wide range of vapors has already been investigated by the gas-liquid partition method. It would appear that all substances capable of being distilled at a pressure of a few millimeters at the temperature of the column can be satisfactorily chromatographed with existing techniques. The range can be extended readily by use of more sensitive vapor detectors or by raising the temperature of operation of the column. High-temperature columns have been investigated in particular by Cropper and Heywood (5, 6) and by Dijkstra, Keppler, and Schols (7). The former workers achieved analytical separations of the methyl esters of $C_{12}$ to $C_{22}$ fatty acids, using columns containing high-vacuum grease and operated at temperatures between 230° and 300° C.

The lower limit to vapor quantity is set by the sensitivity limits of the vapor detector. A milligram has been the order of sample size for analytical columns. The convenient sample size will, of course, rise with the square of the column diameter. Thus Evans and Tatlow (8) have used 3-cm.-internal-diameter columns for separations of fluorocarbons on the 1 to 10 g. scale.

Analyses are effected rapidly, normally between 10 min. and 2 hr. running time. Sample recovery appears to be complete, and columns containing relatively involatile fixed liquids may be used repeatedly.

### 3.6. Adsorbent Columns: Elution Analysis

The use of adsorbent columns for elution analysis is hampered by the curvature of adsorption isotherms and the skew nature of the resulting chromatogram peaks. The retention volume is no longer such a simple characteristic measure as it is with partition columns, and quantitative analysis is made difficult because of the diffuse nature of the rear portion of the peak. A typical elution chromatogram is illustrated in Fig. 18. The most extensive work in this field has been that of Janak (23), who used a nitrometer technique. One of his chromatograms is reproduced in Fig. 8. Some adsorbent-vapor systems cannot be employed because of irreversible adsorption (21).

### 3.7. Adsorbent Columns: Displacement Analysis

A displacement analysis is illustrated by the chromatogram in Fig. 19. Table III gives some typical analytical results. The identification of a vapor is performed by measurement of its characteristic step height. The position of the vapor in the displacement sequence can be used as a further check. Calibration has hitherto been necessary, but a number of simpler displacement relationships have also been found. Thus substances are displaced from charcoal almost strictly in order of their boiling points (21). The amount of vapor contained in a given step is directly proportional to the step length. Quantitative analysis is therefore very simple, and as the measurement is normally one of time (and independent of the

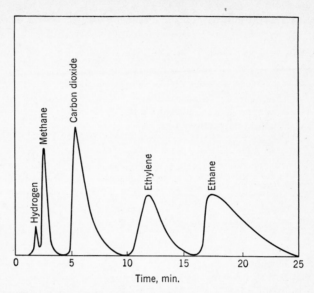

FIG. 18. Separation of hydrogen, methane, carbon dioxide, ethylene, and ethane by elution from a charcoal (adsorbent) column at 40° C. (33).

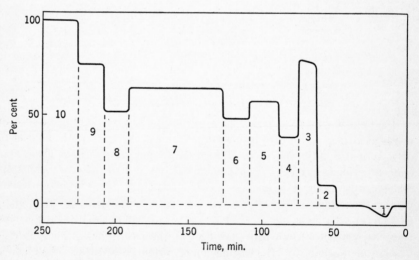

FIG. 19. Displacement analysis on charcoal (A, Table III). Components of mixture: (1) water, (2) diethyl ether, (3) chloroform, (4) ethyl acetate, (5) thiophen, (6) dioxan, (7) pyridine, (8) butyl acetate, (9) chlorobenzene, (10) bromobenzene (displacer) (21).

sensitivity or reproducibility of the vapor detector) it can be made very precisely.

### TABLE III
*Quantitative Analyses with Displacement Gas-Adsorption Chromatography* (21)

Adsorbent: activated charcoal
Flow rate: 46.5 ml. nitrogen/min.
Column temperature: 100° C.
Displacer vapor: Bromobenzene (saturation at 77° C.)

| Analysis | Component | Step height % of displacer | Weight in g. Found | Correct |
|---|---|---|---|---|
| A | Water | no step | 0.0430 | 0.0400 |
| [Fig. 19] | Diethyl ether | 12.0 | 0.0775 | 0.0785 |
| | Chloroform | 77.0 | 0.1920 | 0.1950 |
| | Ethyl acetate | 36.5 | 0.1155 | 0.1170 |
| | Thiophen | 55.0 | 0.2025 | 0.2070 |
| | Dioxan | 45.0 | 0.1650 | 0.1660 |
| | Pyridine | 61.0 | 1.0855 | 1.0800 |
| | Butyl acetate | 50.0 | 0.1830 | 0.1765 |
| | Chlorobenzene | 76.0 | 0.1755 | 0.1770 |
| | | | | |
| B | Benzene | 44.5 | 0.0592 | 0.0588 |
| | Toluene | 55.0 | 3.47 | 3.47 |
| | | | | |
| C | Pentane | 16.0 | 0.0207 | 0.0205 |
| | Benzene | 44.5 | 3.72 | 3.72 |

### 3.8. Comparison of Elution and Displacement Methods

The elution method produces a chromatogram consisting of a series of isolated peaks, the displacement method a chromatogram consisting of a series of adjacent steps. The elution peaks represent low vapor concentrations, but the vapor concentrations in the displacement steps can be quite high. The elution method (especially gas-liquid partition) is ideally suited to the separation of very closely similar substances (e.g., hydrocarbon isomers). Displacement is a useful method for preparative and accurate quantitative work. The self-sharpening properties of displacement (adsorbent) columns make them particularly valuable for the isolation of trace components from a mixture, as is shown by results B and C in Table III. In elution analyses it is important that the whole of the sample be injected into the system instantaneously. In displacement analyses the sample may be introduced over a period of time. Elution columns do not normally require repacking or regeneration between one analysis and the next.

## 4. The Study of Distribution Equilibria

Although the gas-chromatographic methods have been developed largely as analytical tools, it has been pointed out (22) that the analytical results can be used to provide considerable physicochemical information about the nature of the phase-distribution equilibria, upon which the analytical separations depend. Thus distribution coefficients, adsorption isotherms, heats and entropies of solution and adsorption, and vapor pressures can be determined rapidly and with quite simple apparatus.

The distribution coefficients ($\alpha$) are related to the retention volumes and can be calculated directly from the partition chromatograms. An example is given by Bradford, Harvey, and Chalkley (3). From the temperature variation of the retention volumes, heats of solution are derived (26) and hence entropies of solution. Each displacement analysis provides one point on the adsorption isotherms of the displacer vapor and of each of the displaced vapors. The complete isotherms can thus be built up quickly (22). Again from isotherms obtained at two temperatures, heats and hence entropies of adsorption can be calculated.

Vapor pressures may be determined by passing nitrogen (or other inert carrier gas) through the liquid and onto a displacement column for a known time. The step length obtained when this vapor is displaced is then compared with the step length for a known quantity of the liquid applied directly to a similar column. In this way, and in conjunction with the surface-potential detector, a number of low vapor pressures have been determined (10). Gas chromatography would provide a very convenient method for the study of partial vapor pressures in many component systems.

## 5. Conclusion

### 5.1. Comparison with Other Analytical Techniques

Chromatography is primarily a separation technique, and gas chromatography is therefore most directly compared with distillation. Gas-chromatographic analyses are carried out more rapidly and with smaller samples. Highly efficient (up to several thousand theoretical plates) gas-chromatographic columns are readily constructed. Furthermore in distillation the fractionating column has to be filled with some of the material to be separated, and an overlap volume several times the hold-up volume of the column is inevitable. This is very important from the analytical point of view, particularly when some components are present in only trace amounts. Variation of the column fixed phase introduces into gas chromatography a high degree of flexibility.

Analysis by chemical, spectroscopic, or mass-spectrometer techniques tends to become increasingly difficult the greater the number and the similarity of the components in the mixture. These techniques could be very much assisted by conjunction with gas chromatography (3).

Finally it should be emphasized that although the methods of gas chromatography are highly efficient and are rapid in operation, the *last* apparatus required is simple and inexpensive.

## 5.2. Future Developments

Gas chromatography is still in its infancy. The crucial paper by James and Martin (17) appeared only in 1952. Future developments will no doubt include the application of the methods to more involatile compounds by use of high-temperature columns and/or more sensitive detectors. The method should find wide application in preparative as well as in analytical work.

Research is most urgently needed on the relation of separation factors to the chemical nature of the vapors and column fixed phases and on the detailed interpretation of the many factors which affect the theoretical plate efficiencies of columns.

### References

1. Ambrose, D., and Collerson, R. R., *J. Sci. Instr.* **32**, 323 (1955).
2. Berl, W. G., ed., "Physical Methods in Chemical Analysis," Vol. 2, p. 591. Academic Press, New York, 1951.
3. Bradford, B. W., Harvey, D., and Chalkley, D. E., *J. Inst. Petrol.* **41**, 80 (1955).
4. Claesson, S., *Arkiv Kemi* **A23**, No. 1 (1946).
5. Cropper, F. R., and Heywood, A., *Nature* **172**, 1101 (1953).
6. Cropper, F. R., and Heywood, A., *Nature* **174**, 1063 (1954).
7. Dijkstra, G., Keppler, J. G., and Schols, J. A., *Rec. trav. chim.* **74**, 805 (1955).
8. Evans, D. E. M., and Tatlow, J. C., *J. Chem. Soc.* p. 1184 (1955).
9. Griffiths, J. H., James, D. H., and Phillips, C. S. G., *Analyst* **77**, 897 (1952).
10. Griffiths, J. H., and Phillips, C. S. G., *J. Chem. Soc.* p. 3446 (1954).
11. Hagdahl, L., Williams, R. J. P., and Tiselius, A., *Arkiv Kemi* **B4**, No. 10 (1952).
12. Harvey, D., and Chalkley, D. E., *Fuel* **34**, 191 (1955).
13. Hausdorff, H. H., Presented at Symposium, Instrument Society of America, Los Angeles, September 1955. To be submitted to *Analytical Chemistry*.
14. James, A. T., *Research (London)* **8**, 8 (1955).
15. James, A. T., *Biochem. J.* **52**, 242 (1952).
16. James, A. T., and Martin, A. J. P., *Analyst* **77**, 915 (1952).
17. James, A. T., and Martin, A. J. P., *Biochem. J.* **50**, 679 (1952).
18. James, A. T., Martin, A. J. P., and Howard-Smith, G., *Biochem. J.* **52**, 238 (1952).
19. James, A. T., and Martin, A. J. P., *Brit. Med. Bull.* **10**, No. 3, 170 (1954).
20. James, A. T., and Martin, A. J. P., *Biochem. J.* to be published
21. James, D. H., and Phillips, C. S. G., *J. Chem. Soc.* p. 1600 (1953).
22. James, D. H., and Phillips, C. S. G., *J. Chem. Soc.* p. 1066 (1954).
23. Janak, J., Series of papers in *Chem. Listy* **47**, 464 (1953) and later volumes. Also in *Collection Czechoslov. Chem. Communis.* **18**, 798 (1953) and later volumes.

24. Keulemans, A. I. M., Kwantes, A., and Zaal, P., *Anal. Chim. Acta* **13,** 357 (1955).
25. Lichtenfels, D. H., Fleck, S. A., and Burow, F. H., *Anal. Chem.* **27,** 1510 (1955).
26. Littlewood, A. B., Phillips, C. S. G., and Price, D. T., *J. Chem. Soc.* p. 1480 (1955).
27. Martin, A. E., and Smart, J., *Nature* **175,** 422 (1955).
28. Martin, A. J. P., and Synge, R. L. M., *Biochem. J.* **35,** 1358 (1941).
29. Patton, H. W., Lewis, J. S., and Kaye, W. I., *Anal. Chem.* **27,** 171 (1955).
30. Phillips, C. S. G., *Discussions Faraday Soc.* **No. 7,** 241 (1949).
31. Phillips, G., *J. Sci. Instr.* **28,** 342 (1951).
32. Ray, N. H., *J. Appl. Chem.* **4,** 21 (1954).
33. Ray, N. H., *J. Appl. Chem.* **4,** 82 (1954).
34. Scott, R. P. W., *Nature* **176,** 793 (1955).
35. Weaver, E. R., *in* "Physical Methods in Chemical Analysis" (W. G. Berl, ed.),
    Vol. 2, p. 387. Academic Press, New York, 1951.

# Electrochromatography (Zone Electrophoresis, Pherography)

By

THEODOR WIELAND AND KLAUS DOSE

*Institute of Organic Chemistry, University Frankfurt am Main, West Germany*

## 1. HISTORY AND NOMENCLATURE

The movement of electrically charged particles in an electric field is called *ionophoresis* or *electrophoresis*. Utilizing the different mobilities or the movement in opposite directions of charged particles, one can carry out an analytical detection or separation of individual components of a mixture. While the term *ionophoresis* was coined at the end of the last century principally for the movement of small inorganic ions (1, 86, 147–149), the term *electrophoresis* was employed for the motion of charged colloidal particles. The latter can be readily detected in electrophoresis cells by various optical methods (Tiselius, Theorell, Antweiler) as long as convective disturbances are excluded. The diffusional processes which tend to eliminate the front between dense and less dense media are relatively slow. In contrast the fronts of low-molecular substances are unstable, owing to the greater diffusion and can rarely be made sufficiently sharp. Thus for the study of its electrophoretic (ionophoretic) mobility it was recognized that the system had to be stabilized by increasing the viscosity through addition of gelatine or agar-agar. In free electrophoresis (as in a *U* tube) only small amounts of the slowest and fastest components can be obtained in a pure state since zones overlap and are recognizable only through their fronts. In stabilized media, on the other hand, complete separation of a mixture into discrete and homogeneous zones is possible provided the mobilities are sufficiently different.*

The use of agar carrier was proposed in 1907 for the study of proteins of immunobiological interest (138). In the nineteen twenties Kendall *et al.* (67–70) attempted the separation in a similar medium of isotopes, rare earths, barium from radium, hafnium from zirconium after their success with simpler mixtures (SCN⁻/J⁻, Ba⁺⁺/Ca⁺⁺). Only in 1939 the principle of this method was reapplied by Coolidge (23) for the separation of albumins and globulins in a buffer solution stabilized in a powdered-glass column. In the same year Strain (132) succeeded in a complete separation of indicators by applying a potential to the end of a vertical chromatographic tube filled with Super-Cel or cotton and water. The method was designated by him as *electrochromatography*.

The separation of organic substances on a paper strip saturated with an electrolyte carrying a 110 D.C. potential was described by von Klobusitzky and Koenig in 1939 (74) in their attempt to separate snake venoms. A decisive advance in the field came through the work of Consden, Gordon, and Martin in 1946 (20). They demonstrated that amino acids and peptides could be separated on a flat bed of silica gel with strict control of pH. They also developed the theoretical side of the problem. In 1947 Butler and Stephen (16) carried out similar separations on a preparative scale using a horizontal plastic tube in which asbestos was subdivided by paper disks. Subsequently agar (20), starch (36, 78, 79), cotton gauze (147), ion exchangers (131), and cellulose powder (56) were employed. The separation of amino acids received the greatest

---

* Stabilization of zones may also be obtained without any carrier by using a density gradient (135a).

attention. Application of an electric field perpendicular to a descending chromatograph on paper clearly showed the ionophoretic movements of these components (58). In 1948 Wieland (153) designed a simple apparatus for the separation of small amounts of amino acids on buffered filter-paper strips. pH changes at the ends were minimized by use of buffered electrode vessels and diaphragms. Drying was prevented by operation in a closed container. This simple method was applied to the separation of a large class of compounds and has been improved by others. Since 1950 many variants have been described by Cremer and Tiselius (25), Durrum (30, 32a), Kraus and Smith (75), Biserte (3), McDonald, Urbin and Williamson (87, 91), Grassman and Hannig (45), Kunkel and Tiselius (80), Weber (145), Michl (100), Consden and Stanier (21, 22). Silk or rayon can be used in place of paper. Electrophoretic separation of very small amounts of nucleotides ($10^{-10}$ g.) can be carried out on a rayon fiber by a micro technique (33). Larger amounts can be separated by increasing the size of the equipment or by continuous operation. The latter is done by flowing the mixture down a flat carrier and applying a field along the vertical sides. The components will arrive at different points at the lower edge and can be separated continuously. Such arrangements, first with glass powder, were described by Svensson and Brattsten (135) and Grassman and Hannig (46) and on paper by Durrum (31) and Strain and Sullivan (133). Two-dimensional electrophoresis or a combination of chromatography and electrophoretic separation can be carried out on large paper sheets.

A variety of names have been suggested for these procedures, few of which can be misinterpreted. Nevertheless, it is difficult to find references quickly in the scientific literature since the articles are catalogued under the various reference names. It would be desirable, therefore, to establish a single term. The distinction between electrophoresis (motion of colloidal particles) and ionophoresis (small ionic particles) as suggested by Martin and Synge (95) becomes troublesome for substances of intermediate molecular weights (oligopeptides). The expression *electromigration*, which does not concern itself with molecular weight, does not indicate the use of a stabilizing carrier. In accord with the usage of *chromatography*, a typical transport phenomenon, the term *ionography* has been introduced (92). Here, however, the use of an electric field is not emphasized. The same criticism holds for *electrochromatography* (132), which was initially used for a chromatographic technique to which electrical separation was added. It should be reserved for operations where chromatography and electrophoretic separations go hand in hand. The descriptive terms *zone electrophoresis* and *ionophoresis* present difficulties in deriving words describing the results of the operation, as *chromatogram* expresses the result of chromatography. Since the expression (*electro-* or *iono-*) *pherogram* has been accepted widely for the result of the technique, the term *pherography* is suggested. A verb (*to pherograph*) and an adjective (*pherographic*) can be derived. The prefix of the carrier (paper, agar, or starch pherography) can readily identify the nature of the method.

## 2. THEORY

### 2.1. Mobilities

For separation in an electric field it is necessary that the charged particles have different velocities. The velocity $v$ of ions in a carrier-free electrolyte is given by

$$v = \frac{Q \cdot H}{6\pi r \eta} \tag{1}$$

where $Q$ is the charge of the particle, $H$ the field strength, $r$ the ion diameter and $\eta$ the viscosity of the solvent. For charged colloids a similar relation applies except that in the place of $Q$ the product of $\zeta \epsilon r$ is of importance, where $\zeta$ is the electrokinetic potential (phase-boundary potential), $\epsilon$ the dielectric constant of the solvent, and $r$ the diameter of the particle. Equation (1) changes to

$$v = \frac{\zeta \epsilon H}{6\pi \eta} \tag{2}$$

Mobility $V$ is defined as the velocity $v$ in a potential gradient of 1 volt/cm. The mobility can be determined in free electrolytes by dividing the velocity $v$ (where $v = d/t$, the distance traversed in time $t$) by the applied potential

$$V = \frac{dl}{tv} \tag{3}$$

Substances which dissociate in the normally used pH region show a dependence of velocity on dissociation and in their mobilities are influenced by the fraction ionized. The net velocity $V_n$ for a weak acid (HA) is given by

$$V_n = \frac{V \cdot [A^-]}{[HA] + [A^-]} = \frac{VK_a}{[H^+] + K_a} \tag{4}$$

where $K_a$ is the dissociation constant of the acid.

A similar argument holds for weak bases. Thus a strong dependence of mobility on pK is to be expected. Optimum separation of mixtures, particularly of ampholytes, can be achieved by appropriate pH adjustments (20).

The ionic strength of the buffer has an influence on the velocity. With increasing concentration of electrolyte the migration velocity decreases on account of weakening of the field strength. Also, viscosity effects which depend on salt concentration will affect the velocities, increasing with increasing temperature. However, the diffusion of the zones also increases, and the influence of temperature on separation is secondary.

In the presence of a carrier smaller velocities are generally observed. This is due to the longer distance traversed by the charged particle to circumvent obstructions in its path. Thus, in equation (3) one must substitute the actual longer path $d'$ and the adjusted length $l'$ of the carrier length along the potential difference (136) to give

$$V' = \frac{d'l'}{tv} \tag{5}$$

Since $\dfrac{d'}{d} = \dfrac{l'}{l}$ we have

$$V' = \frac{dl}{tv}\left(\frac{l'}{l}\right)^2 \tag{6}$$

Therefore the actual mobility is

$$V' = V\left(\frac{l'}{l}\right)^2 \tag{7}$$

where $V'$ is the mobility determined by experiment, which is always less than $V$ in free electrophoresis. The correction factor $(l'/l)^2$, characteristic of a particular carrier, was estimated for paper by Kunkel and Tiselius (80) by measuring the resistance of a known volume of solution of known conductivity. Values of $l/l'$ lie between 0.5 and 0.8 for various papers. Thus the observed mobilities are to be multiplied by 1.5 to 4 to obtain the "free" mobilities. A correction must also be made for concurrent motion by electroosmosis, which may become appreciable. Mobilities and isoelectric points can thus be determined in carrier systems.

Based on these theoretical concepts, the ratios of mobilities of substances should be the same on all papers. As shown by McDonald et al. (87a) this is not generally true. Comparing Munktell paper 20 and Schleicher and Schüll paper 413, they found velocity ratios of 0.8 for $Ni^{++}$, 1 for aspartic acid, and 1.6 for polyvinylpyrrolidinones. Apart from purely capillary effects, other forces, probably electrochemical in nature, appear to play a part.

### 2.2. Electroosmosis

Every carrier material in contact with an electrolyte assumes a charge so that in a potential field a liquid flow is set up, toward one electrode. This electroosmosis is in most cases (including paper) directed toward the cathode and can in consequence alter the position of the zones. The magnitude of this motion can be visualized by simultaneous use of electrically neutral colored substances (dextran dyed with bromophenol blue, hippuric acid nitrile colored red with cinnamic aldehyde -HCl), and appropriate corrections can be made. On paper the motion is toward the cathode increasing with increase in pH. A relation also exists with the nature of the ions, their charge and concentration. Increase in these quantities brings about a stronger endosmosis. Experiments have been carried out (64) to reduce the effect by suitable pretreatment of the paper. On the assumption that anionic groups in the paper are responsible for endosmosis, basic groups were incorporated (coupling with aminoguanidine after introduction of aldehyde groups through peroxide oxidation). Such papers lose their endosmotic properties at approximately pH 5, and acidic papers show osmosis down to a pH of 2. Since on an uncovered paper strip evaporation takes place on account of ohmic heat, there results a buffer current from both sides toward the middle of the paper (113b). Charged particles migrate only up to that part of the strip where electrophoretic migration and counter acting velocity of flow (resulting from an electroosomotic and an evaporation effect) are balanced. Thus, only a certain length of paper is useful for separation. After some time of running the separated components squeeze together in a rather narrow distance (electrorheophoresis of Macheboeuf (93, 94)). A uniform flow of buffer can be achieved by using a sheet of trapeze-shaped-paper (100a). Electroosmotic flow is greatest in ground glass, decreasing in agar, starch, and paper (80a).

### 2.3. Adsorption on the Carrier

In the majority of experiments carried out in aqueous phase adsorption effects are to be expected only on very active surfaces. The materials mentioned thus far belong to the group of weak adsorbents and adsorb negligible amounts of substance. Ion-exchange materials have been investigated systematically in only few cases (96, 131). In some instances special effects may be achieved from a combination of electrophoretic migration and adsorption. Ion exchange is occurring, for example, during the adsorption of multivalent ions on cellulose fibers. $Cu^{++}$ ions in acetate buffer are so strongly adsorbed on paper that ionophoresis is accompanied by severe "tailing." Complexing with the hydroxyl groups of the cellulose may play an important role.

The adsorption of certain proteins on the carriers is particularly annoying. While the human-blood-sera proteins are comparatively weakly adsorbed on paper, salmine and certain plant proteins cannot be separated. Attempts to minimize the disturbances through pretreatment of the paper with diazomethane (134a) or inorganic ions (12) were not successful. Commercial papers differ markedly in their adsorption of globulins. Since a similar difference was noticeable toward $Ca^{++}$, $Fe^{++}$, and $Cu^{++}$, an attempt was made to improve the carrier activity by treatment with a complexing agent (Dose, unpublished). In fact, the adsorption of globulins was almost completely suppressed. A similar result was achieved by adding to the buffer substances that combine with heavy metals (triethanolamine). Questions concerning the theory of paper electrophoresis are discussed by Valmet and Svensson (141b).

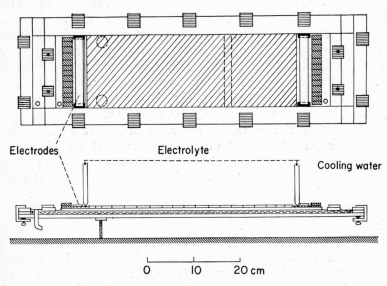

FIG. 1. Apparatus of Consden, Gordon, and Martin (21).

## 3. APPARATUS AND TECHNIQUES

### 3.1. Powdered, Fibrous or Gellike Supports

Thus far the following supports have been used with success: glass powder (9, 23, 46, 135), Hyflo-Super-Cel (132), quartz sand (46), starch, (36, 107), cellulose powder (56), cotton (132), asbestos fibers (16), agar-agar (42, 42a, 67–70, 106, 109), water glass (silica gel) (18, 20).

*3.1.1. Trough Apparatus.* The apparatus shown in Fig. 1 by Consden, Gordon, and Martin (20) consists of clamped glass plates which form a conduit for cooling water. Four strips of glass, made watertight with vaseline, are clamped together tightly to form the sides of a shallow trough into which are introduced the supporting medium and the electrodes (brass cathodes and carbon anodes). For separation of amino acids silica gel is used as support since the acids are difficult to recover from the otherwise more convenient agar-agar. To separate amino acids into the neutral, acidic, and basic constituents, one can operate, for example, in neutral media. One dilutes 28 ml. of a 4.3-$N$ water-glass solution (referred to alkali) to 350 ml. with water, neutralizes with 1.6 $M$ phosphoric acid, and pours the solution into the trough, where it is allowed to set. Space for the electrodes and the surrounding buffer solution is cut at both ends. In the center a 1-cm.-wide strip is removed into which is added the unknown, which was prepared in silica gel in a like manner. The electrodes are then introduced and a stream of buffer solution added through capillaries from a Mariotte bottle. The buffer is discarded into the cooling-water stream by suitable connections and removes the undesirable products of electrolysis. With a voltage of 190 volts a current of 430 ma. will flow. After 4 to 5 hr. the separation is made visible by covering the support with a filter-paper strip and subsequently developing on the strip with ninhydrin. With this as guide the amino acid containing zones, having traveled several centimeters without appreciable broadening, can be cut apart, eluted with water, and recovered with 80 to 100% efficiency. By use of buffers of different pH (9.4, for example) a straightforward separation of monoamino acids is possible, as they have an appreciable difference in their mobility due to varying charges and transport velocity (alanine/methionine; glycine/serine). Synge separated from the hydrolysate of gramicidin and gramicidin $S$ considerable quantities of ethanolamine and ornithine (131). This apparatus permits the separation of approximately 50 mg. of amino acids or dipeptides, which can be obtained in pure state especially if a volatile buffer (ammonium acetate) is used which will sublime in vacuum. For rapid separations the apparatus can be left uncovered. For more extended operations the gel should be covered to prevent drying out. This, however, may lead to disturbances at the points of contact. Different supports can, of course, be used in this apparatus. Several proteins (42) and nucleotides (43) have been separated in agar. Kunkel and Slater (78, 79) have described an arrangement for electrochromatography on starch, which has found use in modified form in the purification of somatotropin (37) and $\alpha$-corticotropin (85). Kunkel suggests for micropreparations a buffer-moistened block of starch between two sheets of waxed paper (80a). Michl also makes use of a thin layer of starch in protein separations. With sufficient cooling, potentials of 50 volts/cm. can be applied (100a). Layers of starch, cellulose powder, and other carriers have been successfully employed in the apparatus used in the authors' laboratory (Fig. 13) (153a).

3.1.2. *Tubular Apparatus.* In designs older than the trough method the support was contained in tubes. This was used at an early date in an attempt to stabilize the buffer in free electrophoresis. Horizontal or vertical arrangement of the tubes is possible.

*Horizontal Techniques:* Following the success of Butler and Stephens (16), who used this principle with asbestos, an effective design was described by Peniston, Agar, and McCarthy (111), who stabilized the horizontal portion by agar (Fig. 2). The separation vessel *A* consists of a horizontal straight glass tube of 8 mm. I.D. and 50 to 75 cm. length. Electrode containers *B* are glass cylinders which are connected to the separation vessel by rubber tubing and contain passages for the entry and outlet of buffer solution *C*. Graphite rods of 2-cm. diameter and 20-cm. length are used as electrodes. The entire apparatus is immersed in a constant-temperature bath. The separation vessel is half filled with a warm 1% agar solution, which is allowed to harden. One cubic centimeter of the mixture in agar is added and the tube filled completely with agar. Connection is then made with the electrode vessels with rubber and a

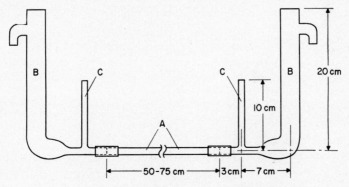

Fig. 2. Apparatus of Peniston, Agar, and McCarthy (111).

glass-wool plug. A 0.1 *M* buffer solution (sodium acetate/acetic acid of pH 4.6 or phosphate buffer at pH 7) is allowed to percolate at a rate of several hundred milliliters per hour. At 10° C. and 390 volts (6.6 volts/cm.) and 20 ma. good separations are obtained in 3 to 4 hr. of 10 to 20γ of aromatic phenol carbonic or sulfonic acids, the position and concentration of which can be determined by UV absorption measurements (111).

*Vertical Techniques:* The principle of this method was described by Strain in 1937, improved by Coolidge (23), and extended by Flodin (36) into a method for zone electrophoresis of proteins. Figure 3 shows the most recent modification based on the apparatus described by Haeglund and Tiselius in 1950 (56). It consists of a demountable *U* tube of 3-cm. diameter and 50-cm. length. One leg is filled with the support (starch) with the protein mixture at the end. The remainder is filled with buffer (veronal, pH = 8.6, $\Gamma/2 = 0.5$) and directly connected with the electrode vessel (Pt electrode in 1 liter buffer). After 15 to 20 hr. at 700 volts, 0.2 cc. of undiluted human-blood serum separates into its components.

For isolation the tube is separated from the remainder of the apparatus and the separate protein fractions are eluted with the same buffer with approximately fifty changes in the receiver. An inverted $U$ tube dipping into buffer works similarly (5).

   *3.1.3. Continuous Separations.* Apparatus developed by Grassman and Hannig (47, 48, 49, 51) in Germany and independently by Svensson and

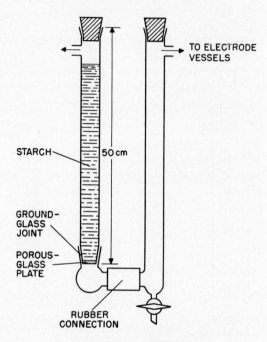

FIG. 3. Apparatus of Flodin (36).

Brattsten in Sweden (135, 9a) allow continuous separation in vertical flow of solution through a carrier and concurrent horizontal separation by means of a horizontal electric field. Having unequal mobilities the various components will arrive at different places at the bottom edge. Figure 4 shows a schematic diagram of the apparatus. The separating chamber $K$, filled with uniform glass powder or sand, is approximately 30 cm. high and 20 cm. wide, with a thickness of only 0.8 cm. to permit adequate cooling from the cooling chambers $W$ on either side. The chamber is separated by glass diaphragms from the electrode spaces $E$ and $E'$, which are irrigated with the same buffer solution as the separating chamber. The flow velocities are higher, though, to wash away the products of electrolysis. The transporting solution (a buffer solution of desired ionic strength and pH) is added at $A$, the solution of the mixture at $B$ or $B'$. Both leave the apparatus via the removal system $C$ consisting of fifty tubes. Voltages of 500 to 1200 volts are applied with 30 to 40 min. travel for low-molecular weight compounds, several hours for proteins. The separated homogeneous fractions appear in three or four neighboring tubes. Figure 5 shows the separation of three amino acids.

The Swedish modification is similar in principle but uses a thicker separating chamber and omits any cooling in its original design. The regu-

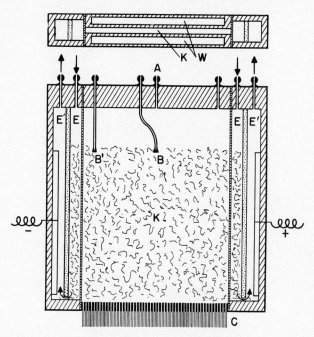

FIG. 4. Apparatus for continuous separation according to Grassmann and Hannig (48).

lation of buffer flow is done hydrostatically by rubber-tube connections which permit adjustments in height relative to the liquid level in the separating chamber. Recently Bradish and Smart (9) have separated satisfactorily globular proteins in a similar apparatus provided with cooling and a very slow injection stream.

A noncontinuous separation can be carried out in a similar arrangement, independent of the constancy of buffer flow and voltage variation. In this "no-flow" method 5 to 10 cc. of the mixture is injected with buffer into the powder bed (veronal or phosphate buffer, pH 7.5 to 9, $\Gamma/2 = 0.04$) forming a vertical column of approximately 1-cm. diameter. The flow is stopped and the current started (300 volts corresponding to

10 volts/cm., 300 ma.). The initially vertical zone separates horizontally into its components (beef serum albumin and gamma globulins separate at 3 to 4 cm./hr.). After several hours the current is stopped and the zones are eluted by vertical buffer flow at a rate of 15 cm./hr. at each of the twenty-seven tubes. As the elution requires 30 min., relatively large amounts of proteins may be separated in this manner. This variant may also be useful for the separation of low-molecular-weight components.

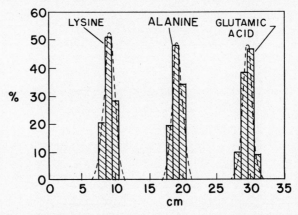

FIG. 5. Separation of lysine, alanine, and glutamic acid: 1/100$m$ acetate buffer, pH 5.5, 750 volts, 150 ma.; throughput 14.7 mg. glutamic acid, 8.9 mg. alanine, and 19.6 mg. lysine/hr.

The same principle of continuous separation has been applied to paper as carrier (*vide infra*).

### *3.2. Paper as Carrier*

*3.2.1. Method of Wieland and Fischer (153).* The simple apparatus consists of a plastic frame and glass plates between which buffer-saturated paper strips are held horizontally (Fig. 6). The ends of the strips dip into two fairly large containers filled with buffer and containing the electrodes. The electrolyte level is made equal at both ends to prevent flow due to syphoning. Initially they were glass tubes closed off with clay into which carbon electrodes were inserted. This measure was introduced to prevent too great a variation in the pH: two platinum electrodes in electrode vessels of sufficient size were found adequate (152). The dimensions of the equipment are variable over wide limits. To prevent sagging of long strips against the bottom of the container, glass or plastic supports may be used. For wide strips multiplication of the number of electrode cells is recommended (138b).

For separating mixtures the following steps are carried out. A strip of paper (cut from good, not too soft filter paper, 8 by 25 cm.) is moistened with buffer of ionic strength $\Gamma/2 = 0.04 - 0.1$. Excess of buffer is soaked up by filter paper. The mixture (approximately 0.05 cc. of a 1–10% solution) is placed in a narrow spot from a round capillary or brush on a marked transverse line near the middle of the strip. Several spots may be added at a distance of 1.5 cm. apart. The strip is suspended tautly between the frame, the end dipped into the electrode vessel, and the current turned on. At 100–300 volts (5–10 volts/cm.) a current of a few milliamperes begins to flow. After 1 hr. low-molecular substances are well separated; after 5–10 hr. high-molecular substances are separated. In this

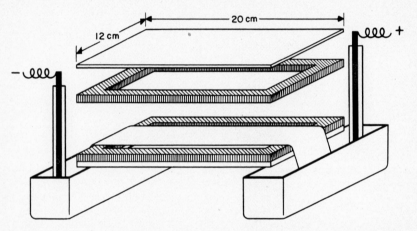

FIG. 6. Apparatus for paper pherography according to Wieland and Fischer (153).

simple apparatus proportionality between time and travel distance exists for a short time only. With time and distance from the center the velocity of the moving components decreases since buffer flows toward the middle to replace the evaporated water. This flow opposes the motion of the substance and adds more electrolyte into the chamber, causing wide variations in salt concentration in the paper. A purposeful use of evaporating (electrorheophoresis) is described by Macheboeuf (93).

Several more recent commercial models are available in handy designs such as the ionograph (USA, 87), Elphor (Germany, 45), Shandon tank (England), LKB apparatus (Sweden) and Pherograph-Frankfurt (Germany) for high voltage electrophoresis on cooled glass plates (Fig. 13) (153a). In several modifications, such as Miettinen's model (102), the chamber extends over the electrodes.

*3.2.2. Method of Durrum.* Durrum described a different modification in 1950 (30) in which 1-cm.-wide paper strips are looped tentlike over a support in a chamber made from three glass cups (Fig. 7). The operations are similar to those of the Wieland apparatus. This design has been modified extensively by widening the narrow strip (94). Particularly simple are the modifications of Sorm *et al.* (130) and Lederer and Ward (84). A further modification of Durrum (32) using a gable principle (Fig. 8) permits the use of several narrow strips or one wide strip for micropreparative work.

3.2.3. *Modification with Contact Cooling.* While in the methods described thus far the ohmic heat was conducted to the air or lost by evaporation, the following modification prevents heating of the paper by direct

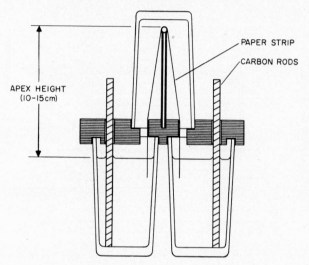

FIG. 7. Apparatus of Durrum (30).

contact with a hydrophobic liquid or by solid plates which are cooled. Cremer and Tiselius (25) placed their strips in chlorobenzene. This technique was taken over by Consden and Stanier (22). Since glass is a relatively good conductor it can be used for cooling. Kunkel and Tiselius squeeze the strip between two silicone-treated glass plates (80) (Fig. 9). This sandwich is in contact with large buffer vessels via thick paper mats. The current is introduced by platinum electrodes through a labyrinth pathway. The apparatus is suitable for separations on thick paper or on several thin sheets. For thin sheets undesirable zone thickening may occur because of capillary and electroendosmotic effects.

Weber (145) has described a modification (Fig. 10A) where the paper *b* is placed directly on the glass *d*. The improvement is due to a marked diminution in the electrolyte content of the paper. While in normal procedure the electrolyte content is 210%, Weber presses out excess liquid down to a moisture content of 150%. This minimizes hydromechanical and capillary effects, which lead to a diffusion of spots. To prevent re-

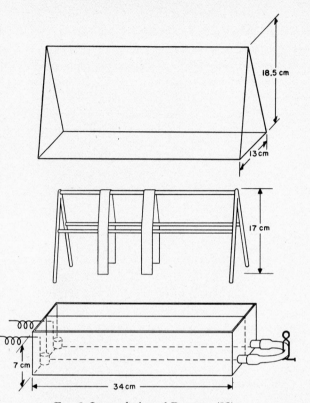

FIG. 8. Large design of Durrum (32).

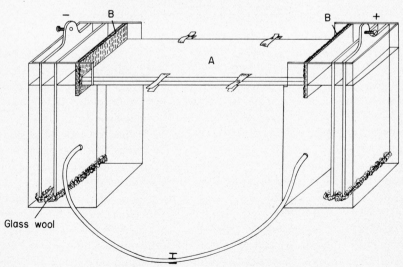

FIG. 9. Apparatus of Kunkel and Tiselius (80).

saturation of the strip through capillary suction from the electrode vessel cellophane tubes and clay plates were added as "brakes" near the ends (Fig. 10B). The separation takes place on the middle of three paper strips laid end to end and thus protected against pH shifts and high moisture content. To obtain the necessary potential gradient (10 volts/cm.) voltages of 1000 to 1500 volts had to be applied at the ends of the 150-cm.-long strips. During operation a second glass plate, resting on the carbon cylinders and clay plates, is added and the space along the edges closed off

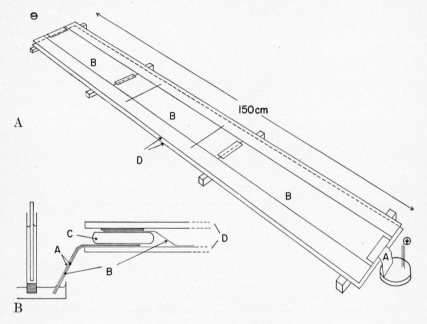

FIG. 10. Apparatus of Weber (145).

with wet filter paper. After 100 min. (10 volts/cm., 3 ma., citrate buffer pH 3.8) histamine separates from cadaverine in spots 1 cm. apart and identifiable in concentrations as low as $10^{-9}$ moles.

In a modified method of filter paper electrophoresis the filter paper strip (60 cm. long, 2.5 cm. wide) is wrapped in spiral fashion round a glass tube through which cold water is running. To minimize evaporation from the strip, it is covered with a strip of thin cellophane of the same width. Humid conditions are maintained by enclosing a portion of the glass tube in a wooden box, lined with filter paper saturated with buffer (162).

*3.2.4. Use of High Voltage.* Since the diffusion process, giving rise to broadening of spots and bands, is minimized during short times of experimentation, the use of high voltage is desirable. Durrum (32) used voltage drops of 30 to 40 volts/cm. in 1951. In the same year Michl (98) described an arrangement (Fig. 11) in which the paper strip *a* hangs down in a beaker from an electrode vessel *b* and dips at its bottom edge into the

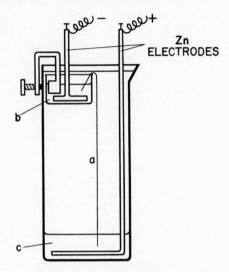

FIG. 11. High-voltage pherography of Michl (98).

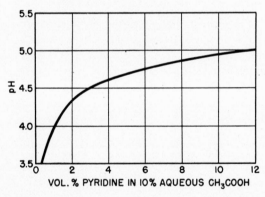

FIG. 12. Dependence of pH on the composition of pyridine–water–acetic acid mixtures (98).

electrolyte *c*. The heat produced at 50 volts/cm. is dissipated by filling the entire vessel with toluene. Michl also uses buffers of low conductivity such as mixtures of pyridine–acetic acid and water, which also have the advantage of volatility. The dependence of pH on composition is shown in Fig. 12. pH variation is plotted as a function of the addition of pyridine (in volume %) to 10% acetic acid. A considerable shortening of time is achieved and thus an increased band sharpness.

Somewhat different is the arrangement of the 56-cm.-long paper strip of Markham and Smith (97), who separated mono-, di-, and trinucleotides at 20 to 25 volts/cm. The paper is submerged as a V in carbon tetrachloride. Turba used toluene as a coolant in a micropreparative pherography. After extended use the toluene must be replaced in consequence of the slight solubility of the buffer. The method is particularly suited to low-molecular substances while proteins undergo changes at the water-toluene interface and exhibit irregular movements. Caution toward fires must be exercised with combustible coolants in the presence of high voltage.

High voltage in the absence of organic coolants can be used if the strips are cooled directly by solid supports which can be cooled separately. An apparatus of this kind was described by Michl (100). It consists of two nylon-lacquer-covered aluminum plates between which are pressed the electrolyte-saturated strips. To avoid sucking up of more buffer the ends are brought in contact with the electrode vessel by Weber's cellophane diaphragms. Cooling is done with water flowing through the cooling chambers mounted on the aluminum plates. Gross (55) described a similar setup (40 to 60 volts/cm.) where the paper strips are laid between water-cooled copper plates insulated by polyethylene, or between two cooled glass plates (55a).

For optimum separation of low-molecular-weight substances it is desirable to work with low moistened paper, with as short a time as possible and at low temperature to minimize diffusion and evaporation. Figure 13 shows an arrangement meeting these requirements and used in the authors' laboratory for analytical and micropreparative separations. It consists of a plastic case supported on a 40- to 50-cm. rectangular glass plate, preferable to plastics in view of its better heat conductivity. The plate closes off a cooling chamber filled with glycol/water that can be cooled down to −10° C. by means of a copper cooling coil. On the opposite ends of the plate two troughs contain buffer and platinum ribbon electrodes. The buffer-saturated and well-squeezed-out paper (38 to 48 cm.) is laid on the cool glass plate and pressed down with a rubber roller. The solution is added at a marked spot by means of a capillary. Connection between paper and electrolyte is established by Weber's cellophane connection, which is pressed on by a second well-fitting glass plate. At 30 to 40 volts/cm. good separations of amino acids and peptides are achieved in 30 to 60 min. (153a).

Working on cooled plastic plates also is successful (147b). Cooling is not necessary even with high voltage if a buffer of very low ionic strength is used. On account of electrolytic decomposition of the buffer in the electrode vessels, it has to be replaced continuously, preferably by circulation. Dilution has no effect on migration of components (125a).

*3.2.5. Multistep Processes.* With square papers and easily removable buffers two-dimensional pherograms can be obtained without difficulty.

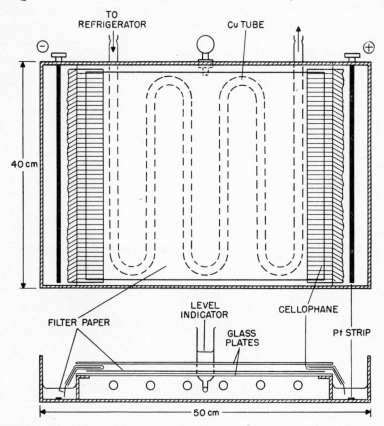

FIG. 13. Apparatus for high-voltage pherography of Wieland and Pfleiderer (153a).

The substance is added first in one corner and pherographed at two different pH values. Durrum described this method in 1951 (32) and was able to separate seventeen amino acids into thirteen spots. Combination of chromatography and pherography can similarly be carried out. One obtains chromatopherograms of amino acids, as shown by Durrum (32) using a strip-transfer technique, and by Kickhöfen and Westphal (71). Haugaard and Kroner (58) combined the two methods by introducing a horizontal field obtained from platinum electrodes mounted along the vertical edge of descending amino acid chromatogram. The method was extended into a continuous one on paper by eliminating the chromatography. Buffer solution was flowed continuously down the paper. The electric field caused a divergent path for the components, which are separated at the serrated bottom (49, 51, 133). Figure 14 shows the simple Strain electrographic cell consisting of filter paper waxed along the vertical edges and containing in the middle a waxed container for the sub-

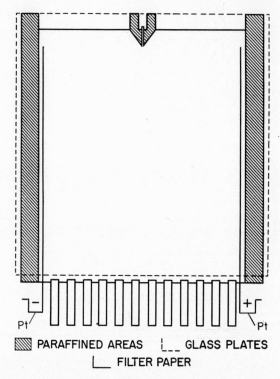

PARAFFINED AREAS   GLASS PLATES
FILTER PAPER

FIG. 14. Electrographic cell according to Strain (133).

stance. The paper is held by clamps between glass plates (133). The platinum-wire electrodes are in direct contact with the paper. In this method strong pH changes occur at the edges. This is true also in the Grassmann apparatus, where the potential is applied via buffer-saturated cotton. In a recent modification (113) this difficulty is avoided. Thicker papers permit separation of large quantities of material. These continuous methods can, of course, be used for the discontinuous no-flow principle.

Detailed descriptions of techniques of paper pherography are found in several special works (i.e. 4a, 24, 59a, 82a, 138b, 160).

3.2.6. *Ultramicro Method of Edström.* A micro method consisting of a 1- to 2-cm.-long rayon fiber can operate with $10^{-5}$ times the normal amount of substance (33). The fiber was prepared from cuprammonium viscose, swelled in alkali, washed with water, and saturated for 24 hr. in a citrate buffer of pH 3.6, made viscous with glycerol and glucose. The saturated fiber was covered with a buffer containing paste at both ends and stretched across a hollow space in a thick glass plate. A hydrochloric acid hydrolysate of ribonucleic acid was added at an arbitrary point, the depression filled with paraffin, the chamber closed with a quartz disk, and the potential applied from microplatinum electrodes with a voltage of 1.2 volts/cm. After 2 hr. adenine, guanine, cytidylic acid, and uridylic acid were definitely separated along 1 mm. of the fiber as shown by UV photography. Photometric measurements permit quantitative estimates of sufficient accuracy so that differences in the nucleic-acid composition of single cells may be detected. Recently Nöller (108a) also designed a similar ultramicromethod to separate proteins.

### 3.3. Quantitative Evaluation

In the preceding sections the quantitative separations of a number of natural and synthetic mixtures have been described. In later sections detailed tests for classes of compounds will be given for the location of the separated components. These indicate only qualitatively results of the separation. Special methods have been developed for quantitative work similar to those of paper chromatography. Only methods specific to paper pherograms will be discussed in detail.

The most accurate results for paper and other carriers will be obtained by eluting the pure components and measuring their concentration by standard methods, such as spectroscopically (directly or of other derivatives), titrimetrically, polarographically, manometrically, biologically, radiometrically, etc.

More details may be found in books on chromatography and paper chromatography including methods for quantitative evaluation directly on the strip. This trades accuracy for gain in time and convenience. Most of the methods have been developed for paper chromatography. Only for one class, the proteins, has paper pherography been shown to be the only separating method. A more detailed description of the quantitative evaluation of such pherograms will follow.

Turba and Enenkel (139) and Durrum (30) showed in 1950 that serum proteins can be cleanly separated into the components in a moist chamber. For visualization protein dyes are added to the strip to color the protein fraction. For quantitative evaluation the components are cut apart, eluted, and determined colorimetrically. The method was quickly adopted in hospitals for routine determinations. Use was made of direct photometric methods which had already been described in 1949 for paper chromatography (14). Serum pherograms dyed with azocarmine or Amido Black 10B (50) are made transparent with paraffin oil and α-bromo-naphthalene, mounted between glass plates and photometered. The photometer consists of a slit light source and photocell. Plotting optical density against distance yields a diagram which gives a quantitative protein composition of the serum. Automatic plotting (146) simplifies the method even further. Reproducible and accurate diagrams are obtained in a few seconds as shown in Fig. 15. A different optical system using cylindrical optics and an absorption wedge was described by Michl (99).

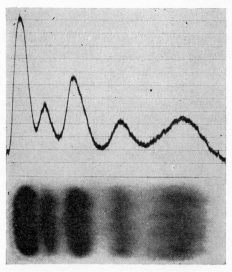

Fig. 15. Quantitative evaluation of a pherogram of serum proteins in lung tumor (146).

The visualization of separated components and direct evaluations are described in section 4.

Retention analysis (153) makes possible quantitative evaluation of protein pherograms (156). In this method a solution of copper acetate in tetrahydrofurane or dioxane is allowed to ascend a pherogram (or chromatogram) perpendicular to the separated component strips. Cupric ion is retained in places where reactive components are present. The sizes of the gaps in the horizontal front of $Cu^{++}$ ascended in the paper are proportional to the concentration of substances in the strip-shaped spots. Many classes of compounds reacting with cupric ions such as amino acids, peptides, hydroxydicarboxylic acids, phosphoric acid esters, etc., can be quantitatively evaluated.

Fluorescing substances can be determined on paper by measuring the intensity of the fluorescing light (128).

## 4. APPLICATION OF THE METHOD

### 4.1. General Detection Methods

Many of the substances do not absorb visible light and have to be identified by suitable techniques. One can use physical, chemical, or biological methods, which may be quite distinct depending upon the particular substances. There exist, however, a number of generally applicable detection principles developed for paper chromatography and described in text books on that method. In this chapter we shall enumerate the methods briefly without citing the very extensive literature.

*Physical Methods:* Pherograms can be observed in UV light to detect fluorescent substances or spots that inhibit the weak self-fluorescence of paper. The extinction of fluorescence is much more pronounced after previous spraying with fluorescing compounds (fluoresceine, acridine). A filtered mercury lamp (255 m$\mu$) is a convenient light source.

The UV absorption can be measured along the paper strip by analysis in a spectrophotometer. Infrared absorption may be used for quantitative analysis, as for amino acids (44).

Radioactive substances can be detected by a sensitive silver bromide film pressed against the strip (autoradiography), by activity measurement along the strip with a Geiger counter or by automatic counting of radioactivity (103). Radioactivity can be introduced by (*a*) use of radioactive mixtures, (*b*) subsequent reaction with radioactive substances and removal of excess reagent, (*c*) introduction of activity through neutron bombardment in sulfur-, bromine-, chlorine-, and phosphorus-containing substances (124, 125).

*Chemical Methods:* Substances can be made visible by reaction with a specific dye or formation of colored or fluorescing derivatives. Indicators may also be used which show pH variations or the presence of reducing or oxidizing substances.

*Biological Methods:* Spraying with enzyme solutions and observation of the occurrence or absence of enzymatic reactions can be used for detection. Also the growth or inhibition of microorganisms (bioautography) can be employed.

### 4.2. Specific Fields of Application

*4.2.1. Amino Acids. Paper as Carrier:* The separation of amino acid mixtures into the acid, neutral and basic constituents is quite simple in acetate buffer at pH 6.7 (approx. 10 volts/cm., 60 to 120 min.). Equally acceptable is pyridine–acetic acid–water buffer, which has the advantage of volatility and smaller electroosmosis. At pH 7.5 lysine and arginine move toward the cathode; histidine remains stationary. At pH 3 aspartic acid moves 'faster toward the anode than glutamic acid (153). Alanine, valine, proline, and tryptophan can be separated in 5 N acetic acid (pH 1.7, 20 to 30 volts/cm., 120 min.) and similarly glycine, isoleucine, phenylalanine, and hydroxyproline (30).

Glycine, alanine, $\alpha$-aminobutyric acid, leucine, serine, threonine, phenylalanine, tryptophane, cysteine, and aspartic acid can be separated in 2 M acetic acid and 0.6 N formic acid (1:1) at pH 1.9 (70 volts/cm., 200 min.) (71, see also 153a).

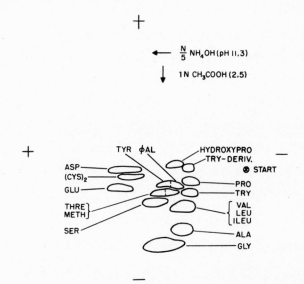

FIG. 16. Two-dimensional pherogram of an amino acid mixture.

*Two-dimensional Pherography:* Separation of a complex amino acid mixture (Fig. 16) is done by developing first in 0.2 N aqueous ammonium hydroxide (pH 11.3, 120 min.), subsequently at right angle in 1 $M$ acetic acid (pH 3.20 to 30 volts/cm., 180 min.) (32).

*Detection and Evaluation:* Ninhydrin reaction and photometry *in situ* or on the extracted dye is recommended. It is desirable (6, 34) to transfer the ninhydrin dyes into their copper complexes (66). 1,2-Naphthoquinone-4-sulfonate (104) forms many different colors with various amino acids. The following other detection methods are available: diazotized sulfanilic acid (histidine, tyrosine), cinnamic aldehyde–HCl gas (tryptophane), Ehrlich's reagent (tryptophane), periodate-Nessler's reagent (hydroxy-amino acids), isatine (proline, hydroxyproline), phthalic dialdehyde (glycine), Sakaguchi's reagent (arginine), sodium nitroprusside (cysteine, with KCN cystine), Millon's reagent (tyrosine), Folin's reagent (reducing amino acids), and detection as chlorimine derivatives with o-tolidine or with benzidine-KI (115, 159b).

Detection is also possible through reaction with 2,4-dinitrofluorobenzene on the paper and bleaching of the yellow dinitrophenol background with HCl gas. Quantitative detection is possible with photospectroscopic determination after elution of the yellow zones and removal of the interfering dinitrophenol with 90% sulfuric acid–benzene (62). Detection is also possible as bivalent copper complexes after separation with rubeanic acid (153).

*Silica Gel as Carrier:* The following separations have been carried out: wool hydrolyzate (approx. 30 mg. amino acids) into acidic, basic, and neutral fractions in phosphate buffer at pH 7 (3 to 4 volts/cm. 200 to 300 min.); glycine and serine in borate buffer at pH 9.7 (3 to 4 volts/cm., 6 hr.); methionine and alanine in borate buffer at pH 9.4 (3 to 4 volts/cm., 4 to 5 hr.); separation of glutamic acid, aspartic acid in acetate buffer at pH 7 (3 to 4 volts/cm., 24 hr.); separation of lysine and histidine in sodium chloride at pH 6.6 (2 volts/cm., 6 hr.); glycine and glycylglycine in aqueous ammonia–ammonium carbonate at pH 9.2 (3 volts/cm., 41 hr.). Detection is accomplished by pressing on of filter paper and ninhydrin reagent (20).

*Continuous Separation on Glass Powder:* Several model mixtures of amino acids have been separated in the apparatus described on page 39.

*4.2.2. Peptides. Separation:* $\alpha$- and $\beta$-Amanitins were separated in sodium acetate buffer after several hours (pH 7, 6 volts/cm.) and observed with cinnamic aldehyde–HCl gas or ammoniacal silver nitrate (157). Glycyl-glycine and glycine-*l*-leucine are separable in 5 N acetic acid (pH 1.7, 30 volts/cm., 120 min.) (30). Many synthetic di- and tripeptides have been separated with high voltage (pH approx. 2, several hours) (71).

High-voltage pherography is successful in the separation of naturally occurring peptide mixtures such as alcoholic extracts of liver and yeast (141a) or the nitrogen-containing nonprotein fraction of blood serum or urine (59). The products of partial hydrolysis of insulin have also been investigated and separated by paper electrophoresis (118a). Figure 17 shows a ninhydrin-colored pherogram of an extract of the anterior lobe of the pituitary. Equally, separations are possible for the peptidelike hormones of the pituitary such as the purification of $\alpha$-corticotropin (85, 89), vasopressin, and oxytocin (133, 137) in acetate buffer (pH 5.7, $\Gamma/2 = 0.1$).

*Detection and Analysis:* Peptides with free amino groups can be detected with ninhydrin. With increasing chain length the color intensity decreases and fails entirely for cyclic peptides. More sensitive is the previously mentioned "chlorine method" (115, 159b). Hormones are detected by biological tests. Polyglutamyl peptides, given off by *B. anthrax* during growth in synthetic nutrients, can be detected with alcoholic bromcresol purple in view of its acidic reaction.

*It should be stated that all filter papers contain ninhydrin negative peptides* (see also 161, 56a), *which may appear as admixed amino acids after hydrolysis of the eluates.*

*4.2.3. Proteins. Electrophoresis on Paper, Separation:* In the protein field paper electrophoresis has proved superior to chromatography. Its low cost, time, and material requirements make it also superior to electrophoresis in unstabilized electrolytes. The method is of particular value

↑
⊹ Start

Fig. 17. Separation of amino acids and peptides of an acetic acid extract of the anterior lobe of the pituitary; acetic acid–formic acid–water buffer (10:5:85), pH 1.9, 40 volts/cm., 50 min., developed with ninhydrin.

in medicine and biology.It is carried out in many laboratories and has led to the publication of several hundred papers, of which only a few can be mentioned in this review. High voltage has been found of little value in protein separation. The "humidity chamber" apparatus (Fig. 6) is best suited. The quality of the paper is of importance in view of differential adsorption effects (99). Composition and ionic strength of the buffer also affect the degree of separation and its sharpness. A 0.1 N veronal buffer according to Dole at pH 8.6 and 0.1 ionic strength is most suitable. A reliable statement concerning specific papers cannot be made. It appears, however, that low-ash papers of thick texture give the best results. Their suitability can be readily determined in preliminary experiments.

*Examples:* The separation of components of human sera plays an important role in the diagnosis of many diseases. The pherogram on page 50 developed with Amido Black 10B can be used as an example. Photoelectric analysis of such strips leads to diagrams resembling those of the moving boundary method even though of different origin.

The proteins of spinal fluid can be separated only after preliminary enrichment, as by acetone precipitation (13). Protein-containing fluids and extracts from all organs of animals can be analyzed similarly. Figure 18 shows the blood serum of a frog, normal and amanita poisoned (153). In whey three distinct protein bands have been demonstrated (142).

Many animal toxins of snakes (52, 100b, 101, 106, 156) and insects (35, 52, 106) have been investigated.

The separation of plant proteins has not in general given good results. The protein separation of potato-tuber extracts proceeds readily at a potential of 10 volts/cm. (127). Several experiments indicate that enzymes can be separated from proteins. Wallenfels and U. Pechmann (144) working with a watery extract of a mold mycelium separated amylase, lipase, phosphatase, and proteinase at pH 6.8 in $m/30$ phosphate buffer. The

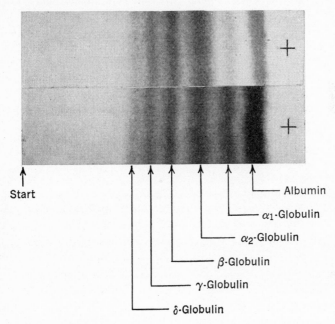

Fig. 18. Serum proteins of a frog poisoned with amanitin (upper) compared with normal animal (lower) (158).

enzymes were specifically demonstrated with sprays of starch solution, $p$-nitrophenyl stearate, and phenolphthalein phosphate and with a strip of gelatine. A technical preparation of hyaluronidase was shown to contain four protein components of which only one, having the shortest path length in 0.05 $M$ veronal at pH 8, had enzymatic activity (17).

Other biologically active proteins have been investigated. The growth hormone somatotropin was shown to be a protein mixture. Isolation on a small preparative scale was carried out on a starch carrier (37).

*Other Carriers:* Starch offers the advantage of smaller protein absorption. For this reason the purification of somatotropin (37) was carried out in a trough apparatus (78, 79) filled with starch. Successful protein separations have been carried out on a variety of carriers, serum albumins from globulins on powdered glass (24), ferritin, hemoglobin, and chicken-egg proteins on agar (42). The use of glass powder for continuous protein separation was discussed on page 38, similarly the use of starch.

*Detection and Analysis:* The protein zones on paper can be detected by means of the relatively insensitive ninhydrin reaction. Other carriers present considerable difficulties. A preferable method is to dye the paper with protein dyes such as azocarmine (139), bromphenol blue–mercuric chloride (75, 80), or Amido Black 10B (50). The pherogram is bathed for some time in an acid solution of these dyes and the solution removed from the nonprotein regions by repeated washing in acid baths.

DIRECTION FOR AMIDO BLACK 10B: Strips are dried at 100° C., placed into the dyeing bath, and stirred for 10 min. The bath consists of a saturated solution of Amido Black 10B

$$O_2N-\langle\bigcirc\rangle-N{=}N-\overset{NH_2}{\underset{NaO_3S}{\bigcirc}}\overset{OH}{\underset{SO_3Na}{\bigcirc}}-N{=}N-\langle\bigcirc\rangle$$

in methanol–acetic acid (9:1). The washing out of excess dye is carried out with methanol–acetic acid (9:1) solutions which are changed several times during the 4-hr. wash. The last wash will remain nearly colorless and the protein-free paper will be slightly blue. Several modifications are possible for the dyeing and washing operation. The following method is particularly suitable: fixing of the strip in methanol–acetic acid (9:1) without dye for 10 min., dyeing with 0.02% dye solution in 2 $N$ aqueous acetic acid at 50° C. for 3 hr., and washing in aqueous acetic acid for 15 min.

Since the dyeing quality is not the same for different proteins, several exploratory experiments with other dyes are reported: Solvay purple (114), "Neu Coccin" (99), Ponceau 2R (118). Ultraviolet illumination may serve for zone localization. The chlorination method of page 53 is also applicable to proteins. For quantitative estimation the elution technique, though clumsy, will give the most dependable results.

A comparison of several proposed methods has been carried out by Röttger (117). For radioactive proteins no dyeing is necessary, as the radioactive detection methods are far superior. A typical example is the detection of $S^{35}$ containing serum proteins obtained in feeding experiments with radioactive methionine (108). Protein high in phosphorus content (casein) can be detected through radioactivity induced by neutron irradiation (124, 125). Evaluation of protein pherograms by ultraviolet-absorption see (72).

*4.2.4. Other High-Polymer Substances.* Relatively few experiments are available in this field. Polyacrylic acid moves readily, using the common protein buffers, and is identified by being dyed with carbol fuchsin from aqueous alcoholic solution (155).

High-molecular-weight acidic polysaccharides (probably sulfonic acid derivatives) have been detected in connective-tissue extracts and made visible by toluidine-blue dyeing (19). Electrophoresis of mucopolysaccharides in a slab of Hyflo Super Cel has also been described (40). Blood-plasma expanders, such as polyvinylpyrrolidone, migrate and can be detected with Lugol solution (90).

The separation of glycogen and galactogen has been demonstrated on silk in veronal buffer at pH 9.3 (41). Paper is unsuitable, owing to its chemical similarity. Hydrolysis carried out on the silk with 2 $N$ HCl at 115° C. gives products which can be localized by means of the Molisch reaction ($\alpha$-naphthol-sulfuric acid).

A separation of hyaluronic acids from chondroitin-sulfuric acid has been demonstrated on a Super-Cel column in acid solution and from heparin, on paper (116).

Humic acids and similar high polymers obtained from hydroquinone by alkaline oxydation may also be separated (147a).

*4.2.5. Sugars and Polyalcohols.* Sugars and polyalcohols carry no electric charge but form anionic borate complexes with increased conductivity (7, 8, 63). The complexing and dissociation constants of the acids depend on the structure of the polyols. This structure also determines the number of boric acid molecules and the charge of the complex. It explains the anodic direction of motion and the structure-dependent velocity. This property was first used by Jaenicke (63) and Consden and Stanier (21) at 10 volts/cm. Figure 19 shows the mobility of a variety of sugars as a function of pH. Here, too, the use of high-potential gradients (40 to 60 volts/cm.) is particularly advantageous for the separation (54). It permits separation of oligosaccharides, which are formed as intermediates during the action of yeast invertase on sucrose (55). A 0.05 $M$ sodium borate buffer of pH > 9 is commonly employed in which most of the investigated saccharides (also methyl, ethyl, and other derivatives) can be separated (39). The method is also applicable to polyalcohols, as shown in the successful separation of glycol, glycerol, and mannitol under similar conditions (100). *o*-Diphenols form particularly strong complexes. Other polyhydric alcohols like sorbitol, mannitol and dulcitol are cleanly separated on paper in 0.05 $M$ borate buffer of pH 9.2 in 1–3 hr. at 2000 volts (55b).

Common natural derivatives of sugars, the glycosides, have been little investigated, following the separation of rutin and quercitrin in borate solution (77). Ten flavonol glycosides were investigated with high potentials in borate buffer (57); naturally occurring cumarine derivatives were similarly separated (76).

The principle of boric acid complexes can be applied to the separation of ribosides. The order of movement toward the anode at pH 9.2 is adenosine, cystidine and guanosine, uridine. In acetate buffer at pH 3.2 the movement is toward the cathode, the basic character gaining the preponderance (63).

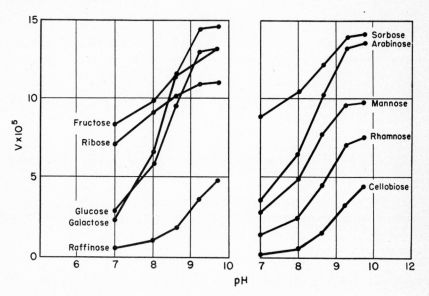

FIG. 19. Mobility of sugars in borate as function of pH (22).

*Detection:* Sugars can be observed with the following reagents: aniline phthalate, ammoniacal silver nitrate, *m*-phenyldiamine, benzidine, 3,4-dinitrobenzoate, triphenyltetrazolium chloride, naphthorescorcinol, permanganate solution or periodate-iodide starch. The use of the last has been reinvestigated by Metzenberg and Mitchell (105). Several of the reagents will also detect glycosides. Quantitative investigations are possible through photoelectric evaluation of the blackness of the reduced silver spot (143). More accurate values are obtained by eluting and photometering the colored compounds obtained with the reagents under standard conditions. Several of the nucleosides have specific ultraviolet absorption peaks.

*4.2.6. Nucleotides and other Phosphoric Acid Derivatives. Separation:* At pH 4 (acetate buffer) adenosine-5-monophosphate (AMP), adenosine-

5-diphosphate (ADP), and adenosine triphosphate (ATP) exist as one, two, and three functional anions. Since ionic radii do not increase uniformly in this series as the electric charge increases, ATP moves most rapidly, AMP most slowly (140). The inorganic ortho-, pyro-, and triphosphates show opposite velocities at pH 10 (sodium borate–sodium hydroxide buffer). Although the velocity differences are small, separation is possible with orthophosphate as the fastest component. Trimeta- and other phosphates can be separated similarly (120). Nucleotides from hydrolysis products of nucleic acids can readily be separated in acid buffers on paper (29, 152) or agar (43). They move with increasing velocity toward the anode in $M/20$ sodium acetate–acetic acid at pH 2.8 in the sequence cytidylic, adenylic, guanylic, and uridylic acid (Fig. 20)

FIG. 20. Pherogram of a mixture (0.5% each) of yeast adenylic acid (A), cytidylic acid (C), guanylic acid (G), and uridylic acid (U), $\frac{1}{20}M$ acetate–acetic acid, pH 2.8, 120 volts, 5 hr. (152).

(152). The technique is so powerful that di- and trinucleotides also separate into sharp zones, particularly at high voltages (97). Adenosine-5-phosphate can be separated in borate buffer from adenosine-3-phosphate in view of the complexing of the former with borate (63). Hydrogenated DPN can be easily separated from DPN at pH 6 owing to its more acid character (Pfleiderer, unpublished). Intermediates of biosynthesis of co-enzyme A from pantothenic acid labeled with $C^{14}$ in microorganisms were analyzed by means of pherography (159a).

Separation of ribo- and deoxyribonucleic acids in veronal buffer at pH 8.6 and 10 volts/cm. proceeds readily in 6 hr., as shown by radioactive analysis using $P^{32}$ (27). Larger amounts can be identified by dyeing with methyl green–pyronin. Ribonucleic acids obtained by different methods from the same cells or by the same method from different cells show different migration speeds. In acid medium at pH 2.5 three different zones are reported (65, 126).

Phosphoric acid esters of sugars can be separated as shown by $P^{32}$ tracing in veronal buffer at pH 8.6 and 10 volts/cm. (123). Figure 21 shows the radiochemical analysis of a separated mixture of fructose-6-phosphate, fructose-1,6-diphosphate, and phosphate.

*Detection:* In contrast to nucleotides the ultraviolet absorption spectrum is weak. Detection of phosphate derivatives is carried out by simultaneous hydrolysis of esters with ammonium molybdate containing $HClO_4$ and HCl (61). The subsequent reduction of the molybdenum phosphate complex to molybdenum blue by hydrogen sulfide is best carried out by exposure to UV light (119). For quantitative detection use of retention analysis is suggested (152).

*4.2.7. Organic Acids, Bases, and Alkaloids.* Although the pK values of many organic acids are remarkably different, only few experiments have been carried out on their pherographic separation. Wieland and

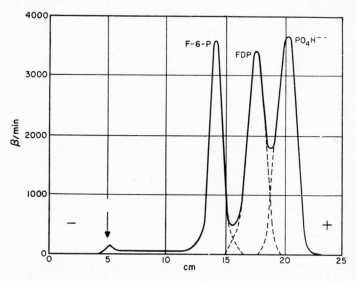

FIG. 21. Pherographic separation of $P^{32}$-fructose-6-phosphate (F-6-P), fructose-1,6-diphosphate (FDP), and phosphate (123).

Feld (151) reported the separation of citric and tartaric acid in 1951 in $\frac{1}{50}$ M acetate buffer at pH 7. Retention analysis was used for detection. Other hydroxy-acids and dicarboxylic acids (lactic acid, oxalic acid succinic acid) were separated in aqueous 2 N ammonia solution with subsequent development with indicators (unpublished). Recently the separation of stearic, palmitic, myristic, and lauric acid was described on an 86-cm.-long cotton wick. The ionophoresis was carried out for 36 hr. in 3 N aqueous ammonia at 300 volts (2). This separation can also be performed on paper (1a). Separation of all fatty acids was possible using 0.2 N NaOH in glycerol at 90° (111a).

An excellent separation of the first five stages of condensation between formaldehyde and *p*-phenol sulfonic acid was carried out on agar and observed spectroscopically at 255 mμ (Fig. 22) (111).

$$
\underset{0}{\overset{\text{OH}}{\underset{\text{SO}_3\text{H}}{\bigcirc}}} + \text{HCHO} \rightarrow
\underset{\text{I}}{\overset{\text{HOCH}_2\ \ \text{OH}}{\underset{\text{SO}_3\text{H}}{\bigcirc}}}
\overset{\text{HCHO}}{\longrightarrow}
\underset{\text{II}}{\overset{\text{HOCH}_2\ \ \text{OH}\ \ \text{CH}_2\text{OH}}{\underset{\text{SO}_3\text{H}}{\bigcirc}}}
$$

$$
\text{I} + 0 \rightarrow
\underset{\text{III}}{\overset{\text{OH}\ \ \text{CH}_2\ \ \text{OH}}{\underset{\text{SO}_3\text{H}\ \ \ \text{SO}_3\text{H}}{\bigcirc\bigcirc}}}
\rightarrow \text{TRIMER}
$$

$$
\text{II} + 0 \rightarrow
\underset{\text{IV}}{\overset{\text{OH}\ \ \text{CH}_2\ \ \text{OH}\ \ \text{CH}_2\text{OH}}{\underset{\text{SO}_3\text{H}\ \ \ \text{SO}_3\text{H}}{\bigcirc\bigcirc}}}
\rightarrow \text{TRIMER}
$$

$$
\text{II} + \text{I} \rightarrow
\underset{\text{V}}{\overset{\text{HOCH}_2\ \ \text{OH}\ \ \text{CH}_2\ \ \text{OH}\ \ \text{CH}_2\text{OH}}{\underset{\text{SO}_3\text{H}\ \ \ \text{SO}_3\text{H}}{\bigcirc\bigcirc}}}
\rightarrow \text{TRIMER}
$$

The separation of dyes in a Hyflo-Super-Cel column was described on page 30. Paper pherography is a convenient and accurate separating technique for the detection of acids in mixtures, such as 3-indole acetic acid in plant extracts (28); of p-amino salicylic acid from isonicotinic acid hydrazide in pharmaceutical preparations (129); or of acid sulfonamides (81). Separation of sulfonphthalein-dyes has also been described (39a).

Basic substances of varied structures can also be successfully handled analytically or preparatively. Weber (145) in the apparatus of page 44 has successfully separated glycine, phenylethylamine, histamine, cadaverine, dimethyl amine, and monomethyl amine in citrate buffer at pH 3.8 (7.5 volts/cm.). Identification is by ninhydrin. The fate of radioactive mescaline and phenylethyl amine in animals was determined similarly (4).

Streptomycin and its basic degradation products could be separated on the basis of their differing cathodic migration at pH 5 and identified with specific reagents (38).

Several basic $B_{12}$-simulating vitamins (microbiological tests) could be identified in feces besides neutral vitamin $B_{12}$ in 2 $N$ acetic acid (pH 2.1, 8 volts/cm., HCN atmosphere, 16 hr.) (60).

In preparative organic chemistry the method has been employed only sparingly. An example is the separation of amino derivatives of fluorene and diphenyl in 20% acetic acid (112). Synthetic acidic or basic dyes not analyzable by standard techniques because of insolubility in aqueous buffers can be separated into sharp zones in nonaqueous electrolytes such as nitromethane, acetic acid, and alcohol (110).

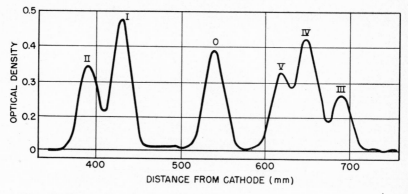

Fig. 22. Separation of early condensation products of formaldehyde and $p$-phenolsulfonic acid in agar (111).

Pherography is of considerable use in the alkaloid field. Several indol alkaloids in calabash curare have been successfully separated (Wieland, unpublished). Particularly useful was the differentiation of quarternary ammonia compounds from other ammonium derivatives. The latter lose their charge in strongly alkaline buffers and stop migrating while the former migrate with undiminished speed toward the cathode (154). Deckers and Schreiber (26) and Burma (15) have described separation of mixtures of various alkaloids.

*4.2.8. Inorganic Ions.* The problem of separating inorganic isotopes was the motivating force behind the construction of the apparatus to be described. In 1923 Kendall and Crittenden (68) attempted separation of chlorine isotopes by placing a sodium chloride containing agar plug in the middle of a long $U$ tube, adding chloride-free agar to the legs of the tube, and putting a potential difference across the tube. The path length chosen was too small for separation in view of the small difference in ionophoretic speed. It demonstrated however that the separation of $SCN^-$ from $I^-$ and of $Ba^{++}$ from $Ca^{++}$ proceeded very readily (69). Considerable enrichment could also be achieved with the rare-earth metals (70). Brewer *et al.* (11) were able to separate the potassium isotopes in a short distance in tubes filled with various materials (sand, glass, wool, etc.) by balancing the electrophoretic movement with a carefully controlled counterflow of electrolyte (countercurrent electromigration). In a cell with a packing consisting of closely spaced diaphragms, whose planes lie perpendicular to the flow of the countercurrent liquid an enrichment of $Rb^{85}$ was attained by Ramirez (114a).

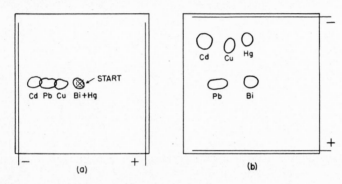

Fig. 23. Two-dimensional pherograms of heavy metal ions (134): (*a*) development with $0.1M$ lactic acid (first phase), (*b*) development with ammonium hydroxide (second phase).

Inorganic ionic mixtures $Rb^+/Na^+$, $Li^+/Na^+$, $Rb^+/Cs^+$, $Li^+/Na^+/K^+$ and organic ions such as acetate and citrate can easily be separated (10).

Strain, who had described the ionophoretic separation of dyes in a column (132), carried his technique over to filter paper and reported successful and continuous separation of ions in a simple electrographic cell (133).

For analytical purposes discontinuous operation suffices. Sensitivity can be increased by a two-dimensional technique using two different buffers (134). Since many ions of heavy metals are adsorbed on most papers, it is necessary to use complex-forming electrolytes, such as lactic acid. A two-dimensional pherogram with cations of the copper group ($Cu^{++}$, $Cd^{++}$, $Hg^{++}$, $Sb^{++}$, $Bi^{++}$) is shown in Fig. 23. Starting at the addition point $X$, the ions were first developed in $0.1\ M$ lactic acid moving toward the cathode. Afterward the mixture was made alkaline with ammonium hydroxide and pherographed again at right angles. Similarly, the metals of the ammonium sulfide group ($Al^{+++}$, $Mn^{++}$, $Fe^{++}$, $Co^{++}$, $Ni^{++}$, $Zn^{++}$, $CrO_4^=$) can be separated, the chromate ion migrating toward the anode. Attempts to separate the rare metals were only partially successful (121). Concurrently Lederer (82) undertook similar separations of the ions of the copper group in 0.5 N HCl. He also made use for the first time of the principle of charge alteration on complexing. Thus cobalt forms an anionic complex with thiocyanate.

An example of separating inorganic anions (phosphate, ortho-, di-, and tri-phosphates) has been given on page 59. Phosphites can be separated from ortho-phosphates owing to their greater mobility at pH 8 (73). The separation of chlorite, chlorate, and hypochlorite proceeds readily in

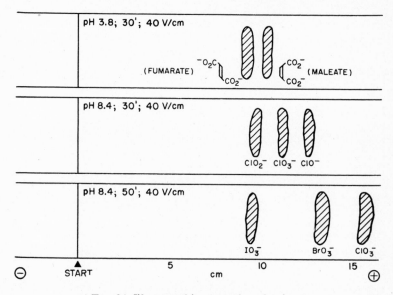

Fig. 24. Pherographic separation of anions.

buffers of triethanolamine acetate at pH 8.4 (Fig. 24). Also shown is the separation of fumarate and maleate and of iodate, bromate, and chlorate (Dose in 153a). Identification can be carried out by the many gaseous or spray reagents developed for the paper chromatography of inorganic ions. The detection of radioactive isotopes is particularly sensitive (122).

*4.2.9. Other Applications.* In addition to separating mixtures of charged particles and their preparative resolution, several other applications are possible.

*a.* The acidic or basic nature of an unknown substance can be determined and quaternary and other nitrogen bases differentiated. The isoelectric point of an unknown ampholyte can be determined provided the magnitude of the electroosmotic flow is determined with a neutral marker.

*b.* Ion migrations can be determined with reasonable accuracy. Complex formations can be deduced from the effect of the nature of different electrolytes.

   c. In view of the rapid movement of inorganic ions in biological systems a convenient desalting technique is available by use of volatile buffers. For this purpose the solution is added in the middle of a 30-cm.-wide filter-paper sheet, saturated with pyridine–acetic acid–water at pH 6 (100 cc. pyridine + 10 cc. acetic acid + 890 cc. water), and pressed out. As shown in Fig. 25, the ions travel to the indicated positions in 15 min. at a potential of 25 volts/cm. The amino acids aspartic acid and ornithine

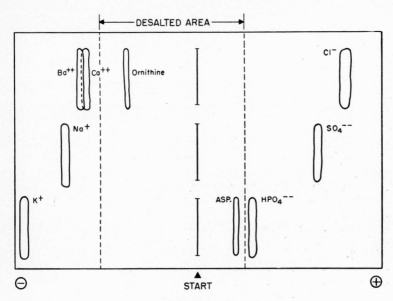

Fig. 25. Ionophoretic desalting on filter paper.

indicate the limit of the desalted region. Succinic acid cannot be separated from phosphoric acid. Varying the pH, as in aqueous ammonia, can make the desalting effective for almost all organic bases and acids, since in that case the phosphoric acid travels more rapidly toward the anode. In the device shown on p. 47 as much as 25 mg. of organic substance can be separated from twice that amount of salt.

### REFERENCES

   1. Arrhenius, S., *Brit. Assoc. Advance. Sci. Rept.* **56**, 334 (1886).
   1a. Barnett, A. J. G., and Smith, D. K., *Nature* **174**, 659 (1954).
   2. Barnett, J. E., Lees, H., and Smith, D. K., *Biochem. J.* **53**, xxxiii (1953).
   3. Biserte, G., *Biochim. et Biophys. Acta* **4**, 416 (1950).
   4. Block, W., *Z. Naturforsch.* **8b**, 440 (1953).

4a. Block, R. J., Durrum, E. L., and Zweig, G., "Paper Chromatography and Paper Electrophoresis." Academic Press, New York, 1955.
5. Bockemüller, W., and Rebling, R., *Chem. Ing. Tech.* **24**, 617 (1952).
6. Bode, F., Hübener, H. J., Brückner, H., and Hoeres, K., *Naturwissenschaften* **39**, 524 (1952).
7. Böeseken, J., *Chem. Ber.* **46**, 2612 (1953).
8. Böeseken, J., *Ber.* **56**, 2411 (1923).
9. Bradish, C. J., and Smart, N. V., *Nature* **174**, 272 (1954).
9a. Brattsten, I., and Nilson, A., *Arkiv Kemi* **3**, 337 (1951).
10. Brewer, A. K., *Chem. Abstr.* **46**, 1373g (1952).
11. Brewer, A. K., Madorski, S. C., and Westhover, J. W., *Science* **104**, 156 (1946).
12. Broda, E., and Schönfeld, T., *Monatsh.* **81**, 459 (1950).
13. Bücher, T., Matzelt, D., and Pette, D., *Naturwissenschaften* **39**, 114 (1952).
14. Bull, B. H., Hahn, J. W., and Baptist, V. H., *J. Am. Chem. Soc.* **71**, 550 (1949).
15. Burma, D. P., *Naturwissenschaften* **41**, 19 (1954).
16. Butler, J. A. V., and Stephen, J. M. L., *Nature* **160**, 469 (1947).
17. Caputo, A., *Nature* **173**, 358 (1954).
18. Choisy, A., Derrien, Y., and Jayle, G., *Compt. rend.* **234**, 1918 (1952).
19. Consden, R., and Bird, R., *Nature* **173**, 996 (1954).
20. Consden, R., Gordon, A. H., and Martin, A. J. P., *Biochem. J.* **40**, 33 (1946).
21. Consden, R., and Stanier, W. M., *Nature* **169**, 783 (1952).
22. Consden, R., and Stanier, W. M., *Nature* **170**, 1069 (1952).
23. Coolidge, T. B., *J. Biol. Chem.* **127**, 551 (1939).
24. Cramer, F., "Papier Chromatographie," 3rd ed. Verlag Chemie, Weinheim 1954.
25. Cremer, H. D., and Tiselius, A., *Biochem. Z.* **320**, 273 (1950).
26. Deckers, W., and Schreiber, J., *Naturwissenschaften* **40**, 553 (1953).
27. Deimel, M., and Maurer, W., *Naturwissenschaften* **39**, 489 (1952).
28. Denffer, D. v., Behrens, M., and Fischer, A., *Naturwissenschaften* **39**, 258 (1952).
29. Dimroth, K., Jaenicke, L., and Vollbrechtshausen, I., *Z. physiol. Chem.* **289**, 71 (1952).
30. Durrum, E. L., *J. Am. Chem. Soc.* **72**, 2943 (1950).
31. Durrum, E. L., *J. Am. Chem. Soc.* **73**, 4875 (1951).
32. Durrum, E. L., *J. Colloid Sci.* **6**, 274 (1951).
33. Edström, J. E., *Nature* **32**, 809 (1953).
34. Fischer, F. G., and Dörfel, H., *Biochem. Z.* **324**, 544 (1953).
35. Fischer, F. G., and Neumann, W. P., *Biochem. Z.* **324**, 447 (1953).
36. Flodin, P., and Porath, J., *Biochim. et Biophys. Acta* **13**, 175 (1954).
37. Fønss-Bech, P., and Li, C. H., *J. Biol. Chem.* **207**, 175 (1954).
38. Foster, M. C., and Ashton, G. C., *Nature* **172**, 959 (1953).
39. Foster, A. B., and Stacey, M., *J. Appl. Chem.* **3**, 19 (1953).
39a. Franglen, G. T., *Nature* **175**, 134 (1955).
40. Gardell, S., Gordon, A. H., and Aqvist, S., *Acta Chem. Scand.* **4**, 907 (1950).
41. Geldmacher-Mallinckrodt, M., and Weinland, H., *Z. physiol. Chem.* **292**, 65 (1953).
42. Gordon, A. H., Keil, B., and Sebesta, K., *Nature* **164**, 498 (1949).
42a. Gordon, A. H., Keil, B., Sebesta, K., and Šorm, F., *Collection Czechoslov. Chem. Communs.* **15**, 1 (1950).
43. Gordon, A. H., and Reichard, P., *Biochem. J.* **48**, 569 (1951).
44. Goulden, J. D. S., *Nature* **173**, 646 (1954).
45. Grassmann, W., *Med. Monatsschr.* **10**, 707 (1951).

46. Grassmann, W., and Hannig, K., *Naturwissenschaften* **37**, 397 (1950).
47. Grassmann, W., and Hannig, K., *Naturwissenschaften* **37**, 496 (1950).
48. Grassmann, W., *Naturwissenschaften* **38**, 200 (1951).
49. Grassmann, W., and Hannig, K., *Angew. Chem.* **62**, 170 (1950).
50. Grassmann, W., and Hannig, K., *Z. physiol. Chem.* **290**, 1 (1952).
51. Grassmann, W., and Hannig, K., *Z. physiol. Chem.* **292**, 32 (1953).
52. Grassmann, W., and Hannig, K., *Z. physiol. Chem.* **296**, 30 (1954).
53. Grassmann, W., Hannig, K., and Knedel, M., *Deut. med. Wochschr.* **76**, 333 (1951).
54. Gross, D., *Nature* **172**, 908 (1953).
55. Gross, D., *Nature* **173**, 487 (1954).
55a. Gross, D., *Nature* **176**, 72 (1955).
55b. Gross, D., *Nature* **176**, 362 (1955).
56. Haeglund, H., and Tiselius, A., *Acta Chem. Scand.* **4**, 957 (1950).
56a. Hanes, S. S., Hird, F. J. R., and Isherwood, F. A., *Biochem. J.* **51**, 25 (1952).
57. Hashimoto, Y., Mori, I., and Kimura, M., *Nature* **170**, 975 (1952).
58. Haugaard, G., and Kroner, T. D., *J. Am. Chem. Soc.* **70**, 2135 (1948).
59. Heilmeyer, L., Clotten, R., Sano, J., Sturm, A., Jr., and Lipp, A., *Klin. Wochschr.* **32**, 831 (1954).
59a. Henley, A., and Schuettler, C. L., "Electrophoresis Bibliography." American Instrument Company, Silver Spring, Md., 1953.
60. Holdsworth, E. S., *Nature* **171**, 148 (1953).
61. Isherwood, F. A., *Nature* **164**, 1107 (1949).
62. Isherwood, F. A., and Cruickshank, D. H., *Nature* **174**, 123 (1954).
63. Jaenicke, L., and Vollbrechtshausen, I., *Naturwissenschaften* **39**, 87 (1952).
64. Jermyn, M. A., and Thomas, R., *Nature* **172**, 728 (1953).
65. Kanngiesser, W., *Naturwissenschaften* **38**, 503 (1951).
66. Kawerau, E., and Wieland, T., *Nature* **168**, 77 (1951).
67. Kendall, J., *Science* **67**, 163 (1928).
68. Kendall, J., and Crittenden, E. D., *Proc. Natl. Acad. Sci. (U.S.)* **9**, 75 (1923).
69. Kendall, J., and White, J. F., *Proc. Natl. Acad. Sci. (U.S.)* **10**, 458 (1924).
70. Kendall, J., and Clarke, B. L., *Proc. Natl. Acad. Sci. (U.S.)* **11**, 393 (1925).
71. Kickhöfen, B., and Wesphal, O., *Z. Naturforsch.* **7b**, 655, 659 (1952).
72. Kimbel, K. H., *Naturwissenschaften* **40**, 200 (1953).
73. Klement, R., and Frieser, H., *Angew. Chem.* **66**, 138 (1954).
74. Klobusitzky, D., and König, P., *Naunyn-Schmiedeberg's Arch. exptl. Pathol. u. Pharmakol.* **192**, 271 (1939).
75. Kraus, K. A., and Smith, G. W., *J. Am. Chem. Soc.* **72**, 4329 (1950).
76. Krebs, K. G., and Wankmüller, A., *Naturwissenschaften* **40**, 623 (1953).
77. Kuhn, R., and Löw, I., *Chem. Ber.* **82**, 474 (1949).
78. Kunkel, H. G., and Slater, R. J., *J. Clin. Invest.* **31**, 677 (1952).
79. Kunkel, H. G., and Slater, R. J., *Proc. Soc. Exptl. Biol. Med.* **80**, 42 (1952).
80. Kunkel, H. G., and Tiselius, A., *J. Gen. Physiol.* **35**, 89 (1951).
80a. Kunkel, H. G., in "Methods of Biochemical Analysis" (D. Glick, ed.), Vol. I, p. 137. Interscience, New York, 1954.
81. Kutzim, H., *Naturwissenschaften* **39**, 135 (1952).
82. Lederer, M., *Nature* **167**, 864 (1951).
82a. Lederer, M., "An Introduction to Paper Electrophoresis and Relative Methods." Elsevier, New York, 1955.
83. Lederer, M., and Cook, J., *Australian J. Sci.* **14**, 56 (1951).

84. Lederer, M., and Ward, F. L., *Australian J. Sci.* **13**, 114 (1951).
85. Li, C. H., Geschwind, I. I., Levy, A. L., Harris, J. I., Dixon, J. S., Pon, N. G., and Porath, J., *Nature* **173**, 251 (1954).
86. Lodge, O., *Brit. Assoc. Advance Sci. Rept.* **56**, 389 (1886).
87. McDonald, H. J., *J. Chem. Educ.* **29**, 428 (1952).
87a. McDonald, H. J., *et al.*, *Clin. Chemist* **5**, 17, 35, 51 (1953).
88. McDonald, H. J., Lappe, R. J., Marbach, E. P., Spitzer, R. H., and Urbin, M. C., *Clin. Chemist* **5**, 35 (1953).
89. McDonald, H. J., and Marbach, E. P., *J. Biochem. (Japan)* **40**, 111 (1953).
90. McDonald, H. J., and Spitzer, R. H., *Circulation Research* **1**, 396 (1953).
91. McDonald, H. J., Urbin, M. C., and Williamson, M. B., *J. Colloid. Sci.* **6**, 236 (1951).
92. McDonald, H. J., Urbin, M. C., and Williamson, M. B., *Science* **112**, 227 (1950).
93. Macheboeuf, M., *Chem. Weekblad* **49**, 237 (1953).
94. Macheboeuf, M., Rebeyrotte, P., and Brunerie, M., *Bull. soc. chim. biol.* **33**, 334, 346 (1951).
95. Martin, A. J. P., and Synge, R. L. M., *Advances in Protein Chem.* **2**, 32 (1945).
96. Manecke, G., *Naturwissenschaften* **39**, 62 (1952).
97. Markham, R., and Smith, J. D., *Nature* **168**, 406 (1951).
98. Michl, H., *Monatsh.* **82**, 489 (1951).
99. Michl, H., *Monatsh.* **83**, 210 (1952).
100. Michl, H., *Monatsh.* **83**, 737 (1952).
100a. Michl, H., *Monatsh.* **85**, 1251 (1954).
101. Michl, H., *Naturwissenschaften* **41**, 403 (1954).
102. Miettinen, J. K., *Suomen Kemistilehti* **A2**, 49 (1953).
103. Müller, R. H., and Wise, E. N., *Anal. Chem.* **23**, 207 (1951).
104. Müting, D., *Naturwissenschaften* **39**, 303 (1952).
105. Metzenberg, R. L., and Mitchell, H. K., *J. Am. Chem. Soc.* **76**, 4187 (1954).
106. Neumann, W., Habermann, E., and Amend, G., *Naturwissenschaften* **39**, 286 (1952).
107. Nikkilä, E. A., Haahti, E., and Pesola, R., *Acta Chem. Scand.* **7**, 1222 (1953).
108. Niklas, A., and Maurer, W., *Naturwissenschaften* **39**, 260 (1952).
108a. Nöller, G., *Klin. Wochschr.* **32**, 988 (1954).
109. Papastamatis, S. C., and Kench, J. E., *Nature* **170**, 33 (1952).
110. Paul, M. H., and Durrum, E. L., *J. Am. Chem. Soc.* **74**, 4721 (1952).
111. Peniston, Q. P., Agar, H. D., and McCarthy, J. L., *Anal. Chem.* **23**, 994 (1951).
111a. Perilä, O., *Acta Chem. Scand.* **9**, 1231 (1955).
112. Peters, J. H., and Gutmann, H. G., *J. Am. Chem. Soc.* **76**, 2267 (1954).
113. Pfeil, E., and Kanngiesser, W., *Z. physiol. Chem.* **296**, 79 (1954).
113a. Porath, J., *Naturwissenschaften* **175**, 478 (1955).
113b. Pučar, Z., *Arkiv Kemi* **25**, 205 (1953); **26**, 29, 41 (1954).
114. Quastel, J. H., and Straten van, S. F., *Proc. Soc. Exptl. Biol. Med.* **81**, 6 (1952).
114a. Ramirez, E. R., *J. Am. Chem. Soc.* **76**, 6237 (1954).
115. Reindel, F., and Hoppe, W., *Chem. Ber.* **87**, 1103 (1954).
116. Rienits, K. G., *Biochem. J.* **53**, 79 (1953).
117. Röttger, H., *Experientia* **9**, B 150 (1953).
118. Röttger, H., *Naturwissenschaften* **39**, 451 (1952).
118a. Ryle, A. P., Sanger, F., Smith, L. F., and Kitai, R., *Biochem. J.* **60**, 541 (1955).
119. Sansoni, B., *Angew. Chem.* **65**, 423 (1953).
120. Sansoni, B., and Klement, R., *Angew. Chem.* **65**, 422 (1953).

121. Sato, T. R., Diamond, H., Norris, W. P., and Strain, H. H., *J. Am. Chem. Soc.* **74,** 6154 (1952).
122. Sato, T. R., Kisieleski, W. E., Norris, W. P., and Strain, H. H., *Anal. Chem.* **25,** 438 (1953).
123. Schild, K. T., and Bottenbruch, L., *Z. physiol. Chem.* **292,** 1 (1953).
124. Schmeiser, K., and Jerchel, D., *Angew. Chem.* **65,** 366 (1953).
125. Schmeiser, K., and Jerchel, D., *Angew. Chem.* **65,** 490 (1953).
125a. Schneider, G., and Sparmann, G., *Naturwissenschaften* **42,** 156 (1955).
126. Schümmelfelder, N., and Heyer, W., *Naturwissenschaften* **41,** 164 (1954).
127. Schwarze, P., *Naturwissenschaften* **40,** 21 (1953).
128. Semm, K., and Fried, R., *Naturwissenschaften* **39,** 326 (1952).
129. Smolarek, W., and Dlugosh, G., *Naturwissenschaften* **41,** 18 (1954).
130. Šorm, F., and Keil, B., *Collection Czechoslov. Chem. Communs.* **16,** 366 (1951).
131. Spiegler, K. S., and Coryell, C. D., *Science* **113,** 546 (1951).
132. Strain, H. H., *J. Am. Chem. Soc.* **61,** 1291 (1939).
133. Strain, H. H., and Sullivan, J. C., *Anal. Chem.* **23,** 816 (1951).
134. Strain, H. H., *Anal. Chem.* **24,** 356 (1952).
134a. Strain, H. H., *et al.*, *Anal. Chem.* **24,** 50 (1952); **26,** 90 (1954).
135. Svensson, H., and Brattsten, I., *Arkiv Kemi* **1,** 401 (1949).
135a. Svensson, H., *Science Tools LKB Instr. J.* **2,** 11 (1955).
136. Synge, R. L. M., *Biochem. J.* **39,** 355, 363 (1945).
137. Taylor, S. P., Jr., Vigneaud, V. du, *J. Biol. Chem.* **205,** 45 (1953).
138. Teague, O., and Buxton, B. H., *J. Exptl. Med.* **9,** 254 (1907).
138a. Tiselius, A., and Flodin, P., *Advances in Protein Chem.* **8,** 461 (1953).
138b. Turba, F., "Chromatographische Methoden in der Protein-chemie," pp. 324–349. Springer, Berlin, 1954.
139. Turba, F., and Enenkel, H. J., *Naturwissenschaften* **37,** 93 (1950).
140. Turba, F., and Enenkel, H. J., *Naturwissenschaften* **38,** 189 (1951).
141. Turba, F., and Esser, H., *Angew. Chem.* **65,** 256 (1953).
141a. Turba, F., and Esser, H., *Biochem. Z.* **327,** 83 (1955).
141b. Valmet, E., and Svensson, H., *Science Tools LKB Instrument J.* **1,** 3 (1956).
142. Vandegaer, J. E., and Miettinen, J. K., *Acta Chem. Scand.* **7,** 1239 (1953).
143. Wallenfels, K., Bernt, E., and Limberg, G., *Angew Chem.* **65,** 581 (1953).
144. Wallenfels, K., and Pechmann, E. v., *Angew. Chem.* **63,** 44 (1951).
145. Weber, R., *Helv. Chim. Acta* **34,** 2031 (1951).
146. Weicker, H., *Klin. Wochschr.* **31,** 161 (1953).
147. Weller, A. L., *Chromatog. Bull.* **7,** 5 (1950).
147a. Welte, E., *Angew. Chem.* **67,** 153 (1955).
147b. Werner, G., and Westphal, O., *Angew. Chem.* **67,** 251 (1955).
148. Wetham, W. C. D., *Phil. Trans. Roy. Soc.* **184A,** 337 (1893).
149. Wetham, W. C. D., *Phil. Trans. Roy. Soc.* **186A,** 507 (1895).
150. Wetham, W. C. D., *Phil. Mag.* **38,** 398 (1894).
151. Wieland, T., and Feld, U., *Angew. Chem.* **63,** 258 (1951).
152. Wieland, T., and Bauer, L., *Angew. Chem.* **63,** 511 (1951).
153. Wieland, T., and Fischer, E., *Naturwissenschaften* **35,** 29 (1948).
153a. Wieland, T., and Pfleiderer, G., *Angew. Chem.* **67,** 257 (1955).
154. Wieland, T., Fritz, H., Hasspacher, K., and Bauer, A., *Ann.* **588,** 1 (1954).
155. Wieland, T., Goldmann, H., Kern, W., *et al.*, *Makromol. Chem.* **10,** 136 (1953).
156. Wieland, T., and Wirth, L., *Angew. Chem.* **62,** 473 (1950).
157. Wieland, T., Wirth, L., and Fischer, E., *Ann.* **564,** 152 (1949).

158. Wieland, T., and Dose, K., *Biochem. Z.* **325,** 439 (1954).
159. Wieland, T., and Turba, F., *in* "Methoden der organischen Chemie" (Houben-Weyl, ed.), Vol. II, 4th ed., p. 860. Thieme, Stuttgart, 1952-1954.
159a. Wieland, T., Maul, W., and Moeller, E. F., *Biochem. Z.* **327,** 85 (1955).
159b. Wieland, T., and Dose, K., *Angew. Chem.* **66,** 781 (1954).
160. Wunderly, C., "Die Papierelektrophorese," Verlag Sauerländer, Aarau, Switzerland, 1954.
161. Wynn, V., *Nature* **164,** 445 (1949).
162. Zentner, H., *Nature* **175,** 953 (1955).

# Electroanalytical Methods in Trace Analysis

BY

W. DONALD COOKE

*Baker Laboratory, Cornell University, Ithaca, New York*

## 1. INTRODUCTION

In recent years scientists in widely different fields of endeavor are becoming increasingly aware of the important role of minor constituents in various phenomena. Extremely small quantities of material, sometimes as low as $10^{-6}\%$, can exert profound chemical and catalytic influences. The effect of microgram quantities of vitamins and hormones has been known for a long time. Traces of various metals are also of great importance in biological systems as well as in various aspects of technology. Cobalt and molybdenum are essential metals for some types of plant life. The minimum amounts of these metals are so small that they are undoubtedly associated with powerful enzyme systems affecting growth. At least eight metallic elements can be found in the human brain, including aluminum, lead, silver, beryllium, and titanium. The function of such metals is still in the realm of speculation, but their balance in some cases can be correlated with certain physiological disorders. Quantities of metals in crude oil stocks, amounting to only a few parts per billion, have deleterious effects on the catalysts used in the cracking process. Many other problems in the fields of atomic energy, corrosion, and catalysis are concerned with minute concentrations of metals. The amounts of material are often vanishingly small, and highly refined analytical methods are usually necessary. Research involving traces of metals is often hampered by the difficulty in developing such analytical methods, and at times progress must wait for the development of reasonable procedures for analysis. It is quite possible that as the analytical chemist develops more sensitive, convenient methods many other instances of the potent influences of trace metals will be discovered.

Many new analytical methods have been devised, and existing procedures extended, to accommodate the analysis of such small quantities of material. Radioactivation analysis (2), isotope-ratio procedures (24), and mass spectrometry of solids (59) are some of the more recent developments. No procedure is universally applicable, and each has specific advantages and disadvantages which vary greatly with the individual sample being analyzed. The purpose of this chapter is to outline some of the more sensitive electrochemical procedures that may be applied to analysis of small quantities of material.

The great advances made in electroanalytical chemistry are due in no small part to the availability of electronic equipment and its adoption by the analytical chemist. The versatility of such apparatus and the fact that low voltages and currents can be easily handled have led to applications that were formerly impossible from an experimental viewpoint.

The term *microanalysis* as currently used, connotes a procedure in which the original sample size is between 0.1 and 10 mg. This usage has been recognized by the Committee on Nomenclature, Division of Analytical Chemistry (21), which has recommended its general acceptance. Unfortunately the term has also been applied to analyses in which the amount of material being determined, regardless of sample size, falls within these limits. It seems that this practice will persist simply because no system of nomenclature is available which is concerned with the amount of the material being determined. The term *trace analysis* is finding increasing application to analyses in which the species being determined comprises only a small percentage of the sample. The word *trace* has been defined by the above-mentioned committee as "a very small quantity of a constituent, especially when not quantitatively determined because of its minuteness." This definition seems to weaken the use of *trace analysis*. Further, there is no quantitative evaluation of such terms in common usage, and what one worker refers to as a "trace" may differ by many orders of magnitude from what is meant by another. It seems that there is no nomenclature available, much less one generally accepted, which is useful to workers who are concerned with the analysis of minor constituents or dilute solutions.

It must be borne in mind that there is a distinct and fundamental difference in the techniques involved in the analysis of a small sample as compared with the analysis of a minor constituent in a relatively large amount of material. With small samples the methods of analysis are often similar to those applied to macroquantities of material. The difference lies in the experimental techniques necessary to the handling of such samples and the application of known methods on a greatly reduced scale.

Many of the methods require marvelous experimental ingenuity and allow investigators to apply analytical methods directly to quantities of material as small as a single cell (18, 28). Gravimetric, volumetric, and colorimetric procedures have been applied to such problems, and the concentration of the material being determined is usually of the same order of magnitude as in conventional macromethods.

In the analysis of minor constituents of samples (which includes dilute solutions) the problems facing an investigator are distinctly different. The difficulty lies in the modification of existing methods and the development of new methods to attain the requisite sensitivity. The apparatus usually presents no problem as in most instances ordinary macroequipment is adequate. For example, ordinary potentiometric titrations can be applied to microanalytical problems by using small electrodes in conjunction with microburettes. In the potentiometric titration of a dilute solution, however, this procedure is inadequate and special methods for detection of the endpoint must be applied. It seems that these useful fields of analysis have little in common.

It might be thought that minor constituents could be isolated as a small volume of concentrated solution and analyzed by microchemical techniques. In some instances this procedure is feasible, but more often the volume of solution after the sample is dissolved, and the large amount of other material present preclude such an approach.

The problem of trace analysis of microsamples is a field which offers interesting possibilities.

## 2. Separation of Minor Constituents

The problem of isolating a minor constituent from a sample is a difficult procedure which is often necessary in trace analysis. Even analytical methods which are highly specific in conventional systems sometimes fall down when the amount of the interfering substance is increased by a factor of $10^4$ or $10^8$. The advent of ion exchange resins and chromatographic techniques, in conjunction with recent developments in analytical extractions, has offered a whole new approach to the problem of trace-component isolation. At present it seems that electrochemical separations cannot compete with these methods in scope, speed, versatility, and convenience. However, since this chapter is concerned with electrochemical procedures, only this type of separation will be discussed even though it is realized that many of the recent advances in trace analysis have been made possible by these other techniques.

The most common usage of electrochemical separations is found in the preliminary removal of an interfering species at a mercury cathode. Particularly in polarographic analysis it is possible to remove a bulk component which yields a reduction wave at more positive potentials than the substance being determined. Ordinarily the large magnitude of the resulting wave would mask the presence of the desired polarogram. The scope of this method has been greatly increased by controlling the cathode potential so that a particular species may be selectively removed (34). Lingane (33) has shown that it is possible by this technique to determine small quantities of lead, tin, nickel, and zinc in copper-base alloys. The copper and bismuth, which would seriously interfere with the polarography of the minor metals, are removed by controlled potential deposition. The lead and tin can be then analyzed, and subsequently removed, so that the nickel and zinc, which have still more negative half-wave potentials, may be determined. The converse problem of small amounts of copper in lead-base alloys offers no difficulty since the polarogram of the copper ion occurs at a positive potential and lead does not interfere.

Recently attempts have been made to recover the deposited metals from the mercury cathode for the isolation of a desired constituent. Furman (14) devised a method by which heavy metals could be plated out of a solution and subsequently recovered by evaporation of the mercury. It is also possible to recover the deposited metals by the anodic decomposition of the amalgam at controlled anode potentials (46, 54).

The electrochemical methods of separation of traces of metals have not been so successful as extraction and ion exchange procedures; however, it has been shown that electrodepositions can be applied to amounts of metal so small that the electrode is covered with less than a complete monolayer (50). It has also been demonstrated that electrochemical laws still hold at dilutions far beyond the scope of current analytical problems ($10^{-12}$–$10^{-15}$ $M$) (20). Future research might well take advantage of these facts and extend the scope and versatility of electrochemical methods of separations.

# 3. POLAROGRAPHY

## 3.1. Dropping Mercury Electrode

Polarographic procedures using a dropping mercury electrode have been widely applied to the determination of a great variety of inorganic as well as organic analytical problems. The method is admirably suited to the analysis of minor constituents when the amount of material is not too small. The large number of elements listed in Table I (*Physical Methods in Chemical Analysis*, Vol. II, p. 6) indicate the scope of the method when applied to the analysis of metals. A large number of organic functional groups can also be determined polarographically, but there have not been as many applications to the analysis of organic minor constituents.

Polarography is valuable because it is essentially a separation procedure combined with a method for determination. Since metals have different half-wave potentials, a high degree of specificity can be obtained for a particular analysis. Chemical separations are unnecessary if the sequence of half-wave potentials is such that the desired constituent is reduced at a more positive voltage than any other species present in solution. It is even possible at times, to change the order of half-wave potentials by the correct choice of supporting electrolyte. For example, in potassium chloride medium copper can be determined in large amounts of lead, while with potassium cyanide as a supporting electrolyte, the copper wave is shifted beyond the lead wave so that small amounts of lead may be determined in copper.

The qualitative information offered by the position of the half-wave potential is particularly useful in trace analysis. The nature of an unsuspected interfering ion or contaminant can be thus ascertained. It is also possible at times to identify and determine more than one metal from a single polarographic analysis.

The concentration range covered by conventional quantitative polarographic procedures is about $2 \times 10^{-5}$ $M$ to $5 \times 10^{-3}$ $M$. This is somewhat above the usual range of concentrations involved in trace analysis although in some cases it is adequate. However, it is possible to use volumes of solution as small as 0.01 ml. (*see Physical Methods in Chemical Analysis*, Vol. II, p. 10) and so the absolute amount of material determined may be quite low; for example, 0.01 ml. of $2 \times 10^{-5}$ $M$ zinc ion contains 0.015 $\mu$g. of metal. It is not always possible to isolate the desired species in a volume as small as 0.01 ml. but concentration to a 1-ml. volume is not difficult. In the analysis of biological samples, the metal can easily be concentrated to a small volume after the sample is ashed or digested.

A word might be mentioned concerning the effect of the presence of residual dissolved oxygen in the polarography of dilute solutions. It seems that reducing the concentration of the dissolved oxygen to a degree that no oxygen wave is obtained is not sufficient deaeration when high sensitivity is desired. The presence of the oxygen causes a different slope to be obtained for the residual current and the plateau of the wave, as shown in Fig. 1a. Under these circumstances it is difficult to know how the diffusion current should be measured. More rigorous removal of oxygen minimizes this difficulty, as shown in Fig. 1b. The author has found that

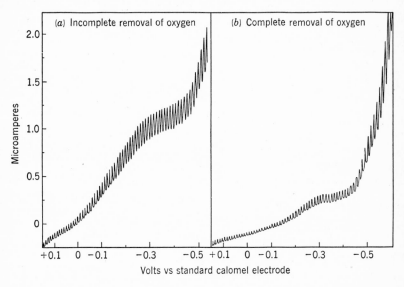

FIG. 1. Effect of traces of oxygen on polarograms. ($3 \times 10^{-7}$ $M$ Mo$^{VI}$ in 2 $M$ HNO$_3$.)

the method of deaeration proposed by Laitenen (32) is very efficient. In this procedure the nitrogen enters the solution through a sintered-glass disk and is dispersed in extremely fine bubbles. The addition of a few per cent of isopropanol allows equilibrium to be attained in less than 1 min. (56).

3.1.1. *Procedures for Extending Sensitivity.* As previously mentioned, conventional quantitative polarographic methods can be applied to solutions with a concentration of $2 \times 10^{-5}$ $M$ or more. A somewhat higher sensitivity is attainable at lower levels of concentration with decreasing accuracy. The factor that limits further extension to more dilute solutions is not the small currents involved, but the relatively high charging or condenser current associated with the dropping mercury electrode. This current is obtained even in the absence of a reducible species and is associated with the continuously renewed mercury-solution interface. The charge of the double layer at the surface of the electrode is supplied by this current, and as each drop falls this charge must be renewed. With $10^{-3}$ $M$ solutions the magnitude of this charging current is small compared with the diffusion current. At lower concentrations of the reducible species, however, the condenser current background becomes more troublesome and the accuracy of the determinations is decreased markedly below $5 \times 10^{-5}$ $M$. A polarogram, recorded for a solution of $5 \times 10^{-5}$ $M$ lead, is shown in Fig. 2 as well as the condenser curve obtained in the

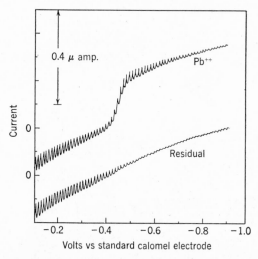

Fig. 2. Polarogram of $2 \times 10^{-5}$ $M$ Pb$^{++}$ and residual current.

absence of lead ion. The idea of using multiple dropping mercury electrodes to increase diffusion currents seems to be of little value. In such cases the ratio of diffusion current to charging current, which is the limiting factor, remains unchanged.

*3.1.2. Catalytic Polarographic Reductions.* In some isolated instances the sensitivity of conventional polarographic procedures can be extended if a catalytic reduction is possible. In such a process the material being determined acts as a catalyst for the electrolytic reduction of some substance which is present in a relatively high definite concentration in the supporting electrolyte. Since the concentration of the material undergoing reduction is large, the polarographic waves obtained are greatly increased in height. As the residual current is not increased, however, greater sensitivity is possible. The heights of such waves vary with the amount of catalyst present although the dependence is usually not linear and a calibration curve must be constructed. The polarographic currents obtained are not controlled by diffusion but by the rate of the catalyzed reaction.

One example of the application of catalytic reductions is the increased sensitivity for the polarography of uranyl ion in the presence of nitrate (22). Nitrate ion, normally not reduced at voltages more positive than $-2$ v. (versus the standard calomel electrode) yields a polarogram with a half-wave potential of $-1.2$ v. when uranyl or uranous ions are present. Since the amount of uranium required to catalyze this reaction is small, solutions as dilute as $10^{-6}$ $M$ can be determined. Unfortunately, a great many ions cause serious interference, and so the method is of limited applicability.

Tungstate, molybdate, and vanadate also yield catalytic reduction waves in the presence of hydrogen peroxide (30). The procedure has a great sensitivity, as evidenced by the fact that an $8 \times 10^{-7}$ $M$ solution of vanadate ion gives a current of about 18 $\mu$a. The shape of this polarogram is unusual, and interferences cause great difficulty.

Catalytic reductions are not always subject to the many difficulties previously discussed. Johnson (26) presented a method for the determination of molybdate in the presence of nitric acid. The author has slightly modified this method and studied some of the interferences involved (5). It appears that the molybdate, or more probably $Mo^V$, is the active species. Upon electrolytic reduction, the product $Mo^{III}$ is reoxidized by nitric acid and the reduction current obtained is not diffusion controlled but is determined by the rate of the reaction between $Mo^{III}$ and nitric acid. The sensitivity obtained is quite high and the shape of the wave is excellent, as can be seen in Fig. 3. The sensitivity of the method is more than one hundred times that of conventional procedures. An important aspect of this catalytic reduction is that very few ions change the height of the wave; for example, 0.1 $M$ solutions of hydrochloric acid, sulfuric acid, and potassium sulfate, have no effect on the molybdenum wave. Complexing agents such as citrate and phosphate when present above 0.01 $M$ must be removed. Because of the positive position of the wave, and the increased sensitivity for molybdenum, no other metals were found which cause serious interference. Copper ion is reduced at essentially the same potential but three times as much copper as molybdenum will increase the wave height by only 5%. This method for molybdenum, being both sensitive and specific, should be of great value in the determination of traces of this metal.

*3.1.3. Compensation Procedures.* Since polarographic methods are limited by the small height of the diffusion wave compared with the charging current, the sensitivity could be extended by reducing the magnitude of these charging currents. Ilkovic and Semarano (23) devised an electrical balancing system consisting of a simple resistance network for compensating the charging current. A circuit of this type used in the

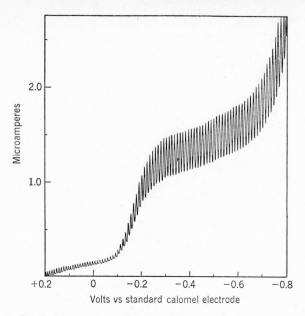

FIG. 3. Catalytic wave for reduction of $2 \times 10^{-6}$ molar molybdate ion.

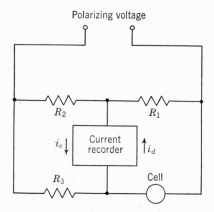

FIG. 4. Resistance network for compensation of residual current (23).

author's laboratory is illustrated in Fig. 4. $R_1$ is a resistance at least one hundred times that of $R_2$, and so essentially all the voltage from the polarizer is applied across the polarographic cell. A small portion of the polarizer voltage, however, appears across $R_2$, and $R_3$ and is of such a value so as to allow a current equal and opposite to the residual current to pass through the current-recording instrument. Figure 5 shows the type of residual currents obtained with and without the compensator. With the uncompensated curve further increase in recorder sensitivity would be difficult because of the already steep curve obtained. A higher sensitivity is possible with the compensated residual recorded in Fig. 5. Approximately a tenfold increase in sensitivity can be gained by the use of such a device (23).

Such compensation however cannot completely eliminate the condenser current background because the variation of this current is not strictly linear with voltage. As the sensitivity of the current recorder is increased in such a compensated system, broad peaks appear in the background and cause distortion of the polarograms.

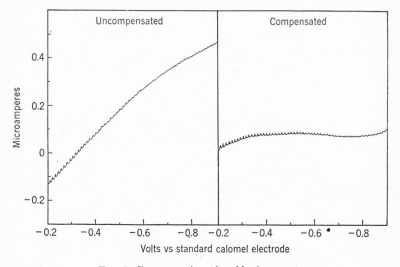

FIG. 5. Compensation of residual current.

A much more elegant technique was devised by Kelley and Miller (27), which is also a compensation technique. The compensation, however, is not limited to a linear function and the device can electrically subtract from a polarogram a residual current that has been previously determined. In this method the background current is first compensated by the technique described above by passing an opposite current through the measuring circuit. Figure 6A shows the uncompensated polarogram as obtained on a highly sensitive recorder scale. After compensation, a background polarogram is obtained as shown in 6B. The broad peak obtained in this fashion is caused by the fact that the condenser current is nonlinear and cannot be exactly compensated by a simple resistance network. With a sensitivity large enough to record the polarograms of $10^{-6} M$ solutions, the effect of nonlinearity is quite pronounced. In order to work with more dilute solutions a further compensation procedure using a curve follower (7) is applied. With this apparatus a separate background is recorded for the supporting electrolyte alone; this information is then stored in the curve follower and subsequently used to subtract electrically the residual current during the recording of a polarogram (6C). A polaro-

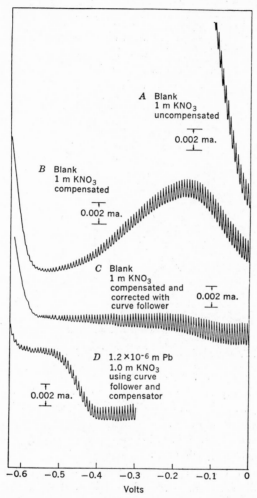

FIG. 6. Highly compensated polarograms (27). Courtesy Analytical Chemistry.

gram of a $1.2 \times 10^{-6}$ $M$ lead ion solution is shown in Fig. 6D. It would, of course, be impossible to obtain such results by conventional methods.

The limitation of this useful method when extended to even more dilute solutions would seem to be the reproducibility of the backgrounds. The shape of the charging current depends on the electrocapillarity zero

of the supporting electrolyte. The observed zero current value would be
dependent on traces of material in solution, for example oxygen, which
may not be removed to the same extent each time. Also traces of organic
material in the sample, which were not present in the pure supporting
electrolyte, would give spurious compensation.

It should be noted that when the sensitivity of a polarographic procedure is greatly increased, the current due to the decomposition of the
supporting electrolyte is magnified. This results in a decrease in the available voltage range, and some metals which can be determined at high
concentrations by conventional methods cannot be analyzed by more

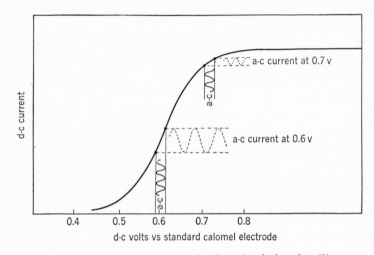

FIG. 7. A. C. polarographic reduction of cadmium ion (3).

sensitive procedures. In Fig. 6 the polarogram shows an appreciable current at approximately −0.6 v. versus the standard calomel electrode,
while by conventional methods, with higher concentrations, a potential
of perhaps −1.5 volts could be reached.

*3.1.4. Methods of Eliminating Capacity Current.* One of the more
recent modifications applied to polarography is the use of an A-C voltage superimposed upon the D-C polarizing voltage (3, 8). In this way a
derivative of the usual polarogram is obtained. To illustrate the principle
involved, Fig. 7 shows a polarographic wave for cadmium which would
be obtained by conventional procedures. If a small A-C voltage is superimposed upon the D-C voltage, the resultant current will have both an
A-C and a D-C component. The magnitude of the A-C current will depend upon the slope of the polarogram, which would be a maximum at
the half-wave potential. At the plateau the slope is zero and the A-C
current output is zero. In practice, only the A-C component of the cur-

rent is measured and when this is plotted against D-C voltage a curve of the type shown in Fig. 8 is obtained. The height of the peak is proportional to concentration, and the potential of the maximum corresponds to the half-wave potential for the particular reduction. The unique features of this type of polarography are that it is applicable to complex

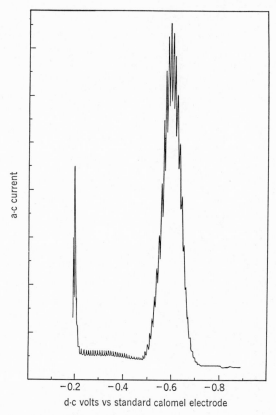

FIG. 8. A. C. polarogram of $4 \times 10^{-5}$ molar $Cd^{++}$ (5).

mixtures and that waves which would be otherwise difficult to resolve may be separated. The method offers no increase in sensitivity over conventional procedures because of the large contribution of the condenser current caused by the low impedance of the double layer to the A-C voltage.

Barker and Jenkins (1) devised a modification of A-C polarography that minimized the charging current background and in this way greatly increased the sensitivity. By superimposing a low-amplitude square wave upon the polarizing voltage instead of a sinesoidal wave, they were able electronically to isolate the diffusion current from the charging current. When the applied voltage is changed, the electrode double layer can be charged and discharged very rapidly, while the diffusion current changes only slowly. If a square wave voltage as shown in Fig. 9A is applied to a dropping mercury electrode, the current response, due to charging of the double layer, can be represented by a rapidly decaying curve as in B. The decrease in diffusion current, however, is much less rapid, as shown separately in 9C. The combination of both 9B and 9C represents the actual

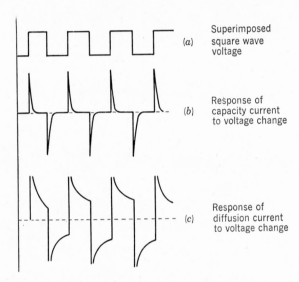

FIG. 9. Current response to superimposed square wave (1).

observed variation of current with time. Measuring the current in the latter part of the cycle, after the charging current has been dissipated, records only the current due to reduction. In this fashion it is possible to analyze solutions as dilute as $5 \times 10^{-6}$ $M$ with the same accuracy as can be obtained with $10^{-3}$ $M$ solutions by conventional methods. Since this is a derivative method it is also true that large quantities of material with a more positive half-wave potential can be tolerated. For example, Barker and Jenkins were able to determine $2 \times 10^{-5}$ $M$ $Pb^{++}$ in the presence of $2 \times 10^{-3}$ $M$ $Cu^{++}$. Aside from the complexity of the equipment, square wave polarography has two limitations to its usefulness. The first is that maximum sensitivity is obtained only with reversible systems, and the second is that small amounts of unsuspected organic material have a serious deleterious effect.

*3.1.5. Other Methods of Increasing Sensitivity.* Conventional polaro-graphic methods have an inherently low sensitivity because of the relatively long diffusion path associated with an unagitated solution. This diffusion layer cannot be reduced by stirring the solution since this causes erratic behavior of the mercury drops. To circumvent the loss in sensitivity associated with the deletion of the reducible species Ishibashi and Fujinaga (25) applied an alternating polarizing voltage to the dropping electrode. Their apparatus, as shown in Fig. 10, consists of a commutator which alternatively applies a potential of value E on one cycle and short circuits the drop to the calomel electrode on the next cycle. When applied

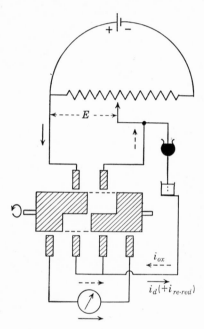

FIG. 10. Apparatus for reversing flow of current in polarography (25).

to reductions of metallic ions the metal is first deposited on and then on the next cycle anodically removed from the mercury drop. The observed current is maintained by passing the anodic current through the same galvanometer. The ion is not depleted at the electrode surface and its concentration at the mercury solution interface is maintained at a high level. Such a procedure has a sensitivity about 20 times greater than conventional methods, as indicated by the polarograms in Fig. 11. It is presumed that this method would be applicable only to the reversible ion-amalgam or ion-ion reductions. Such metals as nickel, which cannot be readily removed after electrodeposition into mercury and organic compounds which are usually irreversibly reduced, would not be amenable to this method.

## 3.2. Use of Other Electrodes

3.2.1. Solid Electrodes. Although the dropping mercury electrode is undoubtedly the most reproducible and useful electrode in the field of polarography, the high charging current, associated with the renewal of the interface, is a distinct disadvantage in the analysis of dilute solutions.

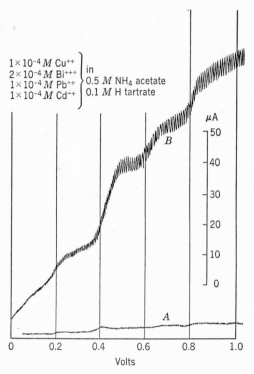

Fig. 11. Increase in polarographic sensitivity by method of Ishibashi and Fujinaga (25).
A—polarogram obtained by conventional procedure.
B—polarogram obtained with commutator.

Solid electrodes have a charging current density which is considerably smaller and is associated with the voltage change applied to the electrode during polarization. The fact that these electrodes can also be used in stirred solution is advantageous in that the diffusion current is increased without the charging current being appreciably raised. A more favorable ratio of signal to background is obtained and hence greater sensitivity is possible. On the other hand, solid electrodes have inherent difficulties involving reproducibility and the necessity of uniform pretreatment that mitigates against their general usefulness. In polarography of substances that are oxidized or reduced at more positive applied potentials, the dropping electrode is unsuitable and recourse must be made to other electrodes.

Solid electrodes of a variety of materials have been applied to various polarographic problems. The first extensive study of such electrodes was that of Kolthoff and Laitenen (29) in which platinum electrodes were used. Other electrodes proposed for polarographic work have been platinized platinum (37, 38), gold, graphite, lead oxide (36), copper, and silver (37). A comprehensive study of the applicability of solid electrodes has been published by Lord and Rogers (36).

In the use of solid metallic electrodes such as platinum, it is essential that the electrode be properly constructed. A platinum wire is usually attached to a steel shaft which is coated with wax to isolate it from the solution. Although such electrodes are adaptable to amperometric titrations, they often do not maintain a constant area over a long period of time and give rise to diffusion currents which are not reproducible. A glass-platinum seal offers better mechanical stability and reproducibility (38). Care must also be exercised with such electrodes since microscopic cracks sometimes appear in the glass and retain small amounts of solutions which give rise to spurious effects. A paper by Kolthoff and Tanaka (31) explains some of the anomalous results previously obtained with platinum electrodes in conjunction with automatic recording polarographs. Sometimes it is not possible to obtain diffusion plateaus for oxidations and reductions at such electrodes because current peaks are superimposed upon the polarograms. These peaks have been shown by the authors to be caused by the films of platinous oxide and adsorbed hydrogen which are formed at high anodic and cathodic potentials respectively. During the recording of a polarogram, the platinous oxide is reduced at a specific voltage, causing a cathodic current to flow. Since a finite amount of material is involved, when it is all reduced the current returns to its normal value and a peak results. A similar effect, giving an anodic peak, occurs with the adsorbed hydrogen.

An excellent application of the use of a large solid electrode has been devised by Toedt (60) for the determination of small amounts of oxygen in solution. By measuring the reduction current at constant potential it was possible to determine concentrations of oxygen below 1 $\mu$g./liter.

In general, the surface effects and pretreatment of solid electrodes are factors which must be considered in their use. The main area of applicability lies in amperometric titration in which a null-point procedure eliminates many troublesome aspects of nonreproducibility. Although great strides are being made in the standardization and understanding of solid electrodes, the lack of long-range reproducibility still limits their usefulness in polarography.

*3.2.2. Mercury Pool Electrodes.* To eliminate the difficulties associated with the surface effects of solid electrodes, various types of nondropping mercury electrodes have been devised (9, 35, 56). Surface effects are minimized since the electrode can be reproduced by simply replacing the mercury. Also, the charging current is comparatively small and a favorable ratio of diffusion current to condenser current is obtained. Such electrodes are reproducible and have a high sensitivity. Lee (35) worked with the first electrode of this type, in which a small amount of mercury in a plastic groove was rotated at high speeds and presented a uniform electrode area. The sensitivity of the method was considerably greater than that obtained by conventional methods. Another mercury electrode (56) of somewhat simpler design is shown in Fig. 12. There is no constant renewal of the mercury surface as in the dropping electrode, and so the charging current density (associated with the voltage scanning) is considerably smaller. Since the diffusion current density is still about the same, the more favorable signal to background ratio allows the analysis of more dilute solutions. The electrode shown in Fig. 12 had an area of about 3 cm.[2] It is possible by use of larger electrodes to obtain higher diffusion currents, but the actual magnitude of the current is unimportant. What is important is the ratio of diffusion current to background current, and this is independent of the area of the electrode. Actually the greater currents obtained at a large electrode have a disadvantage in that the ohmic drop across the cell is larger and causes distortion of the polarograms. Also, at a small electrode, the ratio of electrode area to solution volume is much more favorable and the absolute quantity of material which can be determined is considerably smaller. A cell has been used in the author's laboratory which contains only 1 ml. of solution and has an electrode area of 1 cm.[2]

A polarogram, recorded at such an electrode in a quiet solution, is shown in Fig. 13. The maximum which appears in this polarogram is distinctly different from the usual maximum associated with the dropping mercury electrode in that the shape of the entire curve can be quantitatively predicted (56). The rising portion of the curve is caused by the increasingly applied voltage. At the same time the concentration of the reducible species at the electrode surface is being decreased by electrolysis, causing the diffusion current to be lowered. A leveling off then occurs when the concentration of the reducible species is zero at the electrode surface, and a normal diffusion path is set up. This type of polarogram is a transient phenomenon and depends on the rate of voltage scanning. Hence a reproducible voltage scanning is necessary which precludes the use of a manual polarograph. The waves obtained are predictable by the equations developed for oscillographic polarography (48, 53). That is to be expected since the processes occurring at both electrodes are quite similar. In oscillographic work, the voltage scanning occurs at such a high rate that the electrode can be considered stationary and is thus similar

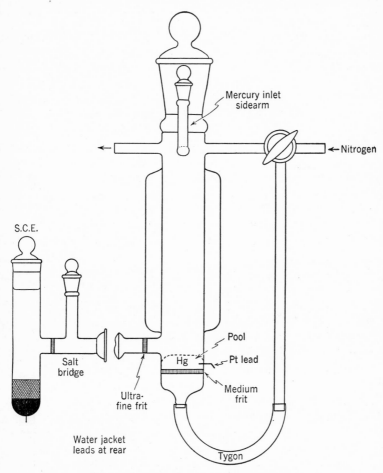

Fig. 12. Cell for mercury pool polarography.

to the quiet pool. The Sevcik equation (53) relating the diffusion current to concentration is

$$i_{\max} = 2.17 A n^{3/2} v^{1/2} D^{1/2} C$$

where

$A$ = electrode area, cm.$^2$

$n$ = number of electrons transferred.

$v$ = rate of voltage scanning, volts/sec.

$D$ = diffusion coefficient, cm.$^2$/sec.

$C$ = concentration, moles/liter.

It is seen from this equation that the peak current is proportional to concentration. The shape of the wave as well as its height varies with the number of electrons transferred and the rate of voltage scanning. In Fig. 14 the effect of variation in $n$ is shown, and it is evident that more

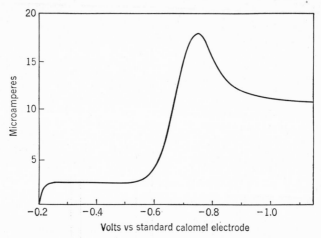

FIG. 13. Reduction of $5 \times 10^{-5}$ molar 1,6 anthraquinone disulfonate at a quiet mercury pool.

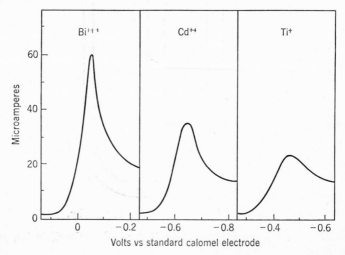

FIG. 14. Effect of $n$ on shape of polarograms of $10^{-4}$ molar solutions (56).

distinct waves are obtained for a three-electron reduction. The increased sensitivity of the quiet pool electrode is evident from the fact that a current of only 6 $\mu$a. is obtained at the dropping mercury electrode with the same concentration of bismuth ion. It can also be seen from this equation that the wave height increases with the rate of voltage scanning, and the magnitude of this effect can be seen in Fig. 15. However, there is a practical limit to increasing the scanning rate, because of a concurrent increase in the charging current, as evidenced by the residual currents in this figure. The voltage range is also decreased at high scanning rates because hydrogen ion is discharged at more positive potentials.

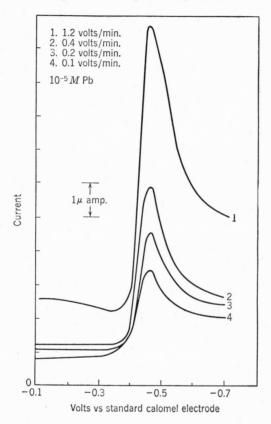

FIG. 15. Influence of scanning rate on shape of polarograms.

Although the potential at which the peak current appears is dependent on concentration, the voltage of the half peak does not vary and can be used to identify the particular metal undergoing reduction. It can be shown also, that for ion-amalgam reductions the half-peak potential agrees within a few millivolts with the half-wave potentials obtained at the dropping mercury electrode.

Polarograms of solutions as dilute as $5 \times 10^{-6}$ $M$ can be obtained by use of the quiet pool electrode. The method has been applied to $Tl^{+}$,

$Cd^{++}$, $Pb^{++}$, $Bi^{+++}$, $Zn^{++}$, $Cu^{++}$, and $In^{+++}$ (56) as well as to $CrO_4^=$, $SeO_3^=$, $Fe^{+++}$, $VO_3^-$, $Ni^{++}$, $Co^{+++}$, and $Sn^{++}$ (45).

The effect of a previously discharged metal on the peak current values of subsequently discharged ions has been studied. At $10^{-4}$ $M$, if the peak height of the initially discharged metal is not more than five times the height of the second, there is little or no effect and in more dilute solutions even higher ratios can be tolerated.

In the reduction of dilute solutions of organic compounds, the waves are similar in shape to those obtained for ion-amalgam reductions. In contrast to the behavior of the latter, the half-peak potentials are often distinctly different from the half-wave potentials obtained at the dropping mercury electrode. At times this difference can be used to advantage in the resolution of mixtures of organic compounds which have similar half-wave potentials. At the pool electrode it is possible that the reduction potentials would be shifted in such a manner that two distinct waves appear. An example of this procedure is the analysis of the gamma isomer of hexachlorocyclohexane (57). At the dropping electrode the half-wave potential of this compound occurs at the same potential as heptachlorocyclohexane. The analysis is possible at the mercury pool electrode because of a shift in reduction potentials.

In the use of mercury pool electrodes, a further increase in sensitivity can be obtained by stirring the solution above the electrode (51). The apparatus is similar to that shown in Fig. 12 except that a glass stirrer driven by a synchronous motor is introduced through the upper ground-glass joint.

In such cases the polarograms are similar in shape to those obtained with the dropping mercury electrode, except that the current fluctuations due to drop growth are absent, and no maxima are present. Because the solution is stirred, there is not appreciable depletion of ions at the electrode surface and the peaks, which are characteristic of the quiet mercury electrode, are no longer evident. The sensitivity of this electrode is considerably greater than that obtained by other electrodes, as is shown by the polarogram reproduced in Fig. 16. In general with this electrode it is possible to attain a 300-fold gain in sensitivity over conventional procedures.

Since the effect of turbulence cannot be quantitatively evaluated in such a system, the use of stirred solutions in conjunction with the mercury pool electrode is an empirical procedure. The geometry of the cell and rate of stirrer speed are, of course, important. In contrast to the results obtained at a rotating platinum electrode (36), the diffusion currents are proportional to stirring speeds even to high values of stirrer rotation. As each individual stirrer varies in efficiency, a calibration curve must be prepared for each one. The distance of the stirrer from the electrode changes the diffusion current, but at a separation greater than 3 mm. this setting is not critical.

In contrast to the quiet pool electrode, the rate of voltage scanning has little effect, and polarograms can be obtained with a manual apparatus.

In the case of ion-amalgam reductions, the half-wave potentials obtained at the stirred poll electrode agree well with those obtained at a

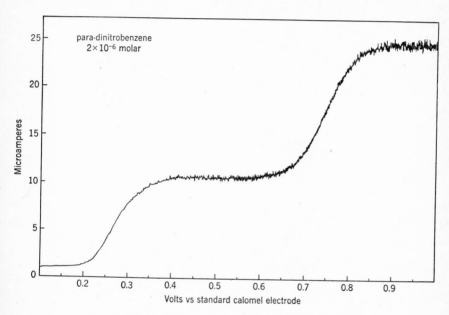

FIG. 16. Polarogram obtained at stirred mercury pool (51).

dropping mercury electrode. This is not true of ion-ion or molecule-molecule reductions, where distinct differences in potentials may be evident. In fact, with some species which give well-defined waves at the dropping mercury electrode, no reduction at all is evident at the stirred pool. Anomalous results are particularly evident with ion-ion reductions.

There is a fundamental difference between the pool electrode and the dropping electrode in that the former is not continuously renewed and the reduced species may be accumulated in the mercury. Under these circumstances the polarogram obtained by scanning the voltage from negative to positive potentials will be different from that obtained by forward current scanning. With cadmium ion a reverse polarogram, shown in Fig. 17, has a characteristic anodic current caused by the oxidation of the cadmium accumulated in the electrode. A plateau is not obtained because the volume of the mercury is small and the cadmium is rapidly depleted, giving rise to a broad peak. If the reduced species is not re-oxidizable, as with nitrobenzene, the same polarogram is obtained regardless of the direction of voltage scanning. When the reduced species is capable of oxidation, as in the case of azobenzene, but is soluble in the electrolyte instead of the mercury, an anodic wave is also obtained; however, in this case the anodic current is smaller in magnitude than the current obtained for amalgam decomposition. These three situations are

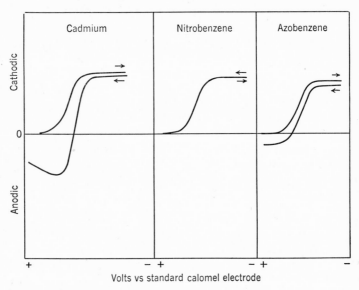

FIG. 17. Effect of reverse voltage scanning on various reductions (51).

depicted in Fig. 17. The application of this phenomenon is useful in qualitative identification of material and throws some light on the properties of the reduced species.

## 4. AMPEROMETRIC PROCEDURES

An amperometric titration is a procedure by which the endpoint of a reaction is determined by polarographic methods. For example, sulfate can be determined with a standard solution of lead ion by following the concentration of the latter ion with a dropping mercury electrode. During the course of the titration the endpoint is recognized by the appearance of a diffusion current caused by the first excess of lead. Although this procedure is more complicated than a straightforward polarographic analysis, it has several inherent advantages, among which are:

1. The polarograph is used essentially as a null-point instrument. It indicates only the presence or absence of a particular species, and

control of conditions such as temperature, drop time, supporting electrolyte concentration, etc., is relatively unimportant. The accuracy of such a titration is therefore greater than that which can be obtained by measurement of the diffusion current alone. For the same reason it is possible to titrate with reasonable accuracy solutions which are somewhat more dilute.

2. Some ions can be determined even though they are not polarographically active, as illustrated in the titration of sulfate with lead.

3. It is possible to carry out amperometric titrations of ions which yield poorly defined waves by conventional polarography. If the wave is not easily resolved from the hydrogen discharge reduction, it is still possible at times to carry out an amperometric titration (42).

By use of the dropping mercury electrode the minimum concentration at which the amperometric titration is applicable is about $2 \times 10^{-5}$ $M$. Replacing the dropping electrode with a mercury pool makes possible extension of the sensitivity of the endpoint detection (42). The apparatus used is shown in Fig. 18. The area of the pool should be large, so as to give high sensitivity, but not so large as to cause appreciable electrolysis of material during the course of the titration. In the work reported here a cathode of 4 cm.$^2$ was used in a cell holding 50 ml. of solution. A smaller electrode would be necessary for a cell containing less solution. Deaeration was accomplished by forcing nitrogen through the sintered-glass tip, which was also used to agitate the solution. The nitrogen was continually passed through the cell and the stirring effect further increased the sensitivity of the electrode. This stirring did not have to be reproducible from determination to determination since the procedure involved a null-point method; however, it was possible to obtain reasonable polarograms by use of this apparatus as shown in Fig. 19. In the amperometric titration of solutions in the micromolar range, a difficulty was experienced which perhaps will be encountered in other similar situations. The oxygen present in the titrant was found to yield a diffusion current, and deaeration of the solution was necessary after each addition of reagents. To circumvent this problem the standard solutions were deaerated and stored under nitrogen.

The above-outlined amperometric method was applied to the titration of a variety of metallic ions with a standard solution of ethylenediamine tetraacetic acid (Versene). A typical titration curve is shown in Fig. 20.

A limitation of the use of the mercury pool cathode in replacing the dropping mercury electrode lies in the fact that the former cannot be

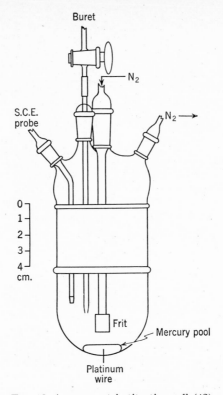

FIG. 18. Amperometric titration cell (42).

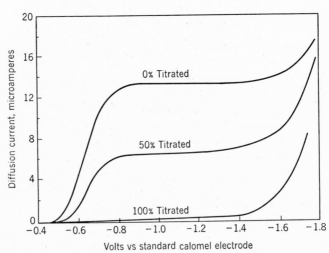

Volts vs standard calomel electrode

FIG. 19. Polarograms of $8 \times 10^{-6}$ molar $Cd^{++}$ at various stages of an amperometric titration with Versene.

applied to precipitation reactions. The precipitated ions settle out on the mercury surface, and reduction of the solid material would occur giving rise to spurious currents. Amperometric precipitation titrations would be difficult in any event because either the solubility of most salts is appreciable in the micromolar range or the rate of nucleation would undoubtedly be slow. It seems that only those systems in which strong complexes are

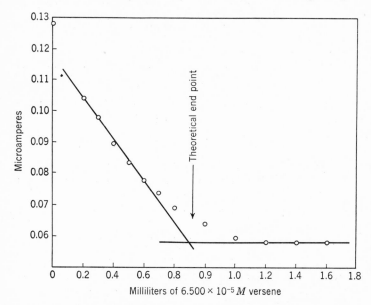

Fig. 20. Amperometric titration of $6 \times 10^{-7}$ molar copper ion (42). Titration of $5.7 \times 10^{-7}$ $M$ $Cu^{++}$ in $10^{-2}$ $M$ $KNO_3$. pH $= 7.0 \pm 1.0$. Potential Applied $= -0.20$ volts.

formed would be amenable to amperometric titrations at extreme dilutions. Such a condition is admirably met with many metallic versenates.

## 5. TITRATION METHODS

Volumetric procedures are widely used in the analysis of macroquantities of material since such procedures are straightforward and can be performed with a minimum amount of equipment. The technique of titration of small volumes of more or less concentrated solutions has reached a high degree of perfection (28). The problems involved in such work are concerned with the experimental difficulties in handling small volumes of material and accurately dispensing minute quantities of titrant. Burettes which are capable of delivering 0.0001 ml. are now commercially available (17).

At times however, it is not feasible to transfer the material to be analyzed to a small volume of concentrated solution, and recourse must be made to the titration of a dilute solution. This aspect of titrimetry is more difficult, because in many cases basic understanding of such processes is still lacking. Few procedures are available for the titration of solutions more dilute than $10^{-4}$ $M$.

With acids and bases, titration of $10^{-3}$ $M$ solutions are possible, but application to much lesser concentrations is extremely difficult. Even if such analysis were possible, it is reasonable to believe that there would be few practical applications for such methods. Acid and basic impurities such as acidic gases and the basic constituents of glassware would often invalidate the usefulness of these samples.

The values of redox titrations are not, in general, invalidated by the forementioned difficulty. Here again, indicators and conventional potentiometric methods are useful to dilutions of about $10^{-3}$ $M$, although it is possible that this range may well be extended by the application of photometric end point techniques (19).

The problems that arise with less concentrated solutions are threefold. There are first, the problem of pretreating the solution so that the desired constituent is in the proper oxidation state, second, the difficulty in storing dilute standard solutions, and third, the detection of the endpoint of the titration. Each of these points will be discussed in some detail.

### 5.1. Preadjustment of Oxidation States

The difficulties in adjusting the oxidation states of a dilute solution of an ion is a problem which has received little or no attention. Many of the conventional techniques applicable to macrotitrations cannot be used. For example, the hydrogen peroxide formed in metallic reductors is no problem in titrations involving macro quantities, because the amount of contamination is relatively small. With more dilute solutions, this error becomes relatively large and this method of reduction is no longer applicable. Oxidation preadjustment, in which the excess oxidizing agent is destroyed, might also present inherent difficulties of a similar nature when applied to dilute solutions. In some instances the presence of oxygen in dilute solution is troublesome and must be removed from the solution being titrated. Many procedures have been published for the redox titration of dilute solutions, but in almost every case the difficult problem of getting the sample in the desired oxidation state has been avoided. Perhaps the recently developed electron exchangers (11) or electrolytic preoxidation and reduction may alleviate some of these problems.

### 5.2. Coulometric Generation of Titrants

To a great extent the problem of storage of dilute titrants has been avoided by the recent developments in the field of coulometric titrations.

The coulometric titration is a procedure by which a titrating agent can be generated, *in situ*, by electrolysis, rather than by dispensing a known volume of reagent from a burette. The method was originally proposed by Szebelledy (58) and developed by Swift and co-workers (12, 39, 52).

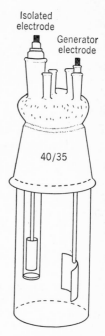

Isolated electrode

Generator electrode

40/35

FIG. 21. Cell for coulometric titrations.

In principle, the coulometric titration is based upon Faraday's law that the number of equivalents of reagent formed by electrolysis can be calculated from the amount of electricity used in the process; for example, oxidizing agents such as permanganate can be titrated with ferrous ion generated from excess ferric salt. A typical titration cell is shown in Fig. 21 in which a potentiometric endpoint is used. Other methods of endpoint detection can also be applied, but electrical methods seem to offer the highest sensitivity. The number of coulombs required for the titration can be conveniently calculated by a constant-current technique in which the time required to reach the endpoint is measured. A wiring diagram of a simple circuit applicable to small generating currents is shown in Fig. 22. The source of constant current is a bank of dry cells in conjunction with a large resistance which will swamp out any changes in cell resistance during the titrations. Closing the switch allows current to flow through the cell and at the same time starts the electric timer. The current can be accurately determined by measuring the IR drop across a standard resistor with a potentiometer. The potential of the indicator electrode is followed during the course of the titration, and, as the endpoint is approached, the generating current can be interrupted to allow equilibrium to be reached. Near the endpoint, small amounts of titrant can be added intermittently, in a fashion analogous to the addition of small increments from a burette.

The titration of ceric sulfate with electrolytically generated ferrous ion can be used to illustrate a typical coulometric titration. Ferric sulfate is added to the unknown ceric solution so that when a current is passed through the cell, ferrous ions will be formed at the cathode. The presence of the ferric ion allows the electrolytic process to occur at 100% efficiency, which is a prerequisite for the successful application of any coulometric method. Ceric ion alone is capable of undergoing direct electrolytic reduction without the ferrous as an intermediate. However, as the ceric ion is depleted by reduction, concentration polarization becomes great enough so that hydrogen gas is concurrently evolved at the cathode, destroying the theoretical efficiency of the process. In the presence of ferric ion, which is in considerably higher concentrations than the substance being reduced, ferrous ion is formed instead of hydrogen evolution. The ferrous ion then reacts with the ceric solution, preserving the overall efficiency of the process.

A source of difficulty in the foregoing system is the nature of the electrolytic process occurring at the anode. If the anode is not isolated

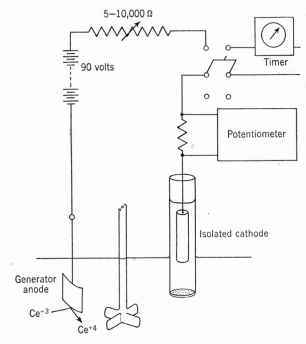

FIG. 22. Simplified source of constant current for small currents (4).

from the electrolysis cell, complications will arise because of reoxidation of the cerous ion produced during the titration. To avoid this problem the anode is placed in a separate compartment and electrical connection made through a sintered-glass disk, as illustrated in Fig. 21.

It is fortunate that a wide variety of titrants can be generated coulometrically. Acids (43) and bases (19, 44) can be readily prepared in almost any desired concentration. Strong oxidizing agents in the form of ceric sulfate (13, 15, 16) and bromine (39) can also be prepared. A mild oxidizing agent, iodine (47), as well as a weak reducing agent, ferrous sulfate (4), can also be generated electrolytically.

The technique of coulometric generation of titrants has recently been extended to include microvolumes of solution (55), which in some cases eliminates the use of microburettes for the delivery of reagents. The apparatus is the same as that previously described on page 99 except that the size of the electrodes is scaled down to appropriate proportions. A typical setup for the titration of hydrochloric acid is illustrated in Fig. 23. A thin platinum wire (0.01 in.) was used as the generator cathode and a silver wire as an attackable anode, and the endpoint was detected by means of an indicator. The background electrolyte was 0.04 ml. of potassium chloride solution into which a sample, usually 0.01 ml., could be titrated. The electrical apparatus was simple and consisted of two 45-v. batteries, a microammeter, and a timer (*see* Fig. 22). No trouble was

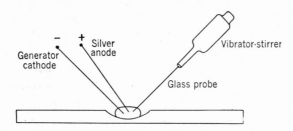

FIG. 23. Coulometric titration of microvolumes of solution.

encountered in obtaining constant current from such a source since low generating currents, about 100 $\mu$a., were sufficient in most cases. This procedure was applied to both redox and acidimetric titrations and amounts of material corresponding to 0.01 ml. of $10^{-3}$ $M$ solution could be handled rather easily. With such titrations a compensated endpoint was used in which the indicator was added to the supporting electrolyte and the solution brought to an endpoint. The unknown material was then added and the titrating agent generated until the endpoint was again reached. This was found to be a more precise procedure than the separate running of a blank titration when dilute solutions are being analyzed and is similar in principle to the pretitration procedure mentioned on page 103. Potentiometric redox titrations were also carried out using small platinum indicator electrodes and a pretitration-compensation procedure. It was possible to handle 0.01-ml. samples of $10^{-4}$ $M$ solutions.

Coulometric titrations are of great value in the titration of dilute solutions because the standardization and storage of such solutions is avoided, the apparatus is simple and compact, and minute amounts of reagent can be conveniently generated. Generating currents as small as 5 $\mu$a., flowing for 1 sec., have been used in the titration of dilute permanganate solutions (6). This corresponds to about $10^{-6}$ ml. of 0.01 $N$

solution. In fact, there seems to be no lower limit to the amount of reagent which can be generated in this manner.

### 5.3. Endpoint Detection

As previously mentioned, one of the problems, and perhaps the limiting one, inherent in the titration of dilute solutions is the difficulty in
the detecting the endpoint. Electrochemical procedures seem to offer considerable promise in this regard. In a redox titration, a platinum indicator
electrode is often used to follow the potential of the solution as the titrant
is added. Theoretically this potential can be calculated from the familiar
form of the Nernst equation,

$$E = E_0 + \frac{0.059}{r} \log \frac{a_{ox}}{a_{red}}$$

There is no concentration term in this equation since the potential is
determined only by the ratio of the concentrations of the oxidized and
reduced species. It would be expected, therefore, that the break obtained
in the titration of a dilute solution, such as $10^{-4}$ $M$, would be similar to
that for a 0.1 $M$ solution. Such is not the case, however, and distinctly
smaller potential breaks are obtained as the concentration of the solution being titrated is decreased. For this reason the conventional potentiometric titration is limited to concentrations of approximately 0.001 $M$.
although in specific instances greater sensitivity can be obtained.

It is possible that this effect is caused by the existence of more than
one potential-determining species being present in solution. For example,
small quantities of oxygen may reduce the magnitude of the potential
change at the endpoint. If a 0.1 $N$ of ferrous ion is titrated with ceric
sulfate, a large break is obtained. In this case the contribution of the
oxygen to the electrode potential would be insignificant. In more dilute
solutions however the oxygen-water as well as the ferric-ferrous couple
affect the potential of the electrode. This situation can exist only because
the solution is not in thermodynamic equilibrium, the rate of reaction
between oxygen and ferrous ion being extremely slow. As the concentration of the material being titrated is decreased, the effect of other
potential-determining species becomes more important and can swamp
the expected change in potential.

In the titration of very dilute solutions the total change in the potential of the indicator electrode may be 1 mv. or less. Obviously
the conventional methods employed in potentiometric titrations are no
longer applicable and recourse must be made to more sensitive adapta-
tions. One method of increasing the sensitivity of a potentiometric titration uses the indicator electrode as a null-point device in conjunction
with a pretitration procedure (6, 40). The apparatus, which is shown in

Fig. 24, is similar to that proposed by Müller (41), in which a sensitive galvanometer is used to detect any unbalance between the cell voltage and a reference potential. The operation of this procedure might be illustrated by the titration of permanganate with electrically generated ferrous ion. The reference voltage impressed upon the cell in this case would be somewhere in the vicinity of the endpoint potential, the exact value being unimportant. The ferric ion solution, from which the reducing agent is generated, is placed in the cell and the galvanometer reading brought to

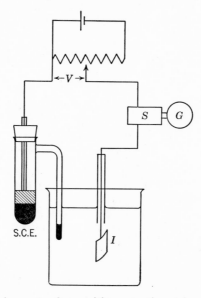

FIG. 24. Apparatus for sensitive potentiometric end-point.

zero either by generating ferrous or adding permanganate. Once this adjustment is made, the unknown oxidizing agent is added to the titration vessel, causing the potential of the solution to change and the galvanometer to deflect. After the preadjustment the permanganate can be titrated with the electrolytically generated ferrous ion. The increase in sensitivity of this method is indicated by the fact that a galvanometer deflection of about 1 cm. is noted for the addition of $10^{-11}$ equivalents of titrant. It is also significant that in some cases the pretitration can be considerable larger than the actual titration of the sample, which indicates that the titration would be impossible without such a precaution.

## 6. Anodic Stripping of Deposited Metals

The anodic dissolution of previously deposited metals from an electrode has been used to determine small quantities of metals (49). The metal is plated into a mercury-coated platinum electrode and subsequently stripped off the electrode under controlled conditions and 100% current efficiency. From the number of coulombs involved in the anodic process, the amount of material can be calculated. This process has an inherently high sensitivity because the metal ion in a large volume of solution is concentrated in a small volume of mercury. The method seems to be limited by experimental difficulties, but if such problems could be overcome it appears that great sensitivity would be attainable.

### ACKNOWLEDGMENT

The author gratefully acknowledges the support of the U. S. Air Force Office of Research and Development under Contract AF18(600)-486. The work performed under this contract has led directly to some of the methods discussed in this chapter, as well as indirectly to the organization and evaluation of much of the material presented.

### REFERENCES

1. Barker, G. C., and Jenkins, I. L., *Analyst* **77**, 685 (1952).
2. Boyd, G. E., *Anal. Chem.* **21**, 335 (1949).
3. Breyer, B., and Gutman, F., *Australian J. Sci. Research* **3**, 558 (1950).
4. Cooke, W. D., and Furman, N. H., *Anal. Chem.* **22**, 896 (1950).
5. Cooke, W. D., Unpublished report.
6. Cooke, W. D., Reilley, C. N., and Furman, N. H., *Anal. Chem.* **23**, 1662 (1951).
7. Coors, T., and Smith, D. C., *Rev. Sci. Instr.* **18**, 173 (1947).
8. Delahay, P., and Adams, T. J., *J. Am. Chem. Soc.* **75**, 5740 (1952).
9. Delahay, P., and Mattax, C. C., *J. Am. Chem. Soc.* **76**, 874 (1954).
10. Epstein, J. H., Sober, H. A., and Silver, S. D., *Anal. Chem.* **19**, 675 (1947).
11. Ezrin, M., and Cassidy, H. G., *Ann. N. Y. Acad. Sci.* **57**, 79 (1953).
12. Farrington, P. S., and Swift, E. H., *Anal. Chem.* **19**, 675 (1947).
13. Furman, N. H., and Adams, R. N., *Anal. Chem.* **25**, 1564 (1953).
14. Furman, N. H., Bricker, C. E., and McDuffie, B. J., *J. Wash. Acad. Sci.* **38**, 5 (1948).
15. Furman, N. H., Bricker, C. E., and Dilts, R.V., *Anal. Chem.* **25**, 482 (1953).
16. Furman, N. H., Cooke, W. D., and Reilley, C. N., *Anal. Chem.* **23**, 945 (1951).
17. Gilmont, R., *Anal. Chem.* **25**, 1135 (1953).
18. Glick, D., "Techniques of Histo- and Cytochemistry." Interscience, New York, 1949.
19. Goddu, R. F., and Hume, D. N., *Anal. Chem.* **26**, 1740 (1954).
20. Gosh-Mazumdar, A. S., and Haissinsky, M., *J. chim. phys.* **51**, 296 (1954).
21. Hallett, L. T. *et al.*, *Anal. Chem.* **24**, 1348 (1952).
22. Harris, W. E., and Kolthoff, I. M., *J. Am. Chem. Soc.* **67**, 1484 (1945).
23. Ilkovic, D., and Samerano, G., *Collection Czechoslov. Chem. Communs.* **4**, 176 (1932).
24. Inghram, M. G., *J. Phys. Chem.* **57**, 809 (1953).
25. Ishibashi, M., and Fujinage, T., *Bull. Chem. Soc. Japan* **24**, No. 2 (1951).
26. Johnson, M. G., and Robinson, R. J., *Anal. Chem.* **24**, 366 (1952).
27. Kelley, M. T., and Miller, H. H., *Anal. Chem.* **24**, 1895 (1952).
28. Kirk, P. L., "Ultramicroanalysis." Wiley, New York, 1950.

29. Kolthoff, I. M., and Laitenen, H. A., *J. Phys. Chem.* **45**, 1061, 1079 (1941).
30. Kolthoff, I. M., and Parry, E. P., *J. Am. Chem. Soc.* **73**, 5315 (1951).
31. Kolthoff, I. M., and Tanaka, N., *Anal. Chem.* **26**, 632 (1954).
32. Laitenen, H. A., and Burdett, L. W., *Anal. Chem.* **22**, 833 (1950).
33. Lingane, J. J., *Ind. Eng. Chem. Anal. Ed.* **18**, 429 (1946).
34. Lingane, J. J., "Electroanalytical Chemistry," p. 316. Interscience, New York, 1953.
35. Lee, T. S., *J. Am. Chem. Soc.* **74**, 5001 (1952).
36. Lord, S. S., and Rogers, L. B., *Anal. Chem.* **26**, 284 (1954).
37. Lydersen, D., *Acta Chem. Scand.* **3**, 259 (1949).
38. MacNevin, W. M., and Levitsky, M., *Anal. Chem.* **24**, 973 (1952).
39. Meier, D. J., Myers, R. J., and Swift, E. H., *J. Am. Chem. Soc.* **71**, 2340 (1949).
40. Meites, L., *Anal. Chem.* **24**, 1057 (1952).
41. Müller, E., "Electrometrische Massanalyse," 6th ed., p. 90. Steinkopff, Dresden, 1942.
42. Nikelly, J. G., and Cooke, W. D., *Anal. Chem.* **28**, 243 (1956).
43. Oelsen, W., and Graue, G., *Angew Chem.* **63**, 557 (1951).
44. Oelsen, W., and Graue, G., *Angew Chem.* **64**, 24 (1952).
45. Peterson, L., M.S. thesis, Cornell University, Ithaca (1953).
46. Porter, J. T., and Cooke, W. D., *J. Am. Chem. Soc.* In press.
47. Ramsey, W. F., Farrington, P. S., and Swift, E. H., *Anal. Chem.* **22**, 332 (1950).
48. Randels, J. E. B., *Analyst* **72**, 301 (1947).
49. Rogers, L. B., and Gardiner, K. W., *Anal. Chem.* **25**, 1393 (1953).
50. Rogers, L. B., and Stehney, A. F., *J. Electrochem. Soc.* **95**, 25 (1940).
51. Rosie, D. J., and Cooke, W. D., *Anal. Chem.* **27**, 1360 (1955).
52. Sease, J. W., Neimann, C., and Swift, E. H., *Anal. Chem.* **19**, 197 (1947).
53. Sevcik, A., *Collection Czechoslov. Chem. Communs.* **13**, 349 (1948).
54. Schmidt, W. E., Univ. Microfilms, No. 8089. From *Chem. Abstr.* **48**, 9863 (1954).
55. Schreiber, R., and Cooke, W. D., *Anal. Chem.* **27**, 1475 (1955).
56. Streuli, C. A., and Cooke, W. D., *Anal. Chem.* **25**, 1691 (1953).
57. Streuli, C. A., and Cooke, W. D., *Anal. Chem.* **25**, 1697 (1953).
58. Szebelledy, L., and Somogyi, Z., *Z. anal. Chem.* **112**, 313, 323, 385, 391, 395, 400 (1938).
59. Tilton, G. R., Aldrich, T., and Inghram, M. G., *Anal. Chem.* **26**, 894 (1954).
60. Toedt, F., *Angew. Chem.* **67**, 266 (1955).

# High-Frequency Method of Chemical Analysis

By

W. J. BLAEDEL

*Department of Chemistry, University of Wisconsin, Madison, Wisconsin*

AND

D. L. PETITJEAN

*Aluminum Company of America, New Kensington, Pennsylvania*

## List of Symbols

$C$ = capacitance through the solution in the vessel, farads (Fig. 2)

$C_c$ = coupling capacitance between solution and electrodes, through the container walls, farads (Fig. 2)

$C_p$ = capacitance of the equivalent parallel circuit of the solution and vessel, farads (Fig. 2)

$C_s$ = capacitance of the equivalent series circuit of the solution and vessel, farads (Fig. 2)

$f$ = frequency, cycles/sec. ($f = \omega/2\pi$)

$f_p$ = resonant frequency of the equivalent parallel circuit of solution and vessel, cycles/sec. (Fig. 3)

$f_s$ = resonant frequency of the equivalent series circuit of solution and vessel, cycles/sec. (Fig. 3)

$K$ = conductance through the solution in the cell, mhos ($K = 1/R$)

$L$ = inductance of the resonant circuit containing the solution and vessel, henries

$N$ = solute normality, equivalents/liter

$R$ = resistance through the solution in the cell, ohms (Fig. 2)

$R_p$ = resistance of the equivalent parallel circuit of the solution and vessel, ohms (Fig. 2)

$R_s$ = resistance of the equivalent series circuit of the solution and vessel, ohms (Fig. 2)

$X$ = cell constant, cm. For a pair of plane parallel electrodes of area $a$ cm.$^2$, and separated by a distance of $l$ cm., $X = a/l$ cm.

$\gamma$ = dimensional constant, for converting electrostatic units of capacitance to farads, $8.85 \times 10^{-14}$ farads/cm.

$\epsilon$ = dielectric constant of the solution

$\kappa$ = specific conductance of the solution, mho/cm. ($\kappa = 1/\rho$)

$\Lambda$ = equivalent conductance, mho cm.$^2$/equivalent

$\rho$ = specific resistance of the solution, ohm cm. ($\rho = 1/\kappa$)

$\omega$ = frequency, radians/sec. ($\omega = 2\pi f$)

## 1. Introduction

### 1.1. Outline of the Method

The high-frequency method of chemical analysis is used to measure, or to follow changes in, the composition of chemical systems. In principle, a vessel containing the chemical system is made a part of, or coupled to, an oscillator circuit resonating at a frequency in the range 1–30 Mc. As the nature or composition of the chemical system changes, the resistance and/or capacitance of the circuit are altered, and changes are produced in oscillator characteristics, such as plate current and voltage, grid current and voltage, and frequency. Any of these characteristics may be easily measured and taken as an indication of the change in composition of the chemical system. The fundamental properties of the chemical system which affect the oscillator characteristics are the dielectric constant and the specific conductance. The advantages of this method over other electrical methods of following changes in composition of a chemical system are that the response is instantaneous and the electrodes are not in direct contact with the solution.

### 1.2. History of the Method

The high-frequency method has long been used empirically to measure the moisture content of various materials, such as textiles, wood, cereals, etc. A detailed summary of such uses has been written by Blake (14).

Blake was probably the first to use the high-frequency principle to follow changes in composition of conducting solutions (14). In the United States, Jensen and Parrack (37) applied the method to follow the course of titrations and provided the stimulus for a considerable amount of later work.

### 1.3. Summary

In this article the theory of the high-frequency method of chemical analysis is presented. Instruments are classified according to the type of response, and the general behavior of each class of instruments is described. A few specific instruments are described. The advantages and limitations of the high-frequency method are given and are compared with other methods of measuring dielectric constant and conductivity. Last, specific applications are discussed.

## 2. THEORY: CLASSES OF INSTRUMENTS AND THEIR GENERAL BEHAVIOR

In this section an attempt is made to show how the response of an A-C circuit is related to the fundamental properties of a solution which is coupled or loaded into that circuit. Various kinds of instruments are classified according to the nature of the response, and the response is related to the dielectric constant and specific conductance of the solution. A few typical instruments of each class are briefly described.

### 2.1. Modes of Coupling Solutions into Electrical Circuits

If direct current is to be passed through a solution, the solution must be resistively coupled to the D-C source, and electrodes must dip directly into the solution. Such direct coupling is required in order to measure the D-C resistance of a solution.

In order that alternating current may be passed through a solution, however, the solution may be either resistively or capacitively coupled to the A-C source. For capacitive coupling, the solution is made to be a part of the dielectric medium of a capacitor in the circuit, and direct, conductive contact of the solution with other elements of the circuit such as electrodes is not necessary. The impedance of the capacitor is dependent upon the dielectric constant and conductivity of the solution, and, being easily measurable, this impedance may be taken as a measure of these solution properties.

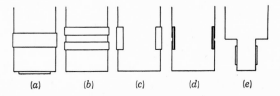

(a)        (b)        (c)        (d)        (e)

FIG. 1. Cell designs for solution containers (49).

Thus, to couple a solution capacitively into an A-C circuit, one places the solution in a vessel or tube which is a capacitive part of the circuit. Figure 1 shows various types of cell design studied by Reilley and Mc-Curdy (49). In cell A, the electrodes are a disk and ring; in cell B, two rings; in cells C and E, the electrodes are pairs of plates attached to the outside of the vessel; in cell D, a pair of plates is attached to the inside of the vessel and then coated with an insulating layer of airplane dope to prevent conductive contact with the solution. The Sargent Oscillometer employs a cell having concentric cylindrical electrodes.

### 2.2. The Equivalent Circuit of the Solution and Container

When capacitively coupled into an A-C circuit, the solution and its container may be represented by the group of electrical elements shown in Fig. 2A, hereafter referred to as the equivalent circuit of the solution and container. No continuous or distributed system, such as the container and solution, can be exactly represented by an equivalent circuit of lumped elements, as in Fig. 2A, but such a representation often serves as a good approximation. In this case, the experimentally observed effects of the solution and container upon the electrical properties of A-C circuits are adequately explained by the equivalent circuit of Fig. 2A.

In Fig. 2A, $C_c$ represents the capacitance through the container walls, $C$ represents the capacitance through the solution, and $R$ represents the resistance through the solution. The resistance of the container walls is assumed to be so high that it may be neglected.

$R$ is simply related to the conductance $(K)$, the specific resistance $(\rho)$ and specific conductance $(\kappa)$ of the solution, and $C$ is simply related to the dielectric constant $(\epsilon)$. The properties $\rho$, $\kappa$, and $\epsilon$ are fundamental ones and are dependent upon composition (34).

$$R = 1/K \tag{1A}$$
$$\rho = RX \tag{1B}$$
$$\kappa = 1/\rho \tag{1C}$$
$$C = \epsilon\gamma X \tag{1D}$$

The constant $\gamma$ is a dimensional one, $8.85 \times 10^{-14}$ farad/cm. (20). The factor $X$ is the cell constant, a geometrical factor determined by the electric field intensity through the solution. If fringe effects are neglected, $X$ may be assumed to be the same for capacitive and conductive paths through the same cell (50).

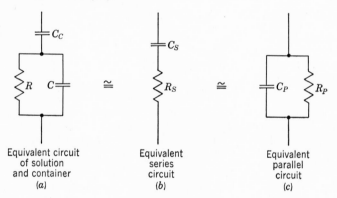

Equivalent circuit of solution and container (a)

Equivalent series circuit (b)

Equivalent parallel circuit (c)

FIG. 2. Equivalent circuits of solution and container.

By the conventional methods of A-C circuit analysis shown in Appendix I, the circuit of Fig. 2A may be represented by the simpler equivalent series circuit shown in Fig. 2B, where

$$R_s = \frac{R}{R^2\omega^2C^2 + 1} \tag{2A}$$

$$C_s = \frac{(R^2\omega^2C^2 + 1)C_c}{(R^2\omega^2C^2 + R^2\omega^2CC_c + 1)} \tag{2B}$$

Similarly, as shown in Appendix II, the circuit of Fig. 2A may be represented by the simpler equivalent parallel circuit shown in Fig. 2C, where

$$R_p = \frac{R^2\omega^2(C + C_c)^2 + 1}{R\omega^2C_c^2} \tag{3A}$$

$$C_p = \frac{C_c[R^2\omega^2C(C + C_c) + 1]}{R^2\omega^2(C + C_c)^2 + 1} \tag{3B}$$

Equations (2) and (3) are useful in interpreting the behavior of the solution and vessel when placed in electrical circuits. The circuits of Fig. 2A, B, and C are all equivalent and offer the same impedance to alternating current, provided the relationships in eqs. (2) and (3) are satisfied.

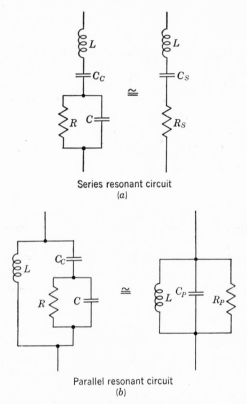

FIG. 3. Series and parallel resonant circuits containing the solution and container.

It is the purpose of the following parts of this section to show approximately how the responses of various classes of high-frequency instruments are related to $R$ and $C$, and thereby to $\kappa$ and $\epsilon$.

### 2.3. Behavior of the Solution and Container in Resonant Circuits

The vessel and solution, represented by the equivalent circuit of Fig. 2A, may be placed in series or in parallel with a pure inductance, $L$, giving a series resonant circuit (Fig. 3A) or a parallel resonant circuit (Fig. 3B). Alternating current circuit analysis of such resonant circuits shows that the resonant frequencies are

$$f_s = \frac{1}{2\pi \sqrt{LC_s}} \qquad \text{(for the series resonant circuit)} \qquad (4A)$$

$$f_p = \frac{1}{2\pi \sqrt{LC_p}} \qquad \text{(for the parallel resonant circuit)} \qquad (4B)$$

On the other hand, the impedances which these resonant circuits offer to the flow of alternating current at resonance are

$$R_s = \text{resonant impedance for the series circuit} \qquad (5A)$$
$$R_p = \text{resonant impedance for the parallel circuit} \qquad (5B)$$

By inserting the solution and container into a capacitive or inductive element of a vacuum-tube oscillator, the characteristic frequency at which the tube oscillates is easily measurable and is given to a good approximation by eq. (4). This measured frequency is related to the properties of the solution through $C_s$ or $C_p$, which is fundamentally dependent upon $\kappa$ and $\epsilon$ through eqs. (1) and (2B) or (3B). On the other hand, the A-C currents and voltages which exist at resonance in the tube circuit are also easily measurable and are related approximately to the solution properties through the resonant impedance, $R_s$ or $R_p$ [eq. (5)].

On the basis of type of response, most instruments used for measurement of $\kappa$ or $\epsilon$ may be classified into three groups. Class I instruments are ones the response of which is dependent primarily upon $R_s$ or $R_p$ and which measure plate, grid, or cathode voltages or currents. The response of class II instruments is dependent primarily upon $C_s$ or $C_p$, and the instruments measure the resonant frequency. Class III instruments are those with a response dependent appreciably upon both $R_s$ and $C_s$ or $R_p$ and $C_p$ and which are operated in a nonresonant condition. These groups of instruments are discussed in greater detail in the following sections.

### 2.4. Class I Instruments and the Dependence of Response upon Properties of the Solution

The response of a class I instrument is approximately proportional (directly or inversely) to the equivalent series resistance, $R_s$, if the solution and vessel are in series with the coil, $L$, or to the equivalent parallel resistance, $R_p$, if the solution and vessel are in parallel with the coil, $L$. The response of a class I instrument is quite independent of $C_s$ or $C_p$. In general, $R_s$ or $R_p$ is a rather complicated function of both $R$ and $C$ [eqs. (2A) and (3A)], and the response of a class I instrument is therefore a rather complicated function of both $R$ and $C$.

In certain cases, however, the dependence of response upon $R$ and $C$ simplifies, or the response becomes dependent primarily upon $R$. These cases are investigated in the following sections, and the general shape of the response curves is described in each case.

*2.4.1. Aqueous Conducting Solutions.* Since it is the objective in this section to relate response to composition, it is advantageous to express $R_s$ and $R_p$ in terms of solution conductance $(K)$, rather than solution resistance $(R)$. The reason for this is that $K$ is approximately proportional to electrolyte concentration, whereas $R$ is inversely proportional. In terms of $K$, eqs. (2A) and (3A) become

$$R_s = \frac{K}{K^2 + \omega^2 C^2} \tag{6A}$$

$$\frac{1}{R_p} = \frac{K\omega^2 C_c{}^2}{K^2 + \omega^2(C + C_c)^2} \tag{6B}$$

When the solution and vessel are in series with the coil, the dependence of $R_s$ upon $K$ may be deduced by considering $C$ and $\omega$ constant. $R_s$ approaches zero as $K$ becomes very large or very small, but $R_s$ is finite for finite values of $K$. Hence, a plot of $R_s$ versus $K$, which passes through a maximum as $K$ varies from very small to very large, has the general shape of the curves shown in Fig. 4. Similar consideration for the case in which the solution and vessel are in parallel with the coil shows that $1/R_p$ passes through a maximum as $K$ varies from very small to very large.

Both $R_s$ and $1/R_p$ have the same form of dependence upon $K$, as shown by inspection of eqs. (6A and B), and so the shapes of the $R_s$ and $1/R_p$ curves are similar. Therefore, response curves for all class I instruments are similar in shape, regardless of whether the solution and vessel are in series or parallel resonance with the coil.

The dependence of $R_s$ or $1/R_p$ upon solute concentration in aqueous conducting solutions is also of the same general shape as shown in Fig. 4. This is so because the specific conductance $(\kappa)$ is related to the solute normality $(N)$ through the equivalent conductance $(\Lambda)$ as follows:

$$\kappa = \frac{\Lambda N}{1000} \tag{7}$$

Since $\Lambda$ is a constant approximately independent of concentration for dilute solutions, it is apparent that a plot of $R_s$ or $1/R_p$ versus $N$ has the same general shape as the plot of $R_s$ or $1/R_p$ versus $\kappa$ shown in Fig. 4. This statement assumes that $C$ is independent of solute concentration. This is permissible for dilute solutions. For example, Falkenhagen (20, p. 220) has shown that for 0.01 $M$ potassium chloride and 0.01 $M$ magnesium chloride, respectively, the values of $\epsilon$ are only 0.5 and 1.3% greater than the value of $\epsilon$ for pure water.*

Figure 4 is an experimental plot of $1/R_p$ against specific conductance (49). Values of $1/R_p$ were measured for aqueous solutions in a cell of the kind shown in Fig. 1A by use of a Twin-T impedance bridge. Conductances of the solutions were measured with a low-frequency conductivity bridge, and specific conductances were computed from these values and the cell constant. It should be added that $1/R_p$ is rather independent of the identity or kind of electrolyte, being dependent only on the specific conductance. This was proved by noting that measurements for solutions

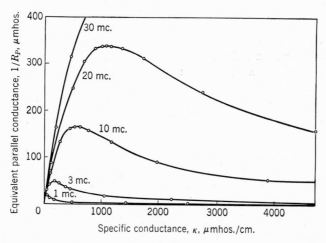

FIG. 4. Dependence of equivalent parallel conductance $(1/R_p)$ upon specific conductance (49).

of KCl, HOAc, and AlCl$_3$ all fell upon the same curve, when measurements were made at 3 Mc. The lack of dependence of $R_s$ upon the identity of the electrolyte has also been proved by other workers (12, 48).

The properties of the response curves of Fig. 4 may be quantitatively explained (*vide infra*) with eq. (6). Comparably precise data do not exist for the equivalent series circuit, but most of the following conclusions are supported experimentally (48).

* In this connection it is assumed that the mode of absorption of radiofrequency energy is the same as that occurring in an ordinary resistor having a resistance equal to that of the solution in the circuit of Fig. 2A. The treatment of this chapter neglects dielectric losses caused by absorption of energy by dipolar molecules oscillating in the alternating field. Such dielectric losses are assumed negligible compared with the resistive losses encountered in conducting electrolytic solutions. In nonconducting solutions, or at very high frequencies, dilectric losses become appreciable, and the equivalent circuit of Fig. 2A is probably inadequate.

The distinguishing characteristics of the response curves of Fig. 4 are the peaks and slopes. Information about these characteristics and their dependence upon $C$, $C_c$, and $\omega$ may be obtained from the first and second derivatives of eq. (6) with respect to $K$. The following conclusions may be drawn from these equations and are supported in part by the experimental curves of Fig. 4. These conclusions and others regarding sensitivity and cell design are derived in the article by Reilley and McCurdy (49).

(1) Setting the first derivatives of $R_s$ and $1/R_p$ with respect to $K$ equal to zero shows that $R_s$ and $1/R_p$ are at maxima when

$$K = \omega C \qquad \text{(for peak } R_s\text{)} \qquad\qquad (8A)$$
$$K = \omega(C + C_c) \qquad \text{(for peak } 1/R_p\text{)} \qquad\qquad (8B)$$

Hence the maximum in the $R_s$ versus $K$ curve comes at a value of $K$ which is independent* of $C_c$ (i.e., independent of cell-wall thickness), whereas the maximum in the $1/R_p$ versus $K$ curve is dependent upon cell-wall thickness.

(2) When the peak $K$ values of eq. (8) are substituted back into eq. (6), the peak values of $R_s$ and $1/R_p$ are found to be

$$R_s = \frac{1}{2\omega C} \qquad \text{(for peak } R_s\text{)} \qquad\qquad (9A)$$
$$\frac{1}{R_p} = \frac{\omega C_c{}^2}{2(C + C_c)} \qquad \text{(for peak } 1/R_p\text{)} \qquad\qquad (9B)$$

The magnitude of the $R_s$ peak value depends inversely upon frequency, whereas the magnitude of the $1/R_p$ peak value depends directly upon the frequency.

(3) The curves of Fig. 4 are all quite steep at low $K$ (i.e., on the low-concentration side of the peak), the slopes approaching $1/\omega^2 C^2$ for the $R_s$ versus $K$ curve and $C_c{}^2/(C + C_c)^2$ for the $1/R_p$ versus $K$ curve, as $K$ approaches zero. For $K$ values above the peak, there is a point of inflection where $R_s$ and $1/R_p$ change most rapidly

---

* It is necessary to point out that this lack of dependence of $K$ at peak $R_s$ upon $C_c$ applies only for the equivalent circuit of Fig. 2A. When the effect of stray capacitance is considered, the circuit of Fig. 2A must be modified by placing a capacitor in parallel with the circuit shown. In such a case, the value of $R_s$, and therefore of $K$, at peak $R_s$ is dependent upon both $C_c$ and the magnitude of the stray capacitance, as well as upon $R$, $C$, and $\omega$.

Such qualifications are necessary in all the conclusions drawn from eqs. (8) to (16), whenever the solution and vessel are made a part of an A-C circuit containing other elements. Equations (8) to (16) and the conclusions obtained therefrom are useful principally for purposes of classifying different kinds of instruments and for showing how the response depends upon the properties of the solution alone. These equations should not be regarded as having strictly quantitative significance, especially when the solution and vessel are only a part of an A-C circuit.

with changes in $K$. These regions of steepest slope are important in considerations regarding sensitivity. The inflection points may be found by setting the second derivatives of $R_s$ and $1/R_p$ with respect to $K$ equal to zero, obtaining

$$K = \sqrt{3}\, \omega C \qquad \text{(for maximum slope in } R_s \text{ vs. } K) \qquad (10A)$$
$$K = \sqrt{3}\, \omega(C + C_c) \qquad \text{(for maximum slope in } 1/R_p \text{ vs. } K) \qquad (10B)$$

It may be seen that the inflection points occur at $K$ values which are proportional to frequency.

(4) For a given solution, the frequency at which the peak $R_s$ value occurs is independent of cell geometry, since from eqs. (8A) and (1),

$$\omega = \frac{\kappa}{\epsilon\gamma} \qquad \text{(for peak } R_s) \qquad (11A)$$

The same is true of the frequency at which the inflection point of the $R_s$ versus $K$ curve occurs, from eqs. (10A) and (1).

However, for the same solution, the frequencies at which the peak and inflection point of the $1/R_p$ versus $K$ curve occur are dependent upon cell geometry, as shown by eqs. (8B), (10B), and (1). Thus, for the case of the peak,

$$\omega = \frac{\kappa X}{\epsilon\gamma X + C_c} \qquad \text{(for peak } 1/R_p) \qquad (11B)$$

*2.4.2. Nonaqueous Conducting Solutions.* The response curve of $1/R_p$ versus $K$ for solutions of potassium chloride in methanol is of the type shown in Fig. 4 (49). What is said in a general way concerning aqueous conducting solutions should also apply to nonaqueous conducting solutions, provided that $\epsilon$ for the solvent is not too low. As $\epsilon$ for the solvent decreases, however, increasing deviations from resemblance to aqueous conducting systems might be expected. Not only do the assumptions of constancy of $\Lambda$ and $C$ become poorer, but the ionization of the solute decreases, $K$ decreases, and the response curves should begin to resemble those of nonconducting systems.

*2.4.3. Nonconducting Solutions.* For the special case of nonconducting liquids, $K$ is small, and eqs. (6) simplify to

$$R_s = \frac{K}{\omega^2 C^2} \qquad (12A)$$

$$\frac{1}{R_p} = \frac{K C_c^2}{(C + C_c)^2} \qquad (12B)$$

Inspection of eqs. (12) show that $R_s$ and $1/R_p$ are each dependent upon both $K$ and $C$. In general, $K$ and $C$ each vary differently with composition, and so the response of a class I instrument is not relatable to any single property of the solution as composition varies, contrary to the case for conducting solutions. Class II instruments do not possess this disadvantage.

*2.4.4. Examples of Class I Instruments.* An example of a class I instrument is that of Anderson *et al.* (1), a simplified schematic of which is given in Fig. 5. The solution and vessel are in parallel resonance with

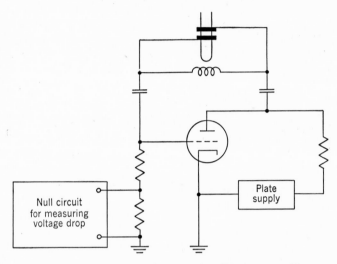

FIG. 5. Schematic diagram of a class I instrument (1).

the coil, and this combination loads a grid dip oscillator. The grid current is measured with a sensitive galvanometer shunting a resistor in the grid circuit. The instrument operates at several selectable frequencies.

Among the references listed at the end of this chapter, the only other example of a class I instrument is that of Hall (30), which is described in section 2.6.

### 2.5. Class II Instruments and the Dependence of Response upon Properties of the Solution

The response of a class II instrument is dependent primarily upon the equivalent series capacitance $C_s$ if the vessel and solution are in series with the coil $L$, or upon the equivalent parallel capacitance, $C_p$, if the vessel and solution are in parallel with the coil. The response is quite independent of $R_s$ or $R_p$. In general, $C_s$ or $C_p$ is a complicated function of the solution properties, $R$ and $C$ [eqs. (2B) and (3B)], and the response of a class II instrument is therefore generally a complicated function of both $R$ and $C$.

In certain cases, however, the response becomes dependent primarily upon $R$, or primarily upon $C$. These cases are investigated in the following sections, and the general shape of the response curves is described in each case.

2.5.1. *Aqueous Conducting Solutions.* For reasons stated in section 2.4, it is advantageous to express $C_s$ and $C_p$ in terms of $K$, rather than $R$, and eqs. (2B) and (3B) become

$$C_s = \frac{(\omega^2 C^2 + K^2)C_c}{\omega^2 C^2 + \omega^2 C C_c + K^2} \tag{13A}$$

$$C_p = \frac{[\omega^2 C(C + C_c) + K^2]C_c}{\omega^2(C + C_c)^2 + K^2} \tag{13B}$$

Semiquantitatively it may be seen that $C_s$ and $C_p$ each approach the limit $CC_c/(C + C_c)$ as $K$ becomes very small, and the limit $C_c$ as $K$ becomes

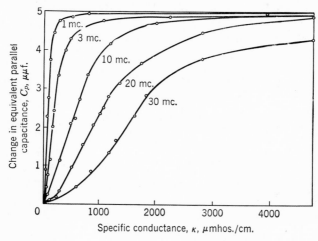

Fig. 6. Dependence of equivalent parallel capacitance $(C_p)$ upon specific conductance (49).

very large. This conclusion is also derivable from inspection of the equivalent circuit of Fig. 2A: as $R$ becomes very small, $C$ is shorted out and the capacitance is that of $C_c$ alone; whereas if $R$ becomes very large, the total capacitance is that of $C$ and $C_c$ in series, or $CC_c/(C + C_c)$.

A plot of $C_s$ or $C_p$ versus $K$ is therefore sigmoid in shape, passing asymptotically between two limits as $K$ varies from very small to very large. Therefore, response curves for all class II instruments are similar in shape, regardless of whether the solution and vessel are in series or parallel resonance with the coil.

Since normality is proportional to $K$, as shown in sec. 2.4.1, plots of $C_s$ or $C_p$ versus $N$ also have the same shape as plots of $C_s$ or $C_p$ versus $K$.

Figure 6 is an experimental plot of changes in $C_p$ against specific conductance, taking $C_p$ for pure water as zero. Data for Fig. 6 were obtained in a manner similar to that for Fig. 4. Comparably precise data do not exist for $C_s$, but most of the following conclusions are supported experimentally (48). For aqueous solutions it has been shown that $C_s$ and $C_p$ are independent of the identity of the electrolyte and are dependent only upon the specific conductance.

The properties of the response curves of Fig. 6 may be quantitatively explained with the aid of eqs. (13). Aside from the separation of the limiting asymptotes, the distinguishing characteristics of the curves of Fig. 6 are the $K$ values at the inflection and midpoints. These may be shown to be

$$K = \frac{\omega}{\sqrt{3}} \sqrt{C(C + C_c)} \qquad \text{inflection of } C_s \text{ curve} \qquad (14A)$$

$$K = \frac{\omega}{\sqrt{3}} (C + C_c) \qquad \text{inflection of } C_p \text{ curve} \qquad (14B)$$

$$K = \omega \sqrt{C(C + C_c)} \qquad \text{midpoint of } C_s \text{ curve} \qquad (15A)$$
$$K = \omega(C + C_c) \qquad \text{midpoint of } C_p \text{ curve} \qquad (15B)$$

The following conclusions may be drawn from eqs. (13) to (15) and are supported in part by the curves of Fig. 6.

(1) The $K$ values at which the inflection and midpoints occur for a particular solution are directly proportional to $\omega$.

(2) Substituting the $K$ values of eqs. (14) back into eqs. (13) reveals that the magnitudes of the slopes of the $C_s$ and $C_p$ curves at their inflection points are inversely proportional to $\omega$.

(3) The $K$ value at the midpoint of the $C_p$ curve is the same as the $K$ value at the peak of the $1/R_p$ curve. There is no such correspondence between the midpoint and peak of the $C_s$ and $R_s$ curves.

*2.5.2. Nonaqueous Conducting Solutions.* The curve of $C_p$ versus $K$ for solutions of potassium chloride in methanol is similar to the curves of Fig. 6. What is said concerning the response of class I instruments to nonaqueous conducting solutions applies similarly to class II instruments.

*2.5.3. Nonconducting Solutions.* For the case of nonconducting liquids, $K$ is small, and eqs. (13) reduce to

$$C_s = \frac{\omega^2 C^2 C_c}{\omega^2 C(C + C_c)} = \frac{CC_c}{C + C_c} \qquad (16A)$$

$$C_p = \frac{\omega^2 C(C + C_c)C_c}{\omega^2(C + C_c)^2} = \frac{CC_c}{C + C_c} \qquad (16B)$$

Equations (16) show that $C_s$ and $C_p$ are each independent of $R$. Figure 7 shows the response of a class II instrument to changes in dielectric constant of nonconducting systems (50). A rather complete analysis of the dependence of response of a class II instrument upon dielectric constant has been made for nonconducting solutions (50).

*2.5.4. Examples of Class II Instruments.* Class II instruments are essentially of two kinds and may be operated in either of two ways:

(1) As $C_s$ or $C_p$ changes, the oscillator remains in resonance but the frequency changes. The frequency change may be measured and taken as a measure of the change in $C_s$ or $C_p$, according to eqs. (4). The instruments of Blaedel and Malmstadt (6, 8), Thomas *et al.* (52), and West *et al.* (47, 54) are of this kind. Each of these instruments possesses two identical high-frequency oscillators,

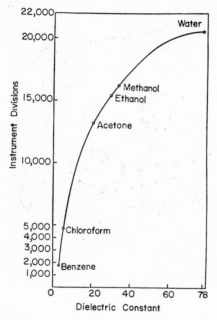

FIG. 7. Dependence of equivalent series or parallel capacitance upon dielectric constant in non-conducting solutions (50).

one being loaded with the vessel and solution and the other being an unloaded reference oscillator. The output frequencies of the two oscillators are heterodyned to give an audio beat frequency. Changes in the beat frequency are taken to correspond to changes in composition of the solution. The beat frequencies are measured with a frequency meter (6, 8, 52) or by finding the frequency of a standard audio oscillator required to give a Lissajou pattern against the audio beat frequency by use of an oscilloscope (47).

(2) As $C_s$ or $C_p$ varies, the resonant frequency of the circuit changes. The circuit is then retuned to its original resonant frequency by varying a compensating precision capacitor in parallel with the

cell. The capacitance changes are measured. The Sargent oscillometer, shown in Fig. 8, is of this type (50). Indication of resonance is given by a discriminator circuit. Hall's instrument also operates on this principle (section 2.6). The instruments of Fischer (21), Wagner and Kaufman (53), and Laskowski and Putscher (43) are probably class II, as are the instruments which are used for precise measurement of dielectric constant. In the latter instruments, the response is made independent of $C_c$ by

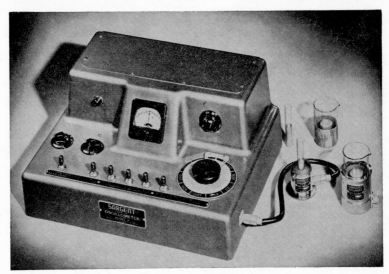

Fig. 8. Sargent oscillometer, with solution vessels.

immersing the condenser directly into the nonconducting liquid, in which case $C_c$ becomes very large, and eq. (16) becomes $C_s = C_p = C$. It is not the purpose of this chapter to describe such dielectric constant measurements. An elementary presentation and source of references are given by Daniels et al. (17, Chapter 12).

### 2.6. Class I–II Instruments

The simple and unique instrument of Hall (Fig. 9) is designed to allow simultaneous measurement of two responses, one proportional to $1/R_p$ and the other proportional to $C_p$ (30). The vessel, in parallel with the coil and compensating capacitors, loads the plate circuit of a crystal controlled oscillator. A 6E5 (magic eye) tube acts both as an oscillator and resonance indicator. A change in composition of the solution causes the oscillator to go out of resonance, as shown by opening of the eye. The oscillator is then retuned to resonance with the graduated capacitors $C_1$ or $C_2$. The change in capacitance required for retuning is proportional to the change in $C_p$, and the change in grid voltage (read on the vacuum-tube voltmeter) after retuning is proportional to the change in $1/R_p$.

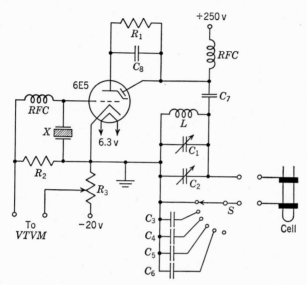

FIG. 9. Schematic diagram of Hall's Class I–II Instrument (30).

$C_1$. 100-$\mu\mu$f. variable capacitor
$C_2$. 30-$\mu\mu$f. variable capacitor
$C_3$. 100-$\mu\mu$f. mica
$C_4$. 40-$\mu\mu$f. mica
$C_5$. 25-$\mu\mu$f. mica
$C_6$. 10-$\mu\mu$f. mica
$C_7$, $C_8$. 0.001-$\mu$f., 450-v. paper
$L$. 42 turns, No. 24 d.c.c. copper wire close wound on $1\frac{1}{4}$ in. form
$R_1$. 150,000 ohms, 1 w.
$R_2$. 41,000 ohms, 1 w.
$R_3$. 10,000 ohms, wire-wound potentiometer
$RFC$. 2.5-mh. radio-frequency choke
$S$. Six-point rotary switch
$X$. 2-Mc. crystal

Of course A-C bridges must be regarded as class I–II instruments, since these are specifically designed to measure both the resistive and reactive parts of the equivalent circuit impedance. The Twin-T bridge is designed to give $R_p$ and $C_p$ for any circuit put across its input terminals; whereas the Schering bridge gives $R_s$ and $C_s$ (26). There are many other types of bridges, each designed for particular purposes (26).

### 2.7. Class III Instruments

Most of the instruments described so far in the literature are designed or operated in such ways that the response is proportional predominantly neither to the equivalent circuit resistance ($R_s$ or $R_p$) nor to the equivalent circuit capacitance ($C_s$ or $C_p$). Such instruments are defined as class III instruments.

Many class III instruments are in principle tunable to resonance and could be used as class I or II instruments, but in practice the oscillator is allowed to deviate from resonance as the composition changes. Such are the instruments of Arditti and Heitzman (3), Flom and Elving (23), Hara (31), Jensen and Parrack (37), and Milner (45).

Other class III instruments are essentially devices which respond to the total impedance of the solution and cell. In the methods of Blake (14) and Kamura (42) alternating current is passed through the cell and solution and is measured as a direct current after rectification. Changes in composition cause changes in impedance, which affect the magnitude of the direct current. Diehl *et al.* (4) measure the radiofrequency voltage developed across a circuit consisting of the solution and vessel in parallel with a transmitter type of inductance coil, when a fixed voltage from a standard oscillator is applied to a part of this coil. The instrument of Fujiwara and Hayashi (24) probably works similarly.

Some class III instruments have curves of response versus concentration which closely resemble the curves of Fig. 4 or 6, but other instruments (23) have response curves intermediate between those of Figs. 4 and 6. A few instruments have response curves with more than one maximum (or minimum), probably owing to the interaction of more than one resonant circuit (24, 37).

### 3. ADVANTAGES AND LIMITATIONS OF THE HIGH-FREQUENCY METHOD OF CHEMICAL ANALYSIS

Before the applications of the high-frequency method are enumerated, it is pertinent to describe generally the advantages and limitations, which is done in this section. Specific advantages and limitations, as pertaining to specific applications, are given in detail in section 4.

The principal advantage of using the high-frequency method to follow changes in composition of a chemical system is that no direct contact is needed between the chemical system and the electrodes, as is needed in the conductometric or potentiometric methods of measurement. Thus all effects due to poisoning, contamination, or polarization of the electrodes are eliminated, as are also effects due to electrolytic decomposition of the system. Measurements may be made on systems *in situ*, by placing the electrodes on the outside of the vessel holding the system, provided that the vessel is nonconducting.

Equipment for the high-frequency method of chemical analysis is usually simpler and less expensive than that for comparably accurate low-frequency measurements.

Potentially at least the high-frequency method is capable of far greater speed than ordinary conductance or potentiometric methods, since the slow process of equilibrating the solution and electrodes does not exist. To utilize this advantage fully, however, instruments involving manual balancing cannot be used. On the other hand, there are several disadvantages to the use of the high-frequency method. First, the response is not linearly dependent upon composition except over limited ranges of composition. In fact, the response is quite insensitive to changes in composition except over certain regions of composition, as may be seen from Figs. 4 and 6. In the case of conducting solutions of electrolytes, the concentration range for good sensitivity is rather low for most instruments—less than 0.1 $N$ sodium chloride, or solutions with equivalent specific conductance.

A second disadvantage is that the response is not generally a simple function of the fundamental properties of the solution ($\kappa$ and $\epsilon$), but is usually dependent upon both. The response of all high-frequency instruments so far described is an empirical function of composition, and the instruments must be calibrated with standard systems before they may be used to measure composition.

Last, the response is nonspecific, being dependent only upon $\kappa$ and $\epsilon$ for the system, and being independent of the specific chemical identity of the substances in the system. This nonspecificity considerably limits the use of the high-frequency method as an analytical tool.

## 4. Applications of the High-Frequency Method of Chemical Analysis

### 4.1. Measurement of the Composition or Fundamental Properties of Chemical Systems

One use of the high-frequency method of chemical analysis is in measuring the composition of chemical systems, with the advantages and limitations described in section 3. The nonspecificity limits the use of the high-frequency method for determining composition to rather simple systems, in which the response is dependent principally upon the concentration of just one component (or group of components).

Jensen and Parrack (37) determine hydrochloric acid (0 to 0.3% by weight) in benzene with a class III instrument. West and co-workers (55) determine water in alcohols with a class II instrument. Mixtures of benzene ($\epsilon = 2.27$) and toluene ($\epsilon = 2.38$) may be analyzed with good precision by the Sargent class II instrument. By use of a variable inductance in series with the vessel, the coupling capacitance $C_c$ (Fig. 2A) may be balanced out, giving increased sensitivity and a response linearly dependent upon composition. Analysis of other binary mixtures is also described (50). Thomas et al. (52) determine the aromatic content of a petroleum refinery stream with a class II instrument (section 4.4).

Conceivably the high-frequency method might also be used in an empirical way to determine fundamental solution properties, such as $\kappa$ and $\epsilon$. Generally, however, this use is limited because response is not simply related to either of these properties and also because response is generally dependent upon both of these properties. Only in the case of nonconducting solutions in class II instruments is the response a simple function of $\epsilon$ alone, and such instruments are widely used to determine $\epsilon$.

With the exception of the above case, measurements of $\kappa$, $\epsilon$, and dielectric loss may be made much more directly, conveniently, and accurately with an A-C bridge (section 2.6). Such bridge measurements have proved of great value in measuring the aforementioned properties to obtain fundamental chemical information. Examples of only a few applications are the following: (1) measurement of the capacitance of the electrical double layer at the interface between mercury and aqueous solutions (27), (2) measurement of complex dielectric constant to give information about the structure of high polymers (22, 25), (3) measurements of a complex dielectric constant to give information about the state of substances (such as water, alcohol, ethylene dichloride, etc.) absorbed upon solid adsorbents (41, 51), (4) A-C bridge measurements, which furnish the most direct and understandable support for the theory of the high-frequency method given in section 2 (28, 49).

### 4.2. Indication of the Endpoint in Titrations

There are many applications of the high-frequency method in detecting endpoints in titrations. The absence of direct contact between electrodes and solution is a very definite advantage, especially in precipitation titrations, but this advantage is partially offset by the nonlinearity and nonspecificity of the response. The disadvantages of nonlinear response or poor sensitivity in certain concentration regions cause inconveniences which may be circumvented by proper choice of titration conditions.

The titration curves obtained with high-frequency instruments are more complicated than ordinary conductometric titration curves and are best explained by Fig. 10 (49). In Fig. 10C are shown three familiar low-frequency titration curves for hydrochloric acid samples with standard sodium hydroxide, for slightly differing sample sizes and dilutions. Figure 10B is a plot of the response of a class I instrument at 10 Mc. over the same conductance range as the plot of Fig. 10C. (Actually, the

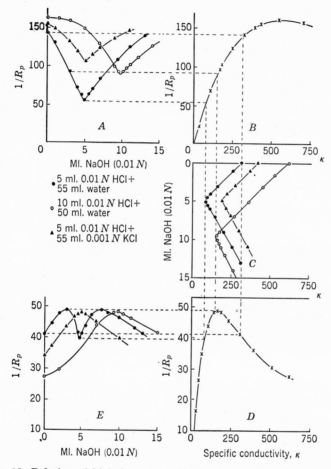

Fig. 10. Relation of high frequency titration curves to ordinary conductometric titration curves (49).

response is that of a Twin-T bridge, which measures $1/R_p$.) The high-frequency curves for the titrations of Fig. 10C which would be given by an instrument with a response like that of Fig. 10B are shown in Fig. 10A. The mode of construction is indicated in the figure. It may be seen that the high-frequency endpoints are sharp, as long as these endpoints fall in conductance regions in which the high-frequency response curve is moderately steep. The wings of the high-frequency titration curves are curved, owing to curvature in the response curve.

The response curve for Fig. 10D is for a frequency of 3 Mc. and is similar to the 10-Mc. curve of Fig. 10B, except that the maximum falls at a lower conductance, in accord with eq. (8B). Figure 10E shows the sort of high-frequency titration curves given by the titrations of Fig. 10C when the conductances during titration fall in the vicinity of the peak

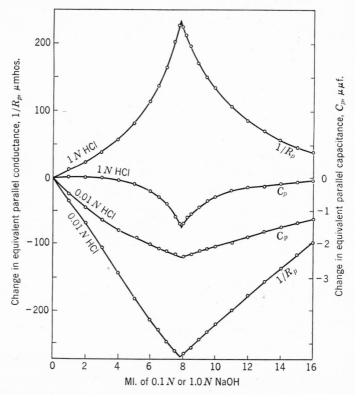

Fig. 11. Effect of concentration on the titration curves for the titration of HCl with NaOH at 6 Mc. (28).

conductance of the response curve. Thus, if the conductance of the titrated solution at the endpoint falls at or near the peak conductance of the response curve, the endpoint may be very poor or may even be obliterated. A pip-shaped titration curve is obtained when the conductance of the titrated solution at the endpoint corresponds to a conductance on the steep part of the response curve but when the conductance before and after the endpoint passes through the peak conductance of the response curve, as shown in Fig. 10E. All plots of Fig. 10 are experimental.

Titration curves obtained with class II instruments are similarly explainable (49), but because the response of class II instruments does not pass through a maximum, pip-shaped titration curves are not obtained. Poor endpoints are obtained if the conductance of the titrated solution falls in conductance regions of low sensitivity, where the response curve has only a slight slope.

The effect of concentration on the slope of the titration curve is brought out somewhat more clearly in Fig. 11 than in Fig. 10. In Fig. 12 the effect of frequency on the shape of the titration curve for a particular

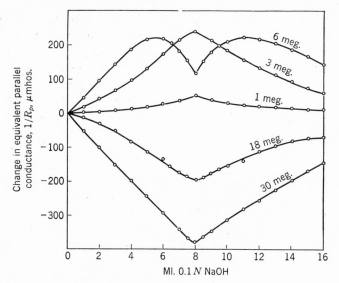

FIG. 12. Effect of frequency on the titration curve for the titration of 0.1 $N$. HCl with 0.1 $N$ NaOH, using a Type I instrument (28).

titration is shown. (The frequency determines the $K$ for peak values in the response curves for class I instruments and the regions of maximum sensitivity for class II instruments, according to eqs. (8), (14), and (15).)

From Figs. 10 to 12, it may be seen that good endpoints will not always be obtained unless titration conditions are properly selected. It is important to select sample size, endpoint volume, and frequency, if possible, so that the endpoint conductance will correspond to the conductance on a steep part of the response curve. The class I–II instrument of Hall is particularly useful in this respect, for the conductance region in which the class I response passes through a maximum and is insensitive is in the region where the class II response has fairly good sensitivity (section 2.6). The nature of the errors encountered in selecting endpoints when the wings of the titration curves are not straight are described by Blaedel and Malmstadt (11), and a method for recording differential titration curves to reduce such errors is presented (10).

The following titrations have been described: argentimetric and mercurimetric titrations of chloride and thiocyanate (7, 8), indirect titration of thorium with sodium oxalate (9), beryllium with standard base (2), sulfate with standard barium nitrate (45), and fluoride with standard thorium nitrate (33, p. 400). Several metals, including calcium and magnesium, have been titrated with the disodium salt of ethylene-diaminetetraacetic acid, or standard soap solution (13, 39). Acid-base titrations have been performed by most of these workers.

Titrations in nonaqueous solutions have also been successfully performed. Weak bases have been titrated with standard perchloric acid in glacial acetic acid solutions (53). Benzoic and o-phthalic acids have been titrated with sodium methylate in methanol (37). The nonspecificity of the high-frequency method precludes accurate results for titrations in solutions containing relatively large amounts of buffering substances and in many titrations which require a relatively high excess of acid or base. The method has therefore not been applied extensively to such titrations.

### 4.3. Measurement of Reaction Rate

The advantage of being able to follow composition changes rapidly and without material contact with the solution makes the high-frequency method very desirable for measuring reaction rates, provided that the limitations mentioned in section 3 are not prohibitive. Class III instruments have been used by Jensen and co-workers (38) to follow the saponification of ethyl acetate and by Diehl and co-workers (18) to study the rate of precipitation of barium sulfate. A class II instrument has been used to determine acetylacetone, based on measurement of its rate of reaction with a known concentration of hydroxylamine in acid solution (48). Flom and Elving (19, 23) have used a class III instrument with a recorded output to measure the rates of alkaline hydrolysis of several esters. The measurable reaction half-times ranged from 2 to 20 sec., the lower limit being set principally by the speed of mixing reactants and the recorder response time. Use of an oscilloscope as a recorder should reduce instrumental response time to only a few microseconds. Melville et al. (15, 44) have used a very sensitive class II instrument to follow free radical formation in photopolymerization reactions of vinyl compounds. The build-up and decay of radical concentration was measured by recording oscillographically a voltage related to the light intensity after irradiation with a light pulse. From the decay curves, radical half-lives in the range 0.1 to 60 sec. could be estimated.

## 4.4. Monitoring

The high-frequency method is desirable for monitoring purposes, since measurements may often be made *in situ*, continuously, and without materially entering the monitored system or stream.

A class II instrument has been used to estimate the content of aromatic hydrocarbons in a petroleum refinery stream. For the aromatics which may be present, $\epsilon$ is 1.9 to 2.1, and for the nonaromatics, 2.3 to 2.6. The instrument operates at resonance, and the frequency is a measure of $\epsilon$ and therefore a semiquantitative measure of the aromatic content of the refinery stream which passes through the cell of the instrument (52).

The high-frequency method has also been applied to the monitoring of adsorption and ion exchange columns (36, 36a). Chromatographic adsorption has been followed in nonaqueous systems (43, 46). Hashimoto and Mori (35) have applied the method to paper chromatography, detecting adsorption zones by passing the paper between two metal condenser plates close together. The high-frequency method has also been used successfully to follow the separation of carboxylic acids in partition chromatographic columns, for which conductometric methods are not easily applicable, since the aqueous phase is dispersed (5).

## 4.5. Miscellaneous Applications

The high-frequency method has been used to study the composition of complex ions, even though the nonlinear and nonselective nature of the response sometimes renders the data uncertain or difficult to interpret (29, 32).

Blake (14) has reviewed a variety of applications, among which are (1) measurement of the rate of diffusion of electrolytes; (2) a device for indicating the position of the interface between two immiscible liquids; (3) instruments for the detection and estimation of water in various materials, such as foods, wood, textiles, lacquer, etc.; (4) a variable capacitive element, for transforming mechanical motion into capacitive changes, so that high-frequency instruments may be used to measure and control such mechanical motion (the application to a balance is described); and (5) biological uses including measurement of changes in composition of plant saps *in vivo* and differentiation between the fertilized and unfertilized eggs of sea urchins and starfish.

The rate of settling of small silica particles in a benzene-nitrobenzene medium has been measured by use of a small capacitor suspended in the region through which the particles fell (40).

The rate of flame propagation has been measured with a class III instrument by noting the voltage pulse developed across a resistor in the plate circuit as the ionized flame front passed through an inductance coil (16).

High-frequency instruments may be used to detect and measure changes in other physical quantities, by using the proper transforming devices to convert the changes into capacitive ones. The instrument of Melville *et al.* (15, 44) should be able to detect relative changes in dielectric constant or pressure of $2:10^8$ and to detect changes in heat or temperature of $3 \times 10^{-5}$ cal. or $10^{-5}$ °C., respectively.

## APPENDIX I

### Derivation of Equation (2)

The complex impedance, $\bar{Z}_{R-C}$, of the parallel combination of $R$ and $C$ in Fig. 2A is

$$\bar{Z}_{R-C} = \frac{R(-j/\omega C)}{R - j/\omega C} \tag{a}$$

The impedance $\bar{Z}_{R-C}$ may be added to that of $C_c$ to obtain the total impedance, $\bar{Z}$, of the entire circuit of Fig. 2A:

$$\bar{Z} = -\frac{jR/\omega C}{R - j/\omega C} - \frac{j}{\omega C_c} \tag{b}$$

When terms are rationalized and gathered, eq. (b) becomes

$$\bar{Z} = \frac{R}{R^2\omega^2C^2 + 1} - j \frac{(R^2\omega^2C^2 + R^2\omega^2CC_c + 1)}{(R^2\omega^3C^2C_c + \omega C_c)} \tag{c}$$

Equation (c) has the form

$$\bar{Z} = R_s - j/\omega C_s \tag{d}$$

where

$$R_s = \frac{R}{R^2\omega^2C^2 + 1} \tag{e}$$

$$C_s = \frac{R^2\omega^2C^2C_c + C_c}{(R^2\omega^2C^2 + R^2\omega^2CC_c + 1)} \tag{f}$$

According to eq. (d), the impedance of the circuit of Fig. 2A is identical to the impedance of a resistor $R_s$ and capacitor $C_s$ in series, as shown in Fig. 2B. The values of $R_s$ and $C_s$ are related to $R$, $C$, $C_c$, and $\omega$ as shown in eqs. (e) and (f), which are the same as eqs. (2A and B).

## APPENDIX II

### Derivation of Equation (3)

The complex admittance, $\bar{Y}_{R-C}$, of the parallel combination of $R$ and $C$ in Fig. 2A is

$$\bar{Y}_{R-C} = \frac{1}{R} + j\omega C = \frac{1 + jR\omega C}{R} \tag{a}$$

The total admittance, $\bar{Y}$, of the entire circuit of Fig. 2A may be obtained as follows:

$$\frac{1}{\bar{Y}} = \frac{1}{\bar{Y}_{R-C}} + \frac{1}{j\omega C_e} = \frac{R}{1 + jR\omega C} + \frac{1}{j\omega C_e} \tag{b}$$

Rationalizing, gathering terms, and rearranging give eq. (b) as

$$\bar{Y} = \frac{R\omega^2 C_e^2}{1 + R^2\omega^2 (C + C_e)^2} + j\omega \left[ \frac{C_e + R^2\omega^2 C^2 C_e + R^2\omega^2 CC_e^2}{R^2\omega^2 (C + C_e)^2 + 1} \right] \tag{c}$$

Equation (c) has the form

$$\bar{Y} = \frac{1}{R_p} + j\omega C_p \tag{d}$$

where

$$R_p = \frac{1 + R^2\omega^2 (C + C_e)^2}{R\omega^2 C_e^2} \tag{e}$$

$$C_e = \frac{C_e + R^2\omega^2 C^2 C_e + R^2\omega^2 CC_e^2}{R^2\omega^2 (C + C_e)^2 + 1} \tag{f}$$

According to eq. (d), the admittance of the circuit of Fig. 2A is identical to the admittance of a resistor $R_p$ and a capacitor $C_p$ in parallel, as shown in Fig. 3C. The values of $R_p$ and $C_p$ are related to $R$, $C$, $C_e$, and $\omega$ as shown in eqs. (e) and (f), which are the same as eqs. (3A and B).

### REFERENCES

1. Anderson, K., Bettis, E. S., and Revinson, D., *Anal. Chem.* **22,** 743 (1950).
2. Anderson, K., and Revinson, D., *Anal. Chem.* **22,** 1272 (1950).
3. Arditti, R., and Heitzmann, P., *Compt. rend.* **229,** 44 (1949).
4. Bever, R. J., Crouthamel, C. E., and Diehl, H., *Iowa State Coll. J. Sci.* **23,** 289 (1949).
5. Blaedel, W. J., and Bauman, F., *Anal. Chem.* **28,** 2 (1956).
6. Blaedel, W. J., and Malmstadt, H. V., *Anal. Chem.* **22,** 734 (1950).
7. Blaedel, W. J., and Malmstadt, H. V., *Anal. Chem.* **22,** 1410 (1950).
8. Blaedel, W. J., and Malmstadt, H. V., *Anal. Chem.* **22,** 1413 (1950).
9. Blaedel, W. J., and Malmstadt, H. V., *Anal. Chem.* **23,** 471 (1951).
10. Blaedel, W. J., and Malmstadt, H. V., *Anal. Chem.* **24,** 450 (1952).
11. Blaedel, W. J., and Malmstadt, H. V., *Anal. Chem.* **24,** 455 (1952).
12. Blaedel, W. J., Malmstadt, H. V., Petitjean, D. L., and Anderson, W. K., *Anal. Chem.* **24,** 1240 (1952).
13. Blaedel, W. J., and Knight, H. T., *Anal. Chem.* **26,** 743 (1954).
14. Blake, G. G., "Conductometric Analysis at Radio-Frequency." Chapman and Hall, London, 1950.
15. Burrell, C. M., Majury, T. G., and Melville, H. W., *Proc. Roy. Soc.* **A205,** 309 (1951).
16. Calcote, H. F., *Rev. Sci. Instr.* **20,** 349 (1949).
17. Daniels, F., Mathews, J. H., and Williams, J. W., "Experimental Physical Chemistry." McGraw-Hill, New York, 1949.
18. Duke, F. R., Bever, R. J., and Diehl, H., *Iowa State Coll. J. Sci.* **23,** 297 (1949).

19. Elving, P. J., "Applicability of Megacycle Frequency Oscillator Circuits to Reaction Rate Measurements." Tech. Rept. No. 3., Project No. NR 051-318, Office of Naval Research, Univ. of Michigan, Jan. 15, 1954.

20. Falkenhagen, H., "Electrolytes." Oxford Univ. Press, New York, 1934.

21. Fischer, R. B., *Anal. Chem.* **19**, 835 (1947).

22. Fitzgerald, E. R., and Miller, R. F., *J. Colloid Sci.* **8**, 148 (1953).

23. Flom, D. G., and Elving, P. J., *Anal. Chem.* **25**, 541 (1953).

24. Fujiwara, S., and Hayashi, S., *Anal. Chem.* **26**, 239 (1954).

25. Fuoss, R. M., *in* "The Chemistry of Large Molecules" (R. E. Burk and O. Grummitt, eds.). Interscience, New York, 1943.

26. General Radio Co., Cambridge, Mass., Catalog N., Jan. 1954.

27. Grahame, D. C., *J. Am. Chem. Soc.* **63**, 1207 (1941).

28. Hall, J. L., *Anal. Chem.* **23**, 966 (1951).

29. Hall, J. L., *Anal. Chem.* **24**, 1236 (1952).

30. Hall, J. L., *Anal. Chem.* **24**, 1244 (1952).

31. Hara, R., *J. Pharm. Soc. Japan* **71**, 1122 (1951).

32. Hara, R., *J. Pharm. Soc. Japan* **71**, 1128, 1134, 1140, 1144 (1951).

33. Harley, J. H., and Wiberley, S. E. "Instrumental Analysis." Wiley, New York, 1954.

34. Harned, H. S., and Owen, B. B. "The Physical Chemistry of Electrolytic Solutions." Reinhold, New York, 1943.

35. Hashimoto, Y., and Mori, I., *J. Pharm. Soc. Japan* **72**, 1532 (1952).

36. Honda, M., *J. Chem. Soc. Japan Pure Chem. Sect.* **73**, 529 (1952).

36a. Honda, M., and Tadano, H., *Japan Analyst* **2**, 456 (1953).

37. Jensen, F. W., and Parrack, A. L., *Ind. Eng. Chem. Anal. Ed.* **18**, 595 (1946).

38. Jensen, F. W., Watson, G. M., and Beckham, J. B., *Anal. Chem.* **23**, 1770 (1951).

39. Jensen, F. W., Watson, G. M., and Vela, L. G., *Anal. Chem.* **23**, 1327 (1951).

40. Jottrand, R., *Chem. Eng. Sci.* **1**, 81 (1951).

41. Kamiyoshi, K. I., and Odake, T., *J. Chem. Phys.* **21**, 1295 (1953).

42. Kamura, Y., *J. Japan. Chemistry* **6**, 771 (1952).

43. Laskowski, D. E., and Putscher, R. E., *Anal. Chem.* **24**, 965 (1952).

44. Majury, T. G., and Melville, H. W., *Proc. Roy. Soc.* **A205**, 323, 496 (1951).

45. Milner, O. I., *Anal. Chem.* **24**, 1247 (1952).

46. Monaghan, P. H., Moseley, P. B., Burkhalter, T. S., and Nance, O. A., *Anal. Chem.* **24**, 193 (1952).

47. Nance, O. A., Burkhalter, T. S., and Monaghan, P. H., *Anal. Chem.* **24**, 214 (1952).

48. Petitjean, D. L., Chemical Analysis by Measurement of Reaction Rate. Doctorate Thesis, University of Wisconsin, 1953.

49. Reilley, C. N., and McCurdy, W. H., Jr., *Anal. Chem.* **25**, 86 (1953).

50. Sherrick, P. H., Dawe, G. A., Karr, R., and Ewen, E. F. "Manual of Chemical Oscillometry." E. H. Sargent, Chicago, 1954.

51. Snelgrove, J. A., Greenspan, H., and McIntosh, R., *Can. J. Chem.* **31**, 72, 84 (1953).

52. Thomas, B. W., Faegin, F. J., and Wilson, G. W., *Anal. Chem.* **23**, 1750 (1951).

53. Wagner, W. F., and Kaufman, W. B., *Anal. Chem.* **25**, 538 (1953).

54. West, P. W., Burkhalter, T. S., and Broussard, L., *Anal. Chem.* **22**, 469 (1950).

55. West, P. W., Senise, P., and Burkhalter, T. S., *Anal. Chem.* **24**, 1250 (1952).

# Field Emission Microscopy

*Department of Physics, The Pennsylvania State University,*
*University Park, Pennsylvania*

## 1. General Background

The condition of a surface is of primary importance in the reaction between solids and gases or liquids. These reactions can be understood in detail only if the atomic fine structure of the surfaces and the acting forces are known with precision. Since the forces are primarily electrical in nature, a survey of surfaces by electrons should be particularly illuminating. The conventional electron microscope is not very useful, as electron energies of 50 to 100,000 volts are much too large to interact appreciably with surface-energy levels that amount to only a few volts. The depth of penetration of such fast electrons is several hundred atomic layers. Only with grazing angles of incidence can electron diffraction give any information about the average condition of the first ten atomic layers. In emission microscopy, on the other hand, the electrons producing the image start with a low velocity from the surface under investigation and are strongly influenced in intensity by localized potential barriers. Emission microscopy is, of course, limited to the investigation of electrical conductors, specifically to metals, but the very sensitivity of this method makes it valuable in studying the nature of thin films as small as a fraction of an atomic layer.

The surface can be studied in a number of ways by electron emission. Historically the first method was by the use of thermionic emission (9, 33). This method has recently been improved thanks to instrumental advances in transmission electron microscopy where stable and flexible equipment has become commercially available (26, 50). The limitation of this approach lies in the fact that a sufficiently strong and constant emission can be obtained only with the metals and oxides of the alkaline earths and of some alkalies. Thus investigations by this method are limited to these substances or surfaces activated by them, within a narrow temperature range. Also the resolution of such emission microscopes (51) is much smaller than that of transmission electron microscopes. Photoelectric electron emission is less temperature dependent, but the current densities are so small that from lack of intensity no substantial magnification can be achieved.

Field emission yields by far the largest current densities. Values of $10^7$ amp./cm.$^2$ can easily be achieved, a million times those of thermionic emission. Furthermore, field emission is almost independent of the cathode temperature, and investigation of a surface can be carried out in the temperature range from liquid-helium temperature to red heat. The necessary field strength of between 20 to 50 million volts/cm. can be obtained with anode voltages of a few thousand volts if the cathode is made in the form of a small tip. If this tip is uniformly curved, for example, in the shape of a hemispherical calotte, the emitted electrons will escape radially and be perpendicular to each surface element. A fluorescent screen several centimeters from the tip will indicate the emission distribution projected from this point source without the need of further electron optics. A magnified picture of the emitting surface is thus obtained (37, 47) (Fig. 1).

Such a field emission microscope can also be operated with positive ions (45) in place of electrons. The resolution of ion microscopes is even better because of the shorter De Broglie wave length of ions and surpasses in this respect all known microscopes. However, since ion microscopy requires field strengths ten times larger than does field electron emission, the technical difficulties are very great and the development of this method is still in its infancy.

## 2. THEORY OF FIELD EMISSION

The mechanism of field emission is easily understood from the point of view of wave mechanics. According to the Fermi-Sommerfeld theory of metals (54), the free electrons are located in a potential trough which they fill at low temperatures to the height of the Fermi level $W_i$ (Fig. 2a). The potential hump on the metal surface is rounded by the image force; i.e., an electron near the surface is attracted back into the metal owing to electrostatic attraction from its image in the metal. At sufficiently high

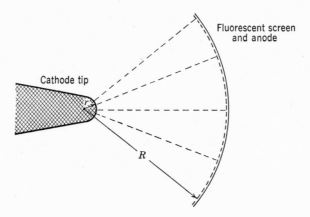

FIG. 1. Diagram of field emission microscope.

temperatures some electrons have energies higher than the Fermi level energy and a small number of electrons whose additional energy is even greater than $\Phi$, the thermal work function, can overcome the potential barrier and leave the metal as thermionic electrons. Electrons whose

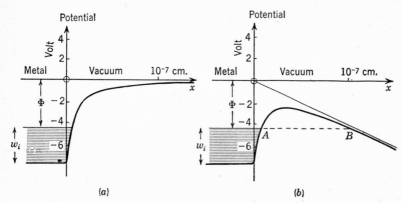

FIG. 2a. Potential on a metal surface.
FIG. 2b. Potential on a metal surface with an external field of 40 Mv./cm.

normal energy content is less than $W_i + \Phi$ will return into the metal. The presence of a strong electric field produces a lowering of the energy barrier, and so thermionic emission increases (Schottky effect). If, however, the field strength is so great that the width of the potential barrier above the Fermi level becomes comparable with the wave length of the electron (Fig. 2b), the total reflection of waves becomes incomplete even at low temperatures and a small electron density is observable at $B$. Electrons appearing there have crossed the barrier by tunneling through $AB$ and, starting with zero velocity at $B$, are accelerated toward the anode. Exact computation of current density is carried out by the method of Fowler and Nordheim (19) by integrating the product of the number of electrons reaching the surface from the interior $N(w)$ with the normal component of energy $w$ and the transmission $D(w)$ of the barrier. One obtains numerically

$$j = 1.55 \cdot 10^{-6} \frac{F^2}{\Phi} e^{-\frac{6.85 \cdot 10^7 \Phi^{3/2}}{F} \cdot f(y)} \tag{1}$$

where $j$ is the current density in amp./cm.$^2$, $F$ the field strength in volts/ cm., $\Phi$ the work function in electron volts, $f(y)$ an elliptical integral (10) the value of which is given in Table I.

TABLE I

| $y = \dfrac{3.62 \cdot 10^{-4} F^{1/2}}{\Phi}$ | 0.0 | 0.1 | 0.2 | 0.3 | 0.4 | 0.5 | 0.6 | 0.7 | 0.8 | 0.9 |
|---|---|---|---|---|---|---|---|---|---|---|
| $f(y)$ | 1.00 | 0.98 | 0.94 | 0.87 | 0.79 | 0.69 | 0.58 | 0.45 | 0.31 | 0.16 |

For the practical case of field emission microscopy one can substitute with sufficient accuracy for eq. (1):

$$i = AF^2 e^{-\frac{B}{F}} \tag{2}$$

Since field strength is proportional to applied voltage $V$, the current-voltage characteristics of a field emission tube can be represented by

$$i = aV^2 e^{-\frac{b}{V}} \tag{3}$$

Taking logarithms gives a convenient form for graphical representation:

$$\log \frac{i}{V^2} = a - \frac{b}{V} \tag{4}$$

Graphs of $\ln i/V^2$ versus $1/V$ give almost straight lines with a slope proportional to $\Phi^{3/2}$. A further simplification is shown in Fig. 3, where $\log i$ is plotted against the reciprocal of the anode voltage $V$. This is sufficient for the location of the current-voltage characteristics and gives, for all practical purposes, straight lines as long as the current is varied over only a few orders of magnitude.

The resolution of the field emission microscope (2, 20, 41) will be estimated on the assumption that tips are ideally smooth down to atomic dimensions. Electrons emitted from a point on the cathode, such as an atom, have a radial as well as a tangential velocity component because the transmission of the barrier is still appreciable somewhat below the Fermi level and the number of electrons rapidly increases for

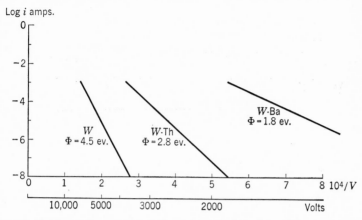

FIG. 3. Field emission current-voltage characteristic for a clean tungsten tip (radius about 2000 Å.), and of the same tip covered with a monolayer of thorium or barium respectively.

lower energy levels. Although the electrons are rapidly accelerated in the radial direction by the applied field, the small velocity component in the tangential direction remains. The electron beam emanating from a point on the tip will broaden out toward the anode and produce a scattering

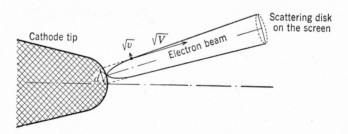

FIG. 4. Scattering disk on the screen from an emitting point on the tip.

disk on the screen the diameter of which determines the sharpness of the image (Fig. 4).

The influence of electron diffraction also has to be considered. This can be done as well by using Heisenberg's uncertainty principle. With the magnification

$$M = \frac{R}{\beta r} \tag{5}$$

($R$ = distance from point to screen, $r$ = tip radius, $\beta$ = factor describing the image compression due to deviation of the geometrical arrangement from the ideal projection between concentric spheres. Practically $\beta$ = 1.5), one obtains the minimum size (236) $\Delta_{min}$ from

$$\Delta_{min}{}^2 = 4v_t{}^2\tau^2 + \frac{2\hbar\tau M}{m} \tag{6}$$

$\left(\tau = R\sqrt{\dfrac{m}{2eV}}\right.$ is the time of flight of the electron, $v_t$ the average tangential velocity $\hbar$, Planck's constant divided by $2\pi$.) The objectside

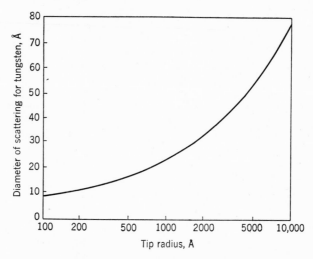

FIG. 5. Diameter of scattering disk (resolving power).

diameter of the smallest image, which we set equal to the resolving power, is then obtained by dividing $\Delta_{min}$ by $M$:

$$\delta = \sqrt{\frac{2\beta^2 r^2 m\bar{v}_t{}^2}{eV} + \frac{2\hbar\beta r}{\sqrt{2emV}}} \tag{7}$$

The tangential velocity component for field electrons has been determined by Richter (52):

$$E = \frac{mv_t{}^2}{2} = 0.67 \cdot 10^{-8} F / \sqrt{\Phi} \tag{8}$$

Using the equations (7), (8) and (10) one can calculate the resolution as given in Fig. 5. For tungsten in a typical case with $F$ = $4 \cdot 10^7$ volt/cm., E = 0.13 e-volt we obtain with a tip radius of 1000 Å. a resolution of 23 Å. With very fine tips and the sacrifice of complete surface cleanliness the resolution can approach 10 Å. The image content, however, defined as the largest possible number of image points of the magnitude of the scattering disk on the tip hemisphere, is also reduced. At a tip of 10,000 Å. the image content consists of 130,000 image points; at a tip of 1000 Å., of 14,000 image points; and at a tip of 100 Å. radius, of only 1100 image points. Hence, projected on the same screen size, the image of a blunt tip looks much more detailed than an image of a very sharp tip, though the resolution of the latter is higher.

By coincidence the practical resolution limits of 10 to 20 Å. for field emission microscopes are of the same magnitude as that of the best transmission electron microscopes. However, the field emission microscope is much more sensitive in the third dimension. It can make visible adsorbed substances even at coverages of less than a monomolecular layer.

## 3. The Field Emission Microscope

The field emission microscope, in contrast to the electron microscope, has not yet been developed into a universal and flexible commercially available instrument. For each application a microscope tube must be specially built, which may present in some cases difficult technical problems.* The practical realization depends in each instance on the feasibility of two manipulations:

(1) The production of a small, smooth, and rounded tip from the metal under observation.
(2) The production of a sufficiently good vacuum so that the surface is not altered by undesired adsorption or sputtering during the course of the observation.

A typical field emission microscope is shown in Fig. 6. The emitting cathode tip is mounted on a wire. The positive high voltage is applied on a metal ring between cathode and screen. The geometry of the anode ring is of no significance. Since some fluorescent screen materials tend to acquire static charges, it is desirable to make the glass wall and a portion of the inner surface of the glass bulb electrically conducting by evaporating of a thin metal film or by the application of a conducting tin oxide layer. Sufficiently large images are obtained for the commonly used tip radii of $10^{-4}$ to $10^{-5}$ cm. and a screen distance of 2 to 5 cm. to make full use of the resolving power even without a very finely grained screen. For demonstration purposes a larger separation distance between tip and screen can be chosen; for example, the cathode can be mounted in a television tube, but the fuzziness, readily calculable from Fig. 5 and the magnification $M = R/r$, amounts in this case to several millimeters.

* A discussion of commercial field electron microscopes (E. Leybold's Nachfolger, Cologne, Germany) is given by Hecht (25).

The surface of the tip is simultaneously the objective and the optical element of the microscope. The image represents directly the distribution of current. This distribution is determined by the local field strength, which in the ideal case of a sperical calotte should be constant everywhere, and by the local work function, which depends on the atomic constitution of the surface, i.e., its crystal structure, chemical nature, and the presence of adsorbed layers.

Satisfactory tips have been prepared only from metals of high melting point. The limitation in durability and the danger of tip destruction during the experiment will be mentioned in more detail below. The pre-

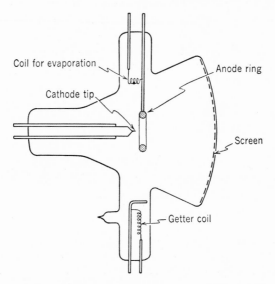

FIG. 6. Sealed off field emission microscope.

liminary sharpening of the cathode is best done by a suitable etching process. Tungsten and molybdenum tips can be obtained in a few seconds by dipping a 4-mil wire into molten sodium nitrite at 300 to 400° C. A 1-mm.-long cone toward the heating loop is desirable. An optical microscope of 100- to 500-fold magnification may be used for control of etching. Electrolytic etching is more readily controlled than etching in salt baths. The tip is usually made the anode. Several electrolytes work satisfactorily with alternating current. Sodium hydroxide or sodium nitrite are recommended for tungsten or molybdenum. Hydrofluoric acid is preferable for tantalum, niobium, zirconium, and titanium. Sometimes dipping of the metal into acid without electrolysis is adequate. Good tips are obtained in this way with nickel in hydrochloric acid or with copper in nitric acid. Iron tips can be formed in electrolytic polishing solutions consisting of perchloric acid-acetic acid (53). Very smooth tips of platinum are obtained by electrolytic etching in molten sodium chloride near 820° C. and at a voltage of several volts (34). Tungsten tips can be obtained by oxidation in a gas flame since the oxide is volatile. In a previously used microscope assembly in which the tip may have acquired a large radius by prolonged heating, resharpening can be accomplished by cautious ion bombardment (36, 47). To accomplish this the tube is filled with a gas giving effective cathode sputtering. Argon or mercury is suitable for this purpose at a pressure of $10^{-5}$ to $10^{-3}$ mm., which can be accomplished for mercury by removal of the liquid-air cold trap. On application of the anode voltage, the electrons emitted from the dull tip ionize the gas and the positive ions fall predominantly on the side of the tip which is eroded by cathode sputtering. This somewhat delicate procedure can furnish tip radii of less than 100 Å. For tungsten and molybdenum subsequent sharpening can be accomplished by oxidation of the hot surface at oxygen pressures of several tenths of a millimeter and removal of the oxide by evaporation (38).

The coarsely sharpened tips prepared by any of the preceding methods must be smoothed down to atomic dimensions. This is done by heating to temperatures where surface motion of atoms on their own lattice becomes noticeable (37, 42). Thus far, only the metals tungsten, molybdenum, tantalum, niobium, platinum, nickel, vanadium, iron, and copper have been successfully used. Iron and copper present difficulties owing to formation of sharp crystal edges, which may be caused by impurities preventing free mobility on the surface. As described below, carbon adsorbed on tungsten shows the formation of sharp edges. Attempts have been unsuccessful thus far to prepare smooth tips of silver. Heating in a gas atmosphere such as nitrogen might be helpful. Metals like zirconium and titanium cause difficulties due to their high reactivity toward the gases that are liberated on baking out. Their oxides, nitrides, and carbides are too stable to be thermally decomposed when the ultimate vacuum is obtained, and the nonmetallic surface does not permit the necessary surface migration. However, it is possible, with some difficulties, to observe the allotropic phase transformation in titanium (8a). A promising metal for studying a hexagonal structure seems to be rhenium (2a). Alloys of various metals, for instance Mo-Zr (10a), can also be used to make cathode tips. The great mechanical strength of whiskers suggests their application as field emitters particularly in the case of iron, copper and silver.

The heat polishing is due to surface migration whereby the protruding points and edges are diminished. The tip tends to assume the shape of minimum free surface energy, but an equilibrium state is never reached.

On heating, the radius of the calotte increases gradually due to migration of atoms toward the rear. For a tungsten tip at 1575° C. about one atomic layer migrated per hour; at 2425° C. the migration rate was one layer per second (42). Heating of several minutes is necessary to obtain a really clean surface. Thus starting with a tip radius of only 100 Å. it is very difficult to obtain a perfect tip much smaller than 1000-Å. radius.

The shape of the calotte is not an equilibrium configuration of the crystal but rather a dissolution form and therefore nearly spherical. From electron micrographs of tungsten tips one can discern a small flattening with rounded edges of the dodecarhomboidal planes (110). The shape of other cubic body-centered metal crystals is similar while cubic face-centered metals form tips with slightly flattened octahedron surfaces

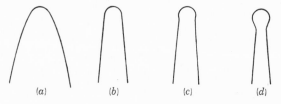

FIG. 7. Different shapes of field emitters, same radius.

(111). From the field emission images one can deduce that several additional planes appear to some extent as surfaces on the calotte: for cubic body-centered metals the (112) and (100) planes, for face-centered crystals the (100) plane. Since the crystallites of the wire are considerably larger than the tip radius, the calotte usually contains only one crystal. Occasionally a crystal boundary is observed which moves on heating as one crystal grows at the expense of its neighbor (46).

Besides the tip radius the angle of the cone is of importance. By proper choice of the etch material and the depth of dipping, one can produce either blunt or slim tips. The blunt tips of Fig. 7a retain their shape even after prolonged heating, but the vertex radius increases relatively rapidly. Tip shapes shown in Fig. 7c, on the other hand, change their radius of curvature only very slowly and gradually obtain a spherical end, which is particularly well formed for very slim tips shown in Fig. 7d. With all tip shapes the curvature and thus the field strength is maximum at the vertex. In Fig. 7a the decrease in field strength with increasing angle away from the vertex is so pronounced that the emission current density has decreased by a half for an angle of 35°. The entire visible image does not include a half angle greater than 55°. For the extreme case of Fig. 7d the decrease in field strength at 35° is less than 2% and the electron image includes a half angle of more than 90°, encompassing more than a hemisphere. In view of the clarity of the picture and the relatively slow increase of radius with heating, the tip shape of Fig. 7d is preferable.

In some instances a knowledge of tip radius is necessary. The most dependable method is the measurement of the tip image in a standard electron microscope (24), which can lead to accuracy in radius determination in the order of 10%. This, however, requires dismantling of the cathode, as the stages of most commercial electron microscopes are not designed to carry the entire cathode loop. A simpler way of determining tip radius is by measuring the field emission itself. For a known, effective average work function of the cathode the field strength required for the emission of a particular current density can be computed from the Fowler-Nordheim theory (19, 54). If, furthermore, one can assume as known the geometrical shape of the tip the conversion factor $f = F/V$ is given for a particular electrode arrangement. This permits the determination of tip radius by a simple measurement of the anode voltage to give a particular current (42). If tip and anode are considered as confocal rotation hyperboloids, one obtains the tip radius

$$r = \frac{0.85 V^{5/4}}{\Phi^2} \tag{9}$$

where $r$ is in angstrom units if the anode voltage for a current of $10^{-5}$ amp. is measured in volts and the work function is likewise expressed in volts. The distance between tip and anode is assumed to be 2.5 cm. in conformity with usual practice. The application of this formula is justified for the hyperboloid tip shape of Fig. 7a. Such a form can be recognized from the small angular image field of the microscope images. If, however, the wide angular field indicates a tip of Fig. 7d, formula (9) will give too small a radius. According to Drechsler and Henkel (13) the following equation is preferable:

$$r = \frac{0.15 V^{3/2}}{\Phi^2}. \tag{10}$$

In view of the uncertainty of the tip shape, absolute radii determined by any of these formulas may be in error by 25%. Relative changes in radius, however, due to surface migration, evaporation, or chemical etching can be followed with great accuracy by determination of anode voltage for a given current, as long as one is certain that the work function has not changed, as is the case for pure surfaces. This is of course easily recognized in the electron image.

Heating of the tip is done through conduction from the cathode loop. Figure 8 shows two constructions of such loops. In Fig. 8a the tip is at the end of a wire which is hooked together with another wire of like material.

The wires are sintered together to make good contact. In Fig. 8b the tip is welded onto the heater loop. Investigations of high-temperature reactions require knowledge of the tip temperature. Calibration of the heating current is done by a micropyrometer. One measures at the middle of the tip cone and includes for accurate determination the temperature decrease

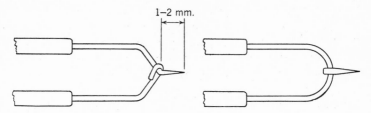

FIG. 8. Cathode heaters with hooked or spotwelded tip.

along the cone toward the tip (42). Examples of the temperature decrease $\Delta T$ between the measuring point at $T$ and the tip calotte 0.5 mm. distant, for a half angle of the tungsten cone of 5°, are shown in Table II. Below 2000° C. the temperature change toward the calotte can be neglected.

TABLE II

| $T$, °C. | $\Delta T$, °C. |
|---|---|
| 900 | 2 |
| 1700 | 20 |
| 2500 | 86 |

During the observation of the field emission microscope image, the tip is usually at room temperature. Heating of the tip by the emission current is negligible as long as one stays in the normal working range of from 1 to 10 $\mu$a. Temperature measurements below red heat present difficulties, particularly if the entire microscope is immersed in a cooling bath of liquid air or helium. After a sufficient cooling time, the tip will assume the temperature of the surroundings, the cooling taking place through heat loss along the heating wires. It is very difficult to obtain a definite intermediate temperature by means of a small heating current. The tip of Fig. 8a can be made into a thermocouple if the two wires are made of two different metals. This may, however, lead to the formation of an alloy during the heating which may influence the adsorptive properties of the tip. A more reliable method is to use a relatively long heater loop with fine potential leads of the same wire material welded on. The temperature is then determined from the resistance of the loop.

## 4. Ultrahigh Vacuum Technique

The field emission microscope is one of the most sensitive methods for detection of adsorption on metals. For example, one thousandths of a monomolecular layer of oxygen is clearly visible. The number of molecules striking a surface in a vacuum of $10^{-6}$ mm. amounts to $4 \cdot 10^{14}$/sec. and cm². Since the number of available adsorption sites on the metal surface is about $10^{15}$/cm.² and since at room temperature practically every molecule reaching the surface is used in the build-up of the monomolecular layer, it requires only 2 sec. at that vacuum to cover the initially clean tip surface in such a way as to give an entirely different emission pattern. In order to study a clean, cool surface for at least several seconds, the partial pressure of oxygen and of other strongly adsorbed gases like water, carbon monoxide, carbon dioxide, and hydrogen must not exceed $10^{-9}$ mm. This requirement eliminates the use of conventional vacuum equipment with greased stopcocks or joints and requires use of a carefully constructed high-vacuum apparatus. It should be emphasized that this is not a limitation of the field emission microscopy technique. If one wants to study cold-metal surfaces under rigorously clean conditions, one must always prevent adsorption due to inadequate vacuum, regardless of the observational technique.

Methods for production of a high vacuum are described in the literature (1, 16, 42). Only a few remarks will be made here. The microscope is preferably constructed wholly from glass with sealed electrodes so that the entire tube may be baked out for at least 1 hr. at 450° to 500° C. The diffusion pump may be operated with oil or mercury. Both pumps require the use of a liquid-air trap. The decomposition products of oil are further cracked on flashing of the cathode, producing tenacious carbon or carbide layers. With clean pumps a vacuum of $10^{-8}$ mm. can easily be reached, sufficient for moderate demands or exploratory experiments. If the adsorption or surface reaction of gases with the tip is under observation, or if substances are to be put on the tip which give off gases on distilling, continuous pumping is necessary. One must attempt to improve the final vacuum as much as possible by careful construction, particularly extended degassing of tube parts likely to get warm, as well as pump connections and the cold trap before it is cooled.

Considerably better vacuums are obtained by removing the carefully outgassed microscope from the pump and continuing the evacuation by a getter or an ionization pump. This separation can be done either by sealing off or, preferably, by means of a greaseless heatable metal valve, according to Alpert (1), so that connection to the pump may be reestablished. The simplest further improvement of vacuum is by the use of getters. For extreme demands the barium getters frequently used in vacuum practice are not adequate. Best results are obtained by slow evaporation of a titanium, zirconium, molybdenum, or tantalum wire in a sidearm of the tube. This wire must, of course, be thoroughly outgassed while the tube is still on the vacuum pump. An ionization manometer connected to the sealed off microscope also produces ultrahigh vacuums and permits a simultaneous determination of the pumping process. An accurate pressure measurement, however, is not essential for field emission microscopes since the tube itself can be used as a vacuum indicator. One determines the time after flashing of the cathode to build up a certain adsorption thickness. Assuming an unchanged composition of the adsorbed residual gas, the time for formation of a particular adsorption image takes $10^5$ longer at a vacuum of $10^{-11}$ mm. than at $10^{-6}$ mm. The process taking place in several seconds on the flashed tip at a pressure barely perceptible on a McLeod gauge will require an entire day at $10^{-11}$ mm. If one cannot wait that long, one can obtain an estimate of the quality of the vacuum by measuring the variation with time of the anode voltage for a constant-emission current. For impurities normally occurring in the vessel, a voltage change of less than 1% in 10 min. represents a vacuum sufficiently good for most purposes. In a vessel with a well-performing getter, this constancy can be maintained for more than 24 hr. For sealed-off tubes that will be used over a period of weeks or years, soft glass should be preferred. It is well established that the diffusion of helium from the atmosphere through Pyrex glass builds up a pressure of $10^{-5}$ mm., which is not being adsorbed by getters and causes severe cathode sputtering of the tip.

## 5. Application of the Field Emission Microscope

### 5.1. Observation of Clean Metal Surfaces

There is hardly another experiment that shows as clearly as field emission microscopy the difficulty of investigating really clean metal surfaces. One notes that almost all experiments dealing with allegedly clean surfaces and their reactions were actually made on surfaces covered with adsorption layers. For most applications of field emission microscopy, the production of really clean and smooth tips is of prime importance. Since the tip in its manufacture is exposed to air, a thick oxide layer is probably existent. The tip can be cleaned in vacuum by heating provided the oxides or other impurities possess a higher vapor or decomposition pressure than the metal so that they disappear before the tip is blunted by surface migration or melts away. Tungsten, molybdenum, tantalum, niobium, platinum, and nickel are easiest to manipulate since their oxides evaporate readily. This is not the case for titanium and zirconium, which do not give good images even if the etching produces a smooth surface. These highly active metals absorb sufficient gas during the baking-out process from the incompletely evacuated system so that the surface is covered with a thick layer of oxides, nitrides, or carbides, which are not decomposed on subsequent heating and do not show the strong surface mobility of the metals themselves. Even metals like tungsten or nickel require a brief heating to very high temperatures to evaporate such impurities as silicon or carbon from initially quite pure material. The presence of impurities can be noted by their diffusion to the surface. If one heats these metals to the maximum allowable temperature and cuts off the heating current quickly, the electron image appears smooth with the characteristic crystal planes since the metal surface is quite clean. If one reheats the tip once more to a lower temperature just sufficient to permit diffusion, the impurities will accumulate on the surface as an adsorption layer. The electron image of this surface will show a characteristic pattern. The impurity can be identified by obtaining a similar image by purposely evaporating or condensing the particular substance onto the tip.

The field emission microscope image of a clean tip in a sufficiently good vacuum is independent of the heating temperature in the distribution of intensities over the various crystal planes. On tungsten one can observe a small increase of the (100) and (112) planes after heat-treating at low temperatures (1200° to 1500° C.), which indicates a temperature-dependent surface-free energy of the different crystal surfaces (3). Only a few surfaces of low index number appear on a clean tip. Figure 9 shows the image from a tungsten tip of $1.5 \cdot 10^{-5}$ cm. radius. Figure 10 shows the corresponding stereographic projection of the cubic lattice. All metals with body-centered cubes have a pronounced dark (011) plane, followed by the (112) and (100) planes. The relative size of the dark areas varies. While tungsten and molybdenum give nearly identical images, tantalum and niobium have an equally pronounced (011) plane but the (100) plane is weak and the (112) plane is barely visible. For cubic, face-centered metals, the (111) plane is the most strongly developed surface with a high work function, i.e., lowest emission, followed by the (100) plane and the less distinct (112) and (110) planes. All these dark planes form small plateaus on the calotte. However, the diminution of the emission is only to a small extent due to the fact that the local field strengths are 1 to 3% weaker on the plateau than on the curved surface. The main reason for the contrast in the pattern is the high work function of some planes. Small differences in work function or contact potential have been known for some time. By field emission it was possible to measure the full extent of the effect which had been previously assumed to be no more than one

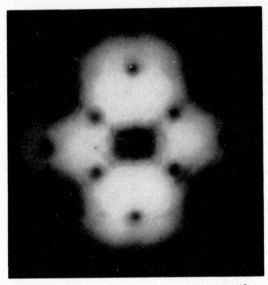

FIG. 9. Pattern of a tungsten tip. Radius 1,500 Å.

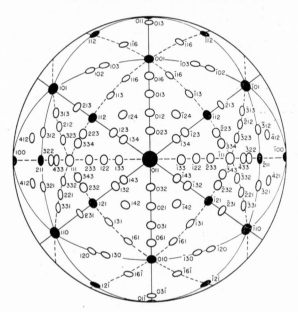

FIG. 10. Crystallographic map of a hemisphere with cubic lattice.

hundredth to one tenth of a volt in magnitude. Probe measurements of current densities on different parts of the field-emission-microscope image have shown that for tungsten the current density in the (011) plane is smaller by four or five orders of magnitude than in the strongly emitting (116) and (130) planes (40, 49). A knowledge of the real magnitude of the potential barrier of crystalline surfaces should be of importance for the solution of a number of topochemical problems and particularly in electrochemistry.

Another application of field emission microscopy of clean surfaces is the observation of surface migration of atoms on their own crystal lattice (42). Two different methods were explored on tungsten. One can observe the increase in tip radius as a function of heating temperature by measuring the anode voltage required to maintain a fixed current, say 10 $\mu$a., and calculating the diameter from eq. (9) or (10). After heating for several seconds or hours, depending on the temperature, the radius is measured again. If one limits the measurements to small radius changes so that the tip geometry is not basically altered, one can deduce what mass has been transported away from the tip per unit time. The logarithm of the mass transport versus inverse temperature is plotted, and the slope gives the activation energy of the process. One must limit the measurements to a relatively small temperature range, approximately below $\frac{2}{3}$ of the absolute melting point. At higher temperatures change in curvature occurs also through volume diffusion, which requires a higher activation energy (27).

The second method for measuring surface migration depends on producing a surface deformation and observing the heating time required for reestablishment of the rounded tip (42). For evaluation one plots the logarithm of velocity as a function of the reciprocal absolute temperature. The activation energy is obtained from the slope while the abscissas of the plot must remain arbitrary since the volume of the distortion can be estimated to only a first approximation. The tip is deformed by evaporating metal from a separate wire onto the tip. On condensing on the cold tip the like metal atoms arrange themselves randomly. If the tip is heated somewhat during the condensation, in the case of tungsten to 1000° C., the atoms have enough mobility to build themselves into the substrate lattice in an orderly way. The tip crystal will then grow with sharp edges. After condensation and turning off of the heating current, an image as in Fig. 11 is obtained. The light rings surrounding the rhombic dodecahedrol planes arise from an increase in field strength on the sharp edges of the (110) planes. The reestablishment of the round tip form on tempering can be followed experimentally. Another, simpler way of deforming the tip is the application of an electric field during heating. The moving surface atoms travel preferentially toward certain crystal surfaces and build up small mounds, which are frozen in after the heating current is turned off (5, 37). When the tip is negative, the process of transformation can be observed directly on the viewing screen, as long as the temperature remains below the thermionic emission. On tungsten tips the (123) plane, located between (112) and (011), is preferentially built up. For positive tips one can employ both higher temperatures and field

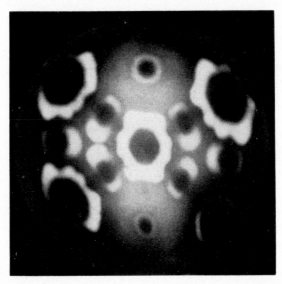

Fig. 11. Evaporated tungsten condensed on a heated tungsten tip.

strengths. Owing to the extreme delicacy of field emission microscopy, one can observe the beginning of movement of atoms on their own lattice at much lower temperatures than with any other method, approximately at one quarter of the absolute melting point. Further use of the method in view of the interest in sintering processes and creep at high temperatures appears promising. One should particularly investigate the effect of adsorbed layers. For example, it was shown that the movement of tungsten on its own lattice is speeded up by a factor of 45 at 1000° C. by the presence of a monomolecular oxygen layer (42). It is conceivable that other layers will block the surface migration. This is the case on molybdenum tips which contain small amounts of silicon. There is no appreciable difference in surface-migration rates for pure molybdenum and silicided molybdenum in high vacuum, however, in the presence of only a monolayer of oxygen, the silicided tip stands unchanged at temperatures that are 200° C. higher.

## 5.2. Observation of Adsorbed Layers

Because of the strong dependence of field emission on work function and the local field intensity, the field emission microscope is one of the most sensitive means for the investigation of adsorbed layers. Since the exponent of the emission formula eq. (1) contains the ratio $\Phi^{3/2}/F$, it is rather improbable that on formation of an adsorbed layer the three-half power of the work function should vary exactly as the local field strength. Thus every adsorption will become noticeable on several of the crystal faces of the substrate by a variation of the relative current density. We cannot interpret or even mention all the adsorption processes observed with field emission microscopy except to treat a few typical cases. Earlier work on adsorption using electron emission phenomena (7) have neglected the specific surface structure of the various crystal planes. Observation with the field emission microscope shows that the influence of the particular surface structure of a crystal surface may overshadow in importance other factors influencing adsorption.

Most adsorption investigations with field emission microscopes have been carried out on tungsten. Stranski and Suhrman (55) as well as Ashworth (2) explain the observed properties of barium, caesium, thorium, sodium, and copper films on the basis of their detailed investigations of the geometrical structure of various tungsten planes as a function of the diameter of adsorbed atoms. Most of these metals are electropositive and produce a particularly strong effect owing to the lowering of the work function. It may also be that, in view of the relative size of the adsorbed atoms, the geometric structure of the substrate is particularly pronounced. This is certainly not the case for films of relatively small molecules, such as hydrogen, nitrogen, or carbon monoxide. For these cases one observes at room temperature a gradual diminution of the current density, which is strongest for tungsten in the region of the vicinals of (112). That geometrical structure alone is not of importance is shown by comparison of adsorption at two different metal tips with the same crystal structure. The pair, tungsten and molybdenum, are particularly interesting since their lattice constants differ by only 0.6%. Nevertheless the adsorption image in the field emission microscope is quite different (47). For such investigations a twin tube is most suitable, i.e., two field emission microscopes with a tungsten and a molybdenum tip connected by a wide tube and exposed simultaneously to the adsorbable gas at a pressure between $10^{-6}$ and $10^{-3}$ mm.

On tungsten the adsorption of hydrogen at room temperature in the pressure range $10^{-6}$ to $10^{-3}$ mm. is pressure independent (50). From the slope of the current-voltage characteristic, one obtains an average work function of 4.93 ev., that of pure tungsten being 4.50 ev. Hydrogen desorbs within several seconds at 430° C. A second clearly observable layer, also pressure independent, is adsorbed on top of the room-temperature stable layer if the adsorption is carried out at liquid-air temperature. If at this low temperature only a small amount of hydrogen is supplied, the adsorption image is similar to that obtained at room temperature. One may deduce that at liquid-air temperature the first layer is deposited as an atomic layer, but the second layer may be molecular. With increasing temperature, it desorbs and disappears at room temperature. Nothing quantitative is known about the degree of coverage. Nitrogen behaves similarly to hydrogen at low temperature. While the latter, however, is uniformly desorbed from all planes as temperature is increased, nitrogen reacts with the base metal at 400° C. Next to the rhombic dodecahedral planes very characteristic dark regions appear corresponding to the (256) crystallographic plane. The formation of such sharply defined regions of high Miller index points toward the formation of a chemical compound, a nitride in this instance, the molecules of which assume a preferred orientation on the particular surface (34). Ordinarily only van der Waal's forces are active. On platinum tips such specific adsorptions do not occur for either hydrogen, nitrogen, or ammonia, which leads to the conclusion that the formation of ammonia on platinum catalysts does not proceed via chemical surface compounds.

Oxygen exhibits a considerable diminution of emission and extraordinarily varied adsorption patterns on different metals. Beginning with the invention of the field emission microscope (37), it has been a favored subject of investigation up to the present time (4, 23, 47, 49a). At room temperature on tungsten a small amount of oxygen causes a decrease of emission on the (123) plane; then the total emission declines and the plane (111) with its surroundings close to (112) becomes uniformly darker. With increasing coverage (112) suddenly darkens and the entire emission around the (100) region decreases. The (111) zones remain lighter and the emission of the otherwise dark (110) plane is fairly strong. Figure 12b shows this stage of saturation, which does not change on pressure increase to $10^{-3}$ mm. and does not disappear on pumping down to $10^{-8}$ mm. If the oxygen-saturated tip is heated in vacuum to a high temperature, the adsorption image is altered considerably and the layer is desorbed by way of many characteristic in-between steps. Figures 12c–i show such layers formed on successive 2-min. heat cycles in the absence of high voltage. The electrical field is applied to the cold tip only after the heater current is turned off, and so frozen-in conditions are observed. The images correspond definitely to different degrees of coverage since all the layers formed between 800° and 1990° C. can be obtained at lower temperature

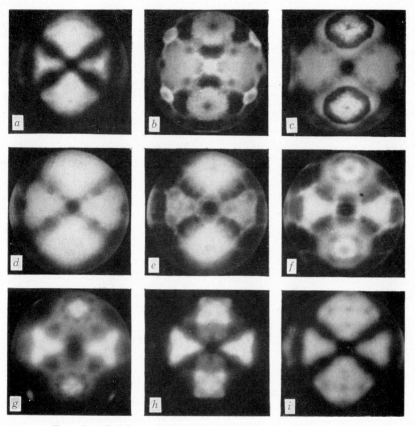

FIG. 12. a–i. Adsorption of an oxygen layer on a tungsten tip.

  a. Small amount of oxygen adsorbed ($10^{-7}$ mm. for 5 sec.).
  b. Surface saturated with $O_2$ ($10^{-3}$ mm.).
  c. Desorption after 2 min. annealing in high vacuum at 600° C.
  d. Heated at 700° C.
  e. Heated at 1100° C.
  f. Heated at 1200° C.
  g. Heated at 1350° C.
  h. Heated at 1600° C.
  i. Heated at 1800° C.

in the inverse sequence if one adds successive small amounts of oxygen to a clean tip. The course of the current-voltage characteristic during desorption is remarkable (Fig. 13). For constant voltage, or field strength, the emission decreases during the build-up of layers by 5 to 7 orders of magnitude, partly because of an increase in the work function to 6.1 ev., averaged over the entire tip, as well as to a decrease in the intercept on the log $J/F^2$ ordinate from $-5.1$ for pure tungsten to $-7.8$. On desorption the work function decreases at first. On heating to 800° C. it amounts to only 5 ev., and cannot be distinguished from that of pure tungsten after it is heated to 1200° C. for 1 min. The intercept on the other hand remains constant up to 1000° C. and then approaches the value of pure tungsten.

One can take advantage of the temperature independence of field emission for the study of adsorption at low temperature. Immersing of the tube into liquid air was useful for the investigation of the adsorption of water vapor on metals (11, 47). Recently Gomer made remarkable progress by using liquid helium as a refrigerant (23). In this way oxygen,

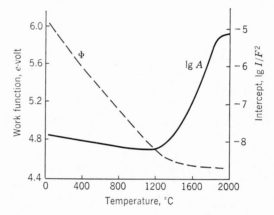

Fig. 13. Changes of field emission characteristic during desorption of oxygen film from tungsten.

for example, can be condensed on one side of the tip only and the spreading out of the first adsorption layer can be observed on heating. Of particular advantage is the radical solution of the vacuum problem, since at this temperature the vapor pressure of all adsorbable gases practically vanishes.

Oxygen adsorption has thus far been investigated thoroughly only on tungsten although most metals promise interesting results, particularly in view of the high-temperature corrosion and creep strength (influence of the oxide film on surface migration). Platinum, too, forms oxygen films whose boundary contracts on desorption at high temperature under certain as yet imperfectly understood conditions (Fig. 14).

During the adsorption of an oxygen containing gas, the oxygen usually displaces the other gas so that one usually obtains only an oxygen film. The purity of other gases must therefore be carefully controlled. Oxygen itself is formed by the decomposition of a grain of potassium permanganate. A pure gas is obtained by diffusion of oxygen from the air through a silver tube at 800° C. Pure hydrogen is diffused through a palladium tube. Pure nitrogen can be formed by the dissociation of azides, sodium nitrate for example. For best results one moves an azide particle by means of an externally operated magnetic slug into the previously carefully out-gassed glass tube. Water vapor as impurity is frozen out with liquid air. All gases required in the adsorption experiments are needed only in very small quantities, at pressures from $10^{-6}$ to $10^{-3}$ mm. If the gas is added

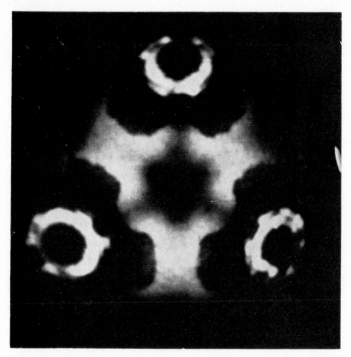

Fig. 14. Oxygen film around (100)-planes of platinum tip ((111) in the center).

during the observation of the image, the pressure must be kept particu-larly low in order to prevent destruction of the tip due to cathode sputter-ing. The positive ions formed in the electron beam react differently with the surface than do the neutral atoms. Normally one will turn off the high voltage during the adsorption process and produce a good vacuum before observation of the image. The reestablishment of a good vacuum takes particularly long with oxygen, since the walls desorb the gas only very slowly. Frequently it is necessary to bake the tube again or to evaporate a getter. The operation of a microscope in the presence of a gas with more than $10^{-7}$ mm. pressure and also with the tip at elevated temperatures has to be done very carefully and by using currents in the microampere range only. Cathode sputtering and the build-up of sharp-edged clusters by field-supported surface migration may cause excessive local current densities which become unstable and initiate the destruction of the tip by a vacuum arc. If the high voltage has been turned off in time, a partly disintegrated tip surface can be recovered by a brief annealing process.

The observation of adsorption of less volatile substances, which can be brought onto the tip by evaporation from a heater coil, is much simpler. One has to watch out that the substance does not react with the

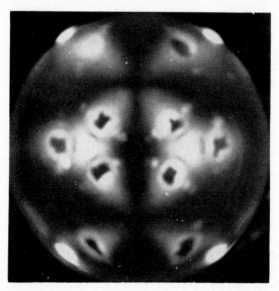

Fig. 15. $UO_2$ adsorbed on tungsten tip, mainly on (112)-planes.

tip or alloy with it. The metal of the evaporation coil itself can be condensed on the tip. In many cases the fluorescent screen has to be protected from the condensation of the vaporized substance by a shield.

During the adsorption of oxides, the presence of condensed films is frequently observed on such planes where the lattice constants of the oxide coincide with those of the substrate. Such cases of epitaxy have been observed between the (112) plane of tungsten and uranium dioxide (Fig. 15) and the (013) plane with cuprous oxide (Fig. 16). Another very characteristic adsorption is the case of the spreading of aluminum oxide on tungsten, in which, as in the two previous cases, the oxygen ions probably face outward, as indicated by the high work function. If one evaporates aluminum oxide onto a tungsten tip and permits surface migration by heating to 700° C., a dark layer is built up in a few seconds starting from the (100) plane, which possesses a preferred square outline corresponding to the structure of the substrate (Fig. 17). It expands by jumps in steps of molecular rows until the entire surface is covered with a complex film. Beryllium oxide also prefers the cubic planes of tungsten but produces an enhanced emission, in contrast with aluminum oxide.

One of the most characteristic adsorption images is formed by the adsorption of carbon on a tungsten tip (31, 32, 47). Carbon remains

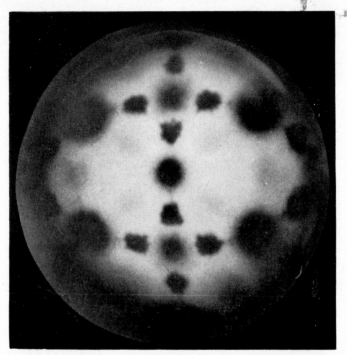

FIG. 16. Cu₂O adsorbed on tungsten tip, mainly on (130)-planes.

when organic molecules are adsorbed and decomposed by heating. This occurs when the diffusion pump is operated without a cold trap. Most advantageously pure carbon can be evaporated from the filament of a light bulb. Fine crystals condense on the cold tip, statistically distributed without reference to the supporting lattice and causing increased emission by their sharp edges. At 760° C. a vigorous surface migration starts on tungsten and the crystallites transform into a monomolecular film. The vicinals of (011) and (112) begin to emit strongly, and the cubic plane and surroundings become completely free of carbon. The increased emission from (011) is due not to a decreasing work function but to an increase in local field strength on the sharp-edged lattice steps. At a suitable carbon

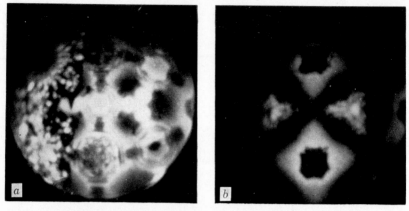

Fig. 17a. Al$_2$O$_3$ evaporated on the left side of the tungsten tip. Tip heated to 700° C. to allow surface migration to begin.

Fig. 17b. Tip with aluminum-oxide heated to 1000° C. Non-emitting mono-film builts up on (100)-planes.

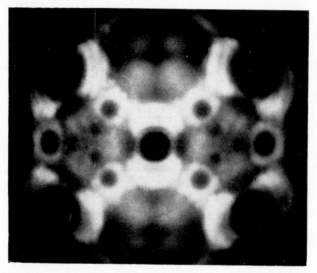

Fig. 18. Carbon film on tungsten tip, after surface migration at 1100° C.

concentration the bright plane resolves into two or three rings (Fig. 18). In the field ion microscope with its much improved resolution, up to eight separable lattice steps could be observed (45). Adsorption of carbon on tungsten proceeds in such a way that surface migration is interrupted and several (011) layers form steps of 10 to 20 Å. in height. By short-heating of the surface to 2500° C. the top layers of carbon evaporate while a part diffuses into the metal. This carbon on tempering at 800° to 1700° C.

rediffuses back to the surface. Measurement of the time required for this process, observed by obtaining the same type of image, as function of the annealing temperature gives an activation energy of 110,000 cal./mole ± 15%. It is possible, however, that the diffusion of carbon into tungsten proceeds more readily and that the rate-determining step is the surface migration of tungsten, for the same activation energy has been measured for the migration of tungsten atoms from growth regions beyond the edges of the (011) plane. The growth of the several lattice steps over the vicinals of (011) might be merely the indicator for the presence of blocking carbon. For small carbon concentrations in the adsorbed layer the planes (334) are particularly characteristic. As the build-up of such planes is not influenced by the presence of the electric field, the growth of these layers can be directly observed with a heated cathode. If the temperature is increased beyond a particular value, for example 900° C., the three spots surrounding the octahedral poles disappear suddenly only to reappear on lowering of the temperature. The critical temperature for the disappearance of the (334) planes is dependent on the concentration of the adsorbed carbon. For a thick layer the planes are stable up to 1200° C.; for very small concentrations they are visible only below 600° C. The explanation for this phenomenon is probably as follows. Below the concentration-determined saturation temperature a two-dimensional graphite lattice crystallizes from the two-dimensional carbon vapor phase, which coincides with the (334) plane of tungsten in such a way that the graphite hexagons are centered on one of the protruding tungsten atoms in the (334) plane. When the critical temperature is passed, the two-dimensional lattice reevaporates into the gaseous mobile phase. With greater carbon concentration, corresponding to a higher two-dimensional pressure, the vaporization point moves toward higher temperatures. The formation of such specific adsorption layers is not entirely a question of isomorphism of the particular planes but is also influenced by chemical considerations. Thus the (334) planes of carbon on molybdenum, with almost the same lattice as tungsten show up only very weakly. The arrangement of the vicinals of (011) and (112) as well as the complete absence of carbon on the surface near (100) is similar for molybdenum and tungsten (Fig. 19a). If carbon is condensed in considerable quantities on a molybdenum tip heated to 1100° C. so that the carbon can diffuse into the interior, one can observe a sudden transformation of the molybdenum lattice into that of hexagonal molybdenum carbide (Fig. 19b) where the basal plane coincides with the previous rhomboid dodecahedral plane (46, 47). In a similar manner the transformation of a niobium or tantalum tip into the nitride crystal can be observed if the metals are heated in nitrogen. Usually more than one crystal is formed on the surface, which gives a less interpretable picture. Another example of a nonmetallic tip probably occurs with iron (53). On strong heating of an iron tip one obtains a striated image which points to the formation of large layers ordered around the cubic planes. On tempering between 600° and 900° C., these stripes disappear entirely, and the image resembles more that of face-centered nickel or platinum rather than that of body-centered tungsten. The picture hardly changes with time in vacuum while a similarly exposed tungsten tip indicates the slow adsorption of impurities. Perhaps

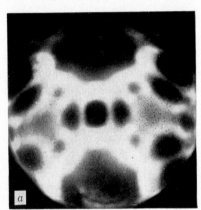 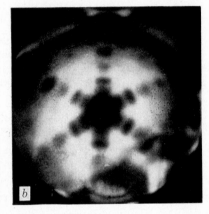

Fig. 19a. Carbon adsorbed on molybdenum tip.
Fig. 19b. Lattice tilts into hexagonal structure of MoC.

the iron tip is completely oxidized and consists of $Fe_3O_4$. The spinel lattice of this oxide resembles that of a face-centered cube. On reduction of the tip in hydrogen one obtains a picture with a pronounced (110) plane belonging to a body-centered $\alpha$-iron crystal. Unfortunately, $\alpha$-$\gamma$ transformation at 900° C. cannot be observed, since the crystal is rapidly deformed at that temperature by the field forces. Figure 20 shows the interaction of a molybdenum tip with silicon at different temperatures.

### 5.3. Reactions on the Cathode Tip

The possibility of investigating chemical reactions and catalytic processes directly on the tip has not been greatly exploited. Adsorption of oxygen on tungsten has already been described on page 154. This layer can be reduced with hydrogen (47, 56) at elevated temperatures and the image reinvestigated after reestablishment of the vacuum. To remove the water formed in the reaction, the entire microscope tube is immersed in liquid air. Below 880° C. no change in the oxygen layer is observable even after 20-min. exposure to hydrogen at $10^{-3}$ mm. At 920° C. the oxygen is attacked on the (116) plane and on the vicinals of the (100) surface. These are the same planes on which the first surface migration of oxygen becomes visible in the oxygen layer. At 1000° C. the reduction commences on the (111) plane and at 1200° C. after 2 min. one obtains a pure tungsten surface. Below $10^{-5}$ mm. the reduction proceeds

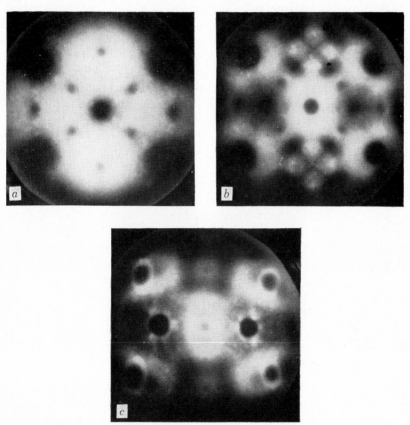

FIG. 20a. Clean molybdenum tip.
FIG. 20b. Small amount of Si evaporated on the Mo-tip, after annealing at 800° C.
FIG. 20c. More Si condensed on 700° C. hot molybdenum tip. Formation of molybdenum silicide indicated by development of (111)-planes.

a little more slowly, and no difference is noticeable between $10^{-3}$ and $5 \cdot 10^{-2}$ mm. Atomic hydrogen produced in the microscope tube itself by contact of molecular hydrogen with a white-hot tungsten wire does not react more rapidly than molecular hydrogen. The presence of atomic hydrogen, however, causes the appearance of carbon on the cathode. Small amounts of hydrocarbons, probably produced from the carbon contained in the cathode leads, decompose on the tip with the formation of carbon. Since cathode sputtering is smaller by orders of magnitude in hydrogen than in other gases, the electron image can be observed directly in the presence of a hydrogen pressure of $10^{-3}$ mm. without destruction of the tip. From the fact that in the presence of hydrogen an oxygen film is already attacked at the temperature of liquid air one must deduce that molecule ions or protons react more easily with adsorbed oxygen than molecular hydrogen. Water vapor, obtained from hydrated copper sulfate or from gypsum on heating and careful dosage in a cold trap is adsorbed in a similar manner as oxygen; however, with tungsten the emission at constant anode voltage decreases by only one order of magnitude. The saturated layer remains unchanged up to 400° C. Beyond that temperature a top layer evaporates off or a rearrangement in the surface takes place. At 1000° C. the adsorption image changes into that of an oxygen film.

Reactions between adsorbed carbon and various gases can be carried out comparatively easily. A carbon film is formed by evaporation from a graphite wire and the surface is allowed to react with oxygen or hydrogen. In the former case the reaction begins at about 700° C. Within several minutes at 800° C. the entire carbon film has disappeared and only an oxygen film remains. The rate-determining step appears to be the breakage of the tungsten-oxygen bond, since the bulk reaction between carbon and oxygen commences at considerably lower temperatures. Adsorbed ammonia reacts with a tungsten substrate at about 400° C. and nitrogen remains on the tip, observable by the formation of the characteristic (256) plane. Very complex conditions are observed during the interaction of carbon monoxide on nickel surfaces.

### 5.4. Visibility of Atoms and Molecules

At low coverage adsorption films of comparatively large atoms or molecules show a granular structure. This is observed not only with elements which decrease the work function, owing to their electropositive character, like the alkali and alkaline earth metals, thorium, uranium, zirconium, and titanium, but also with other materials like sulfur, selenium, barium oxide, and many others (Fig. 21). If such substances are evaporated sidewise onto the tip, they will condense with very irregular granulation. The light-emission regions are readily explainable as caused by locally increased fields above crystallites 10 to 20 Å. in size. If this film is distributed over the entire surface by heating, the crystallites disappear, and planes with the same index assume the same granulation density. The individual grains have the size of the diffraction disk, i.e., about 10 to 30 Å. depending on the tip radius. One can explain them

as diffuse images of single atoms or molecules which are adsorbed on the
surface (38, 44). The possibility of seeing atomic images has been particularly carefully investigated in the case of barium. A difficult question
to resolve is whether the diffraction disk is the blurred image of one
single atom (44) or that of a small cluster of atoms (3). The current
density relative to the surroundings points against the interpretation of
a cluster. A small densely packed barium island of 15 to 30 Å. diameter
should have a very low work function of about 2 ev. and consequently

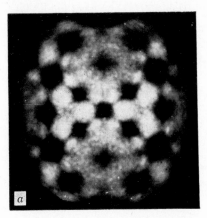 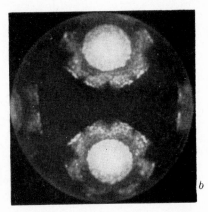

Fig. 21a. Thin film of Ba on tungsten tip. Average degree of covering $\theta = \frac{1}{100}$
of a monolayer.

Fig. 21b. Thin film of Zr on tungsten tip, deposited mainly on and around
(100)-planes.

a current density a million times larger than the surrounding tungsten.
On the other hand, if one calculates the current transfer through the
potential barrier of one single atom and spreads the current over the
area of the diffusion disk, one obtains just the actually observed contrast
of about 30:1. A calculation of the striking probability of positive ions
during cathode sputtering points also to the single atomicity of the small
disk. Another reliable indication of the atomic character is obtained by
counting the number of visible points together with knowledge of the
degree of coverage. In a twin tube, as in Fig. 22, one tip is placed 6.3 times
as far from the point source of vaporized barium as the other. If one
evaporates on the nearby tip enough barium to give a monomolecular
layer, observable from the minimum of the work function, the more
distant tip receives $\frac{1}{40}$ of a monolayer. In a second experiment one produces an equally thin layer on the near tip, as indicated by the similarity
in appearance, and obtains consequently on the second tip a $\frac{1}{1600}$ part
of a monolayer. Assuming that a layer of minimum work function con-

tains $10^{14}$ barium atoms/cm.$^2$ (the exact value is not known and depends on the crystallographic structure of the support), then for a relative coverage of $\frac{1}{1600}$ on a tip hemisphere of $1.5 \cdot 10^{-5}$ cm. radius, approximately 70 atoms should be present. Actually at least 40 diffraction disks could be counted. The remaining barium atoms may be located in holes or other depressions on the surface somewhat shielded electrostatically and consequently not producing local field intensification. It must be emphasized that we are not dealing with the direct image of an atom but that at the spot at which a large atom is adsorbed the local field emission

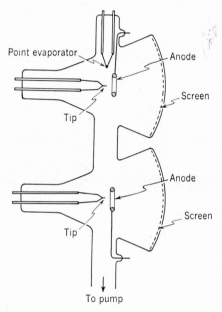

Fig. 22. Twin tube for simultaneous evaporation onto two tips.

of the support has been increased. Nevertheless, a single atom can thus be localized and its surface migration observed at elevated temperature.

The continuous motion of a single atom which proceeds with high speed is not seen, but the particle is observed as it rests at a particular place. Similarly the identity of a particular atom and its path of surface travel cannot be followed. Rather, one observes the fluctuation of the various granulation points. For barium on tungsten the surface migration in the neighborhood of the vicinals of the (110) plane begins at about 200° C., proceeds at 300° C. in the (111) plane, at 400° C. at the vicinals of the cubic planes, such as the (116) plane. At this temperature the atoms on the cube corner (111) are in active motion while the larger binding force on the (100) plane keeps the barium atoms solidly anchored. On this plane the beginning of migration for small coverage begins only at 500° C.

Such differences of the binding at different crystallographic planes of the substrate are also present with other materials, but the initiation of migration and the sequence of planes may be quite different. Sodium on tungsten begins to migrate just above room temperature, but in the case of cesium the tube must be cooled to fix the atoms in place. At room temperature the image is blurred, owing to the rapid motion. Generally the atoms of the adsorbate must be larger than those of the base to prevent their incorporation into the tip lattice and thus their remaining invisible. Only in the case of tungsten was it possible to observe the presence of like atoms on the tip if they were adsorbed on an absolutely flat (110) plane (42). The heat of activation for surface migration on that plane was found to be as low as 30,000 cal./mole. For exchange of position between normal lattice sites, energies of 100,000 cal./mole are necessary, about half of the heat of evaporation. The diffusion disks of single atoms on the (110) plane are very weak and can be seen only with favorable viewing conditions, i.e., with an aluminized fluorescent screen.

Larger molecules should be even more clearly visible than the above-mentioned atoms. In fact with suitable substances at low coverage of the tip, one obtains granular images. Very peculiar situations are met with on evaporation of certain planar substances which gives images with definite structure although their size is below the resolution limit. The first experiment with phthalocyanine (43, 44) showed many quadruplet images very similar to the fourfold symmetry of the molecule (Fig. 23). Hemim and chlorophyll gave similar images while the more extended flat molecules of anthracene, tetracene, and pentacene gave double points (Fig. 24). These images, the details of which may exceed the size of the diffraction disk, represent a unit because they appear all together, rotate jointly around a common center point upon exposure to ion bombardment, and disappear simultaneously by evaporation from a heated tip or through ion impact.

The detailed images usually appear only after the surface has been covered with a certain amount of the substance. They appear to become visible only if the attachment is at some distance from the metal surface, separated from it either by an intermediate layer of molecular dimension or at least by one similar molecule (44, 58). The two or four electron beams constituting the image might be emitted from the protruding edges of the molecule (21); a more likely interpretation, however, is that the image is formed by the scattering of the electron wave going through the molecule (48). Since the molecule is inside the potential barrier, this diffraction process is difficult to visualize. For the splitting up of the electron beam into two or four always equally bright parts, it seems to be important that the molecule possess a $\pi$ electron system which interacts with the spin of the traversing electrons. The similarity of the fourfold

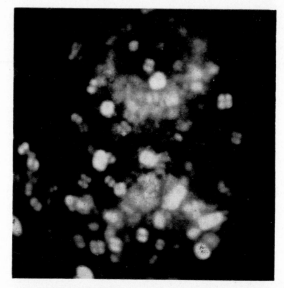

FIG. 23. Phthalocyanine molecules.

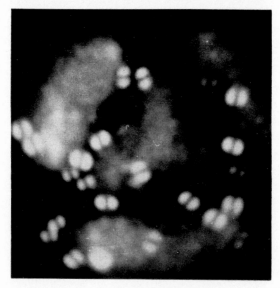

FIG. 24. Anthrachinone molecules.

image of the phthalocyanine with the real molecule may be fortuitous, and indeed further experiments showed that other flat molecules, even the three-sided symmetrical triphenylene, produce quadruplet images as well. However, for stretched molecules only doublets are formed, at least at low degrees of covering. Other less extended flat molecules produce doublets or quadruplets side by side. On thin separation layers the molecule image is aligned with the lattice of the substrate. In Fig. 23, for example, twenty-one of the twenty-three visible molecules are either parallel or perpendicular to the (110) lattice step. It is evident that the two- or fourfold parts of an image always exhibit the same intensity. This could not be expected if the electron distribution in the image ray were determined by the external electric field, since the adsorption along the lattice step produces an unsymmetrical screening of the local field. The

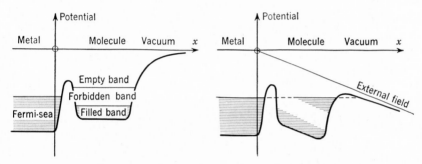

Fig. 25. Energy levels in an adsorbed molecule or small crystal. Tilted energy levels in an external field with easy tunneling through barrier.

beam splitting must therefore occur within the molecule. This also follows from the fact that on subsequent oxygen adsorption only the intensity of the surrounding subtrate is decreased, not that of the molecule itself. The large intensity of the molecule patterns points to a special emission mechanism. Since the large molecule does not approach the metal surface very closely, the energy levels of the electrons of the molecule are not completely broadened. If the ionization potential of the molecule is higher than the work function of the base, the occupied level of the molecule lies below the Fermi level of the metal (Fig. 25). At that height the molecule contains a forbidden region. Presence of the electric field tilts the levels in such a way that the next higher but empty level begins to lie partially below the Fermi level. Electrons from the substrate will then be able to tunnel through the forbidden region and fill the upper level. From this reservoir the electrons can pass the small energy barrier to the outside and yield the observed large current density. This model explains why phthalocyanine molecules appear in the same way whether the support is covered with oxygen and emits at 60 million v./cm. or whether the molecules sit on a barium-activated tip, which emits at 12 million v./cm. Direct field emission from the $\pi$ electron level of the molecule itself, which was assumed to take place at one time (21), would always require the same field strength. This emission model is not only valid for molecules but also applicable to small insulating crystals on the tip. The field is much larger than the break-down voltage of all insulators, and so no difficulty arises about tunneling through the forbidden region. Small "insulating" crystals may therefore emit with very high current density, but one can distinguish them from individual molecules by their almost continuous growth during the condensation. If the insulating crystal is very thin, the unoccupied zone in a field may lie entirely above the Fermi level, and so no reservoir can be filled and no emission occurs. Very tiny aluminum oxide crystals appear dark, while with increasing thickness the emission becomes very strong. In very small crystals the levels of normally conducting bands cannot overlap. One obtains therefore dark "shadow images" even from small carbon or barium crystals of estimated thickness of 10 Å.

The distinction between single molecules or crystals is not generally possible on the basis of the foregoing model. However, in the case of phthalocyanine and many other molecular substances, the frequently observed rotation under the influence of ion impact or heating of the tip would speak for single molecules as well as the effective cross section during cathode sputtering or on sidewise evaporation of copper, whose impulses are sufficient to move the particle. Smaller molecules such as benzene or toluene give on occasion disks with a lighter edge or a ring, which points to rapid rotation in the adsorption layer. During heating of the tip the molecular image remains unchanged up to a fairly high temperature, only to disappear then through evaporation or decomposition. The last of the two- or fourfold images disappears after a 1-min. heating at 650° C., others only at 750° C. (58):

| | |
|---|---|
| Phthalocyanine | |
| Tetraphenyl tetracene | |
| Coronene | stable up to 750° C. |
| Diiodobenzophenone | |
| Hexakosane | |
| Carbon dioxide | |
| Benzene | |
| Naphthalene | |
| Anthracene | |
| Toluene | stable up to 650° C. |
| Acetone | |
| Palmitic acid | |
| Myristic acid | |

In comparison experiments during heating of phthalocyanine and anthracene in evacuated quartz tubes to the stated temperatures, it was found that the substances do not decompose completely. A portion of the blue dye, or clear anthracene crystals, remains. When the decomposition temperature is exceeded on the cathode tip, the typical image of adsorbed graphite is formed. In addition to the substances mentioned in the table, the following substances were investigated: chlorinated phthalocyanines, crystal violet, phenolphthalein, cane sugar, vitamin $B_{12}$, decacyclene, and phosphonitrile chloride. They give usually doublets but sometimes quadruplet images and rarely rings, dumbbells, or three parallel strips. Strangely enough, similar forms were obtained by Ashworth (2) and Becker (4) with oxygen. It is questionable, however, whether they were not dealing with small oxide crystals since the tube was heated with an oxygen layer on the tip to a temperature at which tungstic oxide is mobile on the surface.

### 5.5. Special Applications

With suitable modifications several other applications of the field emission microscope come to mind. The use for the detection of high vacuums has already been mentioned. For this, one can use a very small tube with a screen 1 in. in diameter. A sealed-in wire is sufficient as anode with graphite strip on the glass wall. After heating of the tungsten tip, one can estimate the quality of the vacuum in the region of $10^{-6}$ to $10^{-12}$ mm. from the rate of building up of the adsorption layer.

A measurement of the polarizability (12) of atoms or dipole-free molecules can be carried out in the field emission microscope by sidewise evaporation onto the tip while a voltage is simultaneously applied between tip and anode. Near the tip the field is so strong that particles are attracted to the tip by polarization and then reach the shadow side (Fig. 26). The exact calculation of the particle path is very complex, results accurate to 20% being obtained if one determines the following data for a tungsten tip: $V_1$ the required anode voltage for a clean tungsten tip at a current of $10^{-5}$ amp., the temperature $T$ of the molecular source, the anode voltage $V$, at which the particles begin to appear on the shadow side; then the polarizability $\alpha$ is obtained by

$$\alpha = \frac{7.8 \cdot 10^{-23} V_1 T}{V^2} \tag{11}$$

($\alpha$ in cm.$^3$, if $T$ is measured in degrees Kelvin and $V$ and $V_1$ in volts). For barium atoms one obtains $\alpha = 62 \cdot 10^{-24}$ cm.$^3$, for lithium atoms $\alpha = 16 \cdot 10^{-24}$ cm.$^3$, and for copper phthalocyanine $\alpha = 120 \cdot 10^{-24}$ cm.$^3$.

The use of twin tubes has been mentioned for the preparation of layers of barium of known coverage. Similar field emission microscopy with two tips of different metals in one tube or in two closely connected tubes is very useful for investigation of gas adsorption on different metals under identical conditions of pressure, time, and possible impurities. It could be shown that the initial oxidation of tungsten and molybdenum are quite different although the lattice constants of the metals are nearly similar. For the simultaneous observation of the two images, motion pictures are recommended, which can readily be obtained with emission currents of 10 to 50 μa., good optics, and normal frame speed.

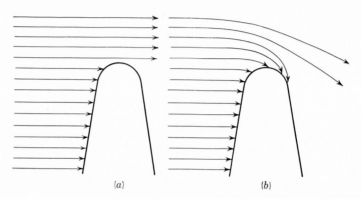

(a)                    (b)

Fig. 26. Evaporation of molecules onto a tip.
a. Without applied field.
b. With applied field. The polarized molecules deposit on the back of the tip too.

It is attractive to make quantitative observations on the screen by photometric measurements. One might thus obtain voltage-current density relations and deduce therefrom the work function of the various crystal planes of pure metals or adsorbed films. The measurement of light intensity is, however, very difficult if large contrasts are encountered. Light scatter from the bright surfaces and total reflection from the glass wall illuminate the dark portions of the image. Wilkinson (57), disregarding this difficulty, obtained with tungsten tips a contrast ratio of 1:30 between the (110) plane and strongly emitting planes. If the optical scattering is diminished by aluminizing the screen, the contrast, according to Dyke (18) and co-workers, rises to 1:2000. Even this ratio is not entirely correct. The dark spaces on the screen are lightened through the aluminum film by secondary electrons or X rays. Exact measurements of current density can be obtained in a special tube, shown in Fig. 27. The electrons passing through the aperture in the viewing screen first go through a grid with a small positive voltage to repel secondaries and then arrive in the collector, where they are measured electrometrically. In this way contrasts of 1:10,000 to 1:100,000 have been obtained depending on the total current (40, 49). The focusing of particular planes on the probe aperture is carried out in this tube by adjusting the position of the anode. One can also construct tubes in which the electron image is shifted by means of a magnetic field relative to the probe aperture or where the

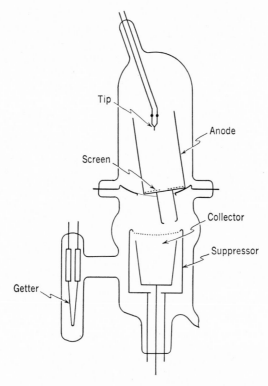

FIG. 27. Diagram of probe tube for measuring current densities in different parts of the pattern.

focusing is done by moving the cathode. The result of the measurement with such tubes is presented in Table III. There is reason to consider these data to be more reliable than those obtained by thermionic methods, particularly for the (011) plane.

For the two last planes the work function depends on the annealing temperature that had been applied before the measurement. At high annealing temperatures the planes are in a dynamic state of disorder due to surface migration, and the planes contain lattice steps which are frozen in if the measurement is made at room temperature. This gives the lower work functions. The high values of the work function are obtained by annealing the tip at 1200° C. only, where the planes are more nearly perfect. Such large differences as 1.7 ev. between the lowest and the highest work functions may as well occur on metals other than tungsten, because their field emission patterns show similar large contrasts at the

TABLE III

| Crystallographic plane | Work function, ev. |
|---|---|
| 116 | 4.30 |
| 013 | 4.31 |
| 012 | 4.34 |
| 111 | 4.39 |
| 123 | 4.52 |
| 112 | 4.65–4.88 |
| 011 | 5.70–5.99 |

(011) plane for the body-centered cubic metals and at the (111) plane for the face-centered cubic metals.

## 6. The Field Ion Microscope

### 6.1. Field Desorption

So far the application of only negative voltage to the tip of the field emission microscope has been described; however, some quite remarkable effects can be studied by making the tip positive. Not more than about 50 Mv./cm. D.C. or 80 Mv./cm. with microsecond pulses can be used at a negative tip because of the large electron emission which would destroy the emitter. As a positive tip the field can be raised to 500 Mv./cm., and the effects of this field on adsorption layers or on the tip metal itself can then be observed in the electron picture on the screen when the tip is made negative again.

The first observations were made with barium on tungsten (39). A film of an average covering of 0.35 is not influenced at all by a positive field of 92 Mv./cm. However, if 94 Mv./cm. are applied for a few seconds, the barium film is torn from the surroundings of the (011) plane of the substrate. For the same film the field desorption from the (111) plane requires 125 Mv./cm. at room temperature. Generally the tearing-off field strength is a function of the degree of covering and the temperature for every crystal plane. This field strength can be measured quite accurately by calibrating the field: voltage ratio with field electron emission from the same tip. It measures the binding force on the particular crystal plane. However, the conversion of tearing-off field strength into heat of adsorption is difficult because of the atomic fine structure of the surface. In principle the ground level of the adsorbed atom has to be lifted by the external field until it reaches the Fermi level of the substrate (30). Then the bonding electron can tunnel into an unoccupied level of the metal and the adsorbed atom leaves the surface as an ion. The actual effective distance is not exactly the atom radius $r$, because the adsorbed atom sits not on an ideal plane, but rather in the corner of a lattice step of the substrate. Also the effective work function $\phi$ is not the average work function of the substrate or of its special crystal plane, but rather an unknown quantity which is valid only for the adsorption under consideration. The data obtained for the heat of adsorption from measurements of field desorption, however, give at least the right order of magnitude.

So far field desorption has been measured with barium, thorium, oxygen, nitrogen, and tungsten in details and with some other adsorbates on an exploratory scale (23b, 49b). Barium at low degrees of coverage is desorbed at room temperature from the vicinals of (011) by a field of 78 Mv./cm., and at full coverage (monolayer, $\Theta = 1$) at 140 Mv./cm. At higher temperatures the desorption field is much lower. For thorium at $\Theta \approx 0$ a field of 235 Mv./cm. is required for desorption, and about 270 Mv./cm. for $\Theta = 0.7$. Field desorption of oxygen requires about 420 Mv./cm. for the second layer and 500 Mv./cm. for the chemisorbed layer on tungsten (49a), while nitrogen comes off at about 350 Mv./cm. from a second adsorption layer and at almost 500 Mv./cm. from the chemisorbed state. Above this field the tungsten surface itself is dissolved at room temperature with a rate of about one monolayer per second.

Field desorption can probably be described as an evaporation of an ion over the potential hump which is formed by the attraction by the image force on the one side and by the external field on the other side (23b, 49a). Thermal agitation helps then to overcome the hump. The binding energy $Q_0$ of a single charged ion is found from the thermionic cycle

$$Q_0 = \Lambda + V_1 - \Phi \tag{12}$$

where $\Lambda$ is the heat of evaporation of the atom, $V_1$ the ionization energy, $\Phi$ the work function of the substrate. The remaining energy hump is then

$$Q = Q_0 - \sqrt{n^3 e^3 F} \tag{13}$$

where the second term describes the reduction of the hump by the external field (Schottky effect), and where the charge of the ion is $n \cdot e$. The time to evaporate a particle over the hump $Q$ is

$$\tau = \tau_0 e^{\frac{Q}{kT}} \tag{14}$$

with $\tau_0 = 10^{-13}$ sec. being the vibration time of the adsorbed particle. This gives the formula for the desorption field

$$F = \frac{1}{n^3 e^3} \left( Q_0 - kT \ln \frac{\tau}{\tau_0} \right)^{\frac{1}{2}} \tag{15}$$

which describes the observed data within the accuracy one can expect from the image force model at these extremely high fields. In the case of barium the assumption of double rather than single charged ions (in the instant of desorption) gives full agreement with the observed data, while thorium and tungsten desorb at fields that are about 20 to 30% lower than that are calculated from the formula above with $n = 1$. Temperature and time dependence (the latter measured for fields applied between microseconds and 300 sec.) are in good agreement with the theoretical expectation.

Field evaporation of metals is a most effective method of polishing and smoothing a field emitter tip. All contaminations and all protruding edges, for instance, from the etching process can be removed at room temperature.

### 6.2. Field Ion Emission

The sudden field desorption of an adsorbed film yields only an almost immeasurable small current pulse of positive ions. The tip of a field emitter holds not more than some $10^4$ barium atoms in a monolayer, corresponding to an ion pulse of some $10^{-15}$ coulombs. A continuous ion emission can be obtained by supplying a constant stream of molecules which can be ionized at the tip. This can be done by operating a positive field emitter in a gas of some microns of pressure (45, 49c). If the field close to the tip is sufficiently high, an approaching neutral gas molecule will be ionized by the tunneling of an electron through its potential barrier toward the tip surface (Fig. 28), while the positive ion follows the field. The ion current is apparently determined by the number of gas molecules arriving at the tip in the unit of time and by the probability of ionization. The number of arriving molecules is proportional to the gas pressure, which is limited at about $10\mu$ to prevent a gaseous discharge breakdown. A favorable effect, enhancing greatly the number of molecules striking the tip, is the attraction of molecules by their induced dipole moment in the inhomogeneous field. The probability of barrier penetration $D$ is approximately given by

$$D_{(W)} = e^{\frac{-2\sqrt{2m}}{\hbar} \int_{x_1}^{x_2} (U - W)^{\frac{1}{2}} dx} \tag{16}$$

where $U$ is the potential and $W$ the kinetic energy of the electron striking the inside of the molecule potential well. The ionization probability becomes appreciable only if the field is extremely high, about 300 Mv./cm. for hydrogen, which is usually described as autoionization, or if the barrier is additionally lowered by the image force close to the surface. The determining quantity is the position of the ground level or the ionization potential of the molecule. If the field is not very high and the molecule is not yet ionized when approaching the tip, the probability of ionization becomes suddenly zero as soon as the ground level sinks below the Fermi level inside the metal.

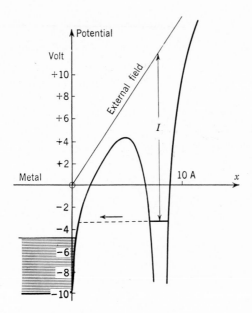

FIG. 28. Atom with ionization potential $I$ approaching a metal surface in an external field of 150 Mv./cm. Valence electron tunnels through barrier.

Field-ion-emission current-voltage characteristics have been measured with hydrogen, helium, neon, argon, krypton, xenon, nitrogen, oxygen, and mercury and are in quantitative agreement with calculations based on the above-developed mechanism. Ion currents up to $10^{-7}$ amp. can be obtained. The required minimum field strengths for a measurable emission are roughly proportional to the $\frac{3}{2}$ power of the ionization potential, requiring 75 Mv./cm. for mercury and 280 Mv./cm. for helium (49c).

A field ion emitter has quite unique properties as an ion source for a mass spectrometer. Since there are no hot electrodes in the ionization tube and the molecules do not have to touch any metal surface before being ionized by the field in front of the tip, there is much less fragmentation than in the conventional electron impact ion sources. Experiments by Inghram and Gomer (28) with a high-resolution mass spectrometer allowed the determination of the velocity distribution of the ions and showed that they originate in part some distance from the tip, while others are being ionized or fragmented directly at the surface.

### 6.3. Field Ion Microscopy

After the ionization in the immediate proximity of the surface, the ions stream away from the tip on nearly the same orbits as the electrons

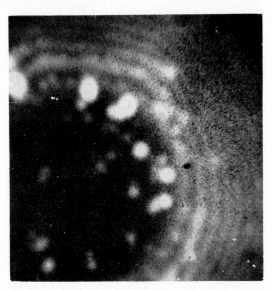

FIG. 29. Helium ion picture of the border of the 110-plane of a tungsten tip. The individual lattice steps are 8 to 12 A apart from each other. Magnification about 2.5 million times.

in the field electron microscope. Since there is not much scattering in the gas because of the low pressure, the ions strike the fluorescent screen and produce an image of the tip surface. The promising fact of this field ion microscope (45) is the very high potential resolution due to the small tangential velocity component of the ions and their small De Broglie wave length. A detailed consideration of the mechanism of field ionization (23b, 49d, 49e) shows that most of the ions originate from rebounding molecules after random elastic collision with the surface. They have then a relatively large tangential velocity component due to the retained dipole attraction energy $\frac{1}{2}\alpha F^2$. This determines the resolution to be about

$$\delta = \pi\beta r^{\frac{2}{3}} \sqrt{\frac{3kT + \alpha F^2}{eF}} \tag{17}$$

where $\alpha$ is the polarizability of the gas. Helium turns out to be most favorable because of its low polarizability and also because of the high ionization potential, which brings the ionization zone as close as 4 to 5 Å. to the surface. At room temperature eq. (17) yields a resolution of 5.5 Å. for a tip radius of 1000 Å. Figure 29 shows the surrounding of the (011) plane of a tungsten tip. About 10 individual lattice steps as the edges of

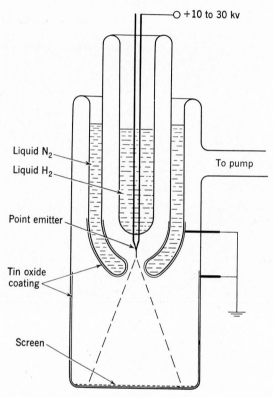

FIG. 30. Schematic diagram of low temperature field ion microscope.

(011) net planes are resolved. In similar pictures, although with less resolution because of the application of hydrogen as operating gas, Drechsler, Pankow, and Vanselow (15) show interesting details in lattice steps which they interpret as spirals caused by screw dislocations.

The unfavorable large tangential velocity component of the ions originating from rebounding atoms can be considerably reduced by cooling the field emitter tip in a microscope tube according to Fig. 30. If the temperature is low enough as to make the accommodation coefficient one, the rebounding helium atoms retain a small tangential velocity corresponding to $kT$ only. This improves the potential resolution to about 1.5 Å. for a 1000 Å. tip, and the actual resolution is now limited by the amount of field ripple within the ionization zone which is produced by the atomic structure of the surface some 4 to 5 Å. below. Cooling the field ion microscope by solid nitrogen or liquid hydrogen improves the resolution so much that the individual lattice steps show up all over the surface of the tip. Moreover, the atoms within the chains that constitute these lattice steps can now be resolved (49d, 49c). Figure 31 shows a

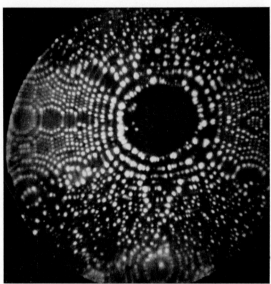

Fig. 31. Helium ion image of small section of a tungsten tip, showing the arrangement of individual tungsten atoms along the lattice steps. Tip radius 510 Å., helium pressure 1.5μ, voltage 12,500 volts, microscope cooled by liquid hydrogen. Magnification about 1.7 million times.

small section of the tip surface between (011) and (112). On similar pictures neighboring tungsten atoms separated by 2.74 Å. have been resolved. With this technique, as limited as the applicability may be at the present time, the field ion microscope is the first microscopical device to reveal the atomic structure of a surface. By field evaporation above 500 Mv./cm. the tip surface can be obtained in a state of perfection that surpasses by far the state that can be produced by heating the tip to the highest temperatures, and subsequently freezing in the thermal imperfections. Dislocations of various kinds can then be produced at will by radiation with heavy particles, by ion bombardment or simply by heat treatment. The arrangement of the individual atoms in the surface can then be studied in the helium ion image.

REFERENCES

1. Alpert, D., *J. Appl. Phys.* **24**, 860 (1953).
2. Ashworth, F., *Advances in Electronics* **3**, 1 (1951).
2a. Barnes, G., *Phys. Rev.* **97**, 1579 (1955).
3. Becker, J. A., *Bell System. Tech. J.* **30**, 907 (1951).
4. Becker, J. A., and Brandes, R. G., *J. Chem. Phys.* **23**, 1323 (1955).
4a. Becker, J. A., *Bull. Am. Phys. Soc.* **30**, 17 (1955).
5. Benjamin, M., and Jenkins, R. O., *Proc. Roy. Soc.* **A176**, 262 (1940).
6. Benjamin, M., and Jenkins, R. O., *Proc. Roy. Soc.* **A180**, 225 (1942).
7. DeBoer, J. H., "Electron Emission and Adsorption Phenomena." Cambridge Univ. Press, London, 1935.
8. von Borries, B., and Ruska, E., *Ergeb. exakt. Naturw.* **19**, 237 (1940).
8a. Brock, E. G., *Phys. Rev.* **100**, 1619 (1955).
9. Brüche, E., and Johannsen, H., *Naturwissenschaften* **20**, 353 (1932).
9a. Dolan, W. W., *Phys. Rev.* **91**, 510 (1953).
10. Burgess, R. E., Kroemer, H., and Houston, J. M., *Phys. Rev.* **90**, 515 (1953).
10a. D'Asaro, L. A., *Phys. Rev.* **100**, 1258A (1955).
11. Drechsler, M., and Müller, E. W., *Metall.* **6**, 341 (1952).
12. Drechsler, M., and Müller, E. W., *Z. Physik* **132**, 195 (1952).
13. Drechsler, M., and Henkel, E., *Z. angew. Phys.* **6**, 341 (1954).
14. Drechsler, M., *Z. Elektrochem.* **58**, 327 (1954).
15. Drechsler, M., Pankow, G., and Vanselow, R., *Z. Physik. Chem.* **4**, 249 (1955).
16. Dushman, S., "Scientific Foundations of Vacuum Techniques." Wiley, New York, 1949.
17. Dyke, W. P., and Trolan, J. K., *Phys. Rev.* **89**, 799 (1953).
18. Dyke, W. P., Trolan, J. K., Dolan, W. W., and Grundhauser, F. J., *J. Appl. Phys.* **25**, 106 (1954).
19. Fowler, R. H., and Nordheim, L. W., *Proc. Roy. Soc.* **A119**, 173 (1928).
20. Gomer, R., *J. Chem. Phys.* **20**, 1772 (1952).
21. Gomer, R., and Speer, D. A., *J. Chem. Phys.* **21**, 73 (1953).
22. Gomer, R., *J. Chem. Phys.* **21**, 239 (1953).
23. Gomer, R., *J. Am. Chem. Soc.* **75**, 4114 (1953).
23a. Gomer, R., and Ingraham, M. G., *J. Am. Chem. Soc.* **77**, 500 (1955).
23b. Good, R. H., Jr., and Müller, E. W. Review article on "Field Emission." *In* "Handbuch der Physik," 2nd ed., Vol. 21. Springer, Berlin, 1956.
24. Haefer, R., *Z. Physik* **116**, 604 (1940).
25. Hecht, K., *Z. Math. u. naturw. Unterricht* **35**, 90 (1952).
26. Heidenreich, R. D., *J. Appl. Phys.* **24**, 1414 (1953).
27. Herring, C., in "Structure and Properties of Solid Surfaces" (R. Gomer and C. S. Smith, eds.), pp. 63–66. Univ. of Chicago Press, Chicago, 1953.
28. Inghram, M. G., and Gomer, R., *J. Chem. Phys.* **22**, 1279 (1954).
29. Jenkins, R. O., *Repts. Progr. Phys.* **9**, 177 (1943).
30. Kirchner, F., *Naturwissenschaften* **41**, 136 (1954).
31. Klein, R., *J. Chem. Phys.* **21**, 1177 (1953).
32. Klein, R., *J. Chem. Phys.* **22**, 1406 (1954).
33. Knoll, M., and Ruska, E., *Ann. Physik* **12**, 607, 641 (1932).
34. Korb, A., Dissertation, University, Berlin (1953); see also (47) p. 337.
35. Langmuir, I., *J. Franklin Inst.* **217**, 543 (1934).
36. Müller, E. W., *Z. Physik* **106**, 132 (1937).

37. Müller, E. W., Z. *Physik* **106**, 541 (1937).
38. Müller, E. W., Z. *Physik* **108**, 668 (1938).
39. Müller, E. W., *Naturwissenschaften* **29**, 533 (1941).
40. Müller, E. W., Z. *Physik* **120**, 261 (1943).
41. Müller, E. W., Z. *Physik* **120**, 270 (1943).
42. Müller, E. W., Z. *Physik* **126**, 642 (1949).
43. Müller, E. W., *Naturwissenschaften* **37**, 333, (1950).
44. Müller, E. W., Z. *Naturforsch.* **5a**, 473 (1950).
45. Müller, E. W., Z. *Physik* **131**, 136 (1951).
46. Müller, E. W., "Modern Research Techniques in Physical Metallurgy," pp. 33–50. American Society for Metals, Cleveland, 1953.
47. Müller, E. W., *Ergeb. exakt. Naturw.* **27**, 290–360 (1953).
48. Müller, E. W., *J. Appl. Phys.* **24**, 1414 (1953).
49. Müller, E. W., *J. Appl. Phys.* **26**, 732 (1955).
49a. Müller, E. W., Z. *Elektrochem.* **59**, 372 (1955).
49b. Müller, E. W., *Phys. Rev.* **101**, April (1956).
49c. Müller, E. W., and Bahadur, K., *Phys. Rev.* **101**, April (1956).
49d. Müller, E. W., Z. *Naturforsch.* **11a**, 88 (1956).
49e. Müller, E. W., *J. Appl. Phys.* **27**, May (1956).
50. Rathenau, G. W., and Baas, G., *Physica* **17**, 117 (1951).
51. Recknagel, A., Z. *Physik* **120**, 331 (1943).
52. Richter, G., Z. *Physik* **119**, 406 (1942).
53. Schleicher, H. W., Z. *Naturforsch.* **7a**, 471 (1952).
54. Sommerfeld, A., and Bethe, H., *in* "Handbuch der Physik," Vol. 24, Part 2, p. 438. Springer, Berlin, 1933.
55. Stranski, I. N., and Suhrmann, R., *Ann. Physik* **1**, 153 (1947).
56. Wiegmann, J., Thesis, Technical University, Berlin (1951); see also (47) p. 337.
57. Wilkinson, M. K., *J. Appl. Phys.* **24**, 1203 (1953).
58. Wolf, P., Z. *angew. Physik* **6**, 529 (1954).

# Theory and Principles of Sampling for Chemical Analysis

By

A. A. BENEDETTI-PICHLER

*Department of Chemistry, Queens College, Flushing, New York*

Sampling for chemical analysis is resorted to since it usually is not practical to submit the whole object of inquiry to a test. After sampling the test is applied to a portion of the object: a particular corrosion spot out of many, a gram of coal out of a shipload, etc. To permit the extrapolation which equates the result of the test on the often very small sample with that which would have been obtained if the whole object had been subjected to the same test, the sample must be a good miniature replica of the whole at least in those features which determine the investigated property. Sampling deals with the preparation of small-scale copies of decisive features of the object of investigation.

## 1. The Theory of Sampling

All matter consists of discrete particles which in turn may be made up of smaller discrete particles, etc. Since it is agreed that chemical and physical properties are determined by the nature, ratio, and arrangement of such entities, a discussion of sampling should start with the defining of the determinative units—in future briefly referred to as units or entities—which are sufficiently different in nature or structure so that variations of their ratio will significantly affect the properties of the object to be investigated.

The size of the unit may vary considerably depending upon the nature of the object. The choice of the unit and its size are determined by the

| Material | Unit | Approximate weight of unit |
|---|---|---|
| Pure substance | Atoms | $10^{-24}$ to $10^{-21}$ g. |
| Molecular dispersions (solutions) | Molecules | $10^{-23}$ to $10^{-19}$ g |
| Colloidal dispersions | Dispersed phase | $10^{-21}$ to $10^{-14}$ g. |
| Suspensions, emulsions | Dispersed phase | $10^{-15}$ to $10^{-3}$ g. |
| Solidified melts of mixtures of several substances, alloys, granite, etc. | Size of crystal grain | $10^{-15}$ g. to kilograms |
| Mixtures of particulate solids | Size of particles | $10^{-15}$ g. to kilograms |

foregoing definition. If a mixture of shavings of two brasses is to be sampled for chemical analysis, the shaving must serve for unit if the two brasses are of different composition, but the grain size of the alloys should be used for unit if they are closely of the same composition. If the two brasses have the same copper content but differ otherwise in chemical composition, the shavings should be the sampling units for determinations of lead, tin, and zinc; the grain size, for determination of copper.

When the unit determining heterogeneity has been decided upon and information is available on the composition and size of the unit and the approximate numerical ratios of units of various kinds, it becomes possible to estimate the size of a sample which may be able to replicate the whole object of investigation within specified limits. An estimate which can satisfy practical requirements may be obtained by starting with a highly idealized example and then finding the conditions under which its solution will apply to actual conditions.

## 1.1. Statement of the Basic Problem

It is assumed that the object consists of $N$ units, $N_1$ of which are of kind A and $N_2$ of which are of kind B, so that the probability of withdrawing at random a unit of kind A is $p = N_1/N$ and the probability of withdrawing a unit of kind B is $q = N_2/N$.

A sample of $n$ units shall be drawn at random so that it contains units A and B in the same ratio as the whole object: $n_1 = np$ units of A and $n_2 = nq$ units of B. Common sense indicates that such a sample may be obtained with certainty only in one way, by making $n = N$, or taking the whole object for sample. If $n < N$, a perfectly representative sample will be obtained only once in a while by accident. As a rule, the composition of the random sample will differ from that of the object, giving rise to the question of within what limits the composition of samples will vary around that of the object and what can be done to keep the variation sufficiently small so that the composition of the object may be assumed practically equal to that of the sample.

Essentially the same problem occupied the mind of an ingenious gambler, who submitted it to the French mathematician Bernoulli. It may be stated in these forms: what reliance can be placed on obtaining 4 black beans when drawing at random 24 beans out of an urn containing a random mixture of 1000 black and 5000 white beans? or what is the chance of throwing 4 aces in 4 throws with 6 dice? Bernoulli (5) found the correct answer concerning the chances of these and any similar betting propositions. The probabilities of obtaining a black or white bean, an ace or a nonace are determined by the ratios of the sought units over the total units in the source: $p = \frac{1}{6}$ and $q = \frac{5}{6}$, respectively. The probabilities of getting 0, 1, 2, 3, etc., black beans or aces in $n$ drawings (throws) are represented by the successive items of the expanded binomial

$$(p + q)^n = \binom{n}{0} q^n p^0 + \binom{n}{1} q^{n-1} p^1 + \cdots + \binom{n}{n} q^0 p^n \tag{1}$$

The binomial shows that the ideal sample representing the composition of the object, 4 black beans (aces) in $n = 24$ drawings (throws), has the highest probability of occurrence:

$$\frac{24 \cdot 23 \cdot 22 \cdot 21}{1 \cdot 2 \cdot 3 \cdot 4} \left(\frac{5}{6}\right)^{24-4} \left(\frac{1}{6}\right)^4 = 0.2133$$

The probabilities for 0, 1, 2, 3, 5, 6, 7, and 8 black beans (aces) are 0.0126, 0.0603, 0.1388, 0.2032, 0.1706, 0.1080, 0.0555, and 0.0236, respectively. Adding the probabilities shows that the probability is 94.97% that any number between 1 and 7 black beans (aces) will be obtained or 98.59% for any number between 0 and 8. This answers also the problem of sampling: there are only 14 chances in 1000 that an actual sample will deviate by more than $\pm 4$ black beans (aces) from the composition of the ideal sample (4 black beans in 24).

The expected variation is much too large ($\pm 100\%$) for practical purposes. To satisfy these, the sample would have to contain a much larger number of units. An attempt to repeat the computation for a sample of $n = 10,000$ units, however, will show that such an endeavor is far too tedious. It is amusing to recognize that the final simple solution of this problem was within the reach of such an ingenious mind as Bernoulli's but for the lack of an apparently minor tool, the definition of a measure of precision. It thus happened that solution had to await the development of a general theory of errors.

For our use, a presentation of the reasoning of Laplace (23) would serve no purpose. It will suffice to develop the argument of Bernoulli in a manner similar to that of Czuber (12).*

In any instance for which $p$ and $q$, i.e., the composition of the original object, is approximately known, one is able to estimate the number $n_1$ of units of A in an ideal sample of $n$ units; it is $n_1 = np$. The deviations from the ideal content $n_1$ may thus be computed for the various possibilities of getting 0, 1, 2, . . . $n$ units of A into an actual sample: $0 - np$, $1 - np, 2 - np, . . . n - np$. The variance (square of the standard deviation) is then obtained by adding the squares of all possible errors after multiplying them by the probability of their occurrence as taken from the expanded binomial of Bernoulli,

$$\nu^2 = \binom{n}{0} q^n(-np)^2 + \binom{n}{1} pq^{n-1}(1 - np)^2 + \cdots + \binom{n}{n} p^n(n - np)^2$$

$$= npq(p + q)^n$$

Since $(p + q) = 1$, the variance to be expected in actual samples becomes

$$\nu^2 = npq \tag{2}$$

The correctness may be easily tested by setting $n = 2$ and substituting this value into the binomial (consider that $1 - 2p = q - p$).

---

* If a sample of $n = 1$ unit is taken, the chance is $p$ for a black bean and $q$ for a white bean to be taken. In the first instance the error in the composition of the sample of 1 bean is $1 - p$ black bean and in the second, $0 - p$ black bean. A variance must be expected equal to $p(1 - p)^2 + q(0 - p)^2 = pq^2 + p^2q = pq(p + q) = pq$. If a second unit is added to the sample, the variance will increase by a like amount, and the variance for a sample of $n$ beans will be $npq$.

## 1.2. The Standard Deviation of Sampling in Terms of Units

The preceding findings may be summarized as follows. An object consists of $N$ concrete units, $N_1$ units of A and $N_2$ units of B. A true miniature replica consisting of only $n$ units should contain $n_1 = pn = nN_1/N$ particles of A and $n_2 = qn = nN_2/N$ particles or units of B. In actual samples removed at random from the object, the number of units of A and B will fluctuate around the most probable values $n_1$ and $n_2$, and this uncertainty is described by the standard deviation

$$\nu = \pm \sqrt{npq} \text{ units} \tag{3}$$

Equation (3) is useful when the ratio of units of different kind is to be determined, i.e., the ratio of black to white beans or the ratio of defective to satisfactory articles of a production line.

## 1.3. The Sampling Error in the Composition

In sampling for chemical or physical testing, the units A and B are usually only the carriers of certain amounts of the property or the substance to be determined.

It shall be assumed that all units have the same volume $v$ and that only two kinds of units are present,

a fraction $p$ of units A, density $d_1$, containing $P_1\%$ of X and
a fraction $q$ of units B, density $d_2$, containing $P_2\%$ of X,

the percentage of which ($\%$ X) in the object is to be determined. The density of the object is then given by

$$d = pd_1 + qd_2 = d_2 + p(d_1 - d_2) = (N_1d_1 + N_2d_2)/N \tag{4}$$

The percentage $P$ of X in an ideal sample of $n$ units, containing $n_1 = pn$ units of A and $n_2 = qn$ units of B, may be readily computed. It is

$$P = 100 \frac{(n_1d_1vP_1/100) + (n_2d_2vP_2/100)}{n_1d_1v + n_2d_2v} \% \text{ X}$$

or

$$P = \frac{n_1d_1P_1 + n_2d_2P_2}{n_1d_1 + n_2d_2} \% \text{ X} \tag{5}$$

Equation (5) is difficult to manage in the differentiation which is to follow but is readily converted into a more suitable form by adding to the right-hand side

$$P_2 - \frac{n_1d_1P_2 + n_2d_2P_2}{n_1d_1 + n_2d_2} = 0$$

The correct percentage of X then becomes

$$P = P_2 + \frac{n_1 d_1 (P_1 - P_2)}{n_1 (d_1 - d_2) + n d_2} \% \text{ X} \tag{6}$$

The sampling error is due to the fact that $n_1 + \Delta n_1$ units of A and $n_2 - \Delta n_1$ units of B are included in the sample instead of the theoretical numbers $n_1$ and $n_2$. The content $P + \Delta P$ of the actual sample is then a function $n_1 + \Delta n_1$. Use of Taylor's theorem for expanding the function $f(n_1 + \Delta n_1)$ into a series and subtraction of $P = f(n_1)$ furnishes the sampling error,

$$\Delta P = \Delta n_1 \frac{d_1 d_2 (P_1 - P_2)}{n d^2} (1 - Q/2 + Q^2/3 - Q^3/4 + \cdots)$$

where

$$Q = \Delta n_1 (d_1 - d_2)/n d$$

Since the total number of units $n$ is always large when compared with $\Delta n_1$, all powers of $Q$ may be neglected and the error in the percentage X becomes

$$\Delta P = \Delta n_1 \cdot d_1 d_2 (P_1 - P_2)/n d^2 \% \text{ X} \tag{7}$$

Substituting from eq. (3) the standard deviation $\nu$ of $n_1$ for $\Delta n_1$, one obtains the standard deviation $\Pi$ of the percentage $P$ of X, which is caused by the sampling error,

$$\Pi = \pm \frac{d_1 d_2 (P_1 - P_2)}{d^2} \sqrt{p_1(1 - p_1)/n} \% \text{ X} \tag{8}$$

The relative standard deviation $\Pi$ in the percentage $P$, which is caused by the sampling error, is (2)

$$\Pi' = \Pi/P = \pm \frac{d_1 d_2}{d^2} \cdot \frac{P_1 - P_2}{P} \sqrt{p(1 - p)/n} \tag{9}$$

### 1.4. Number of Units Required in a Representative Sample

Solving eq. (9) for $n$ gives the number of units to be included in a sample as a function of the relative precision $\Pi' = \Pi/P$ with which the composition of the original object is to be reproduced by the sample:

$$n = p(1 - p) \left(\frac{d_1 d_2}{d^2}\right)^2 \left(\frac{P_1 - P_2}{P}\right)^2 \left(\frac{1}{\Pi'}\right)^2 \text{ units} \tag{10}$$

It appears that the number of units must be increased proportionally to the square of the reciprocal of the permissible relative standard deviation in the percentage of X. Furthermore, the closer the particle ratio approaches $p = 0.5$, the larger the number of units must be. The ratio $(d_1 d_2)/d^2$ arrives at the unit for $d_1 = d_2$ and may increase to a maximum of about 20 where a material of density 1 g./ml. is mixed with a trace of very heavy material of density 20 g./ml. Finally the ratio $(P_1 - P_2)/P$ becomes 0 for $P_1 = P_2$ and may rise to very high values if $P_1 - P_2 = 100$ and $P$ is small. An internal compensation will occur, however, since $p(1 - p)$ must be small if the density ratio or the percentage ratio rises to a high value.

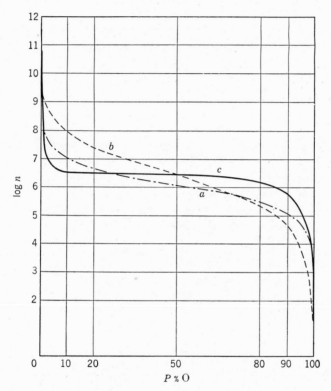

Fig. 1. Number of units in sample as function of the percentage of determined substance. Log $n$ is plotted against $P$ for $P_1 = 100\%$, $P_2 = 0\%$, and $\Pi' = 0.001$. The densities are for curve a: $d_1 = d_2 = 2$; curve b: $d_1 = 20$, $d_2 = 2$; curve c: $d_1 = 2$, $d_2 = 20$.

The effect of this compensation is clearly visible in Fig. 1, which shows the number of units required in the sample as a function of the composition of the object. $P_1 - P_2 = 100$ and $\Pi' = \pm 0.001$ are assumed for all three curves, which, because of the high value for the percentage ratio, must be sensitive to changes of the density ratio or the particle ratio, $p$. Nevertheless, the required number of units, $n$, varies in the range from 10 to 90% X by a factor of only about 10.

## 2. Computation of Sample Size for Actual Materials

Actual objects differ from the assumed ideal mixture in several respects. Often they have such a complex pattern that an exact theoretical treatment, if possible, would lead to a complicated solution too impractical for use. Even such situations, however, may be handled with success by first finding a corresponding ideal mixture.

### 2.1. Mixtures of Several Components

The theoretical treatment assumes two different kinds of units, units of A rich in X and units of B less rich in X. In practice, one will meet objects consisting of several components $a$, $b$, $c$, $d$, etc. It should be possible to obtain reasonable estimates of the weight fractions $F_1$, $F_2$, etc., which these components contribute and also of the percentages $P_1$, $P_2$, $P_3$, etc., of determined X, which they contain. It is then possible to arrange the components in two groups, one rich in X and the other poor in X, and to compute the densities and percentages of X of the representative components A and B as the weighted means of the corresponding data for the actual components. An example may serve for illustration.

| Actual components | Weight fractions | Percentages of X | Densities | | |
|---|---|---|---|---|---|
| a | 0.01 | 100 | 20 | } | A |
| b | 0.05 | 80 | 10 | | fraction, rich in X |
| c | 0.10 | 75 | 9 | | |
| d | 0.001 | 10 | 3 | } | B |
| e | 0.64 | 1 | 2 | | fraction, poor in X |
| f | 0.20 | 0 | 2 | | |

Computed data for representative components A and B:

$$\text{(A) } P_1 = \frac{0.01 \times 100 + 0.05 \times 80 + 0.1 \times 75}{0.01 + 0.05 + 0.10} = 78\% \text{ X}$$

$$d_1 = \frac{0.01 \times 20 + 0.05 \times 10 + 0.1 \times 9}{0.01 + 0.05 + 0.10} = 10 \text{ g./ml.}$$

$$\text{(B) } P_2 = \frac{0.001 \times 10 + 0.64 \times 1 + 0.20 \times 0}{0.001 + 0.64 + 0.20} = 0.8\% \text{ X}$$

$$d_2 = \frac{0.001 \times 3 + 0.64 \times 2 + 0.2 \times 2}{0.001 + 0.64 + 0.20} = 2 \text{ g./ml.}$$

The weight fractions of A and B are $F_1 = 0.16$ and $F_2 = 0.84$, respectively.

If there should be any doubt, the original components may be combined in various sensible ways to see whether or not the difference $P_1 - P_2$

or the density ratio $d_1d_2/d_2$ is significantly affected. As a rule, a representative mixture of A and B can be found, which common sense will accept as a substitute or model of the actual object.

### 2.2. Additional Aids for Computing n

The approximate densities $d_1$, $d_2$, etc., as well as the percentages $P$, $P_1$, $P_2$, etc., of X in the components of the mixture are usually known. The weight fractions may be estimated, and the density $d$ of the mixture is readily determined with sufficient reliability if the object consists of relatively large pieces (alloy, rock). If the object is granular or finely powdered, the density $d$ is more conveniently computed with the use of eq. (12) given below. The particle ratio $p$ is best calculated with eq. (14). This automatically furnishes the particle ratio of the model mixture of two components having units of uniform size.

If $F_1$ is the weight fraction of component A and $F_2 = 1 - F_1$ is that of B, the percentage of X in the mixture is given by

$$P = F_1P_1 + (1 - F_1)P_2$$

The weight fractions are then

$$F_1 = \frac{P - P_2}{P_1 - P_2} \quad \text{and} \quad F_2 = 1 - F_1 = \frac{P_1 - P}{P_1 - P_2} \tag{11}$$

One gram of the mixture then contains

grams of A $= F_1$;        milliliter of A $= F_1/d_1$
grams of B $= 1 - F_1$;    milliliter of B $= (1 - F_1)/d_2$
grams of A $+$ B $= 1$;    volume of A $+$ B $= (F_1/d_1) + (F_2/d_2)$

The average density follows from

$$d = \frac{1}{\dfrac{F_1}{d_1} + \dfrac{1 - F_1}{d_2}} = d_1d_2(P_1 - P_2)/denom. \tag{12}$$

where

$$denom. = d_1(P_1 - P) + d_2(P - P_2) \tag{13}$$

The particle ratio is by necessity identical with the ratio of the volume of component A over the total volume of the mixture:

$$p = \frac{F_1/d_1}{\dfrac{F_1}{d_1} + \dfrac{1 - F_1}{d_2}} = d_2(P - P_2)/denom. \tag{14}$$

The denominator is given by eq. (13).

### 2.3. The Weight of the Representative Sample

After the number $n$ of units required in a representative sample is computed, the weight $S$ of the sample may be readily computed from the volume $v$ of the unit and the average density $d$;

$$S = ndv \text{ units of weight} \tag{15}$$

The average volume of the unit may be estimated by weighing a larger number of units or measuring the volume of liquid displaced by them. If the units are small, various methods for the determination of particle size may be used. There is some latitude permissible in estimating the average volume or average weight $dv$ of the unit, since eq. (16) shows that the actual standard deviation may be expected within 0.5 to 1.5 of the computed (or desired) standard deviation if the estimated volume of the unit is within 0.25 to 2.25 of the proper volume of the unit. Special caution is required, however, when estimating the unit volume from the particle diameter since the above-mentioned volume tolerances reduce to the corresponding cube roots, 0.63 and 1.3, representing the permissible errors in estimation of the particle diameters.

Frequently the volume of the units varies so widely that the selection of an average volume would be highly arbitrary. It is then necessary to estimate from the size distribution the unit volume of an ideal mixture which will give the same sampling error as the actual object of investigation.

### 2.4. Particle Size Distribution and Sampling Error

The usual decision to base the computation of the error upon the volume of the largest particles leads to the use of unnecessarily large samples. A fairer estimate of sample size may be obtained from a consideration of the effects of the presence of particles larger and smaller than particles of a certain intermediate size.

*2.4.1. Mixtures with Two Particle Sizes.* It is assumed that a mixture contains a weight fraction $\phi$ of units of volume $av$ in addition to units of volume $v$. The components A and B are represented in the same ratio regardless of the size of the units. Samples are taken of weight $S$, which has been computed so that $n$ units of volume $v$ will give the permissible standard deviation $\Pi'$. The effect of the units of size $av$ is then calculated.

Actual samples will contain $\phi S$ grams or $n_{av} = \phi S/avd$ units of volume $av$ and the standard deviation of sampling in this fraction is thus given by $\pm \sqrt{pq(\phi S/avd)}$ units of volume $av$ or $\pm a \sqrt{pq(\phi S/avd)}$ units of volume $v$. Actual samples will furthermore contain $(1 - \phi)S$ g. or $n_v = (1 - \phi)S/vd$ units of volume $v$, and so the standard deviation of sampling becomes in this fraction $\pm \sqrt{pq(1 - \phi)S/vd}$ units of volume $v$.

The total variance $\nu^2$ of $n_1$ in terms of units of volume $v$ is then given by the sum of the variances caused in the two size fractions.

$$\nu^2 = (pq \cdot S/vd) \cdot (a\phi + 1 - \phi)$$

The total standard deviation becomes

$$\nu = \pm \sqrt{npq \cdot (1 - \phi + a\phi)} \text{ units of volume } v$$

Comparison with eq. (3) shows that the presence of a weight fraction $\phi$ of units of volume $av$ changes the standard deviation by the factor $\sqrt{1 + \phi(a - 1)}$. If the standard deviation is to remain within the limits $0.5\Pi'$ and $1.5\Pi'$, where $\Pi'$ stands for the relative standard deviation in the percentage of X computed by assuming a uniform unit volume $v$, one arrives at the conditions (2)

$$1.5 \geq \sqrt{1 + \phi(a - 1)} \geq 0.5$$
$$2.25 \geq 1 + \phi(a - 1) \geq 0.25 \tag{16}$$

or, in a more convenient form,

$$\phi \leq 1.25/(a - 1) \qquad \text{if} \qquad a > 1 \tag{17}$$

and

$$\phi \geq 0.75/(1 - a) \qquad \text{if} \qquad a < 1 \tag{18}$$

It follows that $a = 2.25$ or $a = 0.25$ if $\phi = 1$, i.e., that the actual standard deviation will remain between 1.5 to 0.5 of the computed value if as much as 100% of the units have a volume which is either 2.25 times as large as or only 0.25 of the volume assumed in the computation of the size or weight of the sample.

*2.4.2. Selection of Unit Volume for Computation of Sample Size* (4). Table I lists corresponding values of $a$ and $\phi$ and in addition the cube roots of $a$, which represent the multiples of the edge of a cube of volume $v$ that are equal to the edge of a cube of volume $av$. The maximum percentages expressed in numbers of particles have been computed with the obvious equation

$$100 \frac{\text{number of particles of volume } av}{\text{total number of particles}} = \frac{100\phi}{\phi + a(1 - \phi)} \tag{19}$$

Brief inspection of the table reveals some interesting facts. If one is satisfied with maintaining the desired precision within $\pm 0.5$ of its value, up to 75% of particles of infinitely smaller volume than the one used in computation are permissible. The presence of larger particles, however, presents a more serious problem. Only 18% by weight of units with twice the diameter of "normal" particles may be tolerated, and so not more than 5 such particles may be present for 195 particles of volume $v$.

To arrive at a fair decision in the individual instance, the computation of the sample size or weight should be based upon such a unit volume $v$ that the total of larger sizes may bring the actual standard deviation of sampling to 1.5 of the acceptable relative standard deviation $\Pi'$. The presence of a large fraction of smaller units, tending to reduce the un-

## TABLE I

*Permissible Maximum Percentages of Particles Having Volumes av or Diameters $\sqrt[3]{av}$ Instead of the Assumed Dimensions v and $\sqrt[3]{v}$*

| Smaller particles, $a < 1$ | | | | Larger particles, $a > 1$ | | | |
|---|---|---|---|---|---|---|---|
| Submultiples of assumed | | Maximum percentage by | | Multiples of assumed | | Maximum percentage by | |
| Volume $a$ | Diameter $\sqrt[3]{a}$ | Weight $100\phi$ | Number* | Volume $a$ | Diameter $\sqrt[3]{a}$ | Weight $100\phi$ | Number* |
| 0.25 or larger | 0.63 | 100 | 100 | 2.25 or smaller | 1.3 | 100 | 100 |
| 0.10 | 0.46 | 83 | 89 | 3 | 1.4 | 63 | 36 |
| 0.01 or smaller | 0.22 | 75 | 100 | 4 | 1.6 | 42 | 15 |
| | | | | 5 | 1.7 | 31 | 8.3 |
| | | | | 8 | 2 | 18 | 2.6 |
| | | | | 27 | 3 | 4.8 | 0.2 |
| | | | | 64 | 4 | 2.0 | 0.03 |
| | | | | 125 | 5 | 1.1 | 0.01 |
| | | | | 1000 | 10 | 0.1 | 0.0001 |

\* $100\phi/[\phi + a(1 - \phi)]$.

certainty to $0.5\Pi'$, will balance the effect of the large sizes to bring the actual sampling error back within the required limit of $\pm\Pi'$ (4).

EXAMPLE. A mixture of components A and B contains units of the following sizes;

1% by weight of volume $32\mu$

5%             $28\mu$

11%           $24\mu$

22%           $20\mu$

23%           $16\mu$

20%           $12\mu$

18%, volume 8 to $0.1\mu$ and smaller

Several solutions suggest themselves:

(a) selecting $v$ so that 75% of the particles will be smaller than $v$; in the given instance, this leads to

$$v = 24\mu$$

6% of only slightly larger particles and the size of the sample will be unnecessarily large;

(b) selecting $v$ so that it becomes one-half the volume of the largest particles; this leads to

$$v = 16\mu$$

39% larger particles with volumes up to $2v$

28% smaller particles which will hardly compensate the effect of the larger particles;

(c) compromising upon an intermediate value which promises the best compensation of the effects of larger and smaller particles,

$$v = 20\mu$$

17 % larger particles up to $1.6v$

61 % smaller particles so that the actual sampling precision may be somewhat better than the required one.

## 3. Multiple Sampling Operations

When large objects are investigated, it is usually impossible to obtain the test sample in one operation. One to ten million units are often required in the sample to give a satisfactory replica of the original. If the weight of the unit is 10 g., this will easily lead to a sample of several metric tons which could not be subjected to chemical analysis. Thus a smaller sample must be removed from the first sample. If the precision of sampling is to be maintained, a reduction of the size of the unit is required, and $v$ would have to be reduced to one millionth for a sample of a few grams to be obtained immediately, as the weight of the sample is directly proportional to the size of the unit, and the number of units in the sample is fixed by the nature of the object and the needed sampling precision. Such a procedure is impractical; it would not only require the fine milling of a large amount of material, but also would raise a reasonable doubt whether or not the tiny fraction removed as sample has the average composition of the whole; it might have been taken from a stratum in which one of the components accidentally predominated.

It is thus common practice to use in such instances an orderly sequence of sampling, crushing, sampling, grinding, sampling, milling, and sampling operations to obtain laboratory samples, from which finally the actual test samples are taken. A cascade of sampling operations leads from the original object to the final test sample.

At other times the object may consist of many concrete batches: blocks, bales, drums, bags, etc. Samples removed from specified batches are then combined to give a master sample which may have to be reduced by a cascade of sampling operation to obtain the laboratory samples.

*Laboratory samples* shall here be understood to be the portions forwarded to the laboratories; usually they are large enough to furnish material for repeated performance of several tests. *Test samples* are the portions of the laboratory samples which are taken for the performance of tests.

### 3.1. Duplication of the Object by a Master Sample

The object is packaged in concrete lots (bags, drums, tank cars, barges, etc.). Samples are taken from all or from selected lots so that the weights $w_1$, $w_2$, etc., of the samples combined into the gross or master sample are in the same ratio as the weights of the lots which they represent. If $\Pi_1'$, $\Pi_2'$, etc., are the relative standard deviations from the percentages of determined X in the lots caused by taking the individual lot samples, the relative standard deviation of the percentage of X in the master sample from the true content of the sampled lots is then (17)

$$\Pi'^2 = (w_1^2\Pi_1'^2 + w_2^2\Pi_2'^2 + \cdots)/(w_1 + w_2 + \cdots)^2 \qquad (20)$$

If all lots and lot samples are of the same size, the deviation of the master sample from the object is mainly determined by the number of lots sampled. The more lots that are sampled with good precision, the better is the duplication of the object by the master sample. Since we are dealing with an averaging procedure, the returns in precision for the expended effort diminishes rapidly when more than 16 lots are sampled. It may nevertheless be necessary to sample a very large number of lots if the composition varies greatly from lot to lot.

### 3.2. Effect of Cascade Sampling upon the Duplication of the Object by the Test Sample

If the reduction of the object to the test sample requires several steps, for which the relative standard deviations caused in the composition are $\Pi_1'$, $\Pi_2'$, etc., the relative variance in the composition of the test sample from that of the object is given by the sum of the incurred variances,

$$\Pi'^2 = \Pi_1'^2 + \Pi_2'^2 + \cdots \qquad (21)$$

The first variance may be that of a master sample obtained by combining several lot samples.

It is obvious that the duplication of the object will be determined principally by the sampling step which introduces the greatest deviation from the composition it tries to copy. This may be any step in the cascade. Obviously, the laboratory will be inclined—and often rightly so— to suspect the submitted laboratory sample. It must not be forgotten, however, especially when little of the material is taken for the test, that the removal of the test sample may contribute the greatest deviation. Experienced men in the field or plant are well acquainted with odd behavior of the materials of their concern and may be acutely aware of the particular sampling problems. On the other hand, the operator in the laboratory may fail to observe that the submitted laboratory sample has suffered segregation during transport or does not have a particle size small enough to allow further reduction of sample size without preliminary grinding of the whole or a large part of the material received.

## 4. PRINCIPLES FOR THE PRACTICE OF SAMPLING

The theory of sampling is based upon the random removal of a part from an object which contains the various kinds of components either in random distribution or in a uniform arrangement, as found in a crystal lattice. The composition of any large part of the object then approaches the composition of the whole, and it becomes immaterial what particular part is taken for sample.

The number of units which must be contained in a satisfactory sample is dictated by the required precision of duplication, $\Pi'$, and also by the nature of the object as well as of the substance to be determined, both of which fix the density ratio, $d_1 d_2/d^2$, and the percentage ratio, $(P_1 - P_2)/P$, of eq. (10); the particle ratio, $p$, is related via eq. (14) to the percentage ratio. If $P_1$ closely approaches $P_2$, a very small number of particles or units will give a satisfactory sample; the equation leads to the limit $n = $ zero for $P_1 = P_2$. The largest numbers, $n$, of units usually follow from $P_1 - P_2 = 100$ and/or small values of $P$; the determination of traces therefore often requires a very large number of units in a representative sample.

The size or weight of the representative sample being finally determined by the volume of the unit or particle, it may be diminished by reducing the size of the particles. Unit and particle are identical whenever all components are present as grains or definite entities. In the case of dispersions, whether coarse or fine, only the dispersed component is particulate, whereas the dispersion medium forms a continuous matrix. The matrix may then be imagined to consist of units of the size of the particles of the dispersed components. As long as the distribution of the components is uniform, at random or in perfect orderliness, it is of no consequence whether the particles or units change their relative positions (powder, suspension, emulsion) or whether their relative positions are fixed (grains of alloy or rock).

Corresponding with the size of the particles or units, the minimum size of the representative sample must undergo considerable variation. In molecular dispersions, the weight of the unit will rarely exceed $10^{-19}$ g., and a sample of $10^{-10}$ g. will contain a billion or more units corresponding to a relative standard deviation of sampling of $\pm 0.001$ or less, which cannot be detected by quantitative determinations on such a small scale. This prediction will even hold in such unfavorable instances as exemplified by a 0.001% aqueous solution of platinum ion ($d_1 = 20$, $d_2 = 1$, $d = 1$, $P_1 = 100\%$, $P_2 = 0\%$, $P = 0.001\%$, $p = 5 \times 10^{-7}$, $n = 2 \times 10^{12}$ for $\Pi' = \pm 0.001$, and sample weight $S = 6 \times 10^{-11}$ g. for a unit weight of $3 \times 10^{-23}$ g. $=$ weight of a molecule of water). On the other hand, an emulsion of 5% oil in water with oil droplets of 2-$\mu$ diameter will for the same sampling precision require a minimum of $2 \times 10^7$ units, or 0.08 mg. of sample.

For materials containing from 20 to 80% of determined constituent, Fig. 1 suggests an average of 3 million units in the sample if a sampling precision of $\pm 0.001$ is to be obtained. Assuming an average density of 3 g./ml. and units of cube shape, one may readily compute the approximate particle sizes as functions of the desired weight of sample and thus find that the edge of the cube (particle or unit) should be 0.1 mm., 45$\mu$, 22$\mu$, and 4.5$\mu$ if samples of weight 10 g., 1 g., 0.1 g., and 1 mg., respectively, are taken. These figures may provide rough criteria when test samples are taken from a laboratory sample.

Obviously, the application of the theory requires knowledge of the actual particle or unit size. In addition, the practice of sampling may require reduction of the particle size by disintegration of the material, and randomness of the distribution of the components and uniformity of the distribution throughout the whole must always be established before a sample is withdrawn. As an alternative, the sample may be withdrawn in such a manner that the nonuniformity of the object is reproduced in the sample. The rather divergent operations of determination of particle size distribution, disintegration, and mixing will be discussed in separate sections before the splitting of samples is considered further.

## 4.1. Determination of Particle Size

4.1.1. *Particles of Uniform Size*. Equation (16) shows that for all practical purposes size uniformity may be assumed if the variation in the particle volumes does not exceed the ratio 1:9 or if the variation in the particle diameters does not go beyond the ratio 1:2. It will then be fair to set the size of the unit equal to the size of those particles which represent the largest fraction of the object. If the distribution by weight of the sizes is more or less uniform, an intermediate volume may be taken for the volume of the unit.

If the particles are large, the average weight may be determined by weighing a number of particles which are selected to represent fairly the composition of the object. The volume may be estimated by observing the displacement of the meniscus in a graduated tube when a counted number of particles are immersed in a suitable liquid.

Sieves may be used as in the determination of particle size distribution, and the sizes of small particles may be measured under the microscope. In both instances the shape of the particles should be considered in estimating the volume from lineal dimensions.

*4.1.2. Particles of Significantly Different Sizes.* An approximate knowledge of the particle size distribution is needed if the diameter of the particles varies by more than 1:2. A careful determination of the particle size distribution is not necessary, however, since only the fractions of large sizes are of interest. The procedure depends upon the range of the large sizes. Classification by sifting is recommended if the large particles have diameters above $37\mu$. The Palo-Travis particle size apparatus (28, 30) is convenient to use for the range from 44 to $2\mu$. The same size range and the range from 2 to about $0.2\mu$ may be handled by measuring the diameters under the microscope. Particles of smaller sizes will rarely be of practical interest in connection with sampling.

*4.1.3. Sieve Analysis* (4, 34). Use of sieves of a standard series is indicated for sieve analysis. It seems best to start with a sieve which will pass 50 to 80% of the material. The charge and the fraction remaining on the sieve should be weighed with a precision of about $\pm 0.001$. The second sieve is selected according to the outcome of the first sifting operation. If more than 75% of the charge went through the first sieve, as in the example given below, it may be desirable to send the fine material through at least one more sieve. For the rest, the sieves should be selected so that all the material passes through the fifth and coarsest sieve.

EXAMPLE. Charge 10.00 g.

| Sieve opening, mm. | Retained on sieve g. | % | Size range, mm. | Weight fraction, % |
|---|---|---|---|---|
| 0.5 | 0.79 | 7.9 | 2.8 to 2.0 | 0.9 |
| 0.25 | 2.95 | 29.5 | 2.0 to 1.0 | 1.8 |
| 1.0 | 0.27 | 2.7 | 1.0 to 0.5 | 5.2 |
| 2.0 | 0.09 | 0.9 | 0.5 to 0.25 | 21.6 |
| 2.8 | zero | zero | smaller | 70.5 |
| | | | Total | 100.0 |

*4.1.4. Determination of Particle Size by Measurement under the Microscope.* The information required for the purpose of sampling will be frequently obtained by an essentially qualitative procedure. A representative sample is spread on a microscope slide, and the diameters of the largest particles are recorded during a rapid inspection of a large fraction or the whole of the spread sample. Difficulties may be met in preparing a satisfactory microscopical mount which shows a representative cross section through the material so that the boundaries of the particles or of the ultimate working units are clearly recognizable. The ultimate working units are defined by the American Society for Testing Materials as particles or groups of particles which are so firmly held together that they remain intact throughout the sampling process. It is obvious that the particles or ultimate working units should not be broken up when the mount is prepared and that the mount should not contain aggregates of particles or ultimate working units. To facilitate measurement and inspection, the particles should be clearly visible, located in one plane, and free from motion.

The mounting medium and procedure must be found by trial. Consideration of dispersing action, viscosity, and volatility will aid in selection of a suitable mounting medium.

Dry mounts may be obtained by dispersing the material in the solution of a gum or resin in a volatile solvent. After evaporation, the particles are held by the residue of nonvolatile matter, which should form a very thin film (1, 13, 16). Chamot and Mason (9) object to the spreading of materials by rubbing and rely rather upon the action of shearing forces acting when viscous dispersion media are caused to spread between slide and cover slip. For dispersion media, they recommend collodion solution of the consistency of thin syrup and melted gums, dammar or balsam.

Liquid mounts are obtained by essentially the same techniques as used for dry mounts. The dispersing action of water may be improved by addition of wetting agents, and its viscosity may be increased by adding glycerol, which also reduces the volatility. Among other media which have been recommended are glycerol, mixtures of glycerol and alcohols, oils, rubber cement, etc.

The microscopical examination for the purpose of sampling will rarely require the use of high magnifications. Dry objectives with magnifications $2.5\times$, $10\times$, and $20\times$ and micrometer eyepieces with magnifications $7.5\times$ or $10\times$ will usually suffice. It is most convenient to project a small image upon a screen and to perform the measurements on the screen image with the use of a ruler. Illumination of sufficient power may be obtained with a strong incandescent bulb. Information on use and care of the microscope, illumination, projection, and calibration of rulings are given in books on microscopy (9, 31).

The mount is first inspected with the unaided eye. If coarse particles are noticed, they are focused under the microscope with the use of the lowest magnification available. The coarse particles are counted and their average diameters are recorded. If inspection with the unaided eye does not indicate starting points of the search for large particles, the whole mount is first quickly surveyed with the use of the lowest magnification, and any large particles found are measured and recorded. If outstandingly large particles are found, their volume may have to be set equal to the volume of unit, and the size distribution of the small particles may be of no consequence.

If exceptionally large particles are absent, five locations of the mount are selected at random, two at the edge of the mount and three in its interior. Each location is first focused with the lowest magnification, and magnification is increased if advisable. The coarse particles are counted and their average diameters are recorded.

To obtain the weight fraction of the coarse particles, one finally prepares a new mount with a weighed quantity, 1 or 0.1 mg., of the material. Shape and dimensions of the coarse particles are then considered in estimating their volume. The weight fractions are finally obtained by estimates of the densities of the particles.

The same general method may be followed in measuring the grain diameters on polished surfaces of alloys, rocks, etc. This may be combined with the estimation of the ratio of the components (9).

### 4.2. Disintegration of Solid Materials

The great variety of available implements and machines should make it possible to find a satisfactory procedure for the reduction of the particle size of any kind of material. The task is made difficult, however, by the necessity of keeping the composition of the material from undergoing a change during disintegration. A thorough knowledge of the material to be broken up and of the chemical composition and the decisive physical properties of the materials in the tools may permit judging the possible effects of disintegration, but only experiments can prove that the created changes of composition are insignificant. In general, it is wise to carry disintegration not further than necessary for the purpose of sampling and subsequent efficient chemical treatment (4, 18–20, 25).

The tools used should always be harder than the hardest component in the material to be broken. Even the most resistant tools, however, undergo some wear, especially when shearing action is predominant. In the determination of minor or trace constituents, it thus becomes imperative to avoid tools or machines with parts which contain the determined substance.

In this connection it is of interest that not only mortars and pestles (32), but also bucking boards and mullers and grinding plates for the Braun-type sample grinder have been made of alumina which has been sintered at high temperature to attain the hardness of corundum (Mohs' 9). The material is variously referred to as U.S.A. Alumina, levigated alumina, high alumina ceramic, and Diamonite. All of these products may contain more than 99% alumina; amount and nature of the impurities may differ from batch to batch in accordance with variations in the composition of the raw material used. The grinding surfaces may be given a high polish and since even tungsten carbide does not scratch them, one may expect alumina to be definitely superior to agate of hardness 7 and to steel (3, 7).

A mortar and pestle with highly polished grinding surfaces of Kennametal, an alloy of tungsten carbide (hardness above 9) is on the market (14). Around 1940, the same tools have been made (15) of boron carbide, the hardest material next to diamond. If the expense is warranted, objects may be made of pure boron carbide, the powder of which is self-binding at 2400° C.; a mortar, 3/4 in. in diameter, and pestle are offered by Microchemical Specialties Co., Berkeley, Cal.

Thoroughly heterogeneous materials introduce the complication that the various components differ widely in their mechanical behavior. Brittle components will break down readily to give detritus of smaller particle size then required or desired, whereas tough components tend to form a coarse fraction. Soft components may get partly lost by adhering to the surface of the tools; in the most favorable instances the disintegrated material collects without loss in several size fractions which differ in composition and are difficult to mix. In the worst cases some of the brittle components get lost owing to flying particles or dusting, or the soft components produce a rubbery matrix which hinders the disintegration of embedded hard particles.

As a rule, some classification according to size must be combined with the disintegration process since accumulating fine material tends to prevent the breaking of the remaining coarse particles. Most mills provide for the continuous removal of the fraction which has attained the required particle size. If the material is treated in batches, it is best to make the batches so small that the disintegration may be carried to the desired fineness in one operation. Classification according to size, as pointed out in the preceding paragraph, may accentuate the nonuniformity of the product of disintegration.

Grinding may produce considerable heat, which will aid the evaporation of volatile substances during disintegration. It may be necessary to determine moisture (water, other volatile substances) in a large batch of the material before disintegration. The fine grinding will also open most of the fine vacuoles in solids and allow the escape of the gaseous or volatile contents.

Finally the increase of the surface, which is an unavoidable consequence of disintegration, will also proportionally favor all phenomena connected with the surface of the solid such as adsorption of constituents of the atmosphere and reactions with constituents of it, water, oxygen, carbon dioxide.

The implements and machines used in disintegrating must be adapted to the mechanical properties of the materials. Since soft and brittle matter crumbles and offers no problem, an arbitrary but useful classification of materials and the corresponding means of disintegrating them may consider three groups of matter to be broken down: soft and tough materials, hard and tough materials, and hard and brittle materials.

*4.2.1. Soft and Tough Materials.* Materials which are soft, pliable, or elastic and so permit pieces to suffer considerable deformation without breaking apart (wet clay, putty, muscle, hair, fibers, leather, rubber, etc.) are best reduced by cutting or tearing with more or less fast moving knives or other sharp-edged objects. Large objects may be first cut up with a cleaver or knife on a block of maple wood. To get material reasonably fine, one may use grating sets or the rocking motion of a knife or parallel knives with curved cutting edges. Rather widely applicable also are meat choppers which feed the materials by means of a rotating worm or helix to knives which rotate close to the face of a screen. The Latapie type tissue grinders which work on the same principle are now available with capacities of 2, 15, and 70 milliliters (32).

Mills having a set of rapidly rotating knives passing a set of stationary knives are widely applicable. The Wiley Laboratory Mill (35), may be used for cutting and tearing up agar, hair, fur, plastics, cardboard, cereals, bark, dried animal tissue, crab shells, fish scales, leather, organic drugs, seeds, wood, etc. The standard model is provided with three interchangeable brass sieves with openings of 6- to 0.5-mm. diameter. It is operated at 400 to 800 r.p.m. and requires a motor of at least 0.5 hp. The cutting chamber is 8 in. in diameter and 3 in. deep. A micro model (10) is available for use with small samples. Its cutting chamber of 5-ml. capacity is 3.2 cm. in diameter and 1.6 cm. deep, and it is closed with a polished glass plate so that the interior may be observed during operation. The two steel blades may be made to move with speeds up to 5000 r.p.m. The interior of the grinding chamber is easily accessible to permit thorough cleaning and quantitative recovery of the shredded material. The same claim is made for the Labconco Heavy Duty Laboratory Mill of the Laboratory Construction Company, Kansas City, Mo., which has rotating cutting knives arranged in circular plates of hardened tool steel. The distance between the machined plates of 9-cm. diameter may be set with a micrometer adjustment so that the particle size of the product may be regulated from very coarse to fine. The normal speed is 1300 r.p.m. with a motor of 1 hp. The mill is especially adapted to the handling of a variety of agricultural products, and, with most materials, wipers attached to the revolving cutting plate keep the milling chamber clean.

Hammer mills utilize the impact and tearing action of rapidly whirling flailing rods of various shapes and are suited for the disintegrating of a wide variety of materials, hard and soft. The Laboratory Pulverizing Mill of Weber Brothers Metal Works handles salts, asbestos, flowers, glue, gravel, hard rubber, manure, mica, pumice, resins, rock wool, seeds, soft-metal clippings, etc. It takes material of 6-mm. diameter and produces fine powder in a single operation. Six interchangeable stainless steel screens with perforations of 1.25- to 0.2-mm. diameter are supplied. The material is fed by gravity and suction. The Micro-Samplemill of the Pulverizing Machinery Company, Summit, N.J., has the hammers rigidly attached to a rotor which may be run with speeds from 8000 to 12,000 r.p.m. All parts are easily accessible, and it is claimed that loss of material is negligible even with samples as small as 10 g. Lining of mill chamber, rotor, and screens may be of stainless steel. The mill was designed according to the specifications of Ross and Hardesty (29) for the pulverizing of fertilizing materials, mixed feeds, and grains. It may also be used for roots, limestone, coal, chemicals, pigments, and food products. The screens supplied with the unit have round perforations of 1- to 3-mm. diameter.

If the suggested means for disintegration do not seem practical, one may consider changing the mechanical behavior by strong chilling. Most pliable or elastic materials are thus rendered brittle and may then be treated as are materials of the third group.

*4.2.2. Hard and Tough Materials.* For materials which are hard and tough, such as metals and alloys, one usually resorts to some form of cutting action with the use of the customary metal-working tools: saw, drill, lathe, planer, chisel, or file. Special attention must be given to the cleaning of the tool before use and, possibly, to the complete recovery of the disintegrated product. If contamination of the latter by lubricant is suspected, this may be removed by extraction with suitable solvent. Nonferrous material is then usually searched with a magnet for the removal of detritus derived from ferrous tools.

A relatively large amount of work is required for the cutting of hard and tough materials, and it is advisable to search for other means of disintegration especially when large quantities have to be treated. In some instances proper heat treatment may render the material brittle so that it can be crushed and ground. Ductile materials may be rolled to thin sheet or drawn into fine wire, either of which may then be readily cut as desired. Finally, metals and alloys may be obtained in the form of small granules or shot by allowing the molten material to drip from fine orifices. The drops may solidify while traveling through air or they may be caught in a suitable liquid. The procedure is attractive if the melting point is low so that the fusion may be performed without difficulty in an inert atmosphere or under cover of an inert liquid; it has the additional advantage that alloys may be homogenized in the liquid state.

*4.2.3. Hard and Brittle Materials.* Most nonmetallic crystallized matter, glasses, resins, ores, and rocks, are sufficiently brittle to break under nonuniform stress. The material may be crushed between two objects of a harder and tougher substance—if pressure is applied suddenly, a shattering effect is obtained—or it may be ground between two hard surfaces which laterally glide past one another. The material breaks under the impact of shear stress and pressure. If there is a certain roughness of the grinding surfaces, the cutting action of their high points may also be considered.

Large pieces may be broken down by hand on a bucking board with the use of a muller. The board is made of a mixture of pig iron and high carbon steel and is available in two sizes: 45 × 60 cm., 45-kg. weight, and 60 × 90 cm., 68-kg. weight. It is used in a steel trough with high sides which catch flying particles. The muller has a face of 15 × 20 cm.; because of its weight, 23 kg., a satisfactory shattering and crushing effect is obtained by letting it drop. Its weight also gives good grinding action. Large quantities of very coarse material are better broken up in a jaw crusher, such as is in common use for the disintegration of large pieces of rock, coal, etc. The jaws are made of high grade semisteel and mounted and designed so that they may be easily cleaned and readily adjusted to make up for wear. The material is partly crushed and partly ground by a munching motion of the jaw(s). A laboratory model of the Chipmunk Crusher for hand or power operation weighs 130 kg., occupies 35 × 60 cm. bench or floor space, and crushes 20 to 70 kg./hr. to give 1.5-mm. grains from pieces of 8-cm. diameter.

Pieces of 8-mm. diameter or less of hard materials may be shattered in a Plattner diamond mortar. The Ellis mortar (19) is somewhat larger and takes pieces of 10- to 15-mm. diameter. Both mortars are made of hardened tool steel. One piece at a time is placed into the mortar. While ring and pestle are firmly held in position, the pestle is struck vertical blows with a hammer until the material has been converted to a coarse powder, the hammer being first applied lightly and the force of the blows gradually increased until the material starts to break. The pestle of the Ellis mortar is quite heavy, so that a shattering effect may be obtained without the use of a hammer. Crushing and grinding may be carried so far that the material from the Ellis mortar will pass a sieve with 0.15-mm. openings.

Large pieces of not too hard materials may also be broken down by crushing and pounding in a mortar of the tall (bell) form, which may be made of porcelain, brass, bronze, or steel. The mortar of the low form is a crushing and grinding tool in which small charges of coarse powder may be reduced to a very fine powder. Depending upon the hardness of the material, mortar and pestle should be made of glass, porcelain, agate, or steel. The synthetic mineral mullite, $3Al_2O_3 \cdot 2SiO_2$, is harder than agate. The amount of charge is regulated according to the fineness which is to be obtained in one operation. To guard against loss of flying particles, a sheet of cellophane with a hole in the center, is slipped over the handle of the pestle to cover the opening of the mortar.

If the grinding of hard materials to a fine powder is a frequent task, it will be advisable to use a motor-driven mortar grinder such as the ore grinder of the McKenna Brothers Brass Company, Pittsburgh or the streamlined model of the Fisher Scientific Company, Pittsburgh.

Hammer mills, described in section 4.2.1, as well as grinding mills operating on the principle of the old-fashioned coffee mill, may be used to obtain more or less coarse powders. The hand-operated Weatherhead grinder may be used for the preliminary crushing and grinding of small lumps of various materials such as pig iron, ore, rock, coal, clay, etc. It consists of a heavy iron mortar body 26 cm. in diameter, with a toothed tapered boss in the center. Handles are attached to the circular grinding ring, which has teeth on the inner side, corresponding to those of the center boss. Braun sample grinders for operation by hand or power permit the regulation of the fineness of the product by adjustment of lock nuts, and several types of grinding plates are available for use with different materials. The hand-operated model 6-R reduces 120 g. of hard quartz rock to 0.15 mm. within 3 min. The Braun pulverizer type UA works on the same principle but will grind 0.5 kg. of quartz rock/min. On the other hand, the Precision-Shell Sample Pulverizer of the Precision Scientific Company, Chicago, with grinding surfaces of hardened steel and Stellite, has been designed to reduce 3- to 8-g. samples of rock salt, marble, glass, or quartz from 2.5- or 5-mm. size to 0.3 mm. and finer.

Ball mills may be used for the fine grinding and mixing of relatively large quantities of not very hard materials. The charge and an approximately equal volume of grinding balls are placed inside a cylindrical drum or jar, which is then rotated at moderate speed around its axis. The material is broken up by the impact and grinding action of the rolling balls. The speed of rotation must be less for large drums than for small jars and varies from 45 to 85 r.p.m. The grinding jars of the Burrell ball mills are made of porcelain surrounded by a steel jacket and are available with capacities ranging from 1 qt. to 2 gal. The Fisher Minimill uses an 8-oz. glass jar. Grinding balls are furnished of porcelain and of flint with diameters of 1.2 to 4 cm. Both materials have a hardness of 6.5 to 7 (Mohs' scale) and a density of 2.0 to 2.5 g./ml. Higher grinding efficiency is claimed for the Burundum cylinders, Mohs' hardness 9 and density 3.65 g./ml., of U.S. Stoneware, Akron, Ohio. Burundum is a "high-fired ceramic material" with a nonporous surface, resistant to acids and alkalies. The cylinders are available in two sizes, either 2 or 3.1 cm. in diameter and height. Laboratory models (33) of the Bloch-Rosetti type ball mill consist of a jar which rotates around the vertical axis with 300 to 800 r.p.m. Balls of the same material as the jar are kept in rapid motion so that they shatter by impact rather than grind. Soft as well as hard materials may be reduced to colloidal dimensions. Laboratory models which may also serve for mixing and the preparation of emulsions are available with capacities of 3, 10, and 250 milliliters.

### 4.3. Mixing and Blending

Mixing or blending for the establishment of random distribution must frequently precede the removal of the sample. Obviously the greatest difficulties will be met with objects containing several phases.

*4.3.1. Gases and Liquids Forming One Phase.* Stratification may result from various reasons connected with the origin or history of a liquid or gaseous phase. Uniformity of composition will as a rule finally establish itself by diffusion, but this process is extremely slow. Uniformity may be quickly produced by turbulence in the body of the phase, which may be created by mechanical means. A gas is best mixed by the action of whirling propeller blades. Stirring, shaking, and tumbling are customary with liquids. In both instances the required energy grows with the mass and volume of the phase, and mixing may become impractical to impossible for large bodies of liquid which are to be sampled for testing the average composition.

*4.3.2. Mixtures of Liquids and Solids.* A closely representative sample cannot be obtained from coarse emulsions or suspensions which begin to separate as soon as a mechanical dispersing action subsides. One may try to remove a sample while the mixture is kept in turbulent motion by energetic mechanical action. It is more promising, however, either to separate the phases for taking samples of both phases after determining their volume or weight ratio or to produce a higher degree of dispersion so that a stable mixture is obtained. Various means are available to this latter end.

Inexpensive, portable hand homogenizers circulate the mixture by means of a pump which discharges the stream into the bulk of liquid with pressures up to 80 atm. to give stable emulsions. Parts are chromium plated or made of aluminum or steel. A small hand homogenizer (8) may be made of a Pyrex test tube and a closely fitting piston of Lucite. The shearing surfaces do not give off glass powder, as do all-glass apparatus of this type. Teflon pestles with interchangeable stainless steel and aluminum rods are commercially available for emulsifying bacterial cells and soft organs such as liver or brain (32).

Various high-speed blenders and mixers may be used to obtain stable emulsions and suspensions and to prepare juicy plant and animal tissues —fresh fruits, vegetables, canned products, liver, kidney, stomach contents, etc.—for the purpose of sampling. The well-known Waring Blendor uses a propeller of sturdy cutting knives rotating at 10,000 r.p.m. inside a jar. The blades are made of stainless steel, and the jars may be obtained of molded borosilicate glass, Monel metal (nickel, copper, iron), or aluminum alloy in capacities of 250 ml. to 1 liter. It will handle also dehydrated vegetables, confectionery, candy nut bars, softened wood, pulp, and paper, and it has been used for dispersing synthetic rubber and resins in organic solvents. Lamden (22) warns, however, to watch the condition of the metal parts at all times. If the dissolution of traces of heavy metals may affect enzyme systems, vitamin assays, or the determination of trace metals, special precautions may have to be taken. Recommended are plating of the metal parts with platinum-rhodium, replacing the air over the charge by an inert gas, adding reductants to the charge for binding the absorbed oxygen, and adding complexing agents which prevent the catalytic action of metal ions taken up from the parts of the blender.

The Brookfield Counter-Rotating Mixer may be introduced, like an electric stirrer, into any kind of vessel. Two motors drive two propellers which rotate close together around the same axis in opposite directions with relative speeds of 200 to 12,000 r.p.m. The material is drawn into the space between the two propellers, where it is exposed to the cutting action of the whirling blades. Since a vortex does not develop, the liquid level remains approximately constant. All immersible parts are made of 302 stainless steel; the bottom guide bearing is of leaded bronze. The same firm (E. Machlett & Son, New York) offers a Top Drive Laboratory Homogenizer, which is able to handle volumes from 0.2 to 50 ml. The razor-sharp 18-8 stainless steel cutting blades may be given speeds from 100 to 27,000 r.p.m. Shaft, blades, homogenizing flask, and cap may be sterilized as a unit.

The action of the Attritor of the Union Process Co., Akron, Ohio, is similar to that of a ball mill. The grinding tank is stationary, and the charge is rapidly agitated by rotating arms and circulation of the liquid contents by means of a pump. Research Type Model No. 01, operating with stainless steel balls, will furnish 200 to 400 ml. of dispersion within about 1 hr. Without trapping air, solids and semisolids are reduced to an average particle size of $1\mu$ and less.

*4.3.3. Particulate Solids.* A truly random mixture of solid pieces or particles is the more difficult to obtain the more the entities differ in size, shape, or density or have a tendency to cling to one another. Mixing can be effected only by inducing a random movement of the parts relative to one another. When in motion and exposed to the pull of gravity, however, the particles tend to segregate according to size, shape, and density. Adhesion prevents independent random motion of the particles. The various procedures used for mixing solids try to overcome these phenomena, but it should be kept in mind that only experimentation with the particular material can serve as a reliable guide in selecting the most efficient method of mixing. Considerable difficulty may be experienced in mixing very fine powders; it is obviously difficult to impart impulses leading to individual random motion of the extremely numerous population of very small particles. Repeated inspection under the microscope may permit recognition of the approach to randomness or it may show the reason for persistent stratification if particles widely differ in shape.

Methods of mixing large quantities of coarse material are included in the next section, dealing with the practice of sampling, and need not be repeated here. Materials which are very heterogeneous in size or shape may have to be broken up before mixing becomes possible. If there are large differences in toughness and hardness, the incompatible components may have to be separated and weighed to be separately disintegrated, mixed, and sampled; the classification may be performed according to size or density and may be brought about by heat treatment if some components are readily liquefied (metals, alloys, waxes, fats). Metal beads dispersed in dross may be recovered by sending the material through a stamping mill which converts the beads into disks easily separable by screening from the powdery detritus. A melt may be easily homogenized, and segregation on solidifying may be prevented by rapid cooling and forming into a thin slab or conversion to granules or shot. A sample may be removed from the homogeneous melt, and a pistol shaped sampling gun is being offered for the rapid sampling of melts of ferrous and nonferrous metals and alloys (26).

Preparation of a dispersion in a suitable medium may be considered if the material is soft and other methods of mixing do not appear promising.

Disintegration is often combined with mixing, and it may be a prerequisite of the latter if the original particles are conglomerates or show stratification. Thus grinding and mixing are often performed simultaneously in a mortar or in a ball mill, but it will be wise always to suspect the uniformity of the product.

Visibly granular materials may be effectively mixed by repeated pouring through a screen which is coarse enough to permit the ready passage of the whole material. Tumbling in a ball mill without balls and tumbling or shaking in a closed bottle prevent the loss of dust.

The Patterson-Kelley Twin-Shell Laboratory Blender, offered with a rather wide range of capacities, is claimed to give efficient mixing regardless of differences in size, shape, and density of the particles. It is made of Plexiglass so that progress of mixing may be followed with the eye. Two short, wide cylinders are joined to form an upright V, which receives the charge. After the top openings are closed, slow rotation around a horizontal axis exposes the charge to tumbling and folding with a transverse motion. A horizontal, rapidly rotating lug-studded shaft aids by breaking up lumps in the top layer of the material.

If there is a tendency for lumps to form, as is frequently true of fine powders, Crowell and Burke (11) recommend mixing on a rubber mat. The material is alternately spread out by applying pressure with a caulking knife with a wide flexible blade and collected in the center by rolling. At intervals a soft camel's-hair brush is used for collecting in the center all the material that clings to the surface of the mat. The uniformity of the mixture may be tested by spreading with the knife. The spread material should show a uniform smooth texture without regions of different appearance, but this test has proved deceptive in some instances even when the components could be distinguished by their color. Obviously one must guard against contamination by material removed from the mat on mixing of hard materials the particles of which have an abrasive action.

Mixing by rolling may be performed on glazed paper, oil cloth, or tarpaulin, depending on the amount of material. A conical pile is first made at the center of the square sheet. The cone is flattened by pressing its apex vertically down by means of a suitable flat implement, spatula, shovel or board, so that the material flows in a radial direction to give a circular layer of uniform thickness. The material is then rolled by lifting one corner of the square sheet to pull it quickly toward the opposite corner, which is then pulled toward the first corner. This leaves the material rolled into an elongated mound stretching diagonally across the sheet. One corner of this diagonal is then lifted and pulled toward the opposing corner, which in turn is lifted and pulled toward the former. The whole process may be repeated from the beginning, or it may be modified by lifting one side of the sheet and pulling it toward the opposite side, etc. The material may be again collected in the center of the sheet by simultaneously raising all four corners of the sheet.

Frequently one will be tempted to apply various methods of mixing, and there is still ample room for invention and improvisation. Emphasis, however, must be placed on continuous close observation of the effects. It is essential that the material flow freely for mixing, and drying may have to precede this operation.

### 4.4. Sampling Techniques

A material consisting of a uniformly composed phase—whether gas, liquid, or solid—does not offer a problem in sampling for analysis. Any part of it, no matter how small, will suffice since the limitations mentioned on page 184 fall outside the range of the customary testing practice. If the material contains several phases in uniform and perfect random distribution, the minimum size of sample is determined by eq. (10) as a function of the composition of the material, the weight of the unit, and the required sampling precision.

If the material shows stratification, a sample of at least the size required by eq. (10) must be taken in such a manner that it contains a representative cross section of the whole object; for example, a metal button or regulus is sawed in half along a plane of symmetry as a preliminary to the removal of shavings or filings from the exposed cross section. A segment should be removed since it is better representative of the composition of the whole body than a plane-parallel disk cut to include the axis.

*4.4.1. Extraction of Gross Sample from a Large Object.* The removal of a truly representative sample of the average composition of a large heterogenous object may pose a formidable problem. Even if the particle or unit is not very large, an amount may have to be taken which exceeds that indicated by eq. (10) in order to ensure the inclusion of a representative cross section. Only the including of such a cross section can, as a rule, ensure that the sample is representative of the object since mixing is impossible and one may never be certain of the complete absence of stratification or segregation. Often far more than the theoretically required number of particles or units will be grabbed for the gross sample, and the amount will be the greater the more obvious the nonuniformity of the object. The expense of sampling must mount with the quantity included in the gross sample. Since the working up of a sample pile of more than 1 ton in weight is inconvenient, several sample piles may be collected and reduced independently; the resulting samples may be tested separately or combined in the weight ratio of the original gross sample piles.

The sampling of large objects is most economical when combined with an otherwise required transfer. Pipes through which gas or liquid is flowing may be tapped for the continuous removal of a small sample fraction. This, however, assumes that the flowing medium has the same composition over the whole cross section of the conduit. If stratification is suspected, the removal of the sample portion is better performed by a manifold placed in the path of the medium with intake openings systematically distributed over the cross section of the flow. Even this device is not reliable because the intake openings cannot be made to operate with like efficiency or, better, with efficiencies graded in proportion to the rate of flow in the part of the cross section which they serve. Manifolds should consequently be preceded by mixing devices installed upstream. A gas conduit may be equipped with vanes extended from the wall to the center of the flow or to near the opposite wall; the gas may be made to pass through a fan, the blades of which may be kept revolving by the motion of the gas. Similarly, a liquid stream is best sampled near the exit end of a pump and at the point of maximum turbulence if subsiding of the latter would permit segregation (27).

Interesting complications are encountered in sampling the very hot exhaust gases from the combustion chamber of jet engines. The gases are produced at a very high rate and in sonic waves of varying pressure, density, temperature, and composition. Blackshear (6) dealt with the difficulties met in trying to obtain meaningful temperature readings. Withdrawing samples for chemical analysis should give satisfactory results if the probe inlet is well sharpened and the velocity of the gas at the inlet of the probe (referred to as sampling velocity) is equal to the velocity in the stream. Leeper (24) has pointed out, however, that it is difficult to determine the velocity of a stream of very heterogeneous gas and that errors in the measurement of the inside diameters of narrow probes lead to significant errors in computed gas velocities. Furthermore, if the pressure at the inlet of the probe varies with time in some periodic fashion, the gas within the probe will vibrate and the sampling velocity must fluctuate. Depending upon the variations in the stream and the characteristics of the probe, the fluctuations in the sampling velocity may be large or small and of simple or complex nature. Experience indicated that the inlet tube of the probe should be either shorter than one-quarter density wave length (moving with sampling velocity) or longer than two density wave lengths. For best results in a stream of constant velocity, the probe should have a high resonant frequency. The sampling velocity should be adjusted as near stream velocity as possible so that any error will cause the sampling velocity to be above stream velocity. Any probe should also be checked by sampling a representative stream with several sampling velocities near stream velocity.

Solids may be sampled in transfer by the primitive expedient of transferring every $n$th shovel load or every $n$th load of a wheelbarrow to the sample pile. As this leaves the selection of the material for the

$n$th portion to some extent to the whim of the workmen, any automatic arrangement operating on the general principle of the riffle is preferable (27). Chutes may be employed which send a definite fraction of the material to a sample bin or platform. Buckets may be made to travel through a stream of falling material to grab at random a cross section of it. Mills usually permit efficient incorporation of the sampling process into the scheme of their operation.

The sampling of large objects in storage is always somewhat uncertain and often expensive. Even with supposedly homogeneous liquids, samples are best taken immediately after shipment or transfer from one tank to another, at a time when one may reasonably expect that the contents have been thoroughly mixed. Even in such instances prudence may advise the use of a sampling tube, which must be employed if stratification or separation of layers of immiscible liquids may be expected. An open tube is slowly inserted so that it encloses part of a cross section from the surface to the bottom of the tank or drum. The lower opening is closed when the tube reaches the bottom of the container, whereupon the tube is withdrawn with its contents. If the bottom of the container is level and its walls are perpendicular, the tube will contain the various layers in the same proportions as the storage vessel. The various types of thief samplers permit taking samples from predetermined locations or depths; whether or not a mixture of thief samples taken from several locations truly represents the average composition is a matter of speculation.

FIG. 2. LaMotte, Hankinson-Hester type soil-sampling tube.

A sampling tube, auger, or drill is also used to obtain representative cross sections of solid materials spread out, packed in drums or bags, or formed into bars or ingots. The soil-sampling tube shown in Fig. 2 is graduated at 6-in. intervals and has a beveled cutting edge of hardened steel. A slight taper permits easy removal of the sample when the tube is inverted and tapped. The listed tools doubtlessly furnish cross-section samples, but it must be left to experience and discriminating intuition to select the representative cross sections. If the material is spread out in a more or less level layer, one may place on its surface a coarse net with knots marked in a predetermined manner and remove an auger or tube sample at every marked knot. As an alternative, a trench may be dug through the whole material in a chosen direction and every $n$th shovel load placed on the sample pile. Obviously it will not always be possible to make the walls of the trench as perpendicular as would be desirable. If the material has been dumped to form a conical pile, the fine material will have collected underneath the chute and large lumps have tended to roll down the side of the cone. Removal of a segment of the pile for the gross sample would be the most accurate procedure if flattening and quartering are not feasible. Several trenches may have to be dug if the material has been banked.

The sampling of geologic formations, soil, rock, outcroppings, and the bottoms of bodies of water is thoroughly discussed by Krumbein and Pettijohn (21).

*4.4.2. Preparation of the Laboratory Sample.* Preparation of a representative aliquot of a thoroughly mixed gross sample will usually not be difficult with liquids. One may be forced, however, to separate and measure immiscible parts of the gross sample and to forward samples of each layer. A similar procedure has to be followed with grossly heterogeneous solids which cannot be properly mixed or disintegrated as a mixture. In such instances the separation of the incompatible components is preliminary to the reduction of the sample size as outlined below.

Reduction of a large gross sample of heterogeneous solid material is usually performed in several steps, in each step a cross section being taken to eliminate the effects of possible stratification. The procedure is dictated by the amount of material to be handled, and disintegration is resorted to whenever required to obtain in the sample the necessary number of units indicated by eq. (10). Also the disintegration is usually performed in several steps, separated by sampling procedures reducing the amount of material, so as to avoid the fine milling of large quantities and the resulting various difficulties. One may have to start with 1 ton of a gross sample consisting of large pieces and face the task of preparing laboratory samples of about 10 to 500 g.

The alternate-shovel method may be used until the size of the sample is reduced to about 150 kg. A shovelful of the material is taken from the conical pile and spread in a rectangular area the width of the shovel and 2 to 4 meters long. The next shovelful is spread on top of the first but from the opposite direction. This is continued until all material has been collected in the form of a long pile.

The next step is to make two conical piles, of which A contains all odd and B all even numbers of shovel loads taken from the rectangular pile. The workman starts at one end of the rectangular pile and takes one shovelful from the bottom of it. Moving always in the same direction around the pile, the workman advances one shovel width for each portion taken from the rectangular pile. All material is taken from the base of the pile, which is thus gradually reduced in a uniform manner. Finally one of the two conical piles is arbitrarily rejected.

Coning and quartering is used for quantities from 150 to 60 kg. Thorough mixing is first obtained by repeatedly "coning." Each time the material is removed from the base of the old cone by shovelfuls around its circumference, and deposited on top of the new cone. When sufficient mixing seems assured, the last cone is flattened by pressing its apex down vertically by means of a board or shovel so that the material flows in a radial direction until a circular layer of uniform thickness is obtained. Two diameters intersecting at right angles at a point directly under the apex of the flattened cone are marked on the surface, and a coin is flipped to decide which pair of opposite quarters is to be rejected. These sectors are removed, and the parts of the platform which they occupied are brushed clean. The two remaining sectors are shoveled into a cone, starting in a systematic manner at the circumference of the sectors and following each shovelful from one sector with one from the other.

Rolling and quartering serve for quantities less than 70 kg. and are useful also for the dividing of small quantities of fine powder in the laboratory. The conical pile is formed at the center of a large sheet of tarpaulin, rubberized cloth, rubber, or glazed paper. The cone is flattened and the material mixed by rolling. Finally the material is collected in the center by simultaneously raising all four corners of the sheet. The resulting pile is flattened out and one half of it is rejected by the quartering procedure.

The riffle is available in a variety of sizes and may be used in the last stages of the preparation of the laboratory sample. It halves and cross-sections the charge fed to the grating by the simple device of adjacent chutes discharging in opposite directions. The material should be delivered to the grating so that all slots receive an approximately equal amount of it. To this end, the stream from the pan may be made to oscillate slowly back and forth over the grating. After all material has been added, the dust remaining on pan, shovel, or sheet is brushed into the grating. The grating is brushed into the chutes, and material clinging to the chutes is brushed into the receiving pans. The material in the collecting pan is quantitatively transferred to a sheet for rolling before the riffling is repeated.

Composite riffles may be made to reduce the amount of sample to one-fourth, one-eighth, etc., in one operation. It is essential, however, that any such sample splitter can be easily cleaned, permits collection of all the material, and guards against the loss of dust. These conditions must be especially well satisfied by micro sample splitters, several types of which have been described in the literature (21).

*4.4.3. Preparation of the Test Sample.* It is an obvious precaution to inspect the received laboratory sample and the seal of the container. In addition, one should investigate whether the properly prepared and delivered laboratory sample is in a condition to permit the immediate removal of a test sample by means of a spoon or spatula. Further disintegration may be necessary, and a distinctly heterogeneous solid may require further mixing and the reducing of the laboratory sample to the size of the test sample by cross-sectioning in several steps. A riffle may be used for the initial steps if the laboratory sample is large. The final splitting operations, which may be preceded by grinding or milling, are best performed by rolling and quartering. The size of the test sample is indicated by eq. (10), a fact which must be kept in mind especially when tests are performed on a small scale.

REFERENCES

1. Baily, E. D., *Ind. Eng. Chem. Anal. Ed.* **18**, 365 (1946).
2. Baule, B., and Benedetti-Pichler, A., *Z. anal. Chem.* **74**, 422 (1928).
3. Barnett, P. R., Huleatt, W. P., Rader, L. F., and Myers, A. T., *Am. J. Sci.* **253**, 121 (1955).
4. Benedetti-Pichler, A. A., "Essentials of Quantitative Analysis," Ronald, New York, 1956.
5. Bernoulli, J., "Ars Conjectandi," Basel, 1713; translation into German by R. Haussner, "Ostwald's Klassiker der exakten Wissenschaften," Akad. Verlags-Ges., Leipzig, 1899.
6. Blackshear, P. L., Jr., *Am. Soc. Mech. Eng., Paper* No. 52-SA-38 (1952).
7. Bloom, H., and Barnett, P. R., *Anal. Chem.* **27**, 1037 (1955).
8. Brendler, H., *Science* **114**, 61 (1951).
9. Chamot, E. M., and Mason, C. W., "Handbook of Chemical Microscopy," Vol. 1, 2nd ed., Wiley, New York, 1938.
10. Cook, W. H., Griffing, C. P., and Alsberg, C. L., *Ind. Eng. Chem. Anal. Ed.* **3**, 102 (1931).
11. Crowell, W. R., and Burke, S., Preparation of Unknowns for Quantitative Analysis, manuscript, University of California, Los Angeles, 1937.
12. Czuber, E., *in* "Sammlung der mathematischen Wissenschaften," Vol. IX, Part 1. B. G. Teubner, Leipzig, 1932.
13. Dunn, E. J., Jr., *Ind. Eng. Chem. Anal. Ed.* **2**, 59 (1930).
14. Fisher Scientific Company, Pittsburgh.
15. Fisher Scientific Company, Pittsburgh: *The Laboratory* **15**, No. 4.
16. Green, H., *Ind. Eng. Chem.* **16**, 677 (1924).
17. Griffin, M. L., *J. Soc. Chem. Ind.* **28**, 192 (1909).
18. Hempel, W., *Z. angew. Chem.* p. 843 (1901).
19. Hillebrand, W. F., *U.S. Geol. Survey Bull.* **No. 700** (1919).
20. Hillebrand, W. F., Lundell, G. E. F., Bright, H. A., and Hoffman, J. I., "Applied Inorganic Analysis," 2nd ed., Wiley, New York, 1953.

21. Krumbein, W. C., and Pettijohn, F. J., "Manual of Sedimentary Petrography." Appleton-Century, New York, 1938.
22. Lamden, M. P., *Anal. Chem.* **22**, 1139 (1950).
23. Laplace, Pierre Simon, "Théorie Analytique des Probabilités," Courcier, Paris, 1812.
24. Leeper, C. K., Sampling Gas Streams with Time-Varying Composition, manuscript, Mass. Inst. Technology, Cambridge, November 1949.
25. Lundell, G. E. F., and Hoffman, J. I., "Outlines of Methods of Chemical Analysis." Wiley, New York, 1938.
26. Machlett, E., & Son, New York, N.Y.
27. Patterson, G. D., Jr., and Mellon, M. G., *Anal. Chem.* **22**, 136 (1950).
28. Rose, H. E., "The Measurement of Particle Size in Very Fine Powders," Chemical Publishing, New York, 1954.
29. Ross, W. H., and Hardesty, J. O., *J. Assoc. Offic. Agr. Chemists* **25**, 238 (1942).
30. Schaar & Co., 754 W. Lexington Street, Chicago 7, Ill.
31. Schaeffer, H. F., "Microscopy for Chemists," Van Nostrand, New York, 1953.
32. Thomas, A. H., Company, Philadelphia.
33. Vetter, H. W., *Fette u. Seifen* **47**, 424 (1940); laboratory models of the mill are furnished by L. Hormuth, Heidelberg, Germany.
34. Weber, M., Jr., and Moran, R. F., *Ind. Eng. Chem. Anal. Ed.* **10**, 180 (1938).
35. Wiley, S. W., *Ind. Eng. Chem.* **17**, 304 (1925).

### Bibliography

A.S.T.M. "Books of Standards." American Society for Testing Materials, Philadelphia.
A.S.T.M. "Methods for Chemical Analysis of Metals," 2nd ed., American Society for Testing Materials, Philadelphia, 1950.
Association of Official Agricultural Chemists, Official and Tentative Methods of Analysis, Washington, D.C.
Fieldner, A. C., and Selvig, W. A., *U.S. Bur. Mines Tech. Papers* **No. 586.**
Holmes, M. C., and Downs, R., *J. Franklin Inst.* **222**, 337 (1935).
Scott's "Standard Methods of Chemical Analysis" (N. H. Furman, ed.), Vol. 2, 5th ed. Van Nostrand, New York, 1939.
Sharwood, W. J., and von Bernewitz, M. M., *U.S. Bur. Mines Repts. Invest.* **No. 2336** (copies no longer available).
Simon, L. E., *ASTM Bull.* **139**, 17 (1946); *ASTM Proc.* **48**, 877 (1948).
Wilks, S. S., *ASTM Proc.* **48**, 857 (1948).

# Flame Photometry

## By

### KENNETH W. GARDINER

*Central Research and Engineering Division, Continental Can Company, Chicago, Illinois*

## 1. INTRODUCTION AND HISTORICAL BACKGROUND

Flame photometry is a spectroscopic technique for determining microgram quantities of elements by measuring directly the intensity of their flame-produced radiations. The method actually originated over one hundred years ago in the pioneering flame spectroscopic work of Bunsen and Kirchoff. In 1879 Gouy developed in France a simple flame spectroscope that contained an atomizing system for injecting into the flame a vaporized portion of the test solution (60). In this respect, Gouy's instrument was the prototype of the modern flame photometer. It has been reported that a similar arrangement also used for the visual observation of colored flames was developed by Klemperer of Germany in 1910 (91).

With earlier flame instruments, emission spectra were either recorded on photographic plates or observed visually, as in the case of Gouy's and Klemperer's spectroscopes. As early as 1897 Ramage noted that the photographed flame spectra of many elements were quite simple and that the characteristic lines of several metals in a mixture could be easily isolated on the developed plate (107). However, it was not until some thirty years later that the routine usefulness of flame spectroscopy began to attract the attention of analysts. The necessary impetus was supplied by Lundegardh, who extensively explored the quantitative analytical possibilities of the method (84). Aside from Gouy's original technique and prior to the appearance of Lundegardh's flame spectrograph, samples for analysis were generally introduced into the flame in either an impractical or inefficient manner; for example, Ramage employed a mechanical means of introducing a filter paper spill which was impregnated with the test solution (106, 107). As late as 1941, Mitchell applied an improved version of Ramage's technique but only with limited success (92). In principle, Lundegardh's method of sample injection was not unlike Gouy's in that an atomized mist of an aqueous solution was uniformly fed to the source. A tremendous gain in the routine applicability of the method resulted from Lundegardh's development of a technique based on the use of a simple atomizer arrangement for sample injection and the quantitative interpretation of the resulting emitted spectra.

The slow transition from flame spectroscopy, as applied by these earlier workers, to the comparatively simple photometric methods used today has been due chiefly to the fact that the less costly monochromator systems and photoelectric light-measuring devices required for the construction of suitable flame photometers have only recently become readily available. With the availability of such instruments, the use of the previously required expensive spectroscopic equipment was eliminated and the cumbersome and time-consuming photographic procedures were avoided. It is generally conceded that German workers (1935–37) were the first to employ filters and photocells in the assembly of flame photometers containing an atomizer and burner arrangement (68, 74, 119). Descriptions are given in the literature of some of the German flame instruments that were commercially developed from these models prior to 1943 (67, 111, 112, 117).

Elsewhere the development of the method definitely lagged behind the work carried out in Germany. For example, Lundegardh's technique was first used in America by Griggs in 1939 (61) and was still being applied essentially in its original form by others as late as 1945 (29, 45). In 1945 Barnes and co-workers first published details of the construction and use in this country of a flame photometer similar in design to the earlier German filter-photocell instruments (6). Barnes' unit was later developed as the first commercially available model of the Perkin-Elmer flame photometer, which was extensively used for early evaluations of the flame technique (7, 18, 63, 64, 103). Having recognized the inadequacies of this model, several groups described changes that could be made to modify or improve its performance (20, 104, 132).

Shortly following the appearance of the Perkin-Elmer instrument, the Beckman Flame attachment for the model D.U. spectrophotometer became available. The inclusion of this well-known quartz prism spectophotometer as the light dispersing component provided a flame instrument whose spectral isolation properties were substantially superior to those afforded by filter units. It was not until several years after the Beckman instrument appeared that descriptions of either its development or the evaluation of its operating characteristics were published (57, 97). To provide the obvious advantages of prism optics, the Perkin-Elmer photometer was then altered by substituting a dual prism system for the glass color filters originally employed.

In the past few years a great deal of work on the development of comparatively low-cost flame photometers has been carried out with considerable success. There are at least eight different commercial models of well-built instruments now available in this country. A rapidly growing volume of literature on the application of flame analyses is indicative of the increased acceptance of the method. This gain in popularity continues in spite of the many weaknesses and the fact that the origin and nature of the errors and interferences that may be encountered are still not understood. It will be a general aim in the following sections not only to describe the operating characteristics of typical flame-photometer components, as well as the combined units themselves, but also to discuss in some detail the sources and nature of many of these errors. At times this may seem to put undue emphasis on the weak points of flame photometry, but it is felt that the potential user will find application of the method more profitable if he is aware of its faults.

In applying flame photometry, the analyst must often be prepared to treat his problem as a special case and to devote some time to exploring those errors and interferences possible with the particular instrument being used. If proper precautions are taken, the method can be extremely valuable and can do much to simplify many laborious and routine analyses. Although one cannot expect analytical results duplicating those achieved with good gravimetric and volumetric procedures, a precision and accuracy of $\pm \frac{1}{2}\%$ is claimed for many flame determinations (57, 139, 142).

## 2. Basic Working Principles of Flame Photometry

Modern flame photometers are almost exclusively of two basic designs, which can be designated as either single- or double-beam arrangements. A single-beam instrument, as implied, contains only one set of optics, providing a single light path, and includes a single photodetector. With the single-beam system, the observed emitted intensity of a given element's solution of unknown concentration is compared directly with a predetermined calibration curve of intensity versus element concentration. This form of measurement is designated as the direct reading method of flame photometry. A schematic representation of a simple single-beam arrangement is given in Fig. 1. Substitution of the components shown with other light dispersing or filtering devices and different types of photodetectors will provide a schematic picture of the construction of any present-day flame instrument of practical interest.

Double-beam flame photometers contain two sets of optical components and, thus, two distinct light paths. Two photodetector cells are in simultaneous operation with the signal of one tube opposing that of the other through a suitable indicating device. Also shown in Fig. 1 is a typical arrangement of the double-beam units' optics and measuring circuit. The purpose of the double-beam system is to provide a ratio method of comparing and measuring emitted intensities. This is a direct extension of the line ratio, or "internal standard," technique of flame spectroscopy used by Lundegardh (84).

In analyses with a double-beam instrument, a preselected constant quantity of a known emitting element, usually lithium, is added to the calibration samples and to the solutions to be analyzed. One set of optics transmits only the characteristic flame radiation of the internal standard element while the other passes the characteristic emitted light of the particular element being determined. The two photodetector signals are brought into balance with an adjustable potentiometer, and this reading is referred to a predetermined calibration curve for direct conversion to the amount of unknown element present. More pertinent information about the internal-standard technique and its application will be found in section 5.3. A number of internal-standard instruments have been developed and their descriptions are in the literature (7, 18, 50, 65, 114, 138).

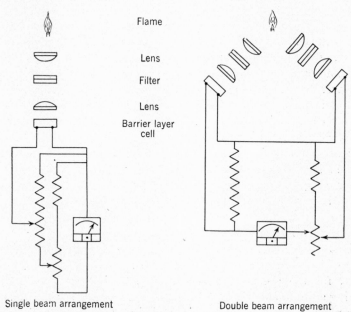

Single beam arrangement          Double beam arrangement

Fig. 1. Simple single beam and double beam arrangements for absolute and internal standard measurements, respectively.

The modern flame photometer is, therefore, a small, compact, and comparatively inexpensive instrument consisting of three major components: (a) a burner to produce an open flame and a system for injecting into the flame the sample to be analyzed, (b) either a single- or double-beam optical arrangement for isolating the burning sample's characteristic radiations, and (c) a photoelectric light-intensity measuring device.

The following discussions of the working principles of flame photometry will be of only a general nature. A more detailed consideration of important instrument components and their operating characteristics is given in section 3.

### 2.1. The Nature of Flame Emissions

As flame photometry is a form of emission spectroscopy, a theoretical treatment of the origin of flame spectra can be basically provided by applying the fundamental concepts used in explaining arc and spark phenomena. Such a fundamental presentation will not be attempted here. Instead, the apparent nature of flame emissions will be described in more general terms.

The major difference between flame emissions and spark- or arc-produced spectra results from the great differences in the thermal energies available for excitation processes. Flame temperatures may vary from about 1800° C. for the ordinary Bunsen-type air-gas flame to approximately 3500° C. obtained with the combustion of oxygen and acetylene. The maximum temperature usable in flame photometry, therefore, produces about one half the thermal energy available from the spectrographic arc. As a consequence, flame spectra are comparatively uncomplicated and usually consist of only one or two visible emission lines or bands for each excited element. This feature fortunately lends itself well to the construction of the simple monochromator and photodetector systems needed if the instrument is to be inexpensive and easily operated.

Table I lists the elements that have been reported determinable with the specific test conditions indicated. Because of the low thermal energies involved, it must be remembered that, except for the alkali metals, the majority of these elements exhibit comparatively weak emissions. The actual number measurable with any given flame source will also be dependent upon other factors as well as flame temperature and the relative emission strengths of the elements. Thus the list of column 3, Table I, for the acetylene flame might conceivably be extended by employing a photodetector system that is more sensitive than the photographic plate originally used. As far as is known, a systematic study of the analytical range of all possible combinations of different flames and available photodetectors has not been reported.

In most practical applications the spectral emissions obtained for each element will consist chiefly of the one or two characteristic radiations at the wave lengths indicated in Table I. Some elements, particularly the alkaline earths, exhibit fairly broad bands of molecular origin (indicated by [a] in Table I) which may often pose spectral-resolution problems in certain determinations. The observed emitted intensity of any given element is dependent upon the number of emitting atoms present in the flame per unit time, and in general luminosity will be found to increase linearly with an increase in the emitter concentration of the test solution. The lowest concentrations measurable will be limited not only by the factors mentioned above but also by the operating efficiency of the particular instrument in use. Specifically, the efficiency of the atomizing system and the over-all transmittance of the optics of the instrument can be very important in determining available sensitivity. For example, sodium is a very strong emitter and with an efficient, modern flame photometer operating under the test conditions indicated in column 1, Table I, measurements in the range of 1 p.p.m. are feasible. Calcium, on the other hand, being a much weaker emitter, is found to be reasonably

TABLE I

*Elements Reported Determinable by Flame Photometry with the Flame and Photodetector Combinations Indicated\**

| Air-gas (1800° C.)[b] Bar ier layer cell (6) | Oxygen-hydrogen (2800° C.)[b] photomultiplier and red sensitive phototube (55) | | Air-acetylene (2400° C.)[b] photographic plate (29, 84) | |
|---|---|---|---|---|
| Ba | Al (484[a]) | Hg (236) | Ba | Mn |
| Ca | Ba (553, 873[a]), [1, 1] | Mo (540, 600), [20, ?] | Cd | Hg |
| Cs | Be (471[a]) | Nd (659[a]) | Ca | Nd |
| Li | Bi (472) | Ni (341, 353), [?, .5] | Cs | Ni |
| Mg | B (548[a]), [5] | Nb (450) | Cr | Pd |
| Na | Cd (326), [10] | Pd (341, 364) | Co | K |
| K | Ca (622,[a] 554[a]), [.1, .02] | K (767, 404), [.01, .2] | Cu | Pr |
| Rb | Ce (481,[a] 493[a]) | Pr (562,[a] 571) | Dy | Rh |
| Sr | Cs (852), [1] | Rh (369) | Gd | Rb |
| | Cr (427, 359), [.1, .3] | Rb (780) | Ga | Ru |
| | Co (341, 353), [1, ?] | Ru (373, 780), [?, .1] | Au | Sc (467, 473) |
| | Cu (325, 327), [.05, ?] | Sm (651[a]) | In | Ag |
| | Dy (522,[a] 570,[a]) | Ag (328, 338), [?, 1] | Fe | Na |
| | Gd (462[a]) | Na (330, 589), [.5, .0002] | La | Sr |
| | Ga (403, 417), [?, .1] | Sr (461, 681[a]), [.005, 1] | Pb | Tl |
| | Au (268) | Te (364,[a] 372[a]) | Li | Y |
| | In (410, 451), [?, .1] | Tl (378), [.1] | Mg | Zn |
| | Fe (372, 386), [1, ?] | Sn (349[a]) | | |
| | La (442,[a] 438[a]) | Ti (497,[a] 518[a]), [?, 10] | | |
| | Pb (368, 406), [?, 3] | U (550) | | |
| | Li (671), [.02] | V (528, 576[a]), [1, ?] | | |
| | Mg (371,[a] 383[a]), [.1, 2] | Y (444,[a] 483[a]) | | |
| | Mn (403), [.01] | Zn (500) | | |

*Principal emisson wave lengths in millimicrons are given in parentheses while detection limits in p.p.m. for each wave length are given in brackets.

[a] Band spectrum.

[b] Approximate values. Flame temperatures may be accurately determined by the line inversion method described by Gaydon (54) and Huldt (71).

measurable, with the same test conditions, only at concentrations of 10 p.p.m. or greater (6). The reported detection limits in p.p.m. are given for some of the more common elements listed in column 2, Table I, but it must be stressed that the values given apply only to the use of the particular flame photometer described.

For wave-length values more exact than those given in Table I, one can refer to the $U_1$ or $U_2$ lines (Raies Ultimes, or most persistent lines) given in any standard wave-length compilation. Very detailed discussions of flame-excitation phenomena and theory are to be found in the published work of Gaydon (54) and Huldt (71).

## 2.2. The Delivery of Material into the Flame

Perhaps the most critical process in flame photometry is the introduction of the sample into the flame. Trustworthy and reproducible calibration curves of emitted intensity versus emitter concentration and the consistently satisfactory determination of analytical samples can be achieved only if a uniform means of sample injection is employed. Gouy's original method, as modified by Lundegardh, for atomizing an aqueous solution and passing the fine mist or smoke formed into the flame has proved to be by far the best means for achieving this end. While Gouy's and Lundegardh's particular atomizer-burner arrangements are now only of historic interest, the aspiration principle of which they made use is the basis for sample injection in all flame photometers of any practical importance today.

There are two distinct ways in which an atomized aqueous sample can be passed into the flame. The already-mentioned Gouy-Lundegardh method depends upon the air-borne transport of the atomized mist by one component of the gas mixture. Thus, if the flame is acetylene and compressed air, the air is used to activate the atomizer and after producing a mist of small droplets carries them through an enclosed system into the region of active combustion. The larger droplets also produced in the process are either returned to the bulk of the remaining sample or diverted to waste. The aspirating gas flow for this system must be carefully regulated and the transported mist must be shielded from contamination or any external influences that might alter its composition.

The alternate method is the direct introduction into the flame of the total volume of atomized solution without separation of the mist from the larger droplets formed. In instruments employing this system, the atomizer and burner assembly is an integral, compact unit (58, 139). The oxygen or compressed air supporting flame combustion is used to create a Venturi effect in a small capillary which dips into the solution to be analyzed. The fine stream of liquid forced through the capillary is sprayed directly into the flame. Obviously an appreciable amount of sample can be introduced per unit time this way, and consequently greater sensitivity is achieved. Each method has unique features which may recommend its particular use for a given problem, but neither will be found ideal for all cases or without some definite limitations and faults. A discussion of the construction and operation of atomizers employing these principles is given in section 3.2.

## 2.3. Methods of Isolating Flame Emissions

The final stage in the over-all flame photometric process is the actual intensity measurement of the spectral lines or bands of the test element appearing in the flame. For analytical purposes, these radiations must be isolated in order to relate a particular emitted intensity to solution concentration. The original flame spectrographs employed the bulky prism or grating monochromator arrangements developed for regular spectroscopic work, and photographic plates were used to record the dispersed spectra. For modern flame photometry, the necessary spectral isolation is achieved by any one of three methods. The simplest, used chiefly in earlier development stages, is the employment of regular glass color filters compounded to permit the transmission of only a selected region of the spectrum (6, 74, 119). To measure the emission of potassium, for example, a red filter that excludes all wave lengths but those in the region of 767 mμ. is used. It will be found that such filters, although still widely used, rarely provide the required degree of monochromaticity needed for the determination of many complex systems. Liquid filters consisting of solutions of selective color-absorbing materials have been developed but do not lend themselves to the construction of more rugged instruments (114).

By far the most efficient transmission filter systems now available for flame photometry are composed of one form or another of an interference filter. These filters are so constructed to permit, when used with collimated light, the transmittance at a selected wave length of only a comparatively narrow region of the spectrum, usually 10 to 20 mμ. pass band measured at one-half maximum intensity. Standard interference filters are effective in the spectral region from about 350 to 800 mμ. Filters of this type at practically any given wave length in the foregoing range are now distributed by a number of optical supply houses in this country and abroad. Several popular commercial flame photometers contain the interference type of optics although their use does not completely eliminate all the resolution inadequacies of color glass filters.

A modification of the single-wave-length interference filter is the Fabry-Perot interference wedge. This form of monochromator has been used in at least one commercial flame photometer and provides, with one compact filter unit, a continuous means of applying the interference effect over the entire visible region.

A somewhat different type of interference filter known as a multilayer filter is now available and is claimed to have a half width of only 7 to

10 m$\mu$. In addition, a maximum transmission of approximately 70% is provided in contrast to the more opaque standard interference type that transmits about 35% of the incident radiation. Consequently, multilayer units are often best suited for isolation of particularly weak emitted radiations or for use in instruments having low detection sensitivities. Because of the nature of the optical interference effect produced in both multilayer and the standard interference filters, it is usually necessary to add one or more ordinary colored glass filters to reduce the amount of side-band transmission. The addition of these auxiliary filters will, depending upon the degree of spectral purity desired, naturally reduce the ultimate total transmittance attainable. Given for comparative purposes in Fig. 2 are typical transmittance curves of the three different types of filters just discussed.

In spite of the improved spectral isolation afforded by interference and multilayer units, it is still not possible to obtain with them the degree of resolution needed to perform certain flame determinations of importance in biology, medicine, and industry. Typically, the determination of calcium at 554 m$\mu$. or 622 m$\mu$. in the presence of the large amounts of sodium found in many biological samples is subject to a sizable error because of the transmittance of some sodium light through the calcium filter. The nearest approach to satisfactory resolution in this case can be made if prism or grating optics are employed. Although the use of these optics requires a somewhat more expensive instrument, this added cost must be assumed if the desired measurement cannot be satisfactorily performed with a filter photometer. Small glass or quartz prisms have been used advantageously in flame work, as is indicated by the many procedures developed with the Beckman and later model Perkin-Elmer units. The dispersion provided, when used in conjunction with good-quality optical slits, makes prism instruments the best choice for the analyses of all systems containing elements with immediately adjacent emission lines or bands. In addition, a quartz prism is capable of covering a wider region of the spectrum than can be normally reached with interference filters, thus giving a greater range in which to select radiations available for measurement. Glass optics, although more limited in their coverage of the spectrum, also are adequate for many flame applications. No commercially available flame photometer has as yet taken advantage of the inexpensive grating replica as a monochromator.

### 2.4. The Measurement of Emitted Intensity

Flame spectroscopy really evolved into flame photometry with the advent of the simple photoelectric cell. The first cells of this kind to be used in simple flame instruments were of the barrier layer type and were found to be capable of responding to light from a very wide portion of the visible spectrum (6, 68, 74). In principle, barrier layer cells convert the dispersed or filtered incident radiation from the flame into a direct current of microampere intensity by the action of the light on a photo-emissive surface. The generated signal can be measured directly with a

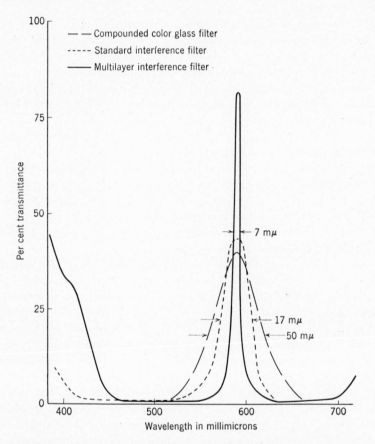

Fig. 2. Typical transmittance curves for the filters most commonly used for spectral isolation in flame photometry.

sensitive galvanometer or microameter, as indicated by the simple circuits of Fig. 1. In general, a linear relationship exists between the current produced by the barrier layer cell and the emitted light intensity from the flame, giving the much desired linear calibration of meter reading versus solution concentration.

A serious limitation of the use of barrier layer cells in flame photometry results from their inherent low resistance, which does not readily allow electronic amplification of the generated signal. Consequently, with instruments containing such cells it is found that satisfactory measurements can be made only of the strongly emitting alkalies and alkaline earths. Descriptions can be found of a number of barrier layer photometers used chiefly for the determination of sodium and potassium (18, 22, 49, 95, 114, 136, 142).

The problem of signal amplification for greater sensitivity was first solved with vacuum phototubes. These tubes have a photoemissive surface much like that of the barrier layer cells but allow the use of an applied voltage and an amplifying circuit to increase the signal intensity. The Beckman model D.U. spectrophotometer was the first instrument in this country to use this type of photoemissive cell for flame photometry. The number of elements thus made available for analysis was substantially increased from the few alkali metals and alkaline earths previously measurable with less sensitive barrier layer units (57). Because of the nature of its photoemissive surface, any given vacuum phototube will have a somewhat restricted spectral response. To achieve good sensitivity over the whole visible region, it is necessary to employ two different tubes—one sensitive in the blue, and the other more responsive in the red, part of the spectrum. The Beckman and the later model Perkin-Elmer flame photometer contain two vacuum phototubes to give full coverage of the spectrum from the near ultraviolet to the near infrared. Still other less commercially important flame instruments have been developed, chiefly abroad, with similar photodetector systems (e.g., 79, 80, 119, 126).

The third type of photoemissive cell to be considered is the electron multiplier phototube. This detector can increase the sensitivity of most flame analyses by a factor of from fifty to one hundred. Multiplication of the current generated by the incident emitted radiation is achieved by a cascade effect in a series of dynodes, each at a fairly large potential drop (70 to 100 v.). To produce the effect, a power supply of from 700 to 1000 v. D.C. is required. Batteries may be used for this purpose, as was done with the detector system of the Weichselbaum-Varney instrument (25b, 139) and the first Beckman photomultiplier attachment for the model D.U. spectrophotometer. A more practical solution is to have an A.C. operated, regulated, adjustable, D.C. voltage supply for the tube, but as yet no flame photometers are sold with this attachment.

A complete circuit for an easily assembled photomultiplier power supply and amplifier developed for use with a Beckman flame photometer has been described in the literature (77). Commercially made line-operated power supplies and photomultiplier assemblies have been available for some time, and at least one of these has been adapted to a flame instrument (31). Signals from photomultipliers can be measured in three ways: direct reading of a galvanometer (2, 91), electronic amplification and measurement with a suitable current flowmeter (24, 109), or electronic recording (77).

Although a large gain in sensitivity is obtained with a multiplier phototube, its use also imposes a sacrifice in the spectral range available for analysis. Present-day photomultipliers do not respond satisfactorily to light in the red region of the spectrum. Thus, some elements—for example, potassium, barium, and cesium—whose most intense radiations occur at wave lengths greater than 700 m$\mu$. cannot be measured with these photodetectors. In addition, great care must be taken to shield the tube from moist air and stray light. In spite of the added attention and equipment required, it is felt that photomultipliers offer the best means of photodetection for flame photometry, and their application will undoubtedly continue to increase.

### 3. Types of Flame Photometers Available

In order to apply flame photometry most successfully, it is usually necessary to make a compromise between the experimental limitations of a particular application and the operating characteristics of those flame photometers available. If, for example, one has only a very limited amount of material to work with, this may well be the determining factor in selecting the type of instrument for use. On the other hand, if sample consumption is no problem, but extremely high spectral resolution is essential because of the complex composition of the test material, an entirely different type of flame instrument may best be employed. No known single model will completely satisfy all the requirements of the large number of different analyses that can be made by the flame method. To provide a system whereby flame photometers may be evaluated as an aid in their selection for any given problem, it is necessary to establish certain criteria that will apply equally to all. While a number of single operating features might be selected for comparative purposes, the two that can be most universally applied are associated with the two experimental conditions noted above. Specifically, the analyst is most apt to be confronted with either the resolution of a complex mixture or the solving of some solution-handling problem. The latter can include not only having a limited amount of sample for analysis but also the effects of contamination, abnormal viscosities, and the ease and rapidity desired in carrying out the determinations. Accordingly, the following two sections consist of the classification of flame photometers based on the type of optics and on the type of atomizer-burner systems used.

### 3.1. Flame Photometers Classed According to the Optics Employed

3.1.1. *Filter Instruments.* Probably the majority of flame photometers now in use have filter optics of one sort or another. Basically, most of these are the double-beam (internal standard) type although many can be converted to single-beam (direct reading) instruments if desired. Certain prototype instruments developed in this country had colored glass filters as well as a special liquid filter for the internal standard radiation of lithium (6, 18, 49). Pratt and Larson found that the all-glass filters provided with the commercial models of these prototypes did not give adequate spectral selectivity and they substituted interference filters in order to resolve better the emitted light of calcium and sodium (104). At least two commercially available flame photometers now widely used contain compounded glass color filters. These instruments are the Barclay (136) and the model designed by Fox (49). A third, less extensively distributed, unit, made by the Process and Instruments Company of Brooklyn, New York, also has color filter optics. These three models are used exclusively for routine sodium and potassium determinations with lithium as the internal standard and none provides filters suitable for the determination of other elements.

To improve the spectral isolation afforded by simple filter systems, the Baird flame photometer, as originally developed by White (142), employs interference filters for the determination of sodium, potassium, and calcium by the internal standard method. This instrument is shown in Fig. 3, but not included is the separate box-type galvanometer used as the indicating meter.

Other models containing both interference and regular glass color filters are also available from Coleman Instruments Inc. (Model 21), Beckman Instruments, Inc. (Beckman Direct-reading Flame Photometer), and North American Philips Co., Inc. (Norelco Flame Photometer). Like the Baird unit, these are designed specifically for sodium, potassium and calcium determinations.

The analysis of calcium in the presence of the large amounts of sodium characteristic of many body fluids and biological specimens cannot be accurately made even with the improvement afforded by interference filter optics. Some workers have observed that the ability of both the interference type and the colored glass filters to screen out the intense sodium 589 m$\mu$. radiation from such samples can be markedly improved by adding a didymium glass filter to the optical system (24, 57, 83, 96). The resultant gain in spectral purity of calcium, while measurable, is still insufficient to provide the error-free performance usually desired.

The flame photometer developed by Weichselbaum and Varney

(25b, 139) contains a wedge interference filter as the monochromator. Although the wedge is a novel and compact filter arrangement, its use does not afford light-resolution properties that are much different from those provided by interference or multilayer systems. Information about

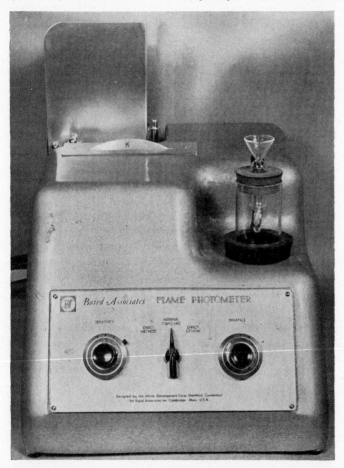

FIG. 3. The Baird flame photometer designed for the internal standard determination of sodium and potassium using standard dielectric and multilayer interference filters. Not shown is the sensitive box-type galvanometer used as the indicating meter.

several other individually constructed flame photometers designed around filter-type optics is available elsewhere (21, 22, 39, 40, 42, 80, 83, 113, 114, 126, 138). These models were constructed with specific needs in mind and thus do not offer much more versatility than is provided by the standard instruments previously discussed.

In general, filter instruments are best suited for sodium and potassium determinations by either the absolute or internal standard techniques, although other periodic group I and II elements are measurable if present in comparatively simple solutions.

*3.1.2. Prism Instruments.* Commercially built flame photometers containing prism monochromators are capable of providing the highest degree of resolution and greatest range of wave-length selectivity so far available. As a more elaborate optical system is involved, prism instruments are somewhat more expensive than filter photometers. There are at the present time three different models of prism-type flame photometers that are widely used. The Perkin-Elmer unit contains two small prisms mounted in series to give, in effect, a double monochromator action. Lithium is usually used as an internal standard, although the instrument can be readily converted for direct measurements. The optics of this instrument are unique in that the beam after passing through the dual monochromator is divided by a beam-splitting mirror. One branch of the divided beam is passed through a fixed slit to isolate the lithium radiation. The other branch can be scanned with a movable slit to give any desired analytical wave length. The monochromator is capable of covering the visible region from approximately 400 to 800 m$\mu$. with the wave-length selection dial being specifically marked to aid in the rapid selection of the principal emission wave length of magnesium, manganese, calcium, chromium, strontium, barium, sodium, lithium, or potassium.

An improved and somewhat simplified version of the above-described unit is also available from the Perkin-Elmer Corporation as their Model 146 Photometer.

The other two readily available prism-type flame instruments have been developed by the Beckman Instrument Company of California. The first is constructed around the prism system of the well-known model D.U. spectrophotometer as shown in Fig. 4. This is a single-beam (direct reading) instrument in which a quartz prism disperses the observed flame radiation. The dispersed spectrum can be passed across an adjustable exit slit by a simple hand-operated drive attached to the prism assembly. In this manner any region of the spectrum from 200 to 2000 m$\mu$. can be centered on the exit slit and hence the photodetector tube.

As the dispersion of the prism is nonlinear, being greater in the blue region than in the red, careful use must be made of the slit settings to assure satisfactory resolution for some flame determinations. To serve as an example, the measurement of potassium at 767 m$\mu$. in the presence of rubidium requires a mechanical slit width of no greater than 0.1 mm. (53). The reason for this is apparent on reference to the plot of dispersion versus wave length available with each model D.U. The plot reveals that in the 770-m$\mu$. region a band width of approximately 6 m$\mu$. is provided by a mechanical slit width of 0.1 mm. As the rubidium emission occurs at 780 m$\mu$., it is evident that a resolution of lines 13 m$\mu$. apart is needed to avoid a sizable inclusion of rubidium emission with the potassium light. Thus the chosen slit width of 0.1 mm. provides suitable spectral isolation without seriously reducing the over-all intensity.

Fig. 4. The Beckman flame spectrophotometer showing model D.U. Quartz spectrophotometer and atomizer-burner attachment.

The importance of good resolution for the measurement of calcium at either of its most persistent band wave lengths (i.e., 554 and 622 m$\mu$.) in the presence of appreciable amounts of sodium has already been mentioned. The sodium emission doublet at 589 m$\mu$. is so intense that even the more efficient prism monochromator will allow a substantial amount of light leak if ordinary slit widths are used. Thus calcium measurements of biological specimens made with this type of prism instrument should always be carried out at the minimum slit width possible and preferably with a didymium filter placed before the entrance port of the light. The extensive analytical range available with the Beckman flame photometer is suggested by the large number of elements reportedly determinable with it (see second column of Table I).

A second and less expensive type of prism spectrophotometer suitable for flame work is also available from the Beckman Company. This model (model B) contains a glass Ferry prism as the monochromator, and therefore its most effective spectral coverage is limited from about 400 to 800 m$\mu$. (10). The emission wave lengths given in Table I suggest that the restricted analytical range of glass optics will allow the model B flame photometer to determine about one half the number of elements that are detectable with a quartz optics instrument.

Other prism flame photometers have been described (29, 65, 110, 115, 118) but aside from the Lundegardh-type of apparatus (84) have probably had only restricted use. The instrument developed by Heidel and Fassel is worth special mention as it employed a constant-deviation prism monochromator (65). With this arrangement it was found possible to have the properties of a double-path optical system with just a single set of optics. Thus, the instrument could be used as an internal standard unit that contained a convenient means of easily selecting various emission lines for internal standard reference. As far as is known, Heidel and Fassel's arrangement has not had very wide use in the field of flame photometry.

*3.1.3. Special-Design Flame Photometers.* In addition to the standard designs just discussed, a fairly large number of what will be considered special flame instruments have been developed. Some offer novel and useful ideas but have not been exploited commercially, as the actual gains derived seem hardly worth the added expense entailed. In this category can be placed the various proposed forms of multichannel flame photometers. With a multichannel unit, a number of elements can be determined simultaneously by assigning a photodetector and indicating meter to each of the several selected emission wave lengths (channels) of interest.

A very simple multichannel arrangement has been assembled by Hermann in which three separate lens and interference filter combinations are spaced around the flame source (66). Three photocells and indicating galvanometers complete the unit. The three filters were selected to allow sodium, potassium, and calcium to be determined simultaneously in a given sample. A similar idea has been suggested by Mitchell, who employed a quartz prism monochromator to disperse the flame radiation (91). Photomultiplier tubes are positioned at the principal calcium and sodium wave lengths, and individual galvanometers indicate the magnitude of the emitted intensity of each element. It was pointed out by Mitchell that this arrangement could be used for the simultaneous determination of more than the two elements mentioned. Ramsay and coworkers in England have also successfully applied the multichannel principle to the simultaneous determination of sodium and potassium in very small volumes of solution (110). In view of the additional cost of each separate channel, multichannel photometers cannot be considered so desirable as the conventional units, which require only a change in the monochromator to select any given analytical wave length.

In conclusion, the development by Walsh and Wolff (137) will be briefly described as it represents quite a departure from the usual type of flame photometric optics. These workers employ a unique system of heterochromatic photometry for the determination of sodium. In effect, use is made of the internal standard principle but only one beam of light from the flame is observed. The required optics consist of a complicated system containing first a lens and stationary glass filter that allows only the sodium and lithium wave lengths to pass. This filter is followed by a movable color wedge, which is actually a liquid filter of variable depth, for absorbing the sodium radiation. Finally, a slowly rotating disk containing both sodium and lithium filters is placed before the single phototube detector. Emitted intensity is related to solution concentration by the amount of displacement of the wedge needed to produce a balance in the pulsed sodium and lithium signals in the photodetector circuit. With the proper selection of filters and the adjustable wedge, the method might find use for other internal standard determinations although none has been reported.

*3.2. Flame Photometers Classed According to the Type of Atomizer-Burner System Used*

The second feature to be given consideration in selecting a flame photometer, whether it be an available commercial model or an individually constructed unit, should be the type of atomizer-burner assembly that will be best suited for the intended applications. As previously stated, both the amount of material available and the physical properties of the solution to be atomized will be factors of great importance. As flame photometry is best suited for the determination of concentrations ranging from 1 to 100 p.p.m. for the more strongly emitting elements, it is apparent that there is a definite limitation to the dilutions that may be employed in practice. If a particular sample is of such initially low concentration that a final diluted volume of only 10 ml. is possible, an atomizer having a low rate of sample consumption must be used. Also, it is best to employ an atomizer that will not clog readily if solutions containing suspended matter are to be run without previous filtering. In selection of the type of flame to be used, consideration of the suggestions made in section 2.1 will be of help in the choice of a fuel combination that will be adequate for the particular elements to be determined.

*3.2.1. Discharge-Type Atomizers.* The design of a typical modern discharge atomizer is represented by A in Fig. 5. It will be recognized that in operating principle this unit is not unlike Gouy's original atomizer (60). In the discharge unit comparatively large jet orifice diameters are usually employed, and the atomized stream is apt to be coarse, consisting of both mist and a distribution of larger solution droplets. The introduction of

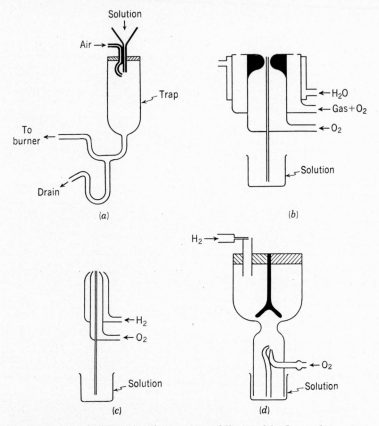

Fig. 5. Four typical atomizer-burner assemblies used in flame photometry.
A. Discharge atomizer requiring separate burner.
B. Weichselbaum-Varney total consumption atomizer and flame source.
C. Integral burner total consumption atomizer developed for the Beckman flame photometer.
D. Reflux atomizer with attached simple burner for hydrogen-oxygen flame.

the entire atomized stream into the separate burner attachment is impractical and the bulk of the fairly large volume of liquid droplets produced must be removed. This is achieved by having a trap with a drain between the atomizer jet and the burner, as shown by Fig. 5A. Sample consumption of discharge units is comparatively high, ranging from 4 to 10 ml./min. Of this amount, probably no more than 5% actually enters the flame, with the rest being diverted to waste. Thus, the ultimate sensitivity for the somewhat weaker emitting elements, such as calcium and magnesium, will be limited with the use of discharge systems. It is possible that a large portion of the wasted atomized solution could be recovered and recirculated through the atomizer to reduce the high rate of sample consumption. This practice, however, is not generally advisable because of the many precautions that must be taken to avoid contamination, particularly between successive changes of samples. Possible plugging of the solution feed capillary may be considered as a somewhat less serious drawback here because the capillary diameters chosen will permit the passage of reasonable amounts of suspended matter. The solution feed tube and the aspirating air tube are most frequently made of glass, but steel hypodermic needles have served as suitable replacements (6, 63).

Commercially available flame photometers employing the discharge atomizer include the Baird, Perkin-Elmer Models 52C and 146, Barclay, Fox, Norelco and the unit distributed by the Process and Instruments Company. In these instruments the atomizer is used in conjunction with a standard Meeker-style burner with either illuminating gas or bottled gas as the fuel, and compressed air provides the aspirating and atomizing action. To avoid excessive contamination of the atomized mist reaching the flame, care should always be taken to make sure that the compressed-air supply is oil and dust free. Some commercial units provide suitable traps to be placed in the line between the compressor and the atomizer, and this practice is recommended for all instruments that are not already so equipped. The flame of the Meeker burner obtains its air supply not only from the atomizer stream but also from the surrounding room atmosphere. If the atmosphere includes a considerable amount of dust, it is advisable to employ a closed air system for the entire burner attachment. If the air supply contains unfilterable dust suspensions, the use of a simple electrostatic precipitator has proved beneficial (100). Both the Baird and Barclay units have shielded-burner systems, and satisfactory results have been reported for other arrangements developed by various workers for eliminating air contamination (13, 124).

A less practical design of the discharge system just described has also been used extensively but is not to be found in any widely distributed flame photometer. This modification differs in that gravity flow of the sample is not taken advantage of and the material to be atomized is carried to the atomizing jet solely by aspiration through a capillary tube that dips into the sample solution. Aside from this difference, dip-type versions are similar in general construction and performance to the more conventional gravity-flow systems. Dip-type atomizers appear to have been much more widely used in Europe than in this country in the construction of flame photometers (2, 21, 39, 42, 111, 114, 126).

Efforts to increase the volume of aspirated material produced by instruments employing either type of discharge atomizer have led a number of workers to suggest the placing of a small baffle immediately in front of the jet (12, 39, 42, 80, 83, 111, 126, 143). The atomized stream strikes the baffle and the larger solution droplets are further dispersed. The net result is an apparent increase in sensitivity because of the larger amount of material now capable of being transported and injected into the flame.

*3.2.2. Total-Consumption-Type Systems.* Total-consumption atomizers are distinguished from discharge atomizers by the fact that the entire amount of solution aspirated by the former is fed into the flame and none is diverted to waste. As a much greater amount of material enters the flame per unit time, greater analytical sensitivity is achieved with instruments employing such systems. Figures 5B and C are schematic drawings of two currently used total-consumption-style atomizing units.

Before these two particular models are discussed, some comment will be made about the atomizing system first employed with the early Beckman flame photometer (57). While this atomizer has been replaced by the more satisfactory unit represented by Fig. 5C, it was used extensively in the past and still finds an occasional application. It therefore represents a stage in the development of flame instruments in this country and can be considered of historical, if of no other, interest. Although it is a total-consumption unit, in many ways this system strikingly resembles Gouy's original atomizer. The two differ, however, in operating principle in that the Beckman version has much smaller jet orifices which produce a very fine mist quite free of any visible solution droplets. Consequently the entire volume of atomized material produced at the rate of 0.1 to 0.2 ml./min. can be carried into the flame. A preheat chamber for completely vaporizing the mist droplets is placed in series between the atomizer jets and the flame source. Quite recently a German investigator published a description of a very similar atomizer arrangement developed for use with an oxygen-acetylene flame to obtain greater sensitivity (43).

Several pertinent criticisms can be made of these atomizers. For one, the very small bore of the feed capillary tube is easily plugged if any suspended material is present in the aspirated solution. Furthermore, it has been suggested that the possible formation of minute gas bubbles on the walls of such small conduits can alter the liquid flow rate to an extent where sizable errors will result. Finally, there is also the question of whether a long vapor path from the atomizer to the flame is a good feature. The irregular loss of some of the mist by condensation or adsorption on the walls of the conveying system is always possible, and a close control of the heat applied to the vaporizing chamber is necessary if these effects are to be kept at a minimum.

With these deficiencies in mind, Weichselbaum and Varney developed an all-metal, direct-feed, total-consumption atomizer and burner arrangement which has been incorporated in a commercially available flame photometer (25b, 139). While Fig. 5B is a simplified schematic version of the Weichselbaum-Varney unit, it does contain the essential features which distinguish it from the previously discussed concentric, all-glass models. With the Weichselbaum system, the solution is aspirated with oxygen by a Venturi effect through a small (0.028-in. diameter) stainless steel hypodermic needle. The solution needle is part of an all-metal burner that uses premixed propane or illuminating gas and oxygen as fuel. The ejection nozzle of the atomizer is positioned in the center of the burner head to give an absolute minimum path length for the atomized solution. Solution consumption is of the order of 0.75 ml./min., which compares very well with the conservative operation of the glass concentric atomizers.

The all-metal construction of the assembly is most desirable from the standpoint of being rugged, but possible corrosion of the needle by the action of strong acid or salt solutions with attendant sample contamination does represent an undesirable feature. Weichselbaum and Varney found that the restricted diameter of the solution needle produced a capillary effect that had to be overcome to ensure the ready aspiration of solution. This was achieved by adding a small amount (0.04%) of a nonionic surface-active agent to all test solutions. Plugging and the occasional uneven flow of solution as encountered with the original Beckman atomizer may also be experienced with the use of this system.

What might be considered as a practical ultimate in the design of atomizing systems of the Weichselbaum variety has been described by Gilbert (58). A schematic drawing of the modification is shown in Fig. 5C. An atomizer burner of this type is now used with both models of the prism-type Beckman flame photometer. The Venturi aspiration through a metal capillary feed tube, as provided by Weichselbaum's atomizer, is maintained, but the burner arrangement is substantially less complicated. Rather than having a separate burner requiring an individual fuel proportioning system, the acetylene or hydrogen for the Beckman flame is burned directly with the oxygen providing the aspirating action. Thus a less elaborate valve arrangement for the control of fuel and oxygen flow is possible and the whole unit is considerably more compact. The rate of sample consumption is substantially greater (2 ml./min.) than that exhibited by the Weichselbaum unit because of the larger diameter capillary employed. The attendant gain in sensitivity is indicated by the large number of elements reported as measurable with its use (column 2 of Table I).

One undesirable feature characteristic of both developments is that fairly concentrated solutions tend to form a deposit at the jet orifice owing to excessive evaporation caused by the proximity of the flame. These deposits can constitute a serious contamination problem, and the burner must be cleaned regularly if such solutions are used.

*3.2.3. Reflux Atomizers.* Reflux atomizers avoid the major disadvantage of the discharge system, that of large sample consumption, by providing a self-contained means of returning to the sample holder that portion of the atomized solution not actually carried to the flame. Lundegardh first made use of the reflux principle in the development of his flame spectrograph (84). His atomizer-burner arrangement proved to be very efficient and was widely used by others in the construction of various flame instruments (29, 68, 74, 91, 119). The original Lundegardh development was also adapted in a simplified form by Hultgren for his work on the spark-in-flame method of analysis (72).

In these atomizers the sample holder, atomizing jet system, and droplet reflux trap are all contained in a small, compact glass unit. The fine air-borne mist produced is conducted to a separate burner attachment designed for an air-acetylene flame. The only unfavorable criticism that can be made of the Lundegardh-type unit is that cleaning between successive runs is a rather laborious process. The atomizer, being an enclosed assembly, must be disassembled to permit complete flushing of the previously used sample. Although high efficiency and stable operation are readily attained, the difficulty in cleansing is probably the chief reason why no current commercial flame photometers contain this type of atomizer.

Recently another fairly complicated all-glass reflux system has been described, the cleansing problem of which is claimed to be greatly simplified (143). Compressed air is used as the aspirating gas and the essentially "dry" aerosol produced on atomization is fed into an oxygen-propane flame. Sample consumption with this system is only 0.3 to 0.4 ml./min. while excellent stability in the delivery of the atomized sample is claimed.

The design of a very simple glass reflux atomizer is given in Fig. 5D. This unit was developed to avoid previously encountered inconveniences in cleansing, as well as to provide a compact atomizer and burner arrangement that would be stable in operation and conservative in sample consumption (53). The particular model shown was found to give adequate sensitivity when used with an oxygen-hydrogen flame although only 0.1 ml. of solution was consumed per minute. A description of another

TABLE II

Summary of the Classification of Some Commercially Available Flame Photometers

| Model | Flame and type of atomizer used | Type of optics | Type of photodetector | Elements reported to be determinable with the model |
|---|---|---|---|---|
| Baird | Gas-air, gravity-flow discharge type | Interference filters, either single or double beam | Barrier-layer cells | Na, K, Ca |
| Barclay | Gas-air, gravity-flow discharge type | Color glass filters, either single or double beam | Barrier-layer cells | Na, K |
| Beckman model B | $H_2$ or acetylene and $O_2$, integral total-consumption type | Glass prism, single beam | Vacuum phototubes with amplifier | See comment in section 3.1.2 |
| Beckman model D.U. | $H_2$ or acetylene and oxygen, integral total-consumption type | Quartz prism, single beam | Vacuum phototubes or photomultiplier with amplifier | See list in Table I |
| Coleman model 21 | Gas-oxygen, total consumption type | Interference and color glass filters, single beam | Vacuum phototube with amplifier | Na, K, Ca |
| Fox | Gas-air, gravity-flow discharge type | Colored glass filters, either single or double beam | Barrier-layer cells | Na, K |
| Norelco | Gas-air, gravity flow discharge type | Interference and color glass filters, single or double beam | Barrier layer cells | Na, K, Li |
| Perkin-Elmer model 52 C and 146 | Propane or acetylene and air, gravity-flow discharge type | Dual glass prisms, either single or double beam | Vacuum phototubes with amplifier | Mg, Mn, Ca, Cr, Sr, Ba, Na, Li, K |
| Process and Instruments | Propane-air, gravity-flow discharge type | Colored glass filters, double beam | Barrier-layer cells | Na, K |
| Weichselbaum-Varney | Gas-oxygen, total-consumption type | Interference wedge filter, single beam | Photomultiplier with amplifier | Ba, Ca, Co, Cr, Cs, Cu, Fe, K, Li, Mg, Mn, Na, Rb, Sr, Tl |

development of this type of system has appeared recently (44). This particular version, however, does not avoid the cleansing problem posed by the earlier reflux designs.

In brief, the reflux unit of Fig. 5D operates in the following manner. The test solution is contained in a small beaker (5-ml. volume), which is placed around the open bottom of the atomizing tube. Low-pressure air or oxygen aspirates the solution, and the coarse atomized stream is directed against the cone-shaped glass reflux surface positioned immediately above the constricted neck joining the atomizer and the upper cylindrical trap. The bulk of the atomized stream is returned to the sample holder by draining down the walls of the atomizer tube while the mist is carried through the trap and into the burner. Plugging of this atomizer is rarely a problem as the feed tube diameter can be as large as 0.5 mm. Samples can be rapidly changed and the unit is adequately cleansed in most cases by two distilled water flushes of several seconds' duration. Such units are readily adaptable to any number of the photometer arrangements previously discussed.

It has been observed that a progressive fractionation and increase in apparent concentration of the test solution will occur with the prolonged operation of reflux systems if a dry atomizing gas stream is employed (44, 53, 143). The effect is caused by extensive evaporation of the larger liquid droplets produced in the atomization process. The evaporated moisture is included with the sample mist carried to the flame while the enriched droplets remaining are returned for recycling. This undesirable process can be easily eliminated by saturating the atomizing gas stream with water vapor prior to its entry into the atomizer (44, 53). A careful consideration of the type of atomizer to be used will do much to help avoid unnecessary exploratory work for many special applications of the flame method.

In accord with the classification system just discussed, the construction features of ten commercially available flame photometers are summarized in Table II. For convenience, the type of photodetector and the elements reportedly determinable for each instrument are also included.

## 4. Sample Treatment Required for Flame Photometric Determinations

### 4.1. The Use of Aqueous, Organic, and Aqueous-Organic Solutions

Most of the samples treated by the flame method consist of aqueous solutions of the particular cations of interest. This does not mean that organic solutions or mixed water-organic solutions cannot be analyzed. The major difficulty with handling organic solutions is the explosion and fire hazards that may arise from their use. This danger is most prevalent in atomizing systems where premixing of the vapor-laden atomizing stream and the burner fuel takes place before combustion occurs. Even when premixing is not required, there is always the possibility of "back flash" into the atomizing chamber. Apparently no trouble is experienced with organic solvents having fairly high flash points (35). The best atomizer for the more dangerous low-boiling organic solutions is the total-consumption type represented by either B or C of Fig. 5, as premixing of the fuel components does not occur and there is no enclosed part of the system that might contain an explosive mixture. It is reported that the determination of lead in raw gasoline is possible with such a system (56).

As a rule, methods for obtaining an aqueous solution of the test material should be tried first in any preparative treatment for flame photometry. If the material proves to be water insoluble, mixtures of water and such water-miscible organic solvents as methyl, ethyl, or isopropyl alcohol, dioxane, etc., may be found suitable. Water or mixed solvent-insoluble substances can be treated with appropriate pure organic solvents. The use of the latter may create a problem in preparing suitable calibration samples, which must be composed of the same solvent used in dissolving the unknown material. Aqueous calibration samples are easily prepared by adding the required amounts of either the chloride or nitrate salts of the cation being studied. This simple method obviously will not work with most of the pure organic systems. If one of them is encountered, it will be necessary to obtain pure organometallic compounds containing the cation, or cations, of interest and from these to prepare the appropriate calibration samples. In one instance the primary standard used for calibration was an available concentrate of the particular additive being determined in an oil base. Benzene was used exclusively as the diluent (94).

Many materials can be brought into aqueous solution only by strong acid treatment. It is advisable in these cases always to use the minimum amount of acid required for the process to avoid possible excessive anion interference effects. For the best results, calibration samples should have solution properties that will duplicate as nearly as possible the chemical and physical characteristics of the unknown solution. Reference can be made to Table III for a list of several typical procedures in outline form for the preparation of some common materials that can be analyzed flame-photometrically. The cited literature will provide specific details where necessary.

### 4.2. Samples in the Gaseous Form

Although no reports have been made on the direct flame determination of initially gaseous materials, there is no reason why such measurements cannot be made. The most serious limiting factor would appear

## TABLE III

*Typical Outline Procedures for the Preparation of Solutions of Some Common Materials for Flame Photometric Analyses*

| Materials | Sample treatment | Cations determinable | References |
|---|---|---|---|
| Whole blood | Sample diluted 1:20. Trichloracetic acid added. Protein precipitate centrifuged out. Add lithium for internal standard if desired. Make to final volume (total dilution 1:25–1:50). | K, Na, Ca | 16, 102, 122 |
| Serum or plasma, urine | (1) Sample diluted 1:100. Add lithium for internal standard (optional). | K, Na | 16, 25c, 50, 51, 102 |
| | (2) Sample treated with trichloracetic acid. Precipitated proteins centrifuged or filtered. Lithium may be added to supernatant liquid for internal standard. | K, Na | 16, 102, 126 |
| | (3) Serum treated with buffered oxalate solution. Precipitate recovered and washed. Redissolved in acid and diluted. Lithium may be added for internal standard. | Ca | 9, 28, 50, 78 |
| Body tissues | Either wet or dry ash specimen. Dissolve residue in acid solution. Dilute to suitable volume. Add internal standard or read directly. | K, Na | 115, 123, 129 |
| Refractory materials, rocks, minerals, soils | (1) Treat with suitably strong acid (conc. HCl, $H_2SO_4$ + HF). For cements, use HCl, dilute and filter out silica. For glass, use HF and evaporate to dryness. Take up in acid solution. Filter. Dilute to suitable volume. Add lithium as internal standard if desired. | K, Na, Li, Ca | 4, 7, 27, 81 101 |
| | (2) Fuse with calcium carbonate + ammonium chloride. Redissolve in acid solution. Filter. Add lithium and dilute to volume. | Na, K | 19, 52 |
| Plant materials | Wet ash with acids. Digest ash with HCl and dilute. Filter. | K | 62, 75 |
| | Digest with $HNO_3$ and $HClO_4$. Dilute and filter. Add lithium as internal standard. | Ca, Na, K | 134 |

to be the very low emitter concentrations characteristic of most gaseous dispersions. If adequate instrument sensitivity can be obtained, the method might be applied to either of two types of determinations. One would be the analysis of a particular element, for example, iron or nickel, in a stream of a gaseous compound such as iron or nickel carbonyl. Boron in methyl borate might also be a possibility. The other use would be the determination of some dispersed contaminant, such as a sodium or calcium salt dust, in a gas or air stream. Required for these applications would be a system for uniformly feeding the gas stream under a positive pressure into the vapor conduit leading to the flame. The calibration problem here would be somewhat analogous to that previously described for the use of pure organic solvents. The possible adaptation of the flame method for gas stream analysis is one of the applications of flame photometry that does not appear to have attracted much interest.

### 4.3. The Use of Solids or Solid Powders

Mention has already been made of some of the means by which solid samples have been directly introduced into the flame (section 1). Chiefly, these are of historical interest only and represent the early procedures employed prior to the development of atomizing systems. However, as it is conceivable that a situation may arise in which atomization would be impractical or impossible, it might be profitable to consider one of the more efficient methods for solid-sample injection. For example, a substance dissolved or suspended in a limited quantity of solution that could not stand further dilution might be handled by the evaporated film technique developed by Ramsay and co-workers (108–110). In this method a drop of the test solution is evaporated on a length of thin platinum wire, which is then mechanically fed into the flame at a fixed slow rate. Successful results were reported for the determination of sodium in extremely small volumes of solution when treated in this manner (108). Aside from Ramsay's development, very little attention has been given to other means of flaming solid samples directly. As a suggested approach, one might consider the possibility of a gas stream method for solids that could be very finely pulverized and dispersed as an aerosol or dust. If workable, such treatment would eliminate the more time-consuming solution process.

### 5. Factors Affecting Precision and Accuracy in Flame Photometry

In spite of all its apparent advantages, flame photometry is still accepted only with reservation by many analysts. In general, dissatisfaction with the method can be attributed to two causes. The first is the appreciable number of experimental difficulties that may be encountered in obtaining completely satisfactory performance with any given flame photometer. With practically all units, a rigid control of at least several instrumental variables is mandatory if precision and accuracy are to be obtained. Of equal importance is the fact that the correct interpretation of flame photometric data can be difficult even when optimum operating conditions are employed. This is due to the existence of certain spectroscopic interferences that may be unique to the particular determination being made and to the possible complex interaction of these effects with unexpected instrumental errors.

If the user rigorously employs all the precautions regarding cleanliness in sample preparation and handling required in regular microgram determinations, the uncertainties in applying the method can be limited to these two major sources: instrumental errors and spectroscopic interferences. In assessing the value of flame photometric data, one must recognize the nature and origin of each influencing factor.

For the purpose of this discussion, any variation in an emitted intensity reading that is directly attributable to the mechanical operation of the instrument, or to a specific operating characteristic of some instrument component, will be classed as an instrumental error. The term *interference* is reserved to describe only the variations in emitted intensity associated directly with reactions in the flame itself. For example, the suppression or enhancement of an element's emission by the simultaneous presence of another element, or group of elements, is of spectroscopic origin and is thus an interference. Also, the phenomenon of self-quenching whereby a portion of the radiation of an emitting atom is reabsorbed by other atoms of the same species will fall in this category.

Unfortunately, in flame photometry there has not been any consistency in the usage of the term *interference*. Early workers in the field, not being certain of the causes of the errors they encountered, developed the practice of designating as interferences all unexpected changes in emitted intensity. Thus some confusion will arise when flame photometric literature containing a reference to an observed variation in emission behavior is consulted, as very often no distinction is made as to whether the effect could be of instrumental or of true spectroscopic origin. The following sections will serve as a guide in determining the sources of the uncertainties of the method and in evaluating their practical importance.

### 5.1. Instrumental Errors

*5.1.1. Errors Associated with the Atomizer and Burner Operation.* The most critical single component in any flame photometer, from the standpoint of being a source of error, is the atomizer and burner assembly. In all cases, a careful control of the aspirating air stream pressure should be maintained, or fluctuations in emitted intensity will result as the flow of atomized sample varies. This control is more important for those atomizer-burner systems in which the aspirating gas is oxygen and is intended to comprise a definite proportion of the mixture being burned. Here a variation in the flow of oxygen not only alters the amount of atomized sample produced but will result in a change in the flame temperature and background intensity. In a like manner, the last two variables will also be noticeably affected by unwanted changes in the fuel flow rate. Many workers have studied or commented on the magnitude of the errors introduced by atomizing stream and fuel pressure fluctuations with different atomizer and burner combinations, and these contributions should be referred to for detailed information (6, 18, 20, 27, 41, 45, 49, 70, 97, 138, 142).

For those systems in which compressed air is used, it must be remembered that the supply should be free of dust and other air-borne contaminants, which may enter the flame and influence the emitted radiation. Perhaps a more serious form of air-borne contamination is that occurring from the atmosphere surrounding the open flame. In some industrial areas the extent of atmospheric contamination may necessitate the use of an air-conditioned room for many flame photometric determinations. The ease with which a typical flame measurement can be influenced by room air contamination is readily demonstrated by observing the enhancing effect of cigarette smoke on the open-flame, 767-m$\mu$. emission of a potassium salt solution.

A factor of less serious import, but one that should nevertheless be considered, concerns the water vapor content of the aspirating air stream prior to its introduction into either reflux- or discharge-type atomizers. The extent of droplet evaporation and the relative amount of material carried to the flame in these systems will be determined by the initial relative humidity of the aspirating air stream. It has been shown that large differences in initial water vapor content can seriously alter atomizer efficiency (44, 53). Experiments with the simple reflux atomizer of Fig. 5D have indicated that its initial atomizing efficiency can vary as much as 35%, depending on whether a dry air stream or one that is presaturated with water vapor at room temperature is used (53). A similar effect might be expected with discharge systems. As the bulk of the sample is constantly recycled in the reflux unit, the extensive droplet evaporation occurring with a dry air stream, particularly tank oxygen, produces a gradual increase in the concentration of the remaining sample. With reflux systems in particular, therefore, it is important that the aspirating gas be presaturated with water vapor if aqueous solutions are being examined. If mixed solvents are used, the presaturating trap should contain a similar solvent mixture. The relationship between aspirating stream humidity and gradual sample concentration does not, of course, exist for discharge units, as the trapped portion of the atomized stream is not returned to the sample holder. The total consumption-style atomizers of more recent design (Figs. 5B and C) are also not subject to such influences, as the total volume of atomized solution is injected directly into the flame.

As all three classes of atomizers depend upon the aspiration of solution through a capillary tube, solution viscosity effects of a similar nature will be common to all. Gouy was probably the first to note the influence of viscosity changes upon atomizer efficiency and the resultant variation in emitted intensity (60). Practically every report of fundamental investigations of the method made since then has contained some reference to the role of viscosity. There appears to be a unanimous agreement in all that an increase in solution viscosity will produce a decrease in measured emitted intensity. It seems logical to expect that the magnitude of any viscosity effect would be directly related to the capillary diameter of the solution feed tube. However, such a straight forward relationship may not always be observed in practice because of the existence of other factors, such as droplet size formation and distribution, which may be more dominant in the particular atomizing system selected (27a). For accurate results, particularly with instruments that do not employ the internal standard principle, and regardless of the atomizer used, it is essential that calibration solution viscosities approximate as closely as possible those of the unknown solutions.

The magnitude of viscosity errors in flame photometry becomes evident on examination of pertinent data. For example, Barnes and co-workers have reported that a fivefold increase in viscosity produces a 42% decrease in the emitted intensity of sodium or potassium when measured by the absolute method, but an 11% lowering is observed if the internal standard technique is used (18). Other comments on viscosity errors and the means for compensating some of them are given in references (8, 20, 27a, 33, 38, 45, 53, 57, 97). Fortunately, for most flame photometric determinations a large dilution factor is tolerable, which tends greatly to reduce the effects of viscosity differences.

A particularly undesirable characteristic of discharge and total-consumption-type atomizers appears as the persistent downward drift in emitted intensity observed during the course of an analysis. This variation is due to the decrease in hydrostatic head in the sample reservoir as the test solution is being consumed. The diminishing hydrostatic pressure results in a corresponding decrease in the rate of aspiration. The drift is particularly noticeable with discharge-type atomizers employing the gravity-aided flow of solution as provided by the unit represented in Fig. 5A. To attain satisfactory analytical precision, it is necessary either to read the emitted intensity value only when the solution level has fallen to a fixed point in the reservoir or constantly to replenish the reservoir so that there is no appreciable change in solution volume. Unfortunately, no published data are available to indicate the magnitude of the errors resulting from the failure to observe either of these precautions. It has been noted, however, that with the less commonly used dip-type atomizer, a drop in the solution level of only 0.9 cm. can produce a decrease of 35% in a measured emitted intensity value, depending upon the aspirating air pressure applied (41). Use has been made of an integral manometer arrangement to aid in determining the rate of sample aspiration and the point at which a reading should be taken for this particular style of atomizer (12).

Total-consumption atomizers are apparently much less subject to a change in efficiency with the drop in sample level; nevertheless, it cannot be assumed that the effect will be entirely lacking. The reflux system represented by D of Fig. 5 is believed to be the only type that is completely free of this source of error, as the sample is constantly subjected to the same air pressure which activates the atomizer (53).

An important aqueous solution property that may seriously affect atomizer efficiency is surface tension, and all atomizing systems will, to different degrees, give a variable response to measurable changes in this property. Generally it will be found that a decrease in surface tension will result in an observed increase in radiation intensity. With the total consumption-type units represented by B and C of Fig. 5, the effect is confined to possible changes in aspiration rate (25b, 139). The lower the surface tension, the greater the rate of aspiration, which in turn yields higher emitted intensity readings. Consequently, it is important, particularly for absolute measurements, that calibration solutions have approximately the same surface tension as the unknown solution. Adjustments in surface tension can be conveniently made with any of a large number of nonionic surface-active agents.

For all atomizers other than the total-consumption types of Figs. 5B and C, droplet formation and size distribution are very critical processes, and surface-tension variations may produce effects which are more subtle and complex than merely a change in the rate of aspiration. A lowering of surface tension will yield a greater number of smaller droplets during solution atomization. For all but total-consumption-type systems, the resulting increase in aerosol concentration coupled with an increase in aspiration rate produces an enhanced emitted intensity (20, 44, 45, 53' 57). However, when low-boiling organic solvents are used, e.g., alcohols, acetone, etc., either in aqueous mixtures or as pure hydrocarbon solutions, there may be some question of to what extent increased solution volatility and the possible raising of the combustion temperature of the flame will affect the light-intensity values.

Some workers have expressed the opinion that a change in surface tension alone cannot account for the magnitude of the errors often attributed to it if one assumes that only changes in aspiration rate and spray nebulosity are involved (18, 44). As evidence, it was found in one case that the addition of a nonionic surface-active agent in an amount sufficient to give a maximum lowering of surface tension produced only a 4% increase in observed emitted intensity (44). This was apparently so in spite of the fact that it has been noted elsewhere that the addition of such compounds can markedly shift the distribution of smaller droplets to favor a substantial increase in the volume of aerosol reaching the flame (53). Undoubtedly, droplet volatility, as well as a nebulosity effect, has some bearing on the ultimate result, and the balance between droplet distribution and extent of evaporation may vary widely under different test conditions. It has been suggested, for example, that the error produced by the presence of an excess of inorganic anions is almost entirely attributable to a lowering of the droplet vapor pressure of the atomized mist, while surface-tension effects are of only secondary importance (44). Because of the resultant reduced rate of droplet evaporation, a greater proportion of unevaporated water enters the flame and causes a depression of emitted intensity by a simple cooling action. In other research, tests made on the supposed cooling effect of excess water injected into the flame failed to substantiate this theory (53).

Regardless of the individual importance of surface tension, droplet vapor pressure, or drop-size distribution, it is reasonably certain that ordinarily the contribution of any single factor will be obscured by its inclusion in an interaction involving all the effects which may contribute to a variation in emission intensity. As a consequence, a complex system of compensating errors may be in force with the net result being an analytical reading not too far from the correct value that would be obtained if no influencing factors existed. If other than ordinary conditions of surface tension, viscosity, or solution volatility are encountered in any series of analyses, naturally their possible individual influence must then be taken into account.

Finally, changes in initial sample temperature may be expected to affect atomizer efficiency in proportion to the extent the solution properties are altered. Using a dip-type discharge atomizer, Smit and co-workers observed a 5 to 10% decrease in the emitted intensity of sodium and potassium solutions for a 20° C. increase in solution temperature (126). With the majority of atomizers, appreciable differences in solution temperature will probably produce errors no larger than these, as the resultant changes in surface tension and viscosity will be small for most aqueous samples. Nevertheless, it is good practice to operate with all samples at a reasonably uniform room temperature.

One interesting temperature effect does occur with the use of reflux systems, and the analyst must be aware of its possible existence. If an aspirating air stream that is not presaturated with water vapor at room temperature is used, or particularly if very dry air or tank oxygen is selected, a definite cooling action due to volatilization of the atomized mist is detected. The entire atomizing assembly and especially the re-turning bulk of the solution will in a few minutes become chilled and may reach a steady low value of 5° to 10° C. (53). It has been observed that for two different types of reflux units the emitted intensity readings taken during this induction period will be untrustworthy and that sufficient time should be allowed for the system to come to equilibrium (45, 53). The increased efficiency detected as the temperature of the recycled solu-tion drops is known to be due to the accompanying increase in the volume of smaller droplets formed and carried into the flame. In contrast, samples at initially elevated temperatures are observed to give large droplets with an attendant decrease in atomizer efficiency (53).

5.1.2. *Errors Introduced by the Type of Optical System Used.* Fre-quently occurring instrumental errors in flame photometry arise from the inadequate spectral isolation provided by the light-dispersing or -filtering system in use. These errors take the form of an enhancement of the particular emitted intensity being measured, because of the in-clusion of excessive amounts of a variable background radiation or of radiation wave lengths characteristic of those other emitting elements present in the solution. While it is true that high spectral resolution is not too essential for measurements of a pure solution containing a single strongly emitting species, there are very few instances in practical flame photometry where such may be the case. To achieve maximum accuracy with the more complex solutions of everyday practice, it is desirable to have the most efficient system attainable for isolating characteristic radiations.

In order to establish whether or not a certain filter arrangement will be adequate for a given determination, reference must be made to the applicable spectral transmission curve for that particular system or, if a prism is used, to the appropriate dispersion data. If the proximity of the emission lines or bands to be resolved is known, the available dispersion or pass band information will indicate how successful the isolation of these radiations will be. Reference to the curves of Fig. 2 will give some idea of the degree of spectral isolation possible with the various types of filter systems that comprise the optics of many low-cost flame photometers. From these curves it can be seen that ordinary colored glass filters would not successfully separate such adjacent emissions as the calcium 554- or 622-m$\mu$. bands from the very strong 589-m$\mu$. sodium radiation. The inadequacy of glass color filters has been noted by many workers not only for determinations made on biological samples, where this resolution problem is particularly prevalent (6, 39, 50, 66, 126, 136, 142), but also for the measurement of sodium, potassium, and calcium in such materials as cements (37), plant and soil extracts (104, 121), and various synthetic inorganic systems (18, 20, 142).

The use of dielectric interference or multilayer filters will reduce the magnitude of some resolution errors but will not eliminate them. For example, in determining small amounts of sodium in the presence of larger amounts of potassium, a positive error of 110% occurs with regular glass filters. This value is reduced to 27% when interference-type filters are used (142). Pratt and Larson were able to halve the sodium error caused by the presence of excess calcium in soil analysis by adding interference filters to the color filter system originally employed (104). Other available data will permit further comparisons to be made between the efficiencies of the various types of filters usable in flame photometry (25b, 37, 118a).

As previously mentioned, prism optics, or gratings if available, will provide an even higher degree of spectral purity. However, significant errors will still be encountered with instruments employing these monochromators. The errors arise from the compromises that must be made involving mechanical slit widths, the known dispersing power of the monochromator, and the photodetector sensitivity available. By increasing slit widths to gain a higher level of emitted intensity for measurement, one increases the effective band width passed by the optical system. As a consequence, depending upon the specific dispersion characteristics of the monochromator, band or line overlap becomes increasingly evident. With prism spectrophotometers, such as that provided with the Beckman flame instrument, the nonlinear dispersion of the prism permits wider slit widths to be used in the blue region of the spectrum with less danger of resolution errors occurring than in the red, where the dispersion is not so great. Grating units, which are much less widely used, give constant linear dispersion throughout the spectrum covered, thus substantially reducing the possibility of resolution errors at near red wave lengths. The importance of always using the minimum possible slit width compatible with sensitivity requirements has been pointed out by several groups of investigators (57, 78, 96, 97, 103a).

In many instances, even a minimum slit width will still provide a measurable error, and other precautions must then be taken. For example, a sizeable enhancement of both the calcium 622- and 554-m$\mu$. emission due to the presence of high sodium concentrations will be in evidence for slit widths as small as 0.1 mm. unless a didymium glass filter is used in conjunction with the prism system (53, 57, 96). It is also reported that the calcium 422-m$\mu$. line emission is subject to a similar influence at a slit width of the same order of magnitude (78). In this case the observed analytical radiation is sufficiently removed in the spectrum from the strong sodium D line to rule out the possibility of a direct line overlap. While the effect may be due chiefly to light leak in the optical system, from a practical standpoint it is no less serious.

For prism instruments having fixed slit widths (e.g., Perkin-Elmer models 52C and 146), the occurrence of line or band overlap is less conveniently eliminated. A considerable amount of work has been done with flame photometers of this design and reference will be made to a few instances where resolution errors were encountered and have been discussed (15, 17, 37, 103a, 134). One group found that calcium enhancement of the sodium intensity reading could be almost completely avoided by adding an interference filter to the double-prism monochromator arrangement (37).

No simple method for anticipating or correcting possible resolution errors can be offered. The extent of the effect will be dependent upon too many different factors to permit this. Such things as the design of the instrument selected, the method of its operation, the nature of the solutions to be treated—particularly the relative concentrations of the emitting elements present and the spectral position of their emissions—will all be important factors. The safest practice when one is first employing the method or investigating a new type of material is to explore the extent of the resolution errors that may be expected with the instrument and solutions to be used.

*5.1.3. Errors Introduced by the Photodetector System.* Aside from more-or-less obvious difficulties such as poor electrical connections and worn-out or broken components, surprisingly few errors will be introduced by the photodetector system of a well-constructed flame photometer. For the simplest systems available, the selenium barrier layer cells used are quite rugged and have an appreciable trouble-free life span if properly shielded. Cell fatigue resulting from extensive exposures to strong light will, however, result in a downward drift in the observed emitted intensity reading. The replacement of a cell may require the reinvestigation

of existing calibration curves because variations in response characteristics may be found from one cell to the next. As amplifying circuits
are not used with such detectors, a barrier layer cell system is easily
maintained.

Detector units employing the photoemissive vacuum tube are somewhat more complicated and may require more attention. These tubes
will also show fatigue characteristics and for best performance they must
be shielded from excessively humid air and sources of electrostatic interference. As the phototube output usually undergoes one or more stages
of amplification, it is necessary to avoid stray light leaks, which when
amplified would add a substantial error to the analytical reading. The
mentioned limited and variable spectral response of these tubes (section
2.3.2.) may result, when they are replaced, in problems similar to those
encountered on the replacement of barrier layer cells. Fairly noticeable
differences in sensitivity, particularly at either limit of the spectral response curve, are possible, and the user cannot assume that the behavior
of an instrument will be the same when one phototube is replaced with
another.

The use of photomultiplier tubes imposes an even greater number of
operating precautions that must be observed. Because of the very high
amplification provided by the multiplier effect in the tube alone, it is
essential that the applied high voltage be regulated to 0.5% or better.
Small fluctuations in dynode voltage will produce sizable surges in the
observed signal when, as is usually done, additional stages of amplification
are applied. The erratic excursions of the indicating meter resulting
from poor regulation cannot be tolerated when even a moderate degree
of precision and accuracy is all that is required. The less practical way
of using dry batteries as the high voltage supply will assure a steady
voltage, but a gradual downward drift in instrument readings can be
expected as the batteries become exhausted. Prior to its incorporation
in a flame photometer, any A-C-operated, regulated power supply to be
used with a multiplier phototube should be checked against existing
operating-line surges. Only in this way can the user be certain that
transient effects from the line will not exceed the regulation provided
and appear as a signal error.

In order to avoid unnecessary experimental difficulties and signal
errors, photomultiplier systems should not be operated at too high voltages (i.e., 1000 volts or greater for tubes of the RCA 931A or 1P22 type).
While a tremendous gain in detectability does result from small increases
in applied voltage at the upper level, this may be more than offset by a
magnification of tube "noise." The generally low signal intensities provided by flame radiations suggest that a compromise upper voltage limit

be accepted in order to have an optimum signal-to-noise ratio without sacrificing too much in sensitivity. Furthermore, this particular feature may vary somewhat from tube to tube, and the user can determine only by investigation the best limit for his particular unit. Because of their extreme sensitivity to light, these tubes must be very carefully shielded from light as well as protected from moist atmospheres and high temperatures. The analytical errors arising from the improper or faulty use of photomultipliers will be of considerable magnitude but can be readily controlled or eliminated.

### 5.2. Spectroscopic Interferences

The existence of certain source interactions involving either the gain or loss of radiant energy of emitting elements is a well-known spectroscopic phenomenon. Flame photometry is not without this effect although the low thermal energies of most flames will tend to lessen its seriousness. A fundamental, systematic study of mutual interferences in those systems best suited for flame analysis, although badly needed, does not appear to have been made as yet. This lack is understandable in view of the difficulty met in trying to determine the causes for emitted intensity variations observed with many of the flame instruments so far developed. Even with the best available models, it is usually unrewarding to try to identify that portion of the radiation's gain or loss arising solely from some instrumental factor and that which results from spectroscopic interaction. At the present time the treatment of flame interferences is, to say the least, quite empirical and there is no available theory that is generally applicable to all known cases. The user will often have to establish his own system for explaining any errors and interferences he may observe on applying his particular instrument and procedures.

5.2.1. Flame Temperature Effects. Variations in flame temperature resulting either from changing fuel proportions or from selecting an entirely different type of fuel mixture can produce substantial differences in emission behavior. Huldt (71) and Gaydon (54) have both given excellent evaluations of the fundamental role of flame temperature in regard to flame emission processes. In addition to the effects induced by altering the fuel mixture, there are variations in radiant intensity that may be found depending upon the region of the flame being observed. It is well known that large temperature differences are encountered in gradient form in any steadily burning flame. With the possible exception of certain band emissions, such as those exhibited by calcium and magnesium, greater emitted intensities result as hotter burning fuels are employed or as a given flame temperature is raised by altering the fuel-oxygen ratio (39, 79, 80, 84, 85, 113). The exceptional behavior of the alkaline earths may be due to the fact that the particular molecular species that give rise to their band spectra can be involved in complicated and possibly competing equilibria in the flame (71). As the temperature is raised, the emitting molecules may be sacrificed by dissociation or reassociation to give a greater proportion of a nonemitting species or one, at least, that does not emit at the particular band wave length being observed.

Finally the maximum radiation for all but possibly the band-emitting elements will appear in the hottest regions of the flame (84, 92). The fact that emission intensity is not constant throughout the entire combustion zone is of little practical importance for most simple filter flame photometers as their optical systems view a good average cross section of the flame. However, if the instrument has an aperture that is slit controlled, the significance of such emission zone variations must not be ignored.

To complicate the picture somewhat, mutual interferences between emitting atoms and other elements may be greatly altered by different temperatures. The situation is not clarified by the fact that pertinent reported data are in wide disagreement with each other over the nature and extent of these interactions. Thus, one can find that many mutual interferences will be accentuated in hotter flames (24, 39, 79, 80, 113). Brealey and Ross report, however, that the effect of certain anions, such as phosphate, on the alkalies will tend to diminish as the temperature is raised (24). Still other workers have suggested that low-temperature flame emissions are more subject to substantial depressions from the presence of excess foreign molecules than are high-temperature radiations (18, 101, 103). It can only be offered that no effort was made in most of these cases to evaluate the interference with respect to the possible instrumental errors that may have contributed to the magnitude and nature of the interaction.

In an attempt to improve this situation, one group studied the depressing action of certain acids and salts in the hot air-acetylene flame and the results obtained show that the effect produced could be part instrumental and part spectroscopic in origin (44). Obviously, considerably more research of this type needs to be carried out before the relationship among flame temperature, instrumental errors, and interference effects will be completely understood. For practical flame work, it has been made adequately clear that a stable flame of the right fuel proportion is essential (6, 28, 138). Flame fluctuations in the absolute method are prohibitive but will be less significant if the internal standard technique is used.

*5.2.2. Source Background Variations.* In the absolute method of flame photometry, the determination made is based on the difference between the intensity of the element's emission and the intensity of the source background. Free-burning flames into which distilled water is sprayed will have characteristic spectra of their own the luminosity and structure of which will be dependent upon the fuel mixture used (54, 144). In general, background curves of the sort illustrated in Fig. 6 are typical of the flames most commonly employed. These spectra are composed of

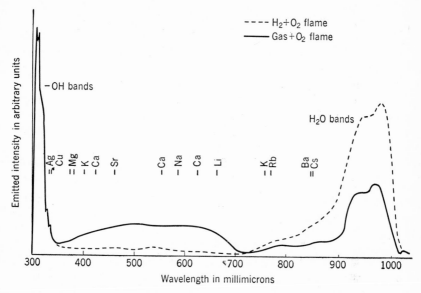

Fig. 6. Background spectra produced by hydrogen-oxygen and gas-oxygen flames showing —OH and H₂O band regions.

the various line, band, and continuous radiations arising from excitation of the products of combustion and the small quantities of impurities that are inevitably carried into the flame. Hydrocarbon fuels are likely to produce a more noticeable continuous background intensity than that observed with a hydrogen flame because of the presence of incandescent carbon particles.

The existence of the pronounced band spectra due to OH and H₂O molecular vibrations noted in Fig. 6 must obviously be taken into account when making measurements in the near ultraviolet or infrared. In these regions the background can constitute an appreciable part of the observed radiation and the operator may expect to have some trouble in obtaining a good signal-to-background ratio. For the determination of copper and silver, whose characteristic emissions appear near the steep portion of the OH band curve, any change in the fuel mixture causing a variation in OH intensity may produce a measurable difference in the analytical reading. This background interference can be reduced considerably if an instrument of high resolving power is used (77). It is fortunate that those elements most commonly determined by the flame method emit in the visible part of the spectrum where the flame background is at a minimum, as is evident from Fig. 6.

Another source of background interference is the increase in luminosity from the combustion of certain materials or elements present in excess in the sample under investigation. A number of earlier workers noted that such elements as sodium, magnesium, and manganese, in particular, would cause a general increase in the light level of the entire visible spectrum (45, 84, 90, 92, 106), as would the presence of large amounts of organic matter (45). Photographic plates were used in these studies to record the emitted radiations, and undoubtedly the resulting accumulative effect was of more serious consequence than is found when similar measurements are made with modern flame photometers. An example of a background interference, and one that is not inconsequential, has been reported for the determination of magnesium in cement with a prism-type flame instrument. The large amount of calcium present produced a measurable increase of the magnesium 371-m$\mu$. emission which could not be accounted for by band overlap in view of the slit width used. Studies with synthetic samples indicated that the background value at 371 m$\mu$. was doubled for a twofold increase in calcium content (30). Similarly another investigation showed that the magnesium determination at 285 m$\mu$. can be seriously affected by the presence of small amounts of sodium. The background increase due to the addition of only 0.1% sodium was found to be equivalent to an apparent gain of 10 to 20 p.p.m. in magnesium concentration (57). Using a similar prism instrument, others found that such background effects could be minimized but not eliminated by working at the smallest slit widths possible (27, 56, 57, 122). In all flame determinations, the background contribution of the source itself, as well as that due to the matrix materials of the sample, must be either subtracted from the analytical signal or compensated by proper synthesis of the calibration solutions.

*5.2.3. Examples of Enhancement or Suppression of Emitted Intensity by Mutual Interaction in the Flame.* The most serious and least understood form of interference is the observed suppression or enhancement of the radiation of an element by the presence of either one or several other different elements. Both cations and anions are capable of causing an effect, although in some cases part of the excess anion interference caused by added acids or salts may be due, as previously mentioned, to spray nebulosity differences. Many determinations for which flame interaction of one kind or another has been observed are reported in the literature. A few typical examples illustrating the most common forms of interference that may be encountered will be presented. A partial list of other interfering systems that are perhaps less frequently met is given in Table IV. No attempt will be made here to analyze any of the individual cases cited for the possible coexistence of instrumental errors that might

### TABLE IV

*Additional Element Pairs for Which a Flame Interference Has Been Reported*

| Element determined (at principal wave length) | Nature of apparent interference + enhancement − suppression | Interfering element (pertinent reference in bracket) |
|---|---|---|
| Na | + | Fe (64, 103, 136); Ca (70, 118a, 136); Sr (103); Mg at high conc. (108). |
| Na | − | Fe (101); Mg (53, 103, 118a); Ca, Cr, Co, Cu, Pb, Mn, Ni, Te, W, Zn (103); Mg at low conc. (108). |
| K | + | Fe, Ca (136); Ba, Cs, Rb (103). |
| K | − | Fe (101, 103); Ca, Cr, Co, Cu, Pb, Mg, Mn, Mo, Ni, Sr, Te, W, Zn (103); Mg (118a). |
| Ca | + | Sr (69); Ba (53). |
| Ca | − | Mg (20, 53). |
| Ba | + | Ca, K (33, 53, 69); Na (53). |
| Mg | + | Na, Ca, Sr, Ba (53). |
| Rb | + | Li, Na, Cs (53). |
| Cs | + | Li, Na, K, Rb (53). |
| Sr | + | Na (53). |
| Sr | − | Na, Mg (125); Ca, Si (37a). |

have influenced the nature of the interference reported. Such an evaluation would only compound the already existing confusion, as in most reports insufficient information is given about the exact experimental and operating procedures employed. The very fact that a specific interference is reported as an enhancement in one case and as a quenching effect in another amply demonstrates that other factors as well as a spectroscopic interaction must have been in force during the two different investigations.

The first interference to be considered will be that occurring in the determination of either sodium or potassium in systems containing both elements. For many of the studies made, particularly those of materials of natural or biological origin, a wide variety of sample preparations has been used. While this varied treatment should not alter the existing ratio of the two elements, the particular method employed would appear to have some effect on the magnitude and nature of the interference noted. Thus changes in the emitted intensities of either sodium or potassium due to their mutual interaction in such systems have been reported to range from negligible (102) to as much as a 70% enhancement (126, 136) or to a possible 50% depression (110) depending upon the preparative treatment of the sample.

The list of biological and natural systems in which an exclusive enhancement occurs for the emitted intensities of both sodium and potassium as a result of a mutual interference is extensive (1, 11, 15, 16, 25a, b, 31, 33, 39, 40, 50, 53, 57, 76, 80, 81, 84, 120, 127a, 136, 139, 142). Still others have found, however, that a mutual suppression exists for many of these (18, 20, 103, 110). Finally, one group of investigators observed that sodium increased the potassium value but that the potassium present had practically no effect on the radiation of sodium (97). It might be added that this study was made on a biological system (serum) for which several of the above-cited references (e.g., 16, 25b, 31, 50, 80, 126) reported definite mutual enhancement.

Studies of the singular effect of sodium on potassium have revealed a suppression of the 767-m$\mu$. emission of the latter in one case (45) and an enhancement in others (14, 23, 24, 38, 49, 70, 102, 127). Measurements of the influence of potassium on the 589-m$\mu$. emission of sodium have reportedly shown only an enhancement (108, 126). The sodium-potassium interference is somewhat distinguished by the fact that at least no one has found a complete lack of some sort of mutual interaction for these elements. In review, the preponderance of evidence favors the occurrence of a mutual sensitization of each element's characteristic radiation when the two are simultaneously present. The extent of the effect will be a function of the concentration ratio of the elements and the over-all concentration level arrived at by dilution of the sample. More specifically, the magnitude of the interference will tend to be larger when either one or both elements are found in appreciable amounts, i.e., 50 to 100 p.p.m. or greater. There is evidence to support the theory that their mutual influence in biological samples will be definitely minimized by working preferably with lower temperature flames and dilutions of 1:10 or greater (6, 15, 50, 80, 126).

The next typical mutual cation interference to be discussed is the effect of sodium and potassium upon the band emission of calcium. A simple and rapid determination of calcium, as might be supplied by flame photometry, is most desirable from the standpoint of biological analyses. The successful use of the method in this respect has been hindered by the apparent large error induced by the existing high sodium-to-calcium ratio. There is no question but that the spurious values often obtained with many of the instruments now in use are partly the fault of inadequate spectral resolution (*see* section 5.1.2.). Aside from this possibility, experimental evidence can be offered for the occurrence of true spectroscopic interactions of sodium or potassium with calcium.

Exclusive of any instrumental error, an appreciable enhancement of the 554-m$\mu$. calcium radiation is said to exist for ratios of sodium to calcium approximating those of certain biological samples (25b, 31, 122). In the course of earlier evaluation work with the Beckman unit, Gilbert *et al.* noted a slight depressing action of sodium on calcium emission at other concentration ratios (57). Gardiner, working with inorganic salt systems, could find no significant change in the 544-m$\mu$. band radiation of calcium, even when sodium-to-calcium ratios as large as 100/1 were tried, provided care was taken to minimize stray light and resolution errors (53).

Potassium, which may be present in substantial quantities in certain biological materials (e.g., urine), is reported to suppress the calcium 622-m$\mu$. band emission (50). In contrast, it has also been found that very small amounts of calcium (3 to 4 p.p.m.) will show an enhanced emitted intensity at 622 m$\mu$. if two to three times as much potassium is present (33).

In view of the above-expressed differences, it is impossible to state definitely whether or not calcium is subject to any true spectroscopic interferences from either sodium or potassium.

An example will be given of a spectroscopic interference for which there appears to be an expressed unanimity of opinion as to its specific nature. This is the marked quenching of the emitted radiation of several elements by aluminum. Those elements for which a measurable suppression has been observed are indium (88a), sodium (25a, 53), calcium (45, 53, 71, 86, 90, 93, 96, 131), strontium (45, 86, 90, 93, 131), barium (131), and lithium (130). As the effect is invariably reported as being negative and fairly large, it is quite certain that aluminum produces a true interference of sufficient intensity to prevent its being completely counterbalanced by any regularly encountered instrumental errors. The exact cause for this intense quenching action is not known with certainty. A theory has been advanced that the progressive increase in the aluminum effect on barium, strontium, and calcium radiation in that order results from an increase in the volatility of the individual alkaline earth-aluminum compound formed in the flame (131). For practical purposes it can be assumed that flame analyses of materials containing aluminum as a constituent will provide low analytical values. The essentially linear depression of both calcium and strontium as a function of aluminum concentration has served as an indirect method for the flame determination of aluminum (93).

To conclude the discussion of mutual cation interferences, comment will be made about some effects noted in systems containing lithium. Special attention to interactions involving this element is warranted in view of its popular usage as an internal standard in flame photometry. The successful application of an internal standard element is dependent upon complete independence of any mutual interferences that might alter emitted intensities. Fortunately lithium appears to be generally free of any serious spectroscopic interactions involving other elements, thus justifying its extensive application. The only exceptions to its nonreactivity seem to occur with certain cations at relatively high concentrations. As an example, at lithium-to-sodium or -potassium ratios of 100/1, positive errors of 7 to 10% were encountered by one group in determining the last two elements (73). At a 10/1 lithium-to-element ratio it has been noted that an approximate 12% increase in the emitted intensity of 100 p.p.m. potassium occurred, but sodium at the same concentration level seemed to be unaffected (53). It is quite possible that a good portion of the potassium increase was due to insufficient spectral isolation of the 767-m$\mu$. line. Parks and co-workers observed that at 10/1 ratios of lithium to sodium or potassium at the 100 p.p.m. level the sodium error was about 3% and negative and the potassium determination was not affected. At a 100/1 ratio the errors are reported by these workers to be potassium, $-35\%$ and sodium, $+37\%$ (103).

For the effect of various elements upon the lithium radiation, the literature reveals that both magnesium and aluminum (130) and sodium and potassium (45a) can effectively quench the lithium characteristic 671-m$\mu$. emission but that sodium will enhance it. At a 10/1 ratio of either magnesium or aluminum to lithium (20 p.p.m.) the lithium intensity has been observed to be depressed by 8% while a ratio of 100/1 produced an approximate 25% reduction (130). For very small lithium contents (about 1 p.p.m.), added sodium concentrations 100 to 200 times greater may result in an apparent 5 to 15% increase in lithium concentration (33). These data, although incomplete, indicate that lithium is not entirely free of possible flame interactions. Therefore, lithium or any internal standard should be applied with caution unless a sufficiently thorough exploratory study has shown the system under investigation to be relatively free of mutual interferences involving the selected reference element.

In addition to cation interactions, anions can also influence the flame-produced emissions of many elements. The effect may be detected as (a) merely the change in radiant intensity of a given concentration of an element depending upon the particular anion associated with it, (b) the gain or loss in intensity as the total anion concentration of the solution is greatly altered by added acids or their ammonium salts, or (c) the modification of a known mutual interference between two or more cations. In the first category only a few specific examples are known to exist. In general, it is found that alkali metal and alkaline earth radiations are independent of the particular associated anion (6, 33, 53). One exception is provided by the observation of Barnes and co-workers that calcium emission in the air-gas flame can be anion dependent (6). For other elements, copper and silver have been noted to exhibit an odd dependence upon anion composition. A systematic decrease in the intensity of the most persistent line (324 m$\mu$.) of copper in the oxygen-hydrogen flame has been found with copper salts in the order chloride, nitrate, acetate, and sulfate, but the second most persistent line (327 m$\mu$.) appeared unaffected. With silver, it was observed that the second most persistent line (338 m$\mu$.) decreased in intensity in the order nitrate, acetate, and sulfate, with the first persistent line (328 m$\mu$.) remaining unaltered (53). No explanation is offered for this phenomenon and it can only serve as a warning that the anion composition of the test solution must be considered in the flame photometric determination of at least some of the more metallic elements.

The second influence, that is, interferences from an added excess of inorganic acids, such as hydrochloric, nitric, sulfuric, or phosphoric, or their nonemitting salts, involves a slightly different problem as there is the possibility of changes in spray nebulosity. As far as is known, all studies of the effects of such additives involved the use of atomizing systems that would be subject to altered spray characteristics. There is evidence that excess anion effects may be avoided by the use of total consumption atomizers that feed the entire spray directly into the flame (139). It will be worth while including a few typical examples of excess anion interferences on the assumption that at least a part of, if not all, the effect observed is of noninstrumental origin.

Several authors have investigated what appeared to be the depression of sodium, potassium, and calcium emissions resulting from the addition of the above-listed acids or their salts (18, 29a, 44, 103, 131). Working under slightly different experimental conditions, others failed to find this depression with such anions as $NO_3^-$, $SO_4^=$, $Cl^-$, $Br^-$, and $I^-$ when present in excess (53, 62, 131, 141). In one of these studies, however, it was observed that large amounts of bicarbonate ion markedly reduced the emitted intensity of calcium (141). If similar investigations have been carried out with other than sodium, potassium, and calcium cations, the results have not been made generally available as yet.

The marked influence of phosphate is of special interest because of its presence in many biological and natural materials often examined by flame photometry. A 24 to 53% lowering of the apparent sodium concentration and a 19 to 29% lower potassium value have been reported for tissue ash analyses because of the presence of naturally occurring phosphate (34). Others were able to reduce this phosphate interference practically to zero for other tissue determinations by employing much greater sample dilutions (64, 123). Working with pure inorganic salts and acids, Parks and co-workers found that a phosphate concentration of approximately 3 M. reduced a known initial sodium content of 80 p.p.m. to an apparent value of 13 p.p.m. and that 80 p.p.m. of potassium analyzed as just 4 p.p.m. With a phosphate content of only 0.001 M. (98 p.p.m.), they found that 80 p.p.m. of sodium appeared as 69 p.p.m. by flame analysis and a corresponding initial potassium concentration was determined as 73 p.p.m. (103). Elsewhere similar observations were also made of the pronounced depressing action of phosphate on sodium (18, 24, 70, 97, 101), potassium (23, 24, 101, 136), and calcium (22a, 76).

The enhancement of sodium and potassium radiations has been reported by Ramsay et al. for comparatively small concentrations of added phosphate. A 25% gain in potassium and a 17% increase in sodium content was apparent for element-to-interferer ratios of 2.5/1 and 0.7/1 respectively (110). Another group has suggested that sodium will show a positive interference effect with phosphate while the potassium emission will be suppressed (136). No phosphate influence on either of these elements exists according to still others (22, 39, 53, 76, 113). As the majority opinion favors a depressing action, it might be assumed that low readings, particularly for sodium, potassium, and calcium, will result when materials containing appreciable amounts of phosphate are analyzed.

The final form of anion interference is comparatively rare and ordinarily will exist only when the interference saturation or radiation buffer method is applied (see section 5.3.4.); for example, the extent of the mutual enhancement of sodium and potassium emissions as a result of their mutual interference is known to be concentration dependent. In measuring one in the presence of a variable or unknown amount of the other, a sufficiently large excess of the interferer is added to eliminate those variations arising from differences in interferer concentration among various samples. This technique may be satisfactory, provided the associated anion of the salt added is carefully selected. It has been observed that if potassium nitrate is added in increasing amounts to a solution of sodium ion, the enhancement of sodium radiation becomes progressively larger and does not appear to reach a plateau. If potassium chloride is used, a definite saturation value is readily achieved above which further changes in potassium content do not affect the emitted intensity of the sodium (53). Additional studies of this sort might disclose the possible existence of other similar anomalies in the radiation-buffer technique. Methods for compensating many of the interferences discussed above are given in section 5.3.

*5.2.4. Suggested Theories for Interference Effects.* No universally applicable theory of flame interference effects has as yet been advanced. It seems unlikely that an all-inclusive explanation for both cation and cation-anion interactions will be forthcoming until the results obtained from a considerably greater amount of additional fundamental research are correlated with the existing extensive body of empirical knowledge. From a practical standpoint there is no straightforward manner in which possible spectroscopic interactions can be predicted with any degree of certainty for a given complex sample. The following is a brief survey of some of the fundamental concepts that must be considered in attempting to explain any specific interference.

The first step in the emission process is, of course, the introduction of the test material into the flame, and it is necessary to start here in determining all possible sources for interference effects. Those instrumental errors resulting from altered spray characteristics and composition, being concerned with just the prior transport of material to the flame, are not to be included in this treatment. Of importance, though, is the dispersion of the material into and throughout the combustion zone, where actual emission will take place. Smit and co-workers, being concerned with what is best described as flame kinetics, suggest that the size of the liquid spray droplets entering the flame can determine to a certain extent the intensity of the observed emission. According to them, the fairly high velocity of passage of material through the source may not give the larger liquid droplets sufficient time to complete the required volatilization and dissociation processes before passing out of a normally positioned photodetector's field of observation (126). While this may not appear to be too important a point, measurements with instruments that observe only a restricted portion of the flame might be subject to error when made under test conditions yielding widely varied spray droplet sizes and requiring high atomizing air pressures.

Assuming the test material is uniformly delivered into the flame at a reasonable velocity, the next step is the production of gaseous molecules of the compound containing the element of interest. These molecules must be dissociated by further heating to give neutral atoms which are the potentially emitting species. Consequently, the boiling points of elements or their compounds do enter as factors of considerable significance in all emission processes. Brode and Timma, working with the direct-current arc, have related the boiling point of an interfering element to the extent of its effect on the emitted intensity of another element (26). The mathematical expression they developed is as follows:

$$\frac{I}{I_0} = 1.32 - 0.284E_i - 0.000747\text{B.P.}_i + 0.000178E_i\text{B.P.}_i$$

where

$I$ = emitted intensity of cation + interferer
$I_0$ = emitted intensity of cation alone
$E_i$ = ionization potential of the interfering cation
B.P.$_i$ = boiling point of the interfering cation

It may be found that under certain conditions this relationship will hold for a given flame interference series, such as the effect of one alkali metal upon another, but it is doubtful whether the interference behavior of other more complex systems can be adequately expressed in such a simple manner. In view of the likelihood of mixed salts or emitting element complexes being formed prior to the gaseous dissociation step (6, 54, 71, 103, 131), the boiling-point relationship for a flame source is no doubt considerably more complicated than has as yet been suggested. Further clarification cannot be given because of the lack of suitable boiling-point diagrams for even the simplest binary systems that may be studied flame photometrically.

The processes occurring after the formation of gaseous molecules can be described by the following equilibria:

atoms in the resonance state
⇅
gaseous molecules ⇌ neutral atoms ⇌ ions + electrons

As the return of excited or resonance atoms to the neutral atom state is the sole source of the element's characteristic flame emission, any factor that will effectively alter the equilibrium involving the two will result in a gain or loss in observed radiant intensity. Typical calculations will reveal that the number of excited atoms at any given time is extremely small, but it is pointed out elsewhere that the number in the nonemitting ionized condition is surprisingly large (71, 126). Thus it becomes apparent that significant changes in emitted intensity can also result indirectly from any applied influence that shifts the neutral atom-ion-electron equilibrium. As a matter of fact, the most coherent theory so far advanced for the cause of mutual cation interferences is based on the effect of induced changes in the neutral atom-ion balance in the flame.

Smit and co-workers (126, 127) and Alkemade (1, 3) have made extensive studies of the interference of sodium on the flame emission of potassium. The enhancement of potassium radiation is explained as being due to the suppression of ionization by the excess electrons from the more readily ionized sodium atoms. Specifically, the neutral atom-ion-electron equilibrium for potassium is shifted to the left in favor of the existence of a larger number of potentially emitting neutral atoms. Huldt (71), Gaydon (54), and Hultgren (72) from other studies have all proposed a similar mechanism to explain the flame interactions they observed. This theory suggests that for a given emitter the addition of a series of interfering elements having a systematic decrease in ionization potential should produce a progressive increase in observed emitted intensity. This relationship does apparently hold for successive pairs of alkali metals (53).

Accordingly, the suppression of a given radiation of interest might be theoretically explained by the reverse process. The more ready acceptance of free electrons by the neutral atom-ion-electron equilibrium of the interfering element should lead to a decrease in the neutral atom concentration of the observed emitter. The fact that the sodium-potassium interaction results in a particularly pronounced mutual enhancement and that other alkali metal pairs behave similarly indicates that this comparatively simple theory is also not adequate. It might be noted that Brode and Timma's mathematical relationship does include the ionization potential of only the interfering cation. Thus it would seem that their expression oversimplifies the contribution of ionization effects in interference reactions and that Smit and Alkemade's theory does not include a consideration of volatility effects. Some combination of the foregoing two theories would probably more nearly express the complicated interference relationships that exist in the flame.

In explaining observed gains or losses in a characteristic emitted intensity, one must also consider the possibility of such other spectroscopic reactions as radiation quenching through absorption by atoms of either the same or different species. For example, Mitchell states that the pronounced depressing action of aluminum in the flame is caused by its ability to absorb readily radiations of other elements (93). Further decreases in radiant intensity can also result from those energy losses due to certain collision processes between potentially emitting atoms and other atoms in the flame. More detailed treatments of this type of phenomenon are given by Gaydon (54) and Huldt (71).

So far nothing specific has been said about possible theories to explain anion interferences. Actually very little information treating cation-anion interactions as a spectroscopic effect is found in available flame photometry literature. The only extensive treatment of this sort appears to be given by Collins and Polkinhorne (32). They suggest that cation emission is depressed by the presence of excess anions through a shift in the equilibrium expressing the reaction in the flame between cations and anions to give molecules. In a manner analogous to that represented by the above-mentioned ionic equilibria, an increase in the number of nonemitting gaseous molecules occurs at the expense of potentially emitting neutral atoms, thereby causing a subsequent decrease in emitted intensity. Obviously anion contributions must be considered in the overall theoretical treatment of interference reactions.

### 5.3. Methods for Compensating Errors and Interferences

A number of methods have been suggested for eliminating or compensating those uncertainties that seem to be inherent in flame photometry. The most direct corrective treatment is to remove by either chemical or physical means the interfering elements or material if they are known. Typically, many investigators working with biological samples have found that the elimination of protein matter by precipitation with trichloracetic acid yielded more accurate sodium, potassium, and calcium determinations (122, 126). Direct ashing of such samples and redissolving of the residue in either acid solution or water are also effective means of removing organic matter. The error caused by calcium in the determination of sodium in plants and soils was eliminated by adding ammonium oxalate to the extracted sample solution and filtering off the calcium oxalate formed (121). Where excess sodium is the interfering element, its removal may be achieved by the triple acetate separation with zinc uranyl acetate as precipitant, provided that such treatment does not produce unwanted changes in the test solution. Filtration of suspended silica in dissolved cement samples proved effective in reducing a previously noted interference in the desired sodium and potassium analyses (37).

An obvious modification of the removal technique is to separate the particular element of interest from the solution rather than to try to remove the interfering substances. Thus many have found that calcium determinations in complex materials are better performed flame photometrically if the calcium is first precipitated as the oxalate, then filtered, and the washed precipitate redissolved in a suitable acid medium. Several have developed procedures for handling plasma and urine samples in this manner (9, 50).

Some attention might be given to the many liquid extraction methods now available for those cases where a direct chemical treatment is not desirable. Great care must be taken in applying separation techniques to avoid either the unsuspected introduction of some new interfering element or material during the treatment or achieving only an incomplete removal of the desired element. In one of the above-mentioned oxalate separations developed for plasma and urine, it was found that an equivalent addition of oxalate ion to all calibration samples was required in order to compensate the observed oxalate-induced depression of calcium emission (50). Any procedure that satisfactorily removes an encountered interference is suitable for the preparation of flame photometric samples provided the work involved is neither time-consuming nor laborious. The advantage of the flame method is generally lost if a 2- or 3-hr. treatment of the test material is needed prior to its actual analysis.

5.3.1. *The Internal Standard Technique.* The nearest approach to an all-inclusive method for compensating for instrumental errors and interferences is the internal standard technique. Here a known amount (usually 50 to 500 p.p.m.) of a reference substance, most commonly a lithium salt, is added to all samples (see 18, 50, 142 for typical procedures with lithium). Also successfully used as internal standard elements in flame photometry have been cobalt (29, 115), manganese (65), strontium (22a), and rubidium, cesium, thallium, and potassium (114). By simultaneously observing both the internal standard radiation and the emission of analytical interest, one may establish an emitted intensity ratio that is relatively independent of flame fluctuations, alterations in the nature and rate of atomization, and other existing instrumental variations. If mutual interference effects are approximately equivalent for the internal standard and those elements in the test sample, a partial compensation of these interactions also results.

Barnes and co-workers found that their standard error of 3% for sodium and potassium determinations obtained by the absolute method could be reduced to only 1.2% if lithium was used as the internal standard (18). White achieved a precision of ±0.3% for the analysis of the same elements by internal standard measurements as compared with ±1% obtained by absolute readings (127). Such excellent results were achieved in these cases because the test conditions selected and the dilutions used greatly reduced the effects of any possible interferences. Under different test conditions, e.g., higher flame temperatures, there is some indication that lithium as the internal standard does not completely compensate the known mutual sodium-potassium interference (14). To apply an internal standard successfully, the user must be certain that, first, the test sample does not already contain measurable amounts of the chosen internal standard element and, second, that there will be no apparent interaction between the added standard and any constituent of the unknown specimen. Details of other typical applications of internal standards are given in the literature for flame determinations of biological specimens (16, 17, 50), soils and plant extracts (8, 52, 121), and refractory materials (19, 105).

*5.3.2. The Dilution Technique.* A method often useful for minimizing both interferences and instrumental errors is simply to dilute the sample as much as possible without exceeding the lowest concentration at which satisfactory measurements can be made. Studies of the sources of error in a typical filter flame photometer have shown that the sodium-potassium interference is noticeably reduced if the sample is less concentrated (20). Others have also noted that many of the unwanted intensity variations encountered in the determination of sodium and potassium in biological fluids could be minimized by use of dilutions of as much as 1:100 or 1:200 (15, 80). Unfortunately the usual initial low concentration of the particular elements of interest, the large dilution errors possible, and the average flame photometer's limited sensitivity will prevent the extensive use of the dilution technique.

*5.3.3. Radiation Buffers.* The purpose of the radiation buffer is to saturate a known interference so that small variations in interferer content from sample to sample will not have significant effects on observed emitted intensities. This is usually achieved by adding a large excess of the interfering ion, or ions, to all solutions. The classical example of an application of radiation buffers is supplied by the determination of sodium, potassium, and calcium in water samples, as discussed by West *et al.* (141). For the sodium measurement, the sodium calibration solutions and a volume of the unknown solution were literally saturated with reagent-grade chlorides of calcium, potassium, and magnesium—the latter being originally present in the water samples as a suspected interferer. In a like manner, the calibration solutions for potassium and calcium contained saturation amounts of the appropriate salts while other aliquots of the unknown samples were similarly treated. The results obtained indicated that the previously experienced mutual interferences were adequately compensated in this way.

Mitchell and Robertson found that the quenching of calcium radiation by aluminum could be offset by saturating the test solution with a calcium-free strontium salt. Similarly the negative error in the determination of strontium due to the presence of aluminum was reduced by use of an excess amount of a calcium salt as the additive (93). In the course of similar studies it was found that magnesium chloride was an even more effective buffer for the depressing action of aluminum (96).

The major disadvantage of buffer techniques are the possible inclusion of undesired impurities from the large amount of buffer salt that must be used and the excessive and not necessarily consistent alterations in spray characteristics arising from the drastic increase in the dissolved solids concentration of the test solutions. Also, total-consumption atomizers (Fig. 5B and C) will give contamination errors because of the deposition of salts around the jet orifice from evaporation of such concentrated samples. From experience it will be found that the best results in flame photometry are most often obtained by working with comparatively simple solutions of low total solids content.

*5.3.4. Synthetic Calibration Samples.* If the relative amounts of all interfering ions and materials are known, adequate compensation for their influences may be achieved by compounding the required calibration series to simulate the unknown's matrix composition. Numerous examples of this procedure are to be found in the literature, as many materials are more expediently handled in this way than by trying to remove or otherwise compensate for existing interferences.

The synthetic sample technique is commonly used in the determination of potassium and the alkaline earths in serum and urine. Aside from the presence of appreciable amounts of protein materials, the greatest single interference encountered is provided by the existing large sodium concentration. Improved results have been obtained by using calibration solutions containing an added sodium content approximating the level characteristic of the biological fluids (17, 70, 79, 80, 102). The compensation of suspected errors due to the interaction of the other sample constituents has been achieved by compounding even more complex standards containing added phosphate, glycerol or glucose, potassium salts, etc. (97, 140). The use of synthetic calibration samples has also been advantageously applied to the flame analysis of the alkalies and alkaline earths in ores, clays, mineral products, and similar refractory substances (7, 19, 45a, 88a, 96). Strontium in sea water was successfully determined only after synthetic sea water calibration solutions were prepared (125).

*5.3.5. The Indirect Correction of Errors and Interference Effects.* The final methods to be discussed are indirect methods of compensating for errors and interferences because the undesired changes in emitted intensity are corrected by either graphical or mathematical means. As an example, an interference of varying amounts of element $A$ on the characteristic radiation of $B$ is observed. If the emitted intensity value of $B$ changes linearly with known increment changes of $A$, a correction factor for $A$ at various concentrations can be readily obtained. To analyze the unknown sample, its $A$ content must first be determined and then the corresponding correction factor for that interferer concentration is applied to the subsequently observed value of $B$. This simple method has been successfully used for rapidly correcting the analytical errors resulting from mutual interferences in the determination of calcium, strontium, and barium in plant tissues (69).

A somewhat more complicated method for correcting errors resulting from unpredictable changes in solution viscosity and surface tension, as encountered in concentrated sugar solutions, has also been worked out (8). In this method synthetic calibration samples having physical characteristics similar to those of the test solutions are prepared. Lithium is used as a reference element and its behavior when it is added to the unknown solution is, along with the observed reading of the element being determined, referred to the appropriate family of calibration curves. A deduced correction factor is obtained in this manner, which is in turn applied to the analytical reading. Other indirect methods have been developed for correcting the flame photometric values of milk elements (76) and sodium and potassium determinations from the flame analysis of some rocks and minerals (101).

There is no definite rule to be followed in deciding what type of error or interference compensation might best be employed in a given case. The limitations in sample treatment that must be observed, the type of instrument available, and the magnitude and probable source of the undesired effects will each be of varying importance for every new problem. The least complicated and most direct method for correction or compensation is naturally desired, but often the complexity of the interactions encountered may require that a devious and indirect scheme be developed.

## 6. Uses of Flame Photometry

From the reported applications extant, one can roughly classify the uses of flame photometry as (a) the determination of sodium and potassium in biological specimens or (b) the less frequent analysis of these and approximately a dozen other elements in a variety of natural products and inorganic materials. Such a classification is justified if the numerical distribution of literature references is accepted as the sole criterion for evaluating the usefulness of the method. However, it is felt that the details of many practical industrial applications of flame photometry have not been published or made generally known and that the availability of this information would definitely show that a very extensive range of applications does exist. Reference has already been made in various preceding sections to some of the specific biological systems that have been treated flame photometrically, and it should suffice here to say in summary that sodium and potassium and, to a much lesser extent, calcium can be readily determined in whole blood, plasma, serum, feces, urine, and other body fluids, and body tissues of all types. Other natural products for which similar determinations are frequently reported include plant leaf and fruit extracts (5, 8, 29, 61, 75, 118, 118a, 121, 127a, 134) and soil extracts (29, 52, 88, 89, 90, 116, 128, 133, 135).

Given in Table V are additional examples of flame photometric applications for which definite procedures have been developed, and the cited references can be consulted for working details. Suggested flame analyses

TABLE V

*Other Applications of Flame Photometry for Which Procedures Have Been Developed and Additional References to Some Applications Already Cited in the Text*

| Element determined | Material (pertinent reference in bracket) |
|---|---|
| Li | Glass (27); metals and alloys (99, 130); petroleum oils (33); Portland cement (87), silicate rocks (45a) |
| Na | Boiler waters and scale (120); clays (19); firebrick (19); glass (19, 27, 81); medical products (38); milk (76); organic salts (82); Portland cement (4, 36, 37, 46, 46a, 59, 105); rocks, minerals, and metals (19, 25a, 73, 81, 98, 101); natural waters (29, 59, 108, 141) |
| K | Boiler waters and scale (120); clays (19); fertilizers (23, 47, 48); firebrick (19); glass (19, 27, 81); medical products (38); milk (76); Portland cement (4, 36, 46, 46a, 59, 105); natural waters (29, 59, 141); rocks, minerals, and metals (19, 73, 81, 99, 101) |
| Mg | Body tissues (29); limestone (30); mortar (30); natural waters (29); soils (29, 90); whole blood (29) |
| Ca | Glass (81); milk (76); natural waters (29, 29a, 59, 141); petroleum oils (33, 94); rocks and minerals (65, 69, 81, 96); phosphoric acid (22a) |
| Sr | Natural waters (29, 125, 130a); minerals (69); petroleum oils (33); soils (90); Portland cement (37a) |
| Ba | Minerals (69); petroleum oils (33) |
| Cu | Fruit juices (61); natural waters (29); vegetable juices (29); nonferrous alloys (35a) |
| Pb | Gasoline (56) |
| Al | Soils (93) |
| Mn | Water solution (37b) |
| In | Bronze alloys (88a) |

for which there do not as yet appear to be any definite published data might include the following. The method is ideally suited as a rapid routine means of analyzing and checking the purity of demineralized water produced by ion exchangers or other water-softening treatments. The efficiency of many industrial washing processes could be controlled in those cases where one of the to-be-removed impurities is capable of flame detection. Also the possibility of smoke, flue-gas, and industrial dust determinations has already been briefly touched upon.

The indirect flame determination of such nonemitters as the halides, sulfate, phosphate, carbonate, and other anionic groups for which flame-sensitive precipitants are available should not be overlooked. In each case a measured excess amount of the appropriate precipitating agent, e.g., silver, barium, calcium, etc., is added, and the portion remaining after the separation of the precipitate is then analyzed. Reference might also be made to Mitchell's indirect method of determining aluminum, which is based on the measurement of its interference on a known added amount of either calcium or strontium (93). Suitable calibration of other interferences, which should be measurably large and preferably linear for reasonable additions of the selected interferent, might prove to be a useful added application.

Actually the flame method can be applied to any determination where known flame-emitting elements are involved and the material can be readily brought into solution. The quality of the results obtained will be limited only by the expertness of the operator and his ability to recognize, correctly interpret, and consistently compensate for those errors and interferences that may occur.

## ACKNOWLEDGMENT

The author gratefully acknowledges the criticisms made by Dr. J. T. Funkhouser and Dr. R. P. Buck during the preparation of the manuscript.

## REFERENCES

1. Alkemade, C. T. J., *Physica* **18**, 933 (1952).
2. Alkemade, C. T. J., Smit, J., and Verschure, J. C. M., *Biochim. et Biophys. Acta* **8**, 562 (1952).
3. Alkemade, C. T. J., *Chem. Weekblad* **48**, 699 (1952).
4. A. S. T. M., Method for Portland cement (C228-49T). "Book of Standards," Part 3, p. 133. American Society for Testing Materials, Philadelphia.
5. Attoe, O. J., *Soil Sci. Soc. Amer. Proc.* **12**, 131 (1947).
6. Barnes, R. B., Richardson, D., Berry, J. W., and Hood, R. L., *Ind. Eng. Chem. Anal. Ed.* **17**, 605 (1945).
7. Barnes, R. B., Berry, J. W., and Hill, W. B., *Eng. Mining J.* **149**, 92 (1948).
8. Bauserman, H. M., and Cerney, R. R., Jr., *Anal. Chem.* **25**, 1821 (1953).
9. Beckman Bulletin DU-9-B. Beckman Instruments, Inc. South Pasadena, Calif.
10. Beckman, A. O., and Cary, H., *J. Opt. Soc. Amer.* **39**, 377 (1949).
11. Belke, J., and Dierkesmann, A., *Arch. exptl. Pathol. Pharmakol.* **205**, 629 (1948).
12. Benotti, J., and Detorre, A., *J. Lab. Clin. Med.* **36**, 763 (1950).
13. Benotti, J., in "Standard Methods of Clinical Chemistry" (M. Reiner, ed.), Vol. 1, p. 107. Academic Press, New York, 1953.
14. Bernstein, R. E., *Nature* **165**, 649 (1950).
15. Bernstein, R. E., *Biochim. et Biophys. Acta* **9**, 576 (1952).
16. Bernstein, R. E., *S. African J. Med. Sci.* **17**, 101 (1952).
17. Bernstein, R. E., *J. Lab. Clin. Med.* **40**, 707 (1952).

18. Berry, J. W., Chappel, D. G., and Barnes, R. B., *Ind. Eng. Chem. Anal. Ed.* **18,** 19 (1946).

19. Biffen, F. M., *Anal. Chem.* **22,** 1014 (1950).

20. Bills, C. C., McDonald, F. G., Niedermeier, W., and Schwartz, M. C., *Anal. Chem.* **21,** 1076 (1949).

21. Boon, S. D., "Vlam-Fotometrie." D. B. Centen, Amsterdam, 1945.

22. Bowman, R. L., and Berliner, R. W., *Federation Proc.* **8,** 14 (1949).

22a. Brabson, J. A., and Wilhide, W. D., *Anal. Chem.* **26,** 1060 (1954).

23. Brealey, L., *Analyst* **76,** 340 (1951).

24. Brealey, L., and Ross, R. E., *Analyst* **76,** 334 (1951).

25a. Brewster, D. A., and Clausen, C. L., Jr., *Iron Age* **166,** 88 (1950).

25b. Bulletin No. 151 A. Scientific Instrument Division, Fearless Camera Corp., Los Angeles, Calif.

25c. Bulletin 193B, June, 1948. Beckman Instruments, Inc., South Pasadena, Calif.

26. Brode, W. R., and Timma, D. L., *J. Opt. Soc. Amer.* **39,** 478 (1949).

27. Broderick, E. J., and Zack, P. G., *Anal. Chem.* **23,** 1455 (1951).

27a. Caton, R. D., and Bremner, R. W., *Anal. Chem.* **26,** 805 (1954).

28. Chen, P. S., Jr., and Toribara, T. Y., *Anal. Chem.* **25,** 1642 (1953).

28a. Chen, P. S., Jr., and Toribara, T. Y., *Anal. Chem.* **26,** 1967 (1954).

29. Cholak, J., and Hubbard, D. M., *Ind. Eng. Chem. Anal. Ed.* **16,** 728 (1944).

29a. Chow, T. J., and Thompson, T. G., *Anal. Chem.* **27,** 910 (1955).

30. Close, P., Smith, W. E., and Watson, M. T., Jr., *Anal. Chem.* **25,** 1022 (1953).

31. Collier, H. B., and Barschel, R. P., *Anal. Chem.* **24,** 1030 (1952).

32. Collins, G. C., and Polkinhorne, H., *Analyst* **77,** 430 (1952).

33. Conrad, A. L., and Johnson, W. C., *Anal. Chem.* **22,** 1930 (1950).

34. Crismon, J. M., *Federation Proc.* **7,** 24 (1948).

35. Curtis, G. W., Knauer, H. E., and Hunter, L. E., *ASTM Spec. Tech. Publ.* No. **116** (1951).

35a. Dean, J. A., *Anal. Chem.* **27,** 1224 (1955).

36. Diamond, J. J., and Bean, L., *ASTM Spec. Tech. Publ.* No. **116** (1951).

37. Diamond, J. J., and Bean, L., *Anal. Chem.* **25,** 1825 (1953).

37a. Diamond, J. J., *Anal. Chem.* **27,** 913 (1955).

37b. Dippel, W. A., and Bricker, C. E., *Anal. Chem.* **27,** 1484 (1955).

38. Domange, L., and Longuevalle, S., *Ann. pharm. franc.* **9,** 647 (1951).

39. Domingo, W. R., and Klyne, W., *Biochem. J.* **45,** 400 (1949).

40. Domingo, W. R., Klyne, W., and Weedon, W., *Biochem. J.* **42,** 36 (1948).

41. Dubbs, C. A., *Anal. Chem.* **24,** 1654 (1952).

42. Dunker, E., and Passow, H., *Biochem. Z.* **321,** 152 (1950).

43. Dunker, E., *Klin. Wochschr.* **15,** 280 (1953).

44. Eggertsen, F. T., Wyld, G., and Lykken, L., *ASTM Spec. Tech. Publ.* No. **116** (1951).

45. Ells, V. R., *J. Opt. Soc. Amer.* **31,** 534 (1941).

45a. Ellsted, R. B., and Horstman, E. L., *Anal. Chem.* **27,** 1229 (1955).

46. Eubank, W. R., and Bogue, R. H., *J. Research Natl. Bur. Standards* **43,** 173 (1949).

46a. Ford, C. L., *Anal. Chem.* **26,** 1578 (1954).

47. Ford, O. W., *J. Assoc. Offic. Agr. Chemists* **34,** 660 (1951).

48. Ford, O. W., *J. Assoc. Offic. Agr. Chemists* **35,** 764 (1952).

49. Fox, C. L., Jr., *Anal. Chem.* **23,** 137 (1951).

50. Fox, C. L., Jr., Freeman, E. B., and Lasker, S. E., *ASTM Spec. Tech. Publ.* No. **116** (1951).

51. Frankenberg, B., Hospadaruk, V., and Neufeld, A. H., *Can. Med. Assoc. J.* **65**, 388 (1951).
52. Gammon, N., Jr., *Soil Sci.* **71**, 211 (1951).
53. Gardiner, K. W., Ph.D. Thesis, M. I. T. (1952).
54. Gaydon, E. G., *Quart. Revs. (London)* **4**, 1 (1950).
55. Gilbert, P. T., Jr., *Industrial Laboratories* (1952).
56. Gilbert, P. T., Jr., *ASTM Spec. Tech. Publ.* No. **116** (1951).
57. Gilbert, P. T., Jr., *Anal. Chem.* **22**, 772 (1950).
58. Gilbert, P. T., Jr., *Anal. Chem.* **23**, 676 (1951).
59. Gilliland, J. L., *ASTM Spec. Tech. Publ.* No. **116** (1951).
60. Gouy, C. L., *Ann. chim. et phys.* **18**, 5 (1879).
61. Griggs, M. A., *Science* **89**, 134 (1939).
62. Griggs, M. A., *Ind. Eng. Chem. Anal. Ed.* **13**, 99 (1941).
63. Hald, P. M., *J. Biol. Chem.* **163**, 429 (1946).
64. Hald, P. M., *J. Biol. Chem.* **167**, 499 (1947).
65. Heidel, R. H., and Fassel, V. A., *Anal. Chem.* **23**, 784 (1951).
66. Herrmann, R., *Z. ges. exptl. Med.* **118**, 187 (1952).
67. Herrmann, R., and Lederle, P., *Bodenkunde u. Pflanzenernähr.* **30**, 189 (1942).
68. Heyes, J., *Angew. Chem.* **50**, 871 (1937).
69. Hinsvark, O. N., Wittwer, S. H., and Sell, H. M., *Anal. Chem.* **25**, 320 (1953).
70. Hospadaruk, V., Frankenber, G. B., and Neufeld, A. H., *J. Can. Med. Assoc.* **65**, 264 (1951).
71. Huldt, L., *Astronomi Och Fysik.* **33A**, 1 (1947).
72. Hultgren, R., *J. Am. Chem. Soc.* **54**, 2320 (1932).
73. Inman, W. R., Rogers, R. A., and Fournier, J. A., *Anal. Chem.* **23**, 482 (1951).
74. Jansen, W. H., Heyes, J., and Richter, O., *Z. physik. Chem.* A **174**, 291 (1935).
75. Johnston, B. R., Duncan, C. W., Lawton, K., and Benne, E. J., *J. Assoc. Offic. Agr. Chemists* **35**, 813 (1952).
76. Keirs, R. J., and Speck, S. J., *J. Dairy Sci.* **33**, 413 (1950).
77. King, W. H., and Priestley, Wm., Jr., *ASTM Spec. Tech. Publ.* No. **116** (1951).
78. Kingsley, G. R., and Schaffert, R. R., *Anal. Chem.* **25**, 1738 (1953).
79. Klyne, W., *Proc. Biochem. Soc.*, 23 and 24 July (1948).
80. Klyne, W., *Spectrochim. Acta* **4**, 64 (1950).
81. Knight, S. B., Mathis, W. C., and Graham, J. R., *Anal. Chem.* **23**, 1704 (1951).
82. Knight, S. B., and Peterson, M. H., *Anal. Chem.* **24**, 1514 (1952).
83. Leyton, L., *Analyst* **76**, 723 (1951).
84. Lundegardh, H., "Die Quantitative Spectralanalyse der Elemente," Vols. 1 and 2. Gustav Fisher, Jena, 1929, 1934.
85. Lundegardh, H., *Z. Physik.* **66**, 109 (1930).
86. McClelland, J. A. C., and Whalley, K. N., *J. Soc. Chem. Ind.* **60**, 288T (1941).
87. McCoy, W. J., and Christiansen, G. G., *ASTM Spec. Tech. Publ.* No. **116** (1951).
88. Mehlich, A., and Monroe, R. J., *J. Assoc. Offic. Agr. Chemists* **35**, 588 (1952).
88a. Meloche, V. W., Ramsay, J. B., Mack, D. J., and Philip, T. V., *Anal. Chem.* **26**, 1387 (1954).
89. Mitchell, R. L., *J. Soc. Chem. Ind.* **55**, 267 (1936).
90. Mitchell, R. L., "Spectrographic Analysis in Great Britain." Adam Hilger, London, 1939.
91. Mitchell, R. L., *Spectrochim. Acta* **4**, 62 (1950).
92. Mitchell, R. L., *J. Soc. Chem. Ind.* **60**, 95 (1941).
93. Mitchell, R. L., and Robertson, I. M., *J. Soc. Chem. Ind.* **55**, 269 (1936).

94. Moberg, M. L., Waithman, V. B., Ellis, W. H., and DuBois, H. D., *ASTM Spec. Tech. Publ.* No. **116** (1951).

95. Monvoisin, J., and Mavrodineanu, R., *Spectrochim. Acta* **4**, 152 (1950).

96. Mosher, R. E., Bird, E. J., and Boyle, A. J., *Anal. Chem.* **22**, 715 (1950).

97. Mosher, R. E., Boyle, A. J., Bird, E. J., Jacobson, S. D., Batchelor, T. M., Iseri, L. T., and Myers, G. B., *Am. J. Clin. Pathol.* **19**, 461 (1949).

98. Mosher, R. E., Itano, A., Boyle, A. J., Myers, G. B., and Iseri, L. T., *Am. J. Clin. Pathol.* **21**, 75 (1951).

99. Mullin, H. R., and Sheely, T. P., "The Flame Photometric Determinations of Sodium, Lithium and Potassium in Beryllium." Private communication, 1953.

100. Olney, J. M., and Jones, A. H., *Science* **115**, 244 (1952).

101. Osborn, G. H., and Johns, H., *Analyst* **76**, 410 (1951).

102. Overman, R. R., and Davis, A. K., *J. Biol. Chem.* **168**, 641 (1947).

103. Parks, T. D., Johnson, H. O., and Lykken, L., *Ind. Eng. Chem. Anal. Ed.* **20**, 822 (1948).

103a. Porter, P., and Wyld, G., *Anal. Chem.* **27**, 733 (1955).

104. Pratt, P. F., and Larson, W. E., *Anal. Chem.* **21**, 1296 (1949).

105. Pritchard, L. R., *Pit and Quarry* **41**, 83 (1948).

106. Ramage, H., *Nature* **123**, 601 (1929).

107. Ramage, H., and Harley, W. N., *J. Chem. Soc.* **71**, 533 (1897).

108. Ramsay, J. A., *J. Exptl. Biol.* **27**, 497 (1950).

109. Ramsay, J. A., Falloon, S. W. H. W., and Machin, K. E., *J. Sci. Instr.* **28**, 75 (1951).

110. Ramsay, J. A., Brown, R. H. J., and Falloon, S. W. H. W., *J. Exptl. Biol.* **30**, 1 (1953).

111. Rauterberg, E., and Knippenberg, E., *Bodenkunde u. Pflanzenernähr.* **20**, 364 (1940); *Ernähr. Pflanze.* **37**, 73 (1941).

112. Riehm, H., *Bodenkunde u. Pflanzenernähr.* **28**, 246 (1942).

113. Riehm, H., *Z. Anal. Chem.* **128**, 249 (1948).

114. Robinson, A. R., and Ovenston, T. J. C., *Analyst* **76**, 416 (1951).

115. Robinson, A. R., Newman, K. J., and Schoeb, E. J., *Anal. Chem.* **22**, 1026 (1950).

116. Rogers, L. H., *Soil. Sci. Soc. Amer. Proc.* **12**, 124 (1947).

117. Schmitt, L., and Breitweiser, W., *Bodenkunde u. Pflanzenernähr.* **10**, 750 (1938).

118. Schrenk, W. G., and Smith, F. M., *Anal. Chem.* **22**, 1023 (1950).

118a. Schrenk, W. G., and Glendening, B. L., *Anal. Chem.* **27**, 1031 (1955).

119. Schuhknecht, W., *Angew. Chem.* **50**, 299 (1937).

120. Scott, R. K., Marcy, V. M., and Hronas, J. J., *ASTM Spec. Tech. Publ.* No. **116** (1951).

121. Seay, W. A., Attoe, O. J., and Truog, E., *Soil Sci.* **71**, 83 (1951).

122. Severinghaus, J. W., and Ferrebee, J. W., *J. Biol. Chem.* **187**, 621 (1950).

123. Shapiro, S., and Hoagland, H., *Am. J. Physiol.* **153**, 428 (1948).

124. Sims, E. A. H., and Kaplow, L., *J. Lab. Clin. Med.* **41**, 303 (1953).

125. Smales, A. A., *Analyst* **76**, 348 (1951).

126. Smit, J. A., Alkemade, C. T. J., and Verschure, J. C. M., *Biochim. et Biophys. Acta* **6**, 508 (1951).

127. Smit, J. A., and Vendrik, A. J. H., *Physica* **14**, 505 (1948).

127a. Spector, J., *Anal. Chem.* **27**, 1452 (1955).

128. Standford, G., and English, L., *Agron. J.* **41**, 446 (1949).

129. Stone, D., and Shapiro, S., *Science* **108**, 503 (1948).

130. Strange, E. E., *Anal. Chem.* **25**, 650 (1953).

130a. Taylor, A. E., and Paige, H. H., *Anal. Chem.* **27**, 282 (1955).

131. Török, T., *Z. anal. Chem.* **116**, 29 (1939).

132. Toscani, V., *Anal. Chem.* **19**, 820 (1947).

133. Toth, S. J., and Prince, A. L., *Soil Sci.* **67**, 439 (1949).

134. Toth, S. J., Prince, A. I., Wallace, A., and Mikkelsen, D. S., *Soil Sci.* **66**, 459 (1948).

135. Wallace, A., Toth, S. J., and Bear, F. E., *Soil Sci.* **65**, 249 (1947).

136. Wallace, W. M., Holliday, M., Cushman, M., and Elkington, J. R., *J. Lab. Clin. Med.* **37**, 621 (1951).

137. Walsh, E. G., and Wolff, H. S., *Nature* **167**, 683 (1951).

138. Walsh, E. G., *J. Sci. Instr.* **29**, 23 (1952).

139. Weichselbaum, T. E., and Varney, P. L., *Proc. Soc. Exptl. Biol. Med.* **71**, 570 (1949).

140. Weiner, A. D., and Kuhnes, D. M., *Am. J. Clin. Pathol.* **23**, 1259 (1953).

141. West, P. W., Folse, P., and Montgomery, D., *Anal. Chem.* **22**, 667 (1950).

142. White, J. U., *Anal. Chem.* **24**, 394 (1952).

143. Willits, C. O., and Connelly, J. A., *Anal. Chem.* **24**, 1525 (1952).

144. Wynn, V., Simon, S., Morris, R. J. H., McDonald, I. R., and Denton, D. A., *Med. J. Australia* **37**, 821 (1950).

# Microwave Spectroscopy

By

BENJAMIN P. DAILEY

*Department of Chemistry, Columbia University, New York, New York*

## 1. Introduction

Molecular spectroscopy has been a subject of considerable interest to chemical analysts for many years. The characteristic absorptions and emissions of atomic and molecular systems in regions of the electromagnetic spectrum ranging from X rays through the infrared have been used for identification and for quantitative analysis. The rapid development of microwave spectroscopy since 1946 has aroused interest in the possible application of spectral techniques in this new frequency range to problems of chemical analysis.

Spectroscopy in the microwave region has its own special procedures just as does spectroscopy in the other major regions of the electromagnetic spectrum. Also the range of energy differences giving rise to spectra in the microwave region is different from that of the older forms of spectroscopy. As a result, microwave spectroscopy has its own special advantages and disadvantages. Many of the unique characteristics of microwave spectroscopy originate in the very high resolution available in this spectral region and in the circumstance that the samples are usually gases at low pressures.

Of course certain interesting experiments can be performed in studying the absorption of microwave radiation by solids and liquids. The absorptions of this kind that are probably of greatest chemical interest are those of substances containing electrons with unpaired spins which give rise to paramagnetic resonances in a magnetic field. This subject will be discussed in a separate section of this chapter.

The high-resolution characteristic of the microwave spectroscopy of gases at low pressures makes it possible to measure the frequency of spectral lines with great accuracy. Overlapping of spectral lines occurs infrequently. As a result, microwave spectra are highly specific properties of a molecule. Ordinarily the measurement of the frequency of a single spectral line will serve to identify the molecule to which it belongs.

It should be possible by use of the microwave spectrometer to identify each of a large number of components in a complex gas mixture by means of nondestructive measurements on a sample as small as a few micrograms. If one rather arbitrarily assumes that two lines 0.25 Mc. apart can just barely be resolved and that 17,000 to 40,000 Mc. is the frequency region over which one can conveniently make routine measurements, then 92,000 separate microwave absorption lines could be measured for a single sample. Obviously then, even in a sample with over one hundred components, the chances of interference between one compound and another creating practical difficulties in analysis are vanishingly small.

The usual factor limiting the detectability of a component of a sample by means of microwave spectroscopy is not interference by other components of the sample but the low intensity of the absorption of the pure substance. A few substances, such as $H_2O$, $NH_3$, and $CH_3OH$, may have intensities of the order of $10^{-4}$ cm.$^{-1}$. If the minimum absorptions which can be detected by an ordinary microwave spectrometer are $10^{-9}$ cm.$^{-1}$, these substances could be identified when present at a concentration of 10 parts per million or better. Unfortunately most molecules, especially large and complex ones, have much smaller absorption coefficients. This means that a great many complex molecules can be detected only when present at a concentration of better than 10% or indeed may not be detectable at all. In the most fortunate case of ammonia, however, the microwave spectrometer can detect as little as $10^{-12}$ moles of the gas even when present as a trace impurity in a complex mixture.

The high resolution of the instrument makes it easily possible to separate the spectra due to different isotopic forms of a molecule. It is usually possible to carry out isotopic analyses by converting the material being investigated into a favorable chemical form. If the material is converted into a molecule with strong microwave absorption it becomes possible to do isotopic analyses with a microwave spectrometer.

As the techniques of microwave spectroscopy are electronic rather than optical in nature, they have certain advantages for rapid analysis and control. The output of the lock-in amplifier, which is normally indicated on an oscilloscope or recorder, can be used to operate an automatic-control device. For all but the weakest absorptions a scanning frequency of several cycles a second is used so that the response time of the system to changes in concentration of the ingredient of the flow stream being monitored need be only a fraction of a second.

## 2. THE THEORETICAL BACKGROUND OF MICROWAVE SPECTROSCOPY

For the most part microwave spectra are molecular rotational spectra. It is true, however, that some microwave spectra involve molecular vibration, as in the inversion spectrum of $NH_3$, and in a few cases transitions between electronic-energy levels interact with microwave radiation, as in $O_2$ and NO.

Rotating molecules, since they obey the laws of quantum mechanics, have a discrete, rather than a continuous, pattern of stationary energy states. A line occurs in the microwave spectrum of a molecule possessing a permanent electric dipole moment when a transition between two adjacent stationary energy states is induced by microwave radiation. The difference in the energy of the two states determines the frequency, $\nu$, of the spectral line in a manner indicated by the following equation

$$\nu = (E_2 - E_1)/h$$

where $h$ is Planck's constant.

For the purpose of discussing the patterns of rotational energy levels molecules may be divided into two main groups. One of these groups, which includes linear and symmetrical rotor molecules, has a relatively simple pattern of rotational levels. The other group, consisting of asymmetrical rotor molecules, gives rise to a rather more complicated situation. Molecules are described as linear rotors if one of their three principal moments of inertia is zero, as symmetrical rotors if two of the moments of inertia are equal, and as asymmetrical rotors if all three moments of inertia are different.

Symmetrical rotors are divided into oblate rotors and prolate rotors. If we define the rotational constants

$$A = \frac{h}{8\pi^2 c I_A} \qquad B = \frac{h}{8\pi^2 c I_B} \qquad C = \frac{h}{8\pi^2 c I_C}$$

and label the three principal moments of inertia $I_A$, $I_B$, $I_C$ in order of increasing size, then for a prolate rotor $B = C$, for an oblate rotor $A = B$. The rotational energies of a prolate rotor are given by the equation

$$\frac{E_r}{hc} = BJ(J + 1) + (A - B)K^2$$

and for oblate rotors

$$\frac{E_r}{hc} = BJ(J + 1) + (C - B)K^2$$

In these equations

$E_r$ = the rotational energy in ergs

$c$ = the velocity of light

$J \dfrac{h}{2\pi}$ = total angular momentum

$K \dfrac{h}{2\pi}$ = the component of the total angular momentum along the molecular symmetry axis

To obtain the microwave spectrum of a molecule a plot is made of the amount of microwave radiation transmitted by the sample as a function of frequency. For symmetrical rotors the quantum mechanical-selection rules permit only transitions for which

$$J \to J + 1$$
$$K \to K$$

Therefore the equation for the frequencies of the lines in the rotational spectrum takes on the simple form

$$\nu(\text{cm.}^{-1}) = 2B(J + 1)$$

For linear molecules in the ground vibrational state the angular momentum about the molecular axis is zero, and so the rotational energy reduces to

$$\frac{E_r}{hc} = BJ(J + 1)$$

and the formula for the frequencies of the rotational transitions is the same as the one already given for symmetrical rotors.

The majority of molecules lack the special symmetry that would make them linear or symmetrical rotors and are therefore asymmetrical rotors. For such molecules it is no longer possible to write simple explicit algebraic expressions for the rotational energy levels. However, it is still possible with the use of published tables to calculate good approximate values for the energy. In one generally useful approach due to King et al. (6), the rotational energy is written as

$$E_r = \frac{(A + C)}{2} J(J + 1) + \frac{(A - C)}{2} E(\kappa)$$

where $\kappa$ is an asymmetry parameter defined by the relation

$$\kappa = \frac{(2B - A - C)}{(A - C)}$$

and the energy quantities $E(\kappa)$ have been tabulated for a range of $\kappa$ values.

For the large class of molecules which are nearly symmetrical rotors and the asymmetry parameters of which are small, it is frequently useful to calculate the rotational energies by use of a series expansion in terms of an asymmetry parameter. One such expansion is

$$E_r = \alpha J(J + 1) + \beta E(b)$$

where

$$E(b) = K^2 + C_1 b + C_2 b^2 + \cdots$$

For the case of a nearly prolate rotor

$$\alpha = \frac{B + C}{2}, \qquad \beta = A - \frac{B + C}{2}, \qquad \text{and} \qquad b = \frac{C - B}{2A - B - C}$$

For the case of a nearly oblate rotor

$$\alpha = \frac{A + B}{2}, \qquad \beta = C - \frac{A + B}{2}, \qquad \text{and} \qquad b = \frac{A - B}{2C - A - B}$$

In the absence of complications to be mentioned later, microwave absorption spectra are patterns of lines which are determined by the values of the molecular moments of inertia and the rotational quantum numbers. This relation is a simple one for linear and symmetrical rotor molecules, more complicated for asymmetrical rotors.

Since the principal moments of inertia of a molecule depend on the atomic masses and on their arrangement within the molecule, it is possible to determine internuclear distances and bond angles from the measurements of microwave spectroscopy. For a molecule of even moderate complexity the number of structural parameters is greater than the number of moments of inertia (at most three) which can be determined by use of a single molecular species. Frequently additional structural parameters can be determined by obtaining the spectra of isotopically substituted versions of the molecule if the assumption is made that the internuclear distances and bond angles do not change with a change in the atomic masses.

The resolution obtainable in microwave spectroscopy is so great that two different isotopic versions of a molecule frequently have widely separated spectra. As a result the possibility presents itself of using microwave spectra in favorable cases for isotopic analysis.

It is important to note that microwave spectra are sensitive to the over-all size and shape of a molecule rather than to the kinds of molecular groupings which occur within the molecule. It might be possible, however, to determine the functional groups present in a molecule from a study of its infrared and nuclear magnetic resonance spectra and to determine the arrangement of those groups by means of data obtained from the microwave spectrum.

In actual cases a number of factors may complicate the relatively simple picture described above. The existence of molecules in excited vibrational states gives rise to a fine structure in the rotational spectrum. The rotational constant depends on the vibrational state through the equation

$$Bv = Be - \sum_i \alpha_i \left(n_i + \frac{d_i}{2}\right)$$

where $n_i$ is the vibrational quantum number, $d_i$ is the degeneracy of the vibration, and the $\alpha_i$ are constants. The intensity of the lines in the vibrational fine structure is a function of the fundamental vibrational frequencies, and in general it is only the lower vibrational frequencies which give rise to lines of appreciable intensity.

For halogen compounds, or for any molecule containing a nucleus with an electric quadrupole moment, a different spectral complication arises. The change in rotational energy for a molecule due to the different possible orientations of a nuclear quadrupole is given by an expression of the form

$$\Delta E_r = eQqf(J,K,I)$$

where $eQ$ is the nuclear quadrupole moment, $q$ is a factor related to the distribution of electronic and nuclear change in a molecule, and $f(J,K,I)$ is a function of the angular-momentum and nuclear-spin quantum numbers.

If large values of the quantum numbers are involved or if there is more than one nucleus in the molecule having an electric quadrupole moment, the resulting hyperfine structure may become quite complex, with the result that no one absorption line in the pattern has more than a small fraction of the total intensity. Since microwave spectra are usually not very intense, this might make the spectrum for a given complicated molecule rather difficult to observe.

Although values of $eQq$ may be obtained only by means of a rather detailed and complicated analysis of the microwave spectrum, it has been shown to be possible to interpret these constants in terms of the molecular electronic structure (2, 12). Thus, for special cases at least, it is sometimes possible to gain information about a part of the molecule from the data of microwave spectroscopy.

The pattern of absorption lines observed in microwave spectroscopy is of primary importance in the applications to qualitative analysis. In the applications to quantitative analysis it is necessary to consider the intensities of the observed spectral lines. The intensity of an absorption line in a molecular rotational spectrum is given by the equation

$$\alpha = \frac{8\pi^2 n \nu^2}{3ckt} |\mu_{ij}|^2 \left[ \frac{\Delta\nu}{(\nu - \nu_0)^2 + (\Delta\nu)^2} + \frac{\Delta\nu}{(\nu + \nu_0)^2 + (\Delta\nu)^2} \right]$$

where

$\alpha$ = absorption coefficient in cm.$^{-1}$ at frequency
$n$ = number of molecules per cubic centimeter in the lower state $i$
$c$ = velocity of light
$t$ = absolute temperature
$k$ = Boltzmann constant
$\Delta\nu$ = half width of spectral line
$|\mu_{ij}|$ = dipole-moment matrix element for the absorption transition
$\nu_0$ = center frequency of absorption line
$n = \dfrac{Nge^{-E_{r_i}/kt}}{Z}$

$N$ = total number of molecules per cubic centimeter
$g$ = statistical weight of the lower state $i$
$Z$ = rotational partition function for the molecule

At pressures below 1 mm. and when the frequency $\nu$ is near the center frequency of the line $\nu_0$, it is permissible to neglect the second term within the brackets and, if we let $\nu = \nu_0$, the following simple expression for the peak intensity of an absorption line is obtained:

$$\alpha_{\max} = \frac{8\pi^2 |\mu_{ij}|^2 \nu^2}{3ckt\,\Delta\nu} \frac{Nge^{-E_{r_i}/kt}}{Z}$$

The application of this equation to the example of the linear OCS molecule may be illuminating. For a linear molecule the previous equation reduces to the form

$$\alpha_{\max} = 2.09 \times 10^8 \frac{\mu^2 \nu^3 \eta^{\frac{1}{2}}}{T^{\frac{5}{2}} \sigma^2}$$

where

$\mu$ = dipole moment
$M$ = molecular weight
$\sigma$ = molecular-collision cross section

For OCS, $\mu = 0.75$ debye, $M^{\frac{1}{2}} = 7.75$, and $\sigma = 10.7$ (derived from experiment), so that the calculated intensity for the $J = 1$ to $J = 2$ transition occurring at 24,326 Mc. is $6.8 \times 10^{-5}$ cm.$^{-1}$.

A number of significant deductions may be made from a consideration of the foregoing equations. Molecules with zero dipole moment will not give rise to microwave spectra and molecules whose dipole moments are only a few tenths of a Debye unit will not give rise to strong spectra. Large molecules will tend to have weak microwave absorptions because they have large collision diameters and because they have a number of low-lying vibrational states which will give rise to a complex spectrum with the absorption divided among a large number of spectral lines.

Many of the special advantages and disadvantages of microwave spectroscopy as a tool for chemical analysis arise from the way in which the shape and peak height of a line in a microwave spectrum vary with the pressure of the gas sample. This variation is shown in Fig. 1. The integrated intensity of a reasonably narrow line at low pressures is equal to

$$\int_0^\infty \alpha d\nu = \alpha_{max} \Delta\nu = \frac{8\pi^2 n}{3ckt} |\mu_{ij}|^2 \nu^2$$

Since the half-line width $\Delta\nu$ is directly proportional to the pressure, as is $n$, the number of molecules per cubic centimeter, over the usual working

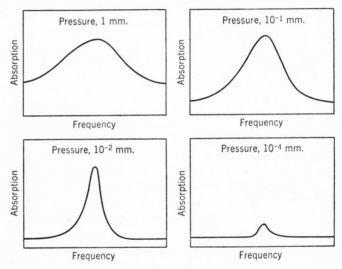

FIG. 1. Effect of pressure on shape of lines.

range of pressure the peak absorption $\alpha_{max}$ will be independent of pressure. This means that no increase in sensitivity will be obtained by increasing the sample pressure and it is generally desirable to work at a pressure of 10 to 100 microns in order to obtain optimum resolution. The optimum sample size for the microwave spectrometer will then be of the order of magnitude of 1 $\mu$mole.

In order to evaluate the significance of the intensity of a given microwave spectrum it is necessary to know the maximum intensity which can be expected and the minimum intensity which can be detected by a microwave spectrometer. The most intense lines so far observed in microwave spectra have had $\alpha$ approximately equal to $10^{-3}$ cm.$^{-1}$. In an absorption cell of the usual length, say 3 meters, this represents an absorption of approximately 15% of the incident microwave radiation. The weakest absorption lines which have been observed and reported so far have had an intensity of about $2 \times 10^{-10}$ cm.$^{-1}$. If a given sample contains a substance having the strongest absorption lines, such as ammonia, then it should be possible to detect its presence at a minimum concentration of one part in $10^7$. This level of sensitivity for a microwave spectrometer requires special technique and is not often attained. However, there is no reason to consider this sensitivity an ultimate limit since theoretical calculations place this limit as low as $10^{-12}$ cm.$^{-1}$.

## 3. Application to Qualitative Analysis

The microwave spectrometer lends itself in a very natural and direct way to the qualitative identification of the components of a micromole sample of a mixture of moderately complex organic molecules. Such a qualitative analysis requires only the measurement of the frequencies of the absorption lines observed over a convenient range of microwave frequencies.

Since lines in a microwave spectrum are usually completely resolved, it is necessary only to compare these measured frequencies against tables of the frequencies observed for known substances. Such a table has been published by the National Bureau of Standards (7), and it is to be hoped that it will be brought up to date from time to time. If the frequencies of the microwave absorption lines are measured with an accuracy of 0.1 Mc. or better, a positive identification can be made if two lines coincide with lines reported for a given substance. In the large majority of cases, identification is possible from the measurement of the frequency of a single line. As an example of this sort of analysis, Hicks (4) by use of a microwave spectrometer identified $H_2O$, HCHO, and HCOOH in the decomposition products of nitrocellulose.

Most sensitive spectrometers employ Stark modulation and display not only the zero-field spectrum but the Stark spectrum, that is, the spectrum under the influence of an electric field, as well. As a result considerable additional information valuable for the qualitative identification of molecules is available. The Stark effect of a given spectral line depends on the size, symmetry and dipole moment of a molecule and may be used readily to differentiate between two spectral lines which are accidentally coincident in frequency.

The question arises over how large a frequency range must a search be made to be reasonably sure of finding a line in a given microwave molecular spectrum? Molecules which have no special symmetry will have their spectral lines scattered over the radiofrequency spectrum somewhat uniformly and will have a high probability of having at least one line falling within a 10,000-Mc. frequency range. Molecules which are linear or symmetrical rotors and which have small moments of inertia will have only a few widely spaced absorption lines, which may all be at frequencies higher than those readily available to the usual microwave spectrometer. Such substances, together with those having zero dipole moment and those that are too large or high boiling will be inaccessible to microwave techniques.

It is desirable to limit the frequency range which must be searched in an analysis using the microwave spectrometer especially if the spectrometer must be operated at maximum sensitivity. One of the serious disadvantages of the microwave spectrometer is the length of time necessary to make such a search. To operate the instrument at a sensitivity level of $10^{-9}$ cm.$^{-1}$ the rate of sweep must not exceed 1 Mc./sec., and it would require nearly 3 hr. to search from 20,000 to 30,000 Mc. With the spectrometers in use at present such a search could not be completely automatic since adjustments of the power level and recentering of the mode must be carried out fairly frequently.

### 4. PROBLEMS CONNECTED WITH QUANTITATIVE ANALYSIS

In an earlier section it was shown that the integrated intensity and the product of the peak height and half width of a microwave absorption line could be related directly to the number of molecules per cubic centimeter present in the given sample of the kind undergoing the absorption. If the total pressure is measured, it is possible to calculate the percentage of abundance in the sample of the particular molecular species. Unfortunately it is not especially easy to measure the spectral quantities. $\alpha_{max}$ can be measured to an accuracy of 5 to 10% by absolute methods. $\Delta \nu$ can be measured to similar accuracy by measuring the difference in frequency of the half-peak points on the absorption line by means of frequency markers.

For most Stark modulation microwave spectrometers the maximum signal produced by an absorption line is proportional to the peak height, $\alpha_{max}$. Since $\alpha_{max} \Delta \nu$ is proportional to $n$, $\dfrac{\alpha_{max} \Delta \nu}{P}$ is proportional to the percentage of abundance of the molecular species in the sample. Under the conditions usually met with in microwave spectroscopy $\alpha_{max}$ is independent of the pressure and $\Delta \nu / P$ is a constant. Therefore the maximum signal from the spectrometer is proportional to the percentage of abundance of the absorbing species in the sample.

Unfortunately in carrying out an analysis on a multicomponent mixture it cannot be assumed that $\Delta \nu$ is independent of composition as well as of total pressure. The following expression gives the dependence of the line breadth on partial pressures:

$$\Delta \nu_1 = k_{11} p_1 + k_{12} p_2$$

where $\Delta\nu_1$ is the half width of an absorption line due to substance 1, $k_{11}$ is the broadening factor of the molecules of substance 1 for collisions with molecules of the same substance, $k_{12}$ the broadening factor of the molecules of substance 1 for collisions with molecules of substance 2. If $k_{11}$ and $k_{12}$ are different, as they usually would be, then $\Delta\nu_1$ will depend on the composition of the sample and it will not be possible to assume that the peak height of the absorption line is directly proportional to percentage of abundance.

There are, therefore, several procedures which can be followed in making a quantitative analysis by use of microwave techniques. Each has its own advantages and disadvantages. One procedure is to measure $\alpha_{max}$ and $\Delta\nu$ for each absorption line and $P$, the total pressure, for the sample as a whole. Here it is difficult to measure $\Delta\nu$ to better than 5% accuracy, and considerable difficulties are met with the measurement of pressure in this range. The gauges normally used to monitor the pressure, thermocouple and Pirani gauges, do not give the true pressure without elaborate calibration. Absorption of sample on glass, metal, and plastic surfaces creates some difficulties in maintaining a constant pressure and in the elimination of sample contamination.

It is possible to escape difficulties associated with line-width measurements by measuring integrated intensities. This gives rise to new problems, however. In order to obtain the complete integrated intensity of a line, it would be necessary to integrate over a very wide range of frequency. In practice it will probably be necessary to integrate between two definite points, say the half-power points, and to multiply the result by an appropriate factor.

The easiest and most straightforward method of doing quantitative analysis with microwave spectrometers of the type used at present seems to be to compare the peak heights of lines for the sample with those for known mixtures which are similar to the sample in composition. It is possible to obtain an accuracy of a few per cent with this method, and perhaps with painstaking attention to details this accuracy could be somewhat improved.

In order to obtain accurate results with this method for a wide range of substances, it is desirable to use a Stark spectrometer which will operate in a stable and reproducible manner. By use of such a spectrometer, uncertainty as to the base line of zero absorption can be eliminated through measuring the total deflection between the peak of the absorption line and the reversed peak of the strongest Stark component.

The use of the Stark spectrometer, however, introduces new uncertainties into quantitative analysis. Unless the modulating field is large enough to move all Stark components out from the central absorption line by several line widths, an inaccurate estimate of peak height and line width will be obtained. These difficulties are made more severe by use of a sine wave modulation instead of a square wave. Insufficient modulation will make the apparent peak height of the line a function of pressure because as the line is broadened by pressure the minimum adequate modulation voltage also increases.

Because of these difficulties it is especially important to use a comparison technique with a Stark modulation spectrometer so that the lines being studied will be subjected to the same modulation. Another difficulty which is minimized by a comparison technique arises from the inevitable presence of reflections in the wave-guide absorption cell. These affect the apparent value of the absorption coefficient, because some of the radiation passes through the absorption cell more than once.

The pattern of reflections in a given wave-guide absorption cell changes rapidly with frequency, which makes it difficult to carry out an accurate measurement of the relative intensity of two lines which are significantly different in frequency.

Isotopic analysis by the comparison method has been carried out by Southern et al. (10) for samples of $NH_3$ and ClCN. Their results indicate the accuracy which can be reasonably expected in this work. For ClCN they were able to determine the $C^{13}/C^{12}$ ratio with an accuracy of 2% for a range of $C^{13}$ concentration between 1.1 and 10%. With $NH_3$ results were not quite so good, giving an accuracy of 3% for the $N^{15}/N^{14}$ ratio over a range of from 0.38 to 4.5% in the $N^{15}$ concentration.

## 5. Apparatus

As in other frequency regions, a microwave spectrometer is made up basically of an energy source, a frequency-measuring device, an absorption cell, and a detector. Since microwave sources are essentially monochromatic, it is possible to detect and display a spectral line by sweeping the source over a range of frequencies and observing the variation in the power received at the detector by means of a meter or other device.

The earliest microwave spectrometers were not much more elaborate than the instrument described above. They suffered, however, from at least two major defects. The presence of reflections in the microwave system sets up a standing wave pattern that is very frequency-sensitive. This gives rise to an irregular zero-absorption base line. When one works at high amplifier gain with weak absorption lines, the lines appear as small deviations on the shoulders of very steep deflections owing to standing waves. Under unfavorable conditions it becomes almost impossible to differentiate the spectral lines from the background of reflections.

Another difficulty experienced in the use of a simple absorption spectrometer comes from the "extra noise" of the crystal detector when the detected signal is of very low frequency. As a result it is quite difficult to obtain high sensitivity with a spectrometer of this type.

Both of the above-mentioned difficulties are avoided by the use of a Stark-modulation instrument of the sort first described by Hughes and Wilson (5, 8, 9). In a Stark spectrometer the absorption line is periodically shifted in frequency by means of an electric field imposed on the sample. This gives rise to a component of the detector current at the modulation frequency in the presence of a molecular absorption. Since the reflections are not sensitive to the presence of the electric field they no longer give rise to difficulty. The output of a receiver tuned to the modulation frequency (assuming square-wave modulation is used) will respond only to the presence of a molecular absorption line or an unusually abrupt change in the source power. To maximize the sensitivity of the instrument the modulation frequency is made as high as possible without at the same time broadening the absorption lines undesirably. Frequencies in the neighborhood of 100 kc. are usually employed. The use of a phase-sensitive detector permits a further increase in sensitivity owing to the elimination of unnecessary noise present in the frequency side bands.

A diagram of a Stark modulation spectrometer is given in Fig. 2. The design and operation of this instrument has been described elsewhere. Certain features of the design present special problems in the use of the microwave spectrometer for analytical purposes.

The usual source of power in microwave spectroscopy is an electronic oscillator of the reflex klystron type. Working data for some of the suitable tubes are given in Table I. These tubes may be tuned electronically over a frequency range amounting to approximately 0.2% of the center frequency and mechanically by means of a device which changes the size of the resonant cavity.

These oscillators have a number of disadvantages when the microwave spectrometer is considered from the point of view of routine chemical analysis. No one tube can be used to cover the entire microwave frequency range, and even within the relatively narrow working frequency range of a given tube there are likely to be places where the tube oscillates poorly. In order to cover a respectable portion of the range of microwave frequencies it may be necessary to have two or three tubes of each of four or five different types of klystron. Since each tube at present costs $300 to $400 and since the working life of a tube may be fairly short the cost of oscillators may become a sizable item.

Another difficulty with experiments of this kind is that it is quite difficult to provide for automatic operation of the microwave spectrometer. The following description will illustrate the number of tuning adjustments that must be made during a search for microwave spectral lines.

The klystron is set to sweep over a 30-Mc. range at a rate of 10 cycles/sec. with a power output of 5 mw. The center oscillation frequency of the klystron is then varied over the desired range by means of a motor-driven mechanical tuner. The variable attenuator must be adjusted periodically

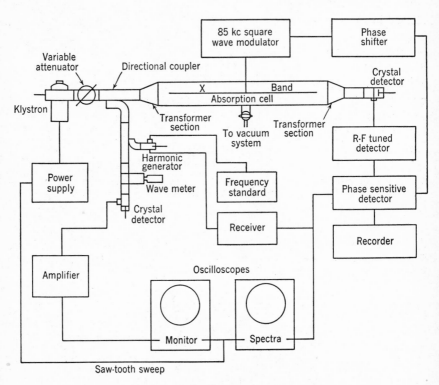

FIG. 2. Stark spectrometer.

to maintain the desired power level so as to avoid saturation phenomena on the one hand and loss of sensitivity on the other. The repeller voltage will have to be reset occasionally to maintain the center frequency of the klystron in the center of the mode. The klystron cavity back plunger may have to be returned to maintain oscillation at an adequate power level.

In addition it may be necessary to repeat the search at more than one level of Stark-modulation voltage. The large voltages needed for a line with a small second-order Stark effect may broaden out and obscure a line having a large first-order Stark effect.

Several attempts have been made to simplify the operation of a microwave spectrometer by using X-band tubes with a harmonic generator as a source of power. This has the advantage that less tuning and adjustment is needed for the oscillator and in general a simpler and more reliable power supply can be used. Unfortunately these advantages are largely lost because of the frequency sensitivity of the critical adjustments on the harmonic generators of which the design has so far been reported.

TABLE I

*Working Data for Microwave Oscillators*

| Type | Beam voltage | Maximum beam current, mamp. | Average power output, mw. | Frequency range, Mc. | Manufacturer |
|------|------|------|------|------|------|
| 2K41 | 300 to 1250 | 15 to 60 | 20 to 2¾ watt | 2660– 3310 | 1 |
| 2K42 | 500 to 1250 | 6 to 50 | 30 to 1450 | 3300– 4200 | 1 |
| 2K43 | 500 to 1250 | 12 to 50 | 125 to 1050 | 4200– 5700 | 1 |
| 2K44 | 500 to 1250 | 14 to 54 | 50 to 1025 | 5700– 7500 | 1 |
| 2K39 | 500 to 1250 | 12 to 50 | 12 to 770 | 7500–10,300 | 1 |
| SRU-54 | 300 | 32 | 20 | 12,500–13,500 | 1 |
| SRU-55 | 300 | 31 | 45–75 | 14,500–17,000 | 1 |
| V-55 | 500 | | 600 | 8,200–11,500 | 2 |
| X-13 | 500 | 65 | 500 | 8,200–12,400 | 2 |
| X-12 | 600 | 65 | 30 | 12,400–17,500 | 2 |
| QK-306 | 1800 | 9 | 40 | 18,000–22,000 | 3 |
| 2K-33 | 1800 | 8 | 40 | 22,000–25,000 | 3 |
| QK-289 | 2250 | 15 | 20 | 27,270–30,000 | 3 |
| QK-290 | 2250 | 15 | 20 | 29,700–33,520 | 3 |
| QK-291 | 2250 | 15 | 18 | 33,520–36,250 | 3 |
| QK-292 | 2500 | 15 | 10 | 35,100–39,700 | 3 |
| QK-293 | 2500 | 15 | 5 | 37,100–42,600 | 3 |
| QK-294 | 3000 | 15 | 5 | 41,200–50,000 | 3 |

1. Sperry Gyroscope Company, Great Neck, New York.
2. Varian Associates, Palo Alto, California.
3. Raytheon Manufacturing Company, Waltham, Massachusetts.

An important instrumental problem connected with the construction of a microwave spectrometer to be used for chemical analysis has to do with the design of the wave-guide absorption cell. A frequent source of difficulty in microwave spectroscopy is the adsorption of gases on the surfaces of the absorption cell. Even a relatively small amount of gas adsorbed onto the cell walls or released from them can make a significant change in the composition of the micromole samples used in microwave spectroscopy. Cells designed to permit Stark modulation are especially bad from this point of view because they have the additional adsorbing surfaces of the central electrode and its insulator strips. It is possible to construct a Stark cell which may be heated to several hundred degrees centigrade and which with thorough pumping may be almost completely degassed. There is still the problem, however, of a change in the composition of the sample due to selective adsorption on the clean walls of the cell.

Adsorption may be minimized by use of a stainless steel cell with Teflon insulators. A resonant cavity may be used for the cell because of the lower ratio of wall surface to volume. In this case, however, care must be taken to avoid power-saturation effects, which would complicate quantitative analysis. Perhaps the most satisfactory solution to the adsorption problem in those cases where sufficient sample is available is to admit several successive samples to the cell and allow them to come to equilibrium with the walls before the actual sample to be analyzed is admitted.

## 6. The Determination of Electron Concentration in Flames

A useful but somewhat special application of microwave techniques to analysis involves the determination of the electron concentration of flames by measurement of their absorption of microwave radiation (11). These results may be used to study directly chemical equilibria in which electrons are involved or in which one of the reacting substances must be in equilibrium with electrons. The critical measurement is that of power attenuation, and fluctuations in frequency are relatively unimportant.

In most of these experiments the reacting substances are contained in the secondary combustion zone of a flame from a Meker burner. The flame gases themselves do not contribute appreciably to the concentration of electrons, which are produced for the most part upon the introduction into the flame of traces of easily ionizable metals or their compounds.

In the simplest experimental arrangement microwaves of 3- or 1.25-cm. wave lengths are passed through a flame which is about 1 cm. thick. The radiation is beamed by horns and the flame portion of the microwave circuit is isolated from the klystron and crystal detector by means of suitable attenuators. The attenuation produced by the flame is measured by comparing it to a calibrated attenuator. Electron concentrations in the range of $10^{10}$ to $10^{12}$ electrons/cc. may be measured with this technique. Somewhat improved sensitivity may be obtained by use of double-beam methods.

It is also possible to use a resonant cavity as a container for the flame. The cavity has holes at either end which are made "radiation tight" by covers of coarse platinum gauze. The cavity is connected by irises to the rest of the waveguide system. The klystron is swept in frequency by a low-frequency saw-tooth voltage. The change in $Q$ for the cavity due to absorption of power by the electron-containing flame is measured by observing the charges in the resonant curve of power transmitted by the cavity. Electron concentrations as low as $10^8/cc.$ may be measured by this method.

The absorption of microwave radiation by gases containing charged particles and ions arises from their interaction with the radiation field to acquire momentum. This momentum is lost by random collisions of the charged particles and ions with molecules. The dielectric constant and the conductivity may be written simply as

$$\epsilon = 1 - \frac{4\pi n e^2}{m} \left( \frac{1}{\omega^2 + \omega_1^2} \right)$$
$$\sigma = \frac{ne^2}{m} \left( \frac{w_1}{\omega^2 + \omega_1^2} \right)$$

in which $n$ is the number of particles per cubic centimeter of mass $m$ and charge $\rho$. $\omega$ is the frequency of the radiation and $\omega_1$ is the molecular collision frequency. Because of the inverse dependence on mass the conductivity is determined largely by the electron concentration, ions having a negligible influence. For the conditions normally encountered in this experiment the attenuation of microwave power by the flame, $\beta$, may be related to the conductivity and through it to the electron concentration by the relation

$$\beta = \frac{17.4\pi\sigma}{c} \, db/cm.$$

## 7. PARAMAGNETIC-RESONANCE SPECTRA

The study of paramagnetic-resonance spectroscopy may be considered as a special part of microwave spectroscopy because it usually involves the absorption of microwave radiation (wave length 3 to 1.25 cm.) by paramagnetic substances in a magnetic field. The paramagnetic materials may be salts of the elements of the transition or rare-earth groups, or they may be free radicals.

The free radicals which can be studied by paramagnetic-resonance techniques vary over a wide range in stability. Certain radicals may have lifetimes of days or weeks or even longer. Other radicals in order to achieve an adequately long life may need to be protected from contact with oxygen or kept at a favorable pH. Perhaps the most interesting free radicals are those which have a transitory existence as reaction intermediates. These are, however, quite difficult to observe and detect. Their extreme reactivity tends to reduce their concentration in a system below the level of $10^{-11}$ moles which can be detected in a paramagnetic-resonance spectrometer. In addition the maximum absorption due to a radical may be decreased by broadening, owing to extremely short lifetimes.

In an elementary discussion of the theory of paramagnetic resonance it is instructive to consider a system of independent electron spins having the magnetic moment $\beta$, where $\beta = eh/2mc$ is the Bohr magneton. This system is quite similar to the set of nuclei having magnetic moments discussed in the chapter on nuclear magnetic resonance. In a magnetic field $H$ the energy states of the system are simply $\pm\beta H$. These correspond to the two allowed values of the spin angular momentum $\pm\frac{1}{2}h/2$. An electromagnetic radiation field of frequency $\nu$ will induce transitions between these two states when

$$\nu = \frac{2\beta H}{h}$$

In a system where orbital momentum and spin momentum both make a contribution, a slightly different situation arises. The total orbital momentum $L$ and the total spin momentum $S$ combine to give a total resultant momentum $J$. The allowed values of the quantum number $M_J$ are $J$, $(J-1)$, . . . $(-J)$ and in a magnetic field these give rise to the energy values $M_J g\beta H$. Since the selection rule is $\Delta M_J = \pm 1$ then

$$\nu = \frac{g\beta H}{h}$$

where $g$ is called the Lande splitting factor. For a free electron it has the value 2.0023. Most free radicals exhibit a $g$ value of very nearly 2. For those systems where $g$ is appreciably different from 2 the difference is said to be due to the contribution of the orbital momentum.

A more complicated pattern of energy levels arises when a paramagnetic ion is situated in a crystal. Neighboring ions and dipoles subject the unpaired electron in the ion to large electric fields. The type of paramagnetic-resonance spectrum which is observed depends on the strength of the crystal field. In the case of transition-element ions of the iron group, there is a moderate crystal field and the spectrum resembles that for a free electron. In the iron group because of the fairly strong interaction with the electric field the spin-orbit coupling is relatively weak. The electric field splits the orbital levels by some 10,000 cm.$^{-1}$, and each orbital level still has a $2S + 1$ degeneracy, which is removed by the external magnetic field, giving rise to a spectrum corresponding to a $g$ value of 2.

In most of the iron-group crystals each ion is octahedrally surrounded with six $H_2O$ molecules, giving rise to an electric field with slightly distorted cubic symmetry. This distortion of the field symmetry together with the spin-orbit coupling gives rise to two new features of crystal paramagnetic-resonance spectra. The $g$ value is no longer equal to 2, and its value now depends on the relative orientation of the crystal and the external magnetic field. Also, if the spin is greater than $\frac{1}{2}$, the spin levels are split by several tenths of a cm.$^{-1}$.

For ions of the platinum and palladium groups the crystal electric field is very strong and the effect of the electric field has to be considered before the interactions between the electrons. In the case of the ions of the rare earths the inner $4f$ electrons are effectively shielded from the crystalline electric field, and the effect of spin-orbit coupling is large compared with the effect of the electric field.

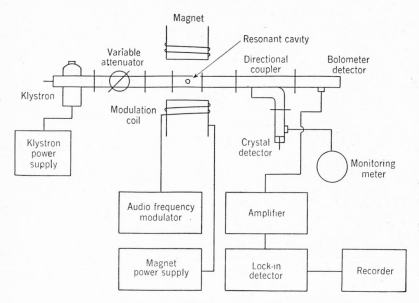

Fig. 3. Paramagnetic-resonance spectrometer.

In a typical experimental arrangement for the observation of paramagnetic resonances a magnetic field of approximately 3,200 oersteds is used. Figure 3 shows a block diagram of a paramagnetic-resonance spectrometer. Microwave power at a frequency of approximately 9,000 Mc. is fed to a transmission type of resonant cavity operating in the $TE_{012}$ mode. The magnetic field is modulated at a low audiofrequency with an amplitude which sweeps over only a small portion of the resonant line. The output signal of the spectrometer is then proportional to the derivative of the absorption line. Use of a modulation system permits the use of a phase-sensitive detector which gives rise to an increase in sensitivity, since the system may be operated with a narrow band width and a resulting higher signal-to-noise ratio.

In the particular experimental arrangement described the signal detector used is a bolometer. The use of a crystal detector with the low audio modulation frequency would be accompanied by excessive noise. In other commonly used spectrometer designs the best signal-to-noise figure is obtained with the use of a crystal.

Some of the advantages and disadvantages of the paramagnetic resonance spectrometer may be summarized as follows. The method may be used to detect and identify very small quantities of paramagnetic material. One such application already mentioned is the detection of free radical reaction intermediates. Another similar case arises when a small amount of paramagnetic impurity exists in a larger amount of diamagnetic material as in the studies of the role of $Mn^{++}$ in phosphors by Hershberger (3). In a somewhat different situation an impurity which is normally diamagnetic may be made into a free radical by irradiation with X rays, neutrons, etc.

Paramagnetic-resonance techniques show considerable promise as a method of studying free radical content in living tissue. The work of Pake and collaborators (1) has correlated the free radical content with the metabolic activity of cells. In work of this kind the water content of the living tissue leads to an excessive nonresonant absorption of the microwave energy with a decrease in the sensitivity of detection. As a result studies are made on lyophilized samples.

Certain limitations to the usefulness of paramagnetic-resonance techniques exist. It is quite difficult to make absolute measurements of absorption in a paramagnetic-resonance spectrometer and as a result quantitative analysis requires the use of comparison standards. One frequently used is diphenyl picryl hydrazyl. The usefulness of these techniques for qualitative analysis suffers from a general sameness of the resonances due to organic free radicals, since all of them exhibit $g$ factors near the value 2.0023.

In some cases a hyperfine structure is present which aids in identifying the molecular species responsible for the observed paramagnetic resonance. If the free radical contains a nucleus having the spin $I$, a hyperfine structure pattern consisting of $2I + 1$ approximately evenly spaced components may be observed. If more than one nucleus has an appropriate spin, even more complex patterns may exist which will not be completely resolved. Venkataraman and Fraenkel (13) have studied hyperfine-structure effects in various substituted semiquinones.

In some cases the use of paramagnetic-resonance techniques is limited by the fact that even though a substance is paramagnetic it may not be possible to observe a resonance. In some of the rare earths the transitions between the well-populated ground-state levels are forbidden. Occasionally lines may be broadened to such an extent by the exchange of energy between spin and lattice vibrational states that the resonance can no longer be observed with ordinary equipment. Sometimes this broadening may be eliminated by cooling the sample down to liquid hydrogen or liquid helium temperatures.

REFERENCES

1. Commoner, B., Townsend, J., and Pake, G. E., *Nature* **174**, 689 (1954).
2. Dailey, B. P., and Townes, C. H., *J. Chem. Phys.* **23**, 118 (1955).
3. Hershberger, W. D., and Feifer, H. N., *Phys. Rev.* **87**, 229 (1952).
4. Hicks, B L., Turner, J. E., Kendrick, W. M., and Fiora, V. C., Ballistics Research Laboratories Memorandum Report No. 703, August, 1953. Aberdeen Proving Ground, Maryland.
5. Hughes, R. H., and Wilson, E B., Jr., *Phys. Rev.* **71**, 562 (1947).
6. King, C. W., Hainer, R. M., and Cross, P. C., *J. Chem. Phys.* **11**, 27 (1943).
7. Kisliuk, P., and Townes, C. H., *J. Research Natl. Bur. Standards* **44**, 611 (1950).
8. McAfee, K., Hughes, R., and Wilson, E. B., Jr., *Rev. Sci. Instr.* **19**, 821 (1949).
9. Sharbaugh, H., *Rev. Sci. Instr.* **21**, 120 (1950).
10. Southern, A. L., Morgan, H. W., Keilholz, G. W., and Smith, W. V., *Anal. Chem.* **23**, 1000 (1951).
11. Sugden, T. M., *Discussions Faraday Soc.* In press.
12. Townes, C. H., and Dailey, B. P., *J. Chem. Phys.* **17**, 782 (1949).
13. Venkataraman, B., and Fraenkel, G. K., *J. Chem. Phys.* **23**, 588 (1955).

GENERAL REFERENCES

Dailey, B. P., *Anal. Chem.* **21**, 540 (1949).
Gordy, W., Smity, W. V., and Trambarulo, R. F., "Microwave Spectroscopy." Wiley, New York, 1954.
Hughes, R. H., *Instruments* **24**, 1352 (1951).
Hughes, R. H., *Ann. N. Y. Acad. Sci.* **55**, 872 (1952).
Townes, C. H., and Schawlow, A. L., "Microwave Spectroscopy." McGraw-Hill, New York, 1955.

# Analytical Applications of Nuclear Magnetic Resonance

## By

## H. S. GUTOWSKY

*Noyes Chemical Laboratory, University of Illinois, Urbana, Illinois*

303

## 1. Introduction

Nuclear magnetic resonance is a spectroscopic technique employing electromagnetic radiation at frequencies of the order of 100 kc. to 40 Mc. These frequencies correspond to wavelengths between 3,000 and 7.5 meters, near the middle of what is usually called the radiofrequency part of the spectrum. Nuclear magnetic resonance was discovered in 1946 by Purcell and his group at Harvard (77) and simultaneously and independently by Bloch and his co-workers at Stanford (13). It is one of the several types of radiofrequency and microwave spectroscopy which have been developed in recent years. Dailey discusses a number of the other branches elsewhere in this volume (Chapter 8).

Nuclear magnetic resonance has its distinctive aspects, but as applied to chemical analysis it is very similar in principle to the spectroscopic procedures incorporating ultraviolet, visible, and infrared radiation which were described in Volume I of this series. The basic premises of these more conventional analytical methods are simple. Atoms and molecules have characteristic sets and varieties of energy levels, and under the proper experimental conditions a sample will emit or absorb electromagnetic radiation at characteristic frequencies corresponding to the transitions from one energy level to another. Qualitative identification is made when an unknown exhibits the same characteristic frequencies and relative intensities as a known sample. Quantitative determinations are based on the relation of the spectral intensities to the concentrations of the chemical species.

Such general premises apply equally well to nuclear magnetic resonance. However, one is restricted here to samples containing magnetic nuclei which are subjected to magnetic fields, for it is a magnetic interaction which gives the energy levels between which transitions are observed. Also, the magnetic energy of a nucleus is influenced by its environment, and the remarkable sensitivity and high resolving power of the experimental methods have revealed a great wealth of detail in the spectral lines. These phenomena are amenable to the analytical investigation of a sample and can give information difficult or impossible to obtain by other methods. By no means all the nuclear magnetic resonance phenomena are of value for chemical analysis. Nonetheless, the utility of a particular method may depend on the absence of disturbing interactions. For this reason it is desirable to give at least a brief survey of all the known types of interactions, as well as to review the general theory and experimental methods. The most completely developed analytical method, high-resolution NMR spectros-copy of liquids, is discussed in detail as it is a val-uable new method for determining molecular struc-ture. Quantitative analysis and several ingenious but specialized applications conclude the chapter.

## 2. General Theory

### 2.1. The Basic Experiment

*2.1.1. Nuclear Magnetism.* To chemists, the mass and electronic structure of atoms are usually more familiar properties than nuclear spin, mag-netic moment, and electric quadrupole moment. The present review requires a general understanding of these nuclear properties. Fortunately, this can be obtained by means of a simplified vector model (4, 67). Suppose the mass, $M$, and the charge, $e$, of a proton are as represented in Fig. 1, both dis-tributed uniformly on a spherical shell which is spinning about a given axis with constant angular velocity. The circulation of the mass generates an angular momentum, **p**, a vector directed along the axis of rotation, while the motion of the charge generates a magnetic field, cylindrically symmet-rical about the axis of rotation. This field is designated conveniently by its magnetic moment, **μ**, which is the product of the magnetic pole strength and the separation between the two poles necessary to reproduce the field. The spinning motion is common to charge and mass, and so the magnetic-moment vector is colinear with and directly proportional to the angular momentum, according to the equation

$$\mathbf{\mu} = \frac{e}{2Mc}\,\mathbf{p} \tag{1}$$

where $c$ is the velocity of light.

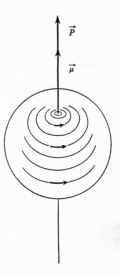

Fig. 1. Classical model of a spinning nucleus. Rotation of the mass produces an angular momentum p, and the circulating electric charge gener-ates a magnetic field which can be described by a magnetic mo-ment μ.

Actual nuclei differ from this simple model in several ways (80). For protons the proportionality between **μ** and **p** is not the $e/2Mc$ of eq. (1), nor does the model apply accurately to any nucleus. There are also anomalies such as the uncharged neutron which has a negative magnetic moment, as do some nuclei. The deficiencies of the model suggest a complex nuclear structure, in which the nuclear components have orbital as well as spinning motions, combining in various ways to give a resultant angular momentum for the nucleus, similar to the coupling of electronic spin and orbital moments in atoms and molecules. Thus, nuclei with an even number of neutrons and protons have zero angular momentum and no magnetic moment, somewhat similar to the nonmagnetic $^1\Sigma$ atomic states in which the electronic magnetic moments are "paired off." Their nonmagnetic nuclear states prevent the use of nuclear magnetic resonance on such chemically important nuclei as $_6C^{12}$, $_8O^{16}$, and $_{16}S^{32}$. For all nuclei the magnetic moment is proportional to the angular momentum. It is convenient to modify eq. (1) to

$$\mathbf{u} = g\,\frac{e}{2Mc}\,\mathbf{p} \tag{2}$$

where $g$ is the nuclear gyromagnetic, or more properly the magnetogyric, ratio; $g$ is a characteristic property of a given nuclear species.

   *2.1.2. Nuclear Magnetic Energy Levels.* In space free of other magnetic fields the energy of a nuclear magnet, or any magnet, does not depend on the orientation of the magnet. But if there is present a magnetic field $\mathbf{H}$, the magnet is subjected to a torque $\mathbf{L}$ which acts to align the magnet parallel with the field, like a compass needle in the earth's magnetic field. Elementary magnetic theory gives the torque as

$$\mathbf{L} = \mathbf{u} \times \mathbf{H} \tag{3}$$

If the magnetic field has a static and uniform value, $\mathbf{H}_0$, over the magnetic dipole, the interaction between the two introduces an energy

$$E = -\mathbf{u} \cdot \mathbf{H}_0 = -\mu_H H_0 \tag{4}$$

where $\mu_H$ is the component of $\mathbf{u}$ along $\mathbf{H}_0$, the latter of magnitude $H_0$.

   Discrete magnetic energy levels occur because the magnetic moment of a nucleus is proportional to its angular momentum, and it is a law of quantum mechanics that "elementary" particles, atoms, and molecules exist only in states with particular values of angular momentum. Experiment has shown that when a direction is established in space for a nucleus, say by the interaction of its magnetic moment with $\mathbf{H}_0$, then $p_H$, the nuclear angular momentum along $\mathbf{H}_0$, has a maximum value of $Ih/2\pi$. $I$ is a characteristic nuclear property, the nuclear spin, which has integral or half-integral values from 0 to at least $\tfrac{9}{2}$ for different nuclei, and $h$ is Planck's constant. The various allowed orientations are summarized by the equation

$$p_H = mh/2\pi \tag{5}$$

where $m$ is the magnetic quantum number, which takes values $I$, $I - 1$, . . . , $-I$, a total of $2I + 1$ in number.

The proportionality of the magnetic moment to the angular momentum in eq. (2) can be rewritten as

$$\mu_H = g \, \frac{e}{2Mc} \, p_H \tag{6}$$

This combines with eq. (5), as shown in Fig. 2, to give a quantization of the magnetic moment along $H_0$

$$\mu_H = mg \, \frac{he}{4\pi Mc} \equiv mg\mu_n \tag{7}$$

Thus, eq. (4) for the magnetic energy becomes

$$E = -mg\mu_n H_0 \tag{8}$$

The last equation describes a set of $2I + 1$ nuclear orientations and energy levels, shown schematically in Fig. 2. These energy levels are

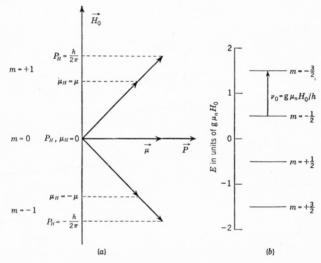

FIG. 2. (a) Quantization along $H_0$ of the nuclear angular momentum **p** and the simultaneous quantization of **μ**, for a nucleus with $I = 1$. ($2I + 1 = 3$ discrete states.) (b) Nuclear-magnetic-energy-level diagram for a nucleus with $I = \frac{3}{2}$. Note that for a positive $\mu$ the lower energy levels have positive $m$, and absorption corresponds to $\Delta m = -1$.

often called nuclear Zeeman levels because of their similarity to those associated with the Zeeman hyperfine structure in atomic spectra. The selection rule for transitions is that $m$ changes by $+1$ or $-1$; so $\Delta E$ is $\mp g\mu_n H_0$. Applying the Bohr frequency condition, $\Delta E = h\nu$, we find the frequency $\nu_0$ corresponding to an allowed change in nuclear magnetic energy to be

$$\nu_0 = g\mu_n H_0/h \tag{9}$$

Before describing how transitions are brought about, we should point out that $\mu_n$, defined in eq. (7) as $(he/4\pi Mc)$, is the nuclear magneton $(5.049 \times 10^{-24}$ erg/gauss). Electronic magnetic moments are measured in terms of the Bohr magneton, which is 1836 times as large because the mass of the electron is used in the denominator of eq. (1) instead of the proton mass. The nuclear magnetic moment $\mu$ is defined by the equation $g = \mu/I$, where $\mu$ is the maximum component of the nuclear moment along $H_0$.

*2.1.3. Larmor Precession and Magnetic Resonance.* In atomic spectra, the Zeeman transitions with $\Delta m = \pm 1$ involve radiation which is circularly polarized in the plane perpendicular to the static magnetic field $H_0$. The nuclear model of Figs. 1 and 2 can be extended (4, 67) to show that this requirement applies equally well to the nuclear magnetic transitions. The magnetic field exerts a torque upon the nuclear magnetic moment, tending to align it parallel to the field. However, this involves a change in the direction of the angular-momentum vector **p**. For such rotational motion, Newton's law states that the time rate of change of the angular momentum equals the torque; that is

$$dp/dt = L \tag{10}$$

Substituting for **L** the value $\boldsymbol{\mu} \times \mathbf{H}$ given in eq. (3), and converting $\boldsymbol{\mu}$ to **p** by eq. (2), we find

$$dp/dt = g(e/2Mc)\mathbf{p} \times \mathbf{H}_0 \tag{11}$$

This equation of motion describes the precession of **p** about $H_0$ with an angular velocity whose magnitude is given by the Larmor equation

$$\omega_0 = g(e/2Mc)H_0 \equiv \gamma H_0 \tag{12}$$

Solving for the precession frequency by substituting $2\pi\nu_0 = \omega_0$ gives

$$\nu_0 = g(he/4\pi Mc)H_0/h = g\mu_n H_0/h \tag{13}$$

This result is identical with the separation, in frequency, of the nuclear energy levels given in eq. (9). An attempt is made in Fig. 3 to picture the nuclear spinning and also to show the precession of the spin axis about $H_0$. A more familiar example is that of a spinning top with its axis "wobbling" about the vertical, because of the torque arising from the gravitational field and the force of reaction where the point of the top rests.

The precession of the nuclear spin axis about a magnetic field suggests a way to change the orientation and, thereby, the magnetic energy of a nucleus. If a small magnetic field $H_1$ is placed perpendicular to $H_0$, the torque exerted by $H_1$ upon $\boldsymbol{\mu}$ will cause the spin axis to precess about $H_1$, changing the orientation of the nucleus or nutating with respect to

$H_0$. However, the sense of this nutation changes with the relative orientations of $H_1$ and $\mu$, as shown in Fig. 3. Therefore, $H_1$ must rotate about $H_0$ in synchronization with the nuclear precession about $H_0$; otherwise the nutation is first in one direction and then the other, giving little or no net effect. That is, the rotation of $H_1$ must be *in resonance with* the Larmor precession about $H_0$.

A rotating magnetic field of this sort is associated with circularly polarized radiation of frequency $\nu_0$. The sense of the Larmor precession depends on the sign of the magnetic moment, with a positive $\mu$ requiring a left circularly polarized $H_1$. In practice an rf current is passed through a small coil mounted perpendicular to $H_0$, producing a magnetic field oscillating along the axis of the coil.

$$H_x = 2H_1 \cos 2\pi\nu t \qquad H_y = 0 \qquad H_z = 0 \qquad (14)$$

But this is equivalent to two circularly polarized fields rotating in opposite directions in the plane perpendicular to $H_0$.

| Right circular | Left circular | |
|---|---|---|
| $H_x = H_1 \cos 2\pi\nu t$ | $H_x = H_1 \cos 2\pi\nu t$ | |
| $H_y = H_1 \sin 2\pi\nu t$ | $H_y = -H_1 \sin 2\pi\nu t$ | |
| $H_z = 0$ | $H_z = 0$ | (15) |

The component which has the correct sense for a given nucleus will satisfy the resonance condition, while the other component has a negligible effect (67). These results agree with the quantum mechanical treatment which provides a quantitative description of the transition probabilities (4, 16).

The essential features of a magnetic-resonance experiment are summarized in Fig. 4. A sample containing magnetic nuclei is placed in a

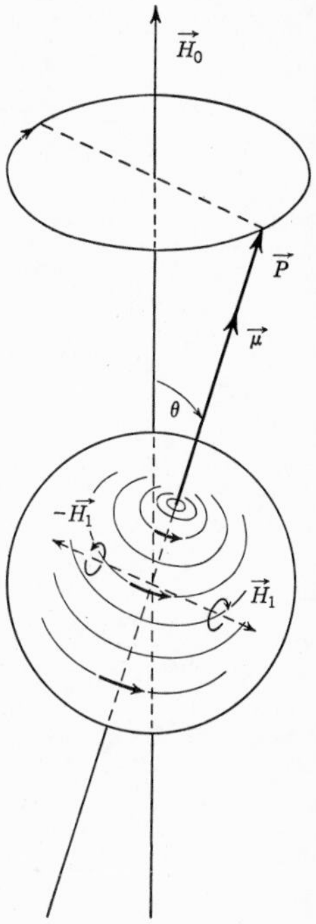

FIG. 3. Larmor precession of the nuclear spin axis about $H_0$. Precession of $\mu$ about the small field $H_1$ changes the angle $\theta$ between $\mu$ and $H_0$ and produces transitions in the nuclear magnetic energy. However, the change in $\theta$ is reversed if the orientation of $H_1$ with respect to $\mu$ is reversed.

static magnetic field, ordinarily several thousand gauss. A coil is mounted with its axis perpendicular to the static field, and enclosing the sample, which is about 1 cc. in volume. A radiofrequency source produces an oscillating current through the coil. The oscillator is set at a fixed frequency and the magnetic field is swept slowly through the resonance condition. The absorption of rf energy by the nuclei at resonance is revealed by a display of the detected rf output on an oscilloscope. Figure 4 shows the proton magnetic-resonance absorption of water obtained in this fashion. Table I lists the resonance frequencies at 10,000 gauss and the nuclear properties for most nuclei of general chemical importance. Experimental details are left to section 3.

### 2.2. Relaxation Effects and Spin-Spin Interactions

*2.2.1. $T_1$, the Spin-Lattice Relaxation Time.* When we turn our attention from a single nucleus to an assembly of nuclei in a magnetic field, a problem arises (16) which is usually unimportant in other types of spectroscopy. How do the nuclear spins attain and maintain thermal equilibrium with their environment? Electronic, vibrational, rotational,

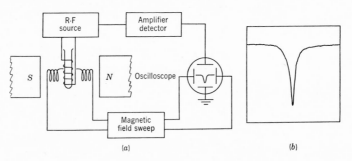

(a)                                                        (b)

Fig. 4. (a) Essential features of a nuclear magnetic resonance experiment. (b) The proton resonance absorption in 0.01 cm.³ of $H_2O$ observed at a fixed frequency of 17.735 Mc. $H_0$ was swept at a rate of 20 milligauss sec.⁻¹, over a total of 100 milligauss. The relatively large apparent line width of about 5 milligauss is due almost entirely to inhomogeneities in $H_0$.

and translational energy are interchanged very readily in "collisions" of one sort or another. However, the nuclei are insulated from their surroundings by the atomic electrons, and the transfer of nuclear magnetic energy to the other degrees of freedom, i.e., to the "lattice," is a relatively slow process. Spontaneous emission is negligible, and induced transitions require a magnetic field oscillating at the Larmor frequency, as shown in the preceding section. If, therefore, there is to be energy transfer from nuclei to lattice, the required oscillating fields must be produced at the nuclei by the thermal motions of the lattice. The efficiency with which the nuclei "relax" from high- to low-energy magnetic states has an important bearing upon the detection of nuclear magnetic resonance.

If one looks closely at the effect of the externally applied oscillating field on the nuclear orientation, it is clear that $H_1$ is as effective in turning the down nuclei up as it is in turning the up nuclei down. If there is to be a *net* absorption of rf energy there must be an excess of nuclei in

## TABLE I

*Nuclear Properties and Magnetic-Resonance Characteristics**

| Isotope | Natural abund., % | $\nu_0$ in $Mc$ at 10,000 gauss | $\mu$ | $I$ | $Q$ | Sensitivity at constant $H_0$ | Sensitivity at constant $\nu_0$ |
|---|---|---|---|---|---|---|---|
| $H^1$ | 99.985 | 42.578 | 2.7927 | $\frac{1}{2}$ | — | 1.000 | 1.000 |
| $H^2$ | 0.015 | 6.536 | 0.8574 | 1 | $2.74 \times 10^{-3}$ | $2.45 \times 10^{-2}$ | 0.409 |
| $Li^6$ | 7.52 | 6.265 | 0.8219 | 1 | $4.6 \times 10^{-4}$ | $2.21 \times 10^{-2}$ | 0.392 |
| $Li^7$ | 92.48 | 16.55 | 3.256 | $\frac{3}{2}$ | $-0.042$ | 0.471 | 1.94 |
| $Be^9$ | 100 | 5.982 | $-1.177$ | $\frac{3}{2}$ | 0.02 | $3.70 \times 10^{-2}$ | 0.702 |
| $B^{10}$ | 18.98 | 4.576 | 1.801 | 3 | 0.111 | $6.06 \times 10^{-2}$ | 1.72 |
| $B^{11}$ | 81.02 | 13.66 | 2.688 | $\frac{3}{2}$ | 0.053 | 0.291 | 1.60 |
| $C^{13}$ | 1.108 | 10.71 | 0.7022 | $\frac{1}{2}$ | — | $3.17 \times 10^{-2}$ | 0.251 |
| $N^{14}$ | 99.635 | 3.077 | 0.4036 | 1 | 0.02 | $3.74 \times 10^{-3}$ | 0.193 |
| $O^{17}$ | 0.037 | 5.772 | $-1.8930$ | $\frac{5}{2}$ | $-0.005$ | $7.89 \times 10^{-2}$ | 1.58 |
| $F^{19}$ | 100 | 40.05 | 2.627 | $\frac{1}{2}$ | — | 0.858 | 0.941 |
| $Na^{23}$ | 100 | 11.26 | 2.216 | $\frac{3}{2}$ | 0.1 | 0.180 | 1.32 |
| $Mg^{25}$ | 10.11 | 2.606 | $-0.8547$ | $\frac{5}{2}$ | ? | $1.09 \times 10^{-2}$ | 0.714 |
| $Al^{27}$ | 100 | 11.10 | 3.639 | $\frac{5}{2}$ | 0.149 | 0.385 | 3.04 |
| $Si^{29}$ | 4.68 | 8.460 | $-0.5549$ | $\frac{1}{2}$ | — | $1.76 \times 10^{-2}$ | 0.199 |
| $P^{31}$ | 100 | 17.24 | 1.131 | $\frac{1}{2}$ | — | 0.104 | 0.405 |
| $Cl^{35}$ | 75.4 | 4.172 | 0.8210 | $\frac{3}{2}$ | $-0.079$ | $1.50 \times 10^{-2}$ | 0.490 |
| $K^{39}$ | 93.08 | 1.987 | 0.3909 | $\frac{3}{2}$ | ? | $2.35 \times 10^{-3}$ | 0.233 |
| $Sc^{45}$ | 100 | 10.344 | 4.7491 | $\frac{7}{2}$ | ? | 0.611 | 5.10 |
| $V^{51}$ | 99.76 | 11.20 | 5.142 | $\frac{7}{2}$ | 0.3 | 0.745 | 5.52 |
| $Mn^{55}$ | 100 | 10.55 | 3.461 | $\frac{5}{2}$ | 0.5 | 0.357 | 2.89 |
| $Co^{59}$ | 100 | 10.10 | 4.639 | $\frac{7}{2}$ | 0.5 | 0.576 | 4.98 |
| $Cu^{63}$ | 69.1 | 11.29 | 2.221 | $\frac{3}{2}$ | $-0.16$ | 0.181 | 1.33 |
| $Ga^{69}$ | 60.2 | 10.22 | 2.011 | $\frac{3}{2}$ | 0.232 | 0.141 | 1.20 |
| $As^{75}$ | 100 | 7.293 | 1.435 | $\frac{3}{2}$ | 0.3 | $6.07 \times 10^{-2}$ | 0.856 |
| $Bi^{81}$ | 49.48 | 11.50 | 2.263 | $\frac{3}{2}$ | 0.26 | 0.211 | 1.35 |
| $Rb^{85}$ | 72.15 | 4.110 | 1.348 | $\frac{5}{2}$ | ? | $3.38 \times 10^{-2}$ | 1.13 |
| $Rb^{87}$ | 27.85 | 13.94 | 2.742 | $\frac{3}{2}$ | ? | 0.306 | 1.64 |
| $Nb^{93}$ | 100 | 10.407 | 6.1435 | $\frac{9}{2}$ | $-0.4$ | 0.976 | 8.07 |
| $Sb^{121}$ | 57.25 | 10.19 | 3.342 | $\frac{5}{2}$ | $-1.3$ | 0.327 | 2.79 |
| $I^{127}$ | 100 | 8.520 | 2.794 | $\frac{5}{2}$ | $-0.75$ | 0.209 | 2.33 |
| $Cs^{133}$ | 100 | 5.584 | 2.564 | $\frac{7}{2}$ | $\leq 0.3$ | 0.123 | 2.75 |
| $In^{115}$ | 95.77 | 9.330 | 5.5072 | $\frac{9}{2}$ | 1.161 | 0.742 | 7.23 |
| $Hg^{199}$ | 16.84 | 7.612 | 0.4993 | $\frac{1}{2}$ | — | $1.35 \times 10^{-2}$ | 0.179 |
| $Tl^{205}$ | 70.5 | 24.56 | 1.611 | $\frac{1}{2}$ | — | 0.253 | 0.577 |
| $Pb^{207}$ | 22.6 | 8.899 | 0.5837 | $\frac{1}{2}$ | — | $2.00 \times 10^{-2}$ | 0.209 |
| $Bi^{209}$ | 100 | 6.842 | 4.039 | $\frac{9}{2}$ | $-0.4$ | 0.342 | 5.30 |

* A more complete wall chart of this type is available from Varian Associates, Palo Alto, California. In the table the units of $\mu$ are $he/4\pi Mc$; of $I$, $h/2\pi$; of $Q$, $e \times 10^{-24}$ cm.$^2$ The relative sensitivities are based on the proton as unity and refer to samples containing the same numbers of nuclei and having the same $T_2/T_1$ ratio for the resonances being compared. Nuclei with an even number of neutrons and protons are omitted because they have no magnetic moments.

the lower energy states. For simplicity we shall suppose that $I = \frac{1}{2}$. An excellent general analysis has been made (56) but is not essential here. When there is thermal equilibrium throughout the sample, the Boltzmann expression shows the relative populations of the two magnetic states to be

$$N_2 = N_1 \exp\left(-\Delta E/kT\right) \tag{16}$$

$N_2$ is the number of nuclei in the high-energy state and $N_1$ that in the low; $k$ is the Boltzmann constant and $T$ the absolute temperature of the

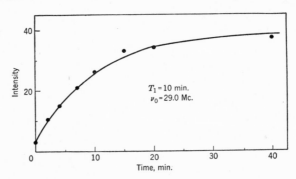

FIG. 5. Spin-lattice relaxation curve for ice at $-180°$ C., showing recovery of proton resonance intensity after saturation (68).

sample. $\Delta E$, the difference in magnetic energy between the two states, is given by eq. (8) as $g\mu_n H_0$. For protons in a field of 10,000 gauss the ratio of populations is, therefore,

$$\frac{N_1}{N_2} = \exp\left(\Delta E/kT\right) = \exp\frac{g\mu_n H_0}{kT} \cong 1 + \frac{g\mu_n H_0}{kT}$$
$$\cong 1 + 7 \times 10^{-6} \tag{17}$$

The slight excess of nuclei in the lower state, seven out of two million in the favorable example cited, gives the net absorption of energy from the radiofrequency field. When rf energy is absorbed some of the excess population in the lower level is transferred to the upper level. This is a radiofrequency heating of the nuclear-spin system. Because of their insulation the nuclei are slow in losing this extra energy to the lattice, and so the excess number of nuclei in the lower state and the absorption steadily decrease in the rf field until a steady state is reached. The nuclear insulation is often good enough that relatively weak rf fields can heat a spin system enough to decrease the absorption significantly, i.e., to saturation. If the rf field is then removed, the spin-lattice relaxation processes cool the spin system exponentially with a characteristic time, $T_1$. The results of such an experiment (68) are plotted in Fig. 5. The protons in ice at $-180°$ C. were saturated with a large rf field. This field was removed, and at short intervals the resonance absorption was observed with an rf field small enough to cause negligible heating. The exponential growth with time of the absorption from this weak field measured the return of protons to the lower energy state. The time constant observed was 10 min., the proton spin-lattice relaxation time. The usual range of nuclear $T_1$ values is $10^{-4}$ to $10^4$ sec. The values depend on temperature, on the state and nature of the sample, and on the static field, $H_0$. The details of the spin-lattice relaxation processes are deferred until section 2.2.3.

*2.2.2. Spin-Spin Interactions and $T_2$.* In addition to their interactions with the lattice, the nuclear spins interact among themselves (16, 100). These spin-spin interactions are a consequence of the small magnetic

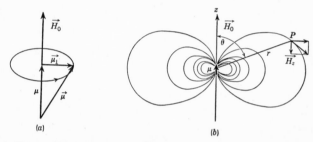

(a)                     (b)

FIG. 6. The rotating and static local magnetic fields about a precessing but otherwise stationary magnetic moment. (a) The precession of $\mathbf{\mu}$ about $H_0$ is equivalent to the rotation of $\mathbf{\mu}_\perp$ in the plane perpendicular to $H_0$. (b) This gives the magnetic field of $\mu$, the static component of $\mathbf{\mu}$ along $H_0$ (77). The field produced in the $z$ direction at $P$ is $(\mu/r^3)(3 \cos^2 \theta - 1)$.

fields, outlined in Fig. 6, which are associated with the magnetic nuclei. We suppose the nucleus to be in a rigid lattice, i.e., in a given location, and consider the field produced at a particular near-by point, $P$. This local field has in general a static and a rotating component. The rotating part is a consequence of the precession of the nuclear magnetic moment $\mathbf{\mu}$ about the external field. The static part arises from $\mu_H$, the component of $\mathbf{\mu}$ along $H_0$, which is $\pm\mu$ for nuclei with $I = \frac{1}{2}$.

The static local field $H_l$ which $\mu$ produces at $P$ depends on $P$'s distance, $r$, and its direction, $\theta$, from the nucleus. $H_l$ is typically of the order of a few gauss; the proton has an exceptionally large nuclear moment and its maximum local field at a distance of 1 Å. is 28.2 gauss. The local field $H_l$ adds to the applied external field $H_a$ to give the net field $H_0$ at $P$. When $H_a \gg H_l$, as is usual, $H_0 \cong H_a + H_{lz}$, where $H_{lz}$ is the component of $H_l$ along $H_a$. $H_{lz}$ is given by the equation

$$H_{lz} = \pm \frac{\mu}{r^3} (3 \cos^2 \theta - 1) \tag{18}$$

and

$$H_0 = H_a \pm \frac{\mu}{r^3} (3 \cos^2 \theta - 1) \tag{19}$$

These local fields produce a splitting or spread in the applied field value $H_a$ necessary to give the resonance field $H_0$. If a sample consists of isolated pairs of nuclei, with $I = \frac{1}{2}$, then according to eq. (19) the resonance at a fixed frequency $\nu_0$ would be split into two equal components separated in gauss by $(2\mu/r^3)(3 \cos^2 \theta - 1)$. If the pairs are oriented at

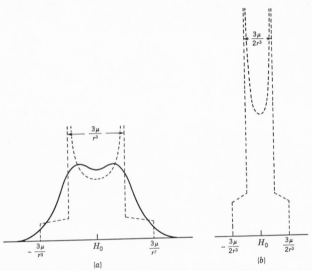

Fig. 7. The absorption line shapes for nuclei with $I = \frac{1}{2}$, occurring as pairs with an internuclear separation $r$. The dashed lines are theoretical curves for a powder sample, neglecting interactions between neighboring pairs; the solid curves indicate the "smoothing out" effects of the neighbors. (a) Assumes stationary nuclei—a rigid lattice (66). (b) Represents the partial motional narrowing produced by rotation of the pairs about axes perpendicular to the internuclear axis (40).

random as in a crystal powder, $\theta$ covers all values and a broadened doublet resonance results. A theoretical calculation (66) of the line shape gives the dotted curve in Fig. 7a. In actual samples the spin-spin interactions between neighboring pairs are appreciable, and this gives additional smoothing out of the resonance, as shown by the solid curve in Fig. 7a.

The rotating components of the local fields can add to the breadth of the resonance, but in a manner somewhat different from the static components. Suppose a pair of identical nuclei, with $I = \frac{1}{2}$, have the same $H_0$ and, therefore, precess at the same Larmor frequency. Each nucleus has a $\mathbf{u}_\perp$, shown in Fig. 6 to be the component of the nuclear moment which rotates in the $x$-$y$ plane. These rotating components generate rotating local fields $H_{1l}$ at each nucleus, which can produce a simultaneous reorientation or flip-flop of both nuclei, interchanging their energy yet conserving the total energy of the pair. The process is often called "spin exchange" or a "spin-spin collision." The spin exchange limits the lifetimes, $\Delta t$, of the nuclear states, giving an uncertainty in energy $\Delta E$, which is related to $\Delta t$ by the Heisenberg principle $\Delta E \, \Delta t \cong h/2\pi$. By analogy with eq. (13), a nuclear spin will precess about $H_{1l}$ and thus change its state at a frequency

$$\nu = g\mu_n H_{1l}/h \tag{20}$$

so

$$\Delta t = \frac{1}{2\pi\nu} = \frac{h}{2\pi} \cdot \frac{1}{g\mu_n H_{1l}} \tag{21}$$

and

$$\Delta E = g\mu_n H_{1l} \tag{22}$$

The rotating fields $H_{1l}$ of $\mathbf{\mu}_\perp$ have about the same magnitude as $H_{zl}$ and, therefore, the spread in energy gives a broadening effect comparable to the static local fields. The quantum mechanical properties of angular momentum lead to

$$\mu_\perp = gI_\perp = (\mu/I)[I(I+1) - m^2]^{1/2} \tag{23}$$

A detailed analysis (100) shows that the rotating fields have half the broadening effect of the static fields; both effects are included in Fig. 7. The spin-exchange effects are important only between nuclei with the same magnetogyric ratios.

Line shapes have been computed for equilateral three- and tetrahedral four-spin systems (5, 11), but the complexity of calculation increases very rapidly with the number of interacting nuclei, and in such cases the crystal powder usually has a simple bell-shaped resonance. However, the second moment, the mean square deviation, $\Delta H_2^2$, of the absorption intensity from the line center in a powder can be calculated readily (32, 100) from the structure of the sample, by the equation

$$\Delta H_2^2 = \frac{6}{5} \frac{I(I+1)}{N} g^2 \mu_n^2 \sum_{j<k} r_{jk}^{-6} + \frac{4}{15} \mu_n^2 \sum_{j,f} \frac{I_f(I_f+1)}{N} g_f^2 r_{jf}^{-6} \tag{24}$$

$I$ and $g$ refer to the nuclei whose resonance is observed, $N$ is the number of such nuclei in the "unit cell" over which the calculation is made, and $f$ refers to other magnetic nuclear species in the cell. Line shapes and second moments can be very useful in determining internuclear distances and crystal structures, but that interesting application is another story, to which references are given in more general reviews (30, 95) than this.

*2.2.3. Lattice Motions and Nuclear Relaxation.* If the nuclei are not stationary, as assumed in the preceding section, but are in motion, the internuclear distances and directions will vary with time and so will the local magnetic fields, giving via eq. (18) for the $z$-components

$$H_{lz}(t) = \pm [\mu r^{-3}(t)][3 \cos^2 \theta(t) - 1] \tag{25}$$

These fluctuations in the local fields have a twofold effect (16). First, they tend to average out the broadening from the spin-spin interactions, thereby producing motional narrowing of the resonance. Second, the lattice motions generate oscillations in the local magnetic fields, and this is one of the most important mechanisms for spin-lattice relaxation. In analyzing the motional narrowing, consider for simplicity a pair of nuclei which in the absence of motion has a doublet resonance separated by $\Delta\nu$. When the pair rotates, with $r$ fixed, then $\theta(t) = f(2\pi\nu_c t)$, where $\nu_c$ is the frequency correlated with the rotation. If the nuclear pair is in a situation where the rotation occurs over all directions uniformly, the average value of $\cos^2 \theta$ is $\frac{1}{3}$. And if the rotation is "fast enough" the $\frac{1}{3}$ can be substituted in eq. (25) to give the effective value of the local field, zero for this particular situation. A similar argument applies to the effects of the rotating components, $H_{1l}$, of the local fields.

There is still the question of how rapid the motions need to be before they reduce the effects of the local fields. Suppose the resonance line width is $\Delta\nu$. If an interacting pair of nuclei are in phase at a given time but are precessing at frequencies differing by $\Delta\nu$, they will be 180° out of phase in a time of the order of $1/2\Delta\nu$ later. In other words, the rate at which the nuclei get out of phase is inversely proportional to the width of the resonance. However, if the local fields change during the time required by the nuclei to get out of phase, then the rate of getting out of phase is changed, and this means a change in line width. Therefore, a resonance will be narrowed when the frequency of motion is the order of the frequency width of the resonance, i.e., when $\nu_c \rightarrow \Delta\nu$. The line width $\Delta\nu$ may be $10^4$ to $10^5$ c.p.s. in rigid lattice solids. But the thermal motions in liquids are much faster than this and also random, which is why resonance lines are usually very narrow in liquids. The frequencies and randomness of motions increase with temperature, and so if a solid is heated from a rigid lattice temperature we should expect the resonance line to narrow as the motions increased. A nice example of this is shown in Fig. 8, where the resonance line width of Li$^7$ observed in the metal is plotted against the temperature (36). In this case the resonance is narrowed by the translational motions of self-diffusion, at temperatures well below the melting point. If the motions are restricted in some manner, then the local fields may be only partially averaged out no matter how fast the motions occur. A nuclear pair restricted to rotation about an axis perpendicular to the internuclear axis has the local fields reduced by a factor of $\frac{1}{2}$, as shown in Fig. 7b. Instances of this sort have been found experimentally (40).

A rigorous analysis of the spin-lattice relaxation mechanisms requires a knowledge of how the coordinates describing the nuclear positions vary in time, so that the oscillations at the Larmor frequency in the local fields in the $x$-$y$ plane may be calculated with equations like eq. (25), and their effect on $T_1$ deduced (16). If the relaxation is produced by one type of lattice motion, such as a molecular rotation, then $T_1$ is given by

$$(1/T_1) = K[\tau_c/(1 + 4\pi^2\nu_0^2\tau_c^2) + 2\tau_c/(1 + 16\pi^2\nu_0^2\tau_c^2)] \tag{26}$$

where $\nu_0$ is the Larmor frequency, $\tau_c$ is the correlation time—the time required for the motion to occur—and $K$ is a constant characterizing the

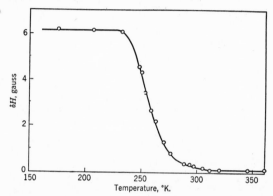

FIG. 8. The temperature dependence of the Li⁷ absorption-line width, $\delta H$, measured between points of maximum slope in solid metallic lithium (36). The narrowing is caused by the translational motions of self-diffusion.

resonance broadening by the local fields in the rigid lattice. It is assumed that the motion influences equally all sources of the local fields. The motional narrowing of the spin-spin broadening is found by a similar analysis to be

$$(1/T_2')^2 = (3/\pi)K \tan^{-1} (2\tau_c/T_2') \tag{27}$$

$1/T_2'$ represents the line-width contribution from spin-spin interactions. $T_1$ also contributes to the line width because it represents a limitation on the lifetimes of the nuclear spin states. In the absence of other effects one finds that

$$(1/T_2) = (2\pi)^{\frac{1}{2}}(1/T_2') + (1/2T_1) \tag{28}$$

Except for a small conversion factor of the order of $1/\pi$, the line width in c.p.s. is $1/T_2$. The symbol $T_2^*$ is sometimes used as an inverse line width including inhomogeneity and other sources of line broadening; we shall use $T_2$ throughout.

$T_1$ and $T_2$ are shown in Fig. 9 as a function of $\tau_c$ for this simplified case. The minimum in $T_1$ occurs for a value of $\tau_c$ where $\nu_c = 1/2\pi\tau_c = \sqrt{3}$ $\nu_0$, and the minimum depends therefore on $H_0$. The physical reason for the minimum is simply that the frequencies on either side are too fast or too slow to induce transitions. The limiting value of $1/T_2$ as $\tau_c \to \infty$ is $1/T_2''$, which is determined by the rigid lattice line width, while as $\tau_c \to 0$, $1/T_2$ and the line width become very small. The temperature dependence

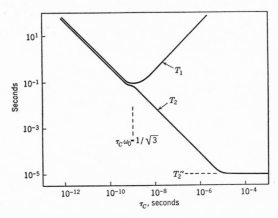

Fig. 9. The influence of $\tau_c$ upon $T_1$ and $T_2$ for the simple model in which all interactions are assumed to have the same $\tau_c$ (16).

of these quantities can be inferred from any valid theory relating $\tau_c$ to the temperature. For instance, if the motions are thermally activated we have

$$\tau_c = \tau_0 \exp (E_a/RT) \tag{29}$$

where $E_a$ is an activation energy for the motion. This gives a plot identical with Fig. 9 except that the abscissa is $\ln \tau_0 + E_a/RT$. Equation (29) is obeyed in many materials except that discontinuities usually occur at transition temperatures. Moreover, the viscosity of a liquid plays an important role in determining its $T_1$. And any actual case will have a distribution of types of motions and of $\tau_c$.

## 2.3. Electronic Effects in Nuclear Resonance

### 2.3.1. Chemical Shifts in the Resonance Positions.
Certainly one of the most important of the nuclear magnetic-resonance phenomena when it comes to analytical applications is the chemical shift. The term "chemical shift" originated with the initial experimental observations (26, 53, 75) that the location of the resonance for a particular nucleus varied from one chemical compound to another. These shifts can be measured either as differences in resonance frequency for a given applied magnetic field

or as differences in the applied magnetic field for a fixed resonance frequency. The latter, which is the more usual experimental arrangement, is assumed here. Magnetic field units can be converted to frequency with the direct proportionality of the Larmor equation, eq. (13). The chemical shifts are rather small and often are obscured in solids by the dipole-dipole broadening of the resonance. Therefore, the shifts are usually observed in the liquid state, in magnetic fields of high homogeneity.

The principle underlying the chemical shift is that the magnetic field at a nucleus is in general not the same as that in the bulk sample. The

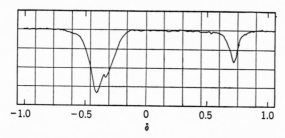

$$-1.0 \qquad -0.5 \qquad 0 \qquad 0.5 \qquad 1.0$$
$$\delta$$

FIG. 10. The proton spectrum of propionic acid, $CH_3CH_2CO_2H$, under conditions of moderate resolution. The resonance was observed in 0.01 cm.[3] of the liquid at a fixed frequency of 17.735 Mc. $H_0$ was swept at a rate of 15 milligauss sec.[-1] over a total of 83 milligauss. $\delta$ is defined as $10^5(H_r - H_c)/H_r$ with $H_2O$ the reference compound.

difference arises from the interaction of the applied magnetic field with the motions of the electrons in the sample and can be represented as

$$H_0 = H_b(1 + \sigma) \tag{30}$$

$H_b$ is the magnetic field in the bulk of the sample, and $\sigma$ is an internal magnetic susceptibility of the electrons about the nucleus. Usually $\sigma$ is negative corresponding to a magnetic shielding of the nucleus or an internal diamagnetism. If nuclei of the same species have different distributions of electrons about them, then the $\sigma$ values will differ. Different applied fields, $H_b$, will be required for resonance. These shifts are referred most easily to some reference compound and given as a field-independent difference, $\delta$, in the nuclear magnetic shielding.

$$\delta = \sigma_r - \sigma_c = H_0(H_c - H_r)/H_rH_c \cong (H_c - H_r)/H_r \tag{31}$$

$H_c$ and $H_r$ are the applied static fields required for resonance in the compound and in the reference, respectively. If a compound has two or more nonequivalent sites, the resonance will have two or more components. This is illustrated in Fig. 10 by the proton resonance in propionic acid, $CH_3CH_2CO_2H$, which has three components with relative intensities of

3:2:1 corresponding to the $CH_3$, $CH_2$ and $CO_2H$ protons. The line for the $CO_2H$ group is displaced considerably from the overlapping lines for the $CH_3$ and $CH_2$ groups, as one might predict from their chemical differences.

The earliest calculations of the nuclear magnetic shielding were made to correct the observed apparent nuclear magnetic moments for the shielding effects. For atoms and monatomic ions the theory is relatively simple (55), giving

$$\sigma = (e^2/3mc^2)v(0) \qquad (32)$$

where $v(0)$ is the electrostatic potential produced at the nucleus by the electrons. $v(0)$ can be calculated from any reasonable set of electronic wave functions. The Fermi-Thomas statistical approximation gives the simple, but nonetheless quite good, result that

$$\sigma = -3.19 \times 10^{-5}Z^{4/3} \qquad (33)$$

where $Z$ is the nuclear charge. More recent calculations (25) give values of $\sigma$ ranging monotonically from $-1.8 \times 10^{-5}$ for hydrogen to $-1.16 \times 10^{-2}$ for uranium.

The nonspherical charge distribution in molecules complicates the calculation of $\sigma$ for molecules, as shown by the general theory (78). It is convenient, although arbitrary, to divide the $\sigma$ for a nucleus in a molecule into two terms. The first is a diamagnetic term, similar to eq. (32) with the provision that $v(0)$ is calculated for all electrons in the molecule. The other term is a second-order paramagnetism; it is caused by the magnetic-field perturbations, which mix excited magnetic electronic states in with the ground state. This effect may cancel out part or all of the diamagnetic shielding or even increase the field at the nucleus above that externally applied. $\sigma$ is ordinarily independent of temperature unless there is a low-lying electronic state or unless there are large molecular interactions which change with temperature (48). The range of $\sigma$ for a nucleus in different molecules is roughly of the same magnitude as $\sigma$ for the free atom or ion. Thus $\delta's$ for protons are of the order of $10^{-5}$ and for thallium, $10^{-3}$.

Elements in the metallic state exhibit a more pronounced but similar resonance shift (53). The shifts in the metals, compared with those in their salts, arise from the paramagnetism of the conduction electrons. The effects range from $2 \times 10^{-4}$ for lithium to $10^{-2}$ for cesium (36) and have proved very useful in studying the electronic nature of metals.

*2.3.2. Indirect Spin-Spin Coupling of Nuclei.* An indirect coupling of the magnetic nuclei by the electrons in a sample often gives rise to a multiplet structure in the resonance (34, 43) which, like the chemical shifts, is rather small and most readily observed in liquids. An example of this effect is shown in Fig. 11, which gives the proton and the fluorine resonance lines in fluorochloromethane, $CH_2FCl$. The two hydrogens in the molecule are equivalent, by symmetry; yet the proton resonance is a doublet, with components of equal intensity. The fluorine resonance is a triplet, the components having intensities in the ratio $1:2:1$. Moreover, the splittings, i.e., the separation of adjacent lines, when expressed in energy units are the same for the proton and fluorine resonances, 38 c.p.s. in this case.

These multiplets arise from an indirect coupling of the nuclear spins via the electrons in the molecule. The coupling may be described qualitatively somewhat as follows. For simplicity consider only two nuclei,

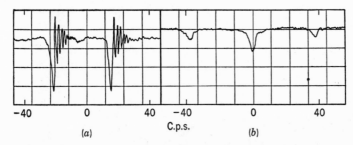

-40　　0　　40　-40　　0　　40
C.p.s.
(a)　　　　　　　　(b)

FIG. 11. The proton and fluorine multiplet resonances in a 0.02 cm.³ sample of fluorochloromethane, $CH_2FCl$. $H_0$ was swept at a rate of 2.9 milligauss sec.⁻¹. (a) The proton spectrum was observed at a fixed frequency of 17.735 Mc. The total sweep is 23.2 milligauss. The beat signals after the resonance are associated with the sweep rate (50) as described in section 3.1.3. (b) The fluorine spectrum was observed at 16.682 Mc. The total sweep is 29 milligauss.

$A$ and $B$, bonded directly to one another. When an electron is in the vicinity of nucleus $A$, the magnetic moment of the electron is oriented to a slight extent by the local magnetic field of $A$. If this "polarized" electron spends any fraction of its time at nucleus $B$, the polarized field of the electron will change the magnetic field from the value which would otherwise have been seen by that nucleus. In different molecules nucleus $A$ will have various orientations with respect to the main magnetic field, $H_0$, and nucleus $B$ will see different local fields. So in a bulk sample the resonance of nucleus $B$ is split into a number of components equal to the orientations of nuclei $A$ in different molecules. The intensities of the components depend on the statistical weights of the various orientations of $A$. Nucleus $B$, of course, exerts a similar effect upon nucleus $A$, and the net effect is a mutual coupling.

The doublet proton resonance in $CH_2FCl$ thus arises from the two spin states of the fluorine; and the intensities are the same because the states have essentially equal probability, as stated in eq. (17). The fluorines, however, are acted upon by two equivalent protons, each with two spin states. The proton spins can combine in three nonequivalent ways, represented schematically as $(++)$, $(+-, -+)$ and $(--)$, with statistical weights of $(1:2:1)$ corresponding to the observed intensities.

These results can be described by an interaction between the nuclei of the form

$$A_{ij}\mathbf{F}_A \cdot \mathbf{F}_B \tag{34}$$

$A_{ij}$ is the coupling constant expressed as the observed splitting in cycles per second. As it is assumed that there may be several nuclei of each type interacting, we have

$$\mathbf{F}_A = \sum_{i=A} I_i \quad \text{and} \quad \mathbf{F}_B = \sum_{j=B} I_j \tag{35}$$

where $\mathbf{F}_A$ and $\mathbf{F}_B$ are the total spin angular momenta in units of $h/2\pi$ for groups $A$ and $B$ respectively. If the resonance frequencies $\nu_A$ and $\nu_B$ differ for the two groups by an amount

$$|\nu_A - \nu_B| \gg A_{ij} \tag{36}$$

which is certainly true for $CH_2FCl$, first-order theory gives the perturbation (34) of the nuclear magnetic levels to be

$$A_{ij}M_A M_B \tag{37}$$

where $M_A$ and $M_B$ are the magnetic quantum numbers describing the spin orientations of nuclei in groups $A$ and $B$. This accounts correctly for the number, splittings, relative intensities, and nondependence upon $H_0$ of the multiplets observed.

Many of the theoretical details are too involved to permit elaboration here, but several of the results are essential for qualitative understanding of the spectra. For example, there is no experimental evidence of coupling between the two protons in $CH_2FCl$. The theory shows that coupling occurs between equivalent nuclei but the effects are not observable except in certain cases. Also, it is to be noted that the splittings are independent of $H_0$ only as long as the condition of eq. (36) is satisfied. In this connection it is not essential that the groups $A$ and $B$ contain nuclei of different species, but only nuclei with different resonance positions. Thus many multiplets arise from coupling between nuclei differing only by a chemical shift $\delta\nu$ in resonance frequency. In this event one often finds $A_{ij} \sim \delta\nu$, and the simple rules embodied in eq. (37) no longer apply. But the more complex spectra can nonetheless be described accurately by more complex theory (9, 43). Another complexity is that $A_{ij}$ is not necessarily the same for all pairs of $A$-$B$ interactions, even though the nuclei in each group are chemically equivalent. In $F_2C = CH_2$, for example, the F-H coupling depends on whether the nuclei are cis or trans; and the simple theory incorporated in eq. (37) must be modified to include this difference (57).

Theoretical values of $A_{ij}$ in general agreement with the experimental have been calculated (34, 79). These calculations are somewhat like those for the chemical shift; the coupling mixes in excited electronic states with spin and/or orbital angular momentum. Like the chemical shift, $A_{ij}$ is independent of temperature unless one of the electronic states contributing to $A_{ij}$ is sufficiently low lying that it makes a temperature-dependent contribution to the normal state. Observed values of $A_{ij}$ range as large as a kilocycle or so for directly bonded nuclei. The coupling is ordinarily attenuated by factors of the order of $\frac{1}{2}$ to $\frac{1}{5}$ per additional bond, and this attenuation can be useful in fixing the location in a molecule of the interacting nuclei. The coupling constants for protons in organic molecules are commonly in the 1- to 25-cycle range, and for fluorine in fluorocarbons $A_{ij}$ may be as much as 100 cycles.

*2.3.3. The Influence of Dynamic Processes.* In section 2.2.3 it was pointed out that molecular reorientations give a motional narrowing of the broad resonances produced by the local magnetic fields in solids. A qualitative argument suggested that the critical reorientation frequency is the frequency equivalent of the perturbation being averaged, the line width in the case of motional narrowing. A similar effect can be produced on the chemical shifts (41) and multiplet lines (34) by dynamical processes of certain types. Suppose protons can exchange chemically or by a molecular rearrangement between two different structural sites. In the absence of the exchange two separate resonance lines are observed, corresponding to the different electronic environments of the two sites. But when exchange occurs at a "fast enough" rate, the different electronic environments average out, and a single resonance line occurs at an intermediate position determined by the relative numbers of protons at each site. The exchange rate required for the averaging is determined by the difference to be averaged. If the resonance components are separated in the absence of exchange by an amount, $\delta\nu$, say 100 c.p.s., then the correlation time, $\tau$, for the exchange must be the order of $1/\delta\nu$, or $10^{-2}$, sec. to average out the chemical shift. The appearance of the spectrum has been predicted theoretically as a function of exchange rate (41), and the results of such a calculation are given in Fig. 12. It is seen that as $\tau \to 1/\delta\nu$, the two resonance components broaden and coalesce, giving a single narrow line when $\tau \ll 1/\delta\nu$.

A similar argument holds for the multiplet splittings except that changes in the spin states are required to average out the interaction.

The splitting of the resonance of nuclei in one group depends on the spin orientations of nuclei in the second group. If the latter change at a frequency comparable with that of the splitting, then the coupling is averaged out and the splitting of the resonance of the first group disappears. The analysis mentioned above for the chemical shift applies to this case provided that $\delta\nu$ is redefined as the splitting and $\tau$ as the nuclear spin lifetime of the nucleus producing the splitting. In some cases chemical exchange will determine $\tau$ (63); in others it may be $T_2$ or the external application of a radiofrequency field to induce transitions (93).

*2.3.4. Paramagnetic Samples.* The term *paramagnetism* refers usually to materials with unpaired electrons. An externally applied magnetic

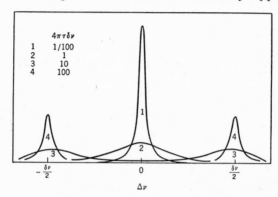

Fig. 12. Theoretical absorption-line shapes in a chemically exchanging two-species system, computed for different lifetimes $\tau$. It is assumed that in the absence of the exchange the sample has two resonance components of equal intensity separated in frequency by $\delta\nu$.

field orients the electronic magnetic moments and gives a net magnetization to the sample. The orientation of nuclear magnetic moments in $H_0$ is entirely analogous except that, as mentioned in section 2.1.2, the nuclear moments are only about $\frac{1}{1836}$ as large as the electronic moment, and so the nuclear paramagnetism is correspondingly less. The effects of electronic paramagnetism are so large compared with those of the nuclear moments that the nuclear resonance is often indetectable in paramagnetic samples. As an illustration, if an atom has an unpaired electron as well as a nuclear magnetic moment, then the local magnetic fields produced by the electron at the nucleus are of the order of $10^3$ to $10^5$ gauss. Splitting of the nuclear magnetic levels by these local fields, and/or spin-lattice relaxation by fluctuations in the local fields, are so great that the nuclear resonance is split and/or broadened past detectability. For such reasons, the observation of nuclear resonance is limited to diamagnetic or weakly paramagnetic systems,

If the paramagnetic centers are dilute, the $1/r^3$ dependence of their local fields may reduce the effects enough to permit observation of nuclear resonance in the sample. In fact, small concentrations ($\sim 10^{-3}$ $M$) of paramagnetic salts have often been added to solutions to reduce $T_1$ and increase the absorption intensities (12). Another effect of paramagnetic ions, in aqueous solutions, is a concentration-dependent nuclear resonance shift (26). The shifts in gauss are linear in $H_0$; positive as well as negative shifts have been observed, and the size of the shifts is about $10^{-4}$ mole$^{-1}$ liter.

*2.3.5. Quadrupole Coupling.* Nuclei with $I > \frac{1}{2}$ have properties which can be ascribed to nonspherically symmetric charge distributions in the nucleus (23). There is symmetry about the axis of spin, but the distribution can be either flattened or elongated at the poles, and this deviation from spherical symmetry of the charge distribution is described by the nuclear electric quadrupole moment, $Q$. Nuclei do not have electric dipole moments, and so the energy of any nucleus is independent of its orientation in a *uniform* electric field. But if the electric field is *inhomogeneous*, then, as described by Dailey in Chapter 8, there will be a net torque exerted on a quadrupolar nucleus tending to align the nucleus along the direction in which the electric field changes, that is, along the gradient of the electric field. The interaction energy is proportional to $eQq$, the product of the electric field gradient, $q$, and the nuclear quadrupole moment, and is as little as a few kilocycles or as much as 2000 Mc., depending on the nucleus and the magnitude of the electric field gradients.

The electric field gradients may originate in the electrostatic fields in crystals or in the distribution of electrons in chemical bonds. Our main concern with the quadrupole coupling is its effect upon the nuclear magnetic resonance. In rigid lattice solids the quadrupole energy adds more or less directly (71) to the nuclear magnetic energy, producing a splitting of the magnetic resonance in a single crystal into $2I$ components. As this splitting is orientation dependent, the magnetic resonance in a crystal powder is often spread over such a range that it is too weak to detect. In liquids and gases molecular reorientations tend to average out the field gradients, which then operate mainly as relaxation mechanisms. But if the quadrupolar energies are large ($\sim 10$ to 20 Mc.; $eQ \sim \pm 0.05 \times 10^{-24}$ cm.$^2$) the averaging may be incomplete or the relaxation so effective that the magnetic resonance is still broadened past detection.

If the environment of a quadrupolar nucleus is sufficiently symmetric, the electric field gradient will be zero at the nucleus, and quadrupole coupling effects will not occur. It is for this reason that the magnetic resonance of nuclei, such as Na, Rb, Cs, Cl, Br, and I, which have appreciable $Q$'s, can nonetheless be observed in cubic crystals and in solutions of ionic compounds. In the solutions, solvation effects disrupt the spherical symmetry of the ions and there is usually appreciable broadening because of quadrupolar contributions to $T_1$. But in molecular compounds, such as liquid $CCl_4$, the chlorine nuclei have a quadrupole coupling of about 35 Mc. with the field gradient of the C-Cl bond, and this prevents the observation of the chlorine magnetic resonance. In general, the successful observation of nuclear magnetic resonance for quadrupolar nuclei requires careful screening of proposed experiments.

Quadrupole effects can also exert an indirect influence on the appearance of the resonance absorption of nonquadrupolar nuclei. An interesting example of analytical interest is that multiplets produced by quadrupolar nuclei are seldom observed. In $CH_2FCl$, for instance, the proton and fluorine resonances show no multiplet structure attributable to the chlorine even though the chlorine nuclei have sizable magnetic moments and their coupling with the protons and fluorine is probably large enough to be observable. The explanation lies in the large quadrupole coupling of the chlorine nuclei with the field gradients of the C-Cl bond. This reduces the lifetime of the various chlorine nuclear spin states well past the limit in which the coupling is averaged out, as described in section 2.3.3. Multiplets produced by quadrupolar nuclei have been observed (63, 64) in cases where the molecular symmetry results in small quadrupole coupling.

## 3. EXPERIMENTAL METHODS

A sizable number of different techniques have been invented for detecting nuclear magnetic resonance. The diversity of resonance phenomena is a complication because the observation of different phenomena requires different arrangements of apparatus. The apparatus used for a particular analytical procedure is outlined under that heading. In this section we calculate the magnitudes of the nuclear signals under various conditions and give a general description of the basic experimental problems and methods.

### 3.1. Nuclear Magnetic Susceptibility

*3.1.1. Nuclear Magnetization.* The magnitudes of the resonance effects are proportional to the extent of nuclear magnetization, which is given by the excess population of nuclei oriented parallel to the external magnetic field (67). For nuclei with magnetic levels designated by $m$, the magnetization $M_H$, per unit volume, along the static field **H** will be

$$M_H = \sum_m \mu_H(m)N_m \qquad (38)$$

where $N_m$ is the number of nuclei with orientation given by $m$, and $\mu_H(m)$ is the component along **H** of the nuclear moment for such nuclei;

$m$, of course, varies by integral values from $I$ to $-I$. Equation (7) has given $\mu_H(m)$ as $mg\mu_n$, and $N_m$ is related by the Boltzmann expression of eq. (16) to the temperature and the energy of the state, $-mg\mu_nH_0$. This converts eq. (38) to

$$M_H = \sum_m mg\mu_nN_0 \exp (mg\mu_nH_0/kT) \tag{39}$$

The constant $N_0$ is readily evaluated by the requirement that the total number of nuclei per unit volume be a given value $N$; so

$$\sum_m N_m = N = \sum_m N_0 \exp (mg\mu_nH_0/kT) \tag{40}$$

But the terms exp ( ) are all very close to 1, and there are $2I + 1$ values of $m$, so

$$N \cong N_0(2I + 1) \tag{41}$$

Substitution of this result in eq. (39) and inclusion of the second term in the series expansion of the exponential give

$$\begin{aligned}
M_H &= \sum_m \frac{N}{(2I + 1)} mg\mu_n(1 + mg\mu_nH_0/kT) \\
&= \frac{N}{2I + 1} (g^2\mu_n{}^2H_0/kT) \sum_m m^2
\end{aligned} \tag{42}$$

The terms in $m$ cancel out. Also, $I$ is integral or half integral, and so

$$\sum_m m^2 = (\tfrac{1}{3})I(I + 1)(2I + 1) \tag{43}$$

and

$$M_H = (N/3kT)g^2\mu_n{}^2I(I + 1)H_0 \tag{44}$$

The magnetization is expressible as the product of a susceptibility and the applied field; so the static nuclear paramagnetic susceptibility $\chi_0$ is identified as

$$\chi_0 = (N/3kT)g^2\mu_n{}^2I(I + 1) \tag{45}$$

As a numerical example, $\chi_0$ for protons in $H_2O$ at room temperature is found in c.g.s. units to be

$$\chi_0 = 3.2 \times 10^{-10} \text{ erg gauss}^{-2} \tag{46}$$

With a magnetic field of 10,000 gauss the magnetization is only $3.2 \times 10^{-6}$ erg gauss$^{-1}$. Such a very small value is exceedingly difficult to detect by static methods; however, radiofrequency methods are more sensitive.

*3.1.2. The Bloch Equations.* The interaction of the nuclear magnetization with the radiofrequency field can be described by a set of equations introduced by Bloch (12, 103). These equations are useful not only for calculating the magnitude of the resonance absorption but also for relating the appearance of the resonance to the conditions of passage through the resonance. In treating the radiofrequency phenomena it is convenient mathematically to use complex quantities (identified by script letters)

$$\mathfrak{X} = \chi' - i\chi'' \tag{47}$$
$$\mathfrak{M} = \mathfrak{M}' - i\mathfrak{M}'' = \mathfrak{X}\mathfrak{K} \tag{48}$$

The oscillating magnetic field applied to the sample is identified as the real part of the complex quantity

$$\mathfrak{K}_x = 2H_1 \exp (i\omega t) \tag{49}$$

The physically observable effects of the interactions between the rf field and the nuclear susceptibility are associated, therefore, with $M_x$, the real part of the magnetization

$$\mathfrak{M} = (\chi' - i\chi'')2H_1 \exp (i\omega t)$$
$$= 2H_1(\chi' \cos \omega t + \chi'' \sin \omega t) - 2iH_1(\chi'' \cos \omega t - \chi' \sin \omega t) \tag{50}$$

And this gives

$$M_x = 2H_1(\chi' \cos \omega t + \chi'' \sin \omega t) \tag{51}$$

The applied rf field is $2H_1 \cos \omega t$, and so the first term in eq. (51) is the in-phase component of the magnetization while the second term is the out-of-phase component, and these involve $\chi'$ and $\chi''$ respectively. The phase lag between the magnetization and rf field can be said to result from "frictional losses" to the nuclei in the sample. This absorption of energy, per unit volume per second, is given as the real quantity

$$A = \nu \int_0^{1/\nu} \mathbf{H}_1(d\mathbf{M}/dt) \, dt \tag{52}$$

$\mathbf{H}_1$ and $\mathbf{M}$ are coplanar in our case; so

$$A = \nu \int_0^{1/\nu} 2H_1 \cos (2\pi\nu t)2H_1 2\pi\nu(-\chi' \sin 2\pi\nu t + \chi'' \cos 2\pi\nu t) \, dt$$
$$= 4\pi\nu\chi''H_1{}^2 = 2\omega\chi''H_1{}^2 \tag{53}$$

This shows that the absorption by the nuclear spin system is proportional to $\chi''$, the out-of-phase component of the nuclear magnetization. The next problem is to calculate the frequency dependence of $\chi''$ and also of $\chi'$.

The equations of motion for the bulk magnetization can be obtained from that for a single nuclear magnetic moment by summing over all nuclei. The equation for a single moment is eq. (11), with $\mathbf{u}$ substituted for $\mathbf{p}$.

$$d\mathbf{u}/dt = g(e/2Mc)\mathbf{u} \times \mathbf{H} \equiv \gamma\mathbf{u} \times \mathbf{H} \qquad (54)$$

$\gamma$ is defined as $g(e/2Mc)$, which also equals $\omega_0/H_0$ or $2\pi\nu_0/H_0$. And for the magnetization $M$, per unit volume,

$$d\mathbf{M}/dt = \gamma\mathbf{M} \times \mathbf{H} \qquad (55)$$

$\mathbf{H}$ is given in the usual magnetic-resonance experiment as

$$H_x = H_1 \cos \omega t \qquad H_y = -H_1 \sin \omega t \qquad H_z = H_0 \qquad (56)$$

Using these values in the cross product of eq. (55) and assuming there are no other interactions involving the nuclei, we find

$$dM_x/dt = \gamma(M_y H_0 + M_z H_1 \sin \omega t) \qquad (57a)$$
$$dM_y/dt = \gamma(-M_x H_0 + M_z H_1 \cos \omega t) \qquad (57b)$$
$$dM_z/dt = \gamma(-M_x H_1 \sin \omega t - M_y H_1 \cos \omega t) \qquad (57c)$$

There is a significant difference between these equations for the bulk magnetization $\mathbf{M}$ and for $\mathbf{u}$, a single nuclear moment. In the absence of an rf field $\mathbf{M}$ has only a $z$ component while $\mathbf{u}$ has $x$, $y$, and $z$ components; the individual nuclei precess about $z$ at random phases, and so the $x$ and $y$ components of $\mathbf{u}$ average to zero in forming $\mathbf{M}$.

So far we have neglected the interactions among the nuclei and between nuclei and lattice. Consider first the spin-lattice effects. $M_z$ is proportional to the excess population of nuclei in the lower energy states, and at thermal equilibrium the value would be $M_0$, the magnetization given in eq. (44). But if $M_z \neq M_0$, the spin-lattice processes change $M_z$ toward $M_0$ at a rate characterized by the relaxation time $T_1$, and

$$dM_z/dt = (M_0 - M_z)/T_1 \qquad (58a)$$

Moreover, $M_x$ and $M_y$ differ from zero only if a group of nuclei are in phase. But the phase relations are destroyed by the spin-lattice and spin-spin interactions, and if we neglect any line-shape peculiarities associated with the local fields, the loss of phase can be characterized by a single relaxation time, $T_2$, and

$$dM_x/dt = -M_x/T_2 \qquad (58b)$$
$$dM_y/dt = -M_y/T_2 \qquad (58c)$$

In any actual experiment the time dependence of the magnetization reflects the combined effects of the externally applied magnetic fields and the interactions within the sample. Therefore, the differential equations describing the actual behavior of the system are obtained by adding the terms in eq. (58) to eq. (57). The resulting equations are the Bloch equations. The manner in which $T_1$ and $T_2$ appear in these equations has led to another terminology besides the phrases *spin-lattice* and *spin-spin* relaxation times used so far. $T_1$ describes the change in magnetization parallel to $H_0$, the $z$-axis, and so it is the longitudinal relaxation time. $T_2$ refers to the magnetization in the $x$-$y$ plane, perpendicular to $H_0$, and so it is the transverse relaxation time.

The solution of this set of differential equations depends on the boundary conditions employed. A particular solution, which applies to most experiments of immediate concern, is obtained by assuming that the resonance is observed under steady-state or slow-passage conditions. In this event the rf absorption is just balanced by energy transfer from nuclei to lattice and so $dM_z/dt = 0$. The solution on this basis is straightforward (12, 67) and gives

$$M_x = \frac{1}{2}\chi_0\omega_0 T_2 \frac{(2H_1 \cos \omega t)(\omega_0 - \omega)T_2 + 2H_1 \sin \omega t}{1 + (\omega_0 - \omega)^2 T_2{}^2 + \gamma^2 H_1{}^2 T_1 T_2} \tag{59a}$$

$$M_y = \frac{1}{2}\chi_0\omega_0 T_2 \frac{2H_1 \cos \omega t - (2H_1 \sin \omega t)(\omega_0 - \omega)T_2}{1 + (\omega_0 - \omega)^2 T_2{}^2 + \gamma^2 H_1{}^2 T_1 T_2} \tag{59b}$$

$$M_z = \chi_0 H_0 \frac{1 + (\omega_0 - \omega)^2 T_2{}^2}{1 + (\omega_0 - \omega)^2 T_2{}^2 + \gamma^2 H_1{}^2 T_1 T_2} \tag{59c}$$

Equation (51) identifies $\chi'$ and $\chi''$ as the coefficients of $2H_1 \cos \omega t$ and $2H_1 \sin \omega t$ in the $M_x$, and taking these coefficients from eq. (59a), we find the frequency dependence of $\chi'$ and $\chi''$ to be

$$\chi' = \frac{1}{2}\chi_0\omega_0 T_2 \frac{(\omega_0 - \omega)T_2}{1 + (\omega_0 - \omega)^2 T_2{}^2 + \gamma^2 H_1{}^2 T_1 T_2} \tag{60}$$

$$\chi'' = \frac{1}{2}\chi_0\omega_0 T_2 \frac{1}{1 + (\omega_0 - \omega)^2 T_2{}^2 + \gamma^2 H_1{}^2 T_1 T_2} \tag{61}$$

For some purposes it is convenient to introduce a function $g(\nu)$ describing the frequency dependence of the absorption, which in this case is

$$g(\nu) = \frac{2T_2}{1 + (\omega_0 - \omega)^2 T_2{}^2 + \gamma^2 H_1{}^2 T_1 T_2} \tag{62}$$

The term $\gamma^2 H_1{}^2 T_1 T_2$ occurs in the denominators of the expressions for $\chi'$, $\chi''$, $M_z$, and $g(\nu)$. This term is called a *saturation factor* because it increases with $H_1$ and thereby reduces the other quantities. It expresses quantitatively the saturation effects described in section 2.2.1. Combining eq. (59c) for $M_z$, evaluated at $\omega = \omega_0$, with eq. (45) for $\chi_0$, we find

$$M_z(\omega_0) = \frac{NH_0 g^2 \mu_n{}^2 I(I + 1)}{3kT(1 + \gamma^2 H_1{}^2 T_1 T_2)} \tag{63}$$

This is identical with the static magnetization if we introduce a spin temperature $T_s$, where

$$T_s = T(1 + \gamma^2 H_1{}^2 T_1 T_2) \tag{64}$$

which increases with the degree of saturation. This model gives a generally satisfactory description of nuclear resonance in liquids, but it has been found not to apply to high degrees of saturation of broad lines in solids (81).

Saturation effects are negligible if

$$\gamma^2 H_1{}^2 T_1 T_2 \ll 1 \tag{65}$$

The term then drops out of eqs. (60) and (61). Plots are given in Fig. 13 of the resulting functions for the susceptibilities $\chi'$ and $\chi''$. The plot of $\chi''$ corresponds to $g(\nu)$ in eq. (62) and, when multiplied by the essentially

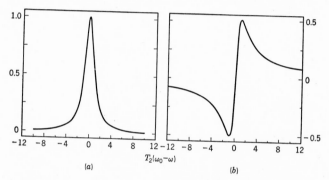

Fig. 13. The Bloch nuclear magnetic susceptibilities (12). The ordinate is in units of $(\frac{1}{2})\chi_0\omega_0 T_2$ and the abscissa is the dimensionless variable $T_2(\omega_0 - \omega)$. (a) $\chi''$, the imaginary part of the susceptibility, which causes the resonance absorption. (b) $\chi'$, the real part of the susceptibility, which causes the resonance dispersion.

constant factor $(\frac{1}{2})\omega H_1{}^2\chi_0\omega_0$, is converted directly to the energy absorbed. $g(\nu)$ is a Lorentz curve, the characteristic line shape for a damped oscillator. The curve for $\chi'$ corresponds to the dispersion which accompanies an absorption band. If the actual absorption line shape $g(\nu)$ is different from the Lorentzian shape assumed here, the dispersion can be calculated by use of the Kronig-Kramers relations (4). The sharply resonant character of the absorption is seen by comparing the line width with $\nu_0$, the frequency of the line center. The full width of the absorption line at half its maximum value is $2/T_2$; and $2/T_2$ may be as small as $10^{-1}$ sec.$^{-1}$ compared with a $\nu_0$ of 1 to 40 Mc.

The increased sensitivity of a radiofrequency experiment compared with the static magnetization is suggested by eq. (61) relating $\chi''$ to $\chi_0$. This gives

$$\chi''(\omega_0) = (\frac{1}{2})\chi_0\omega_0 T_2 \tag{66}$$

which indicates that the rf susceptibility is of the order of $(\frac{1}{2})\omega_0 T_2$ or $10^3$ to $10^7$ times greater than the static susceptibility. The resonance effects observed are associated with the oscillating components of the nuclear magnetization, and these depend on $H_1$ as given in eq. (59). An optimum value for $H_1$ is obtained for the resonance absorption by taking the expression for $M_x$ (or $M_y$) at $\omega = \omega_0$ and setting $dM_x(\omega_0)/dH_1$ equal to zero, to give

$$\gamma^2 H_1^2 T_1 T_2 = 1 \tag{67}$$

Typical values of $T_1$ and $T_2$ for protons in liquids are of the order of 0.1 to 10 sec., for which $(H_1)_{op} = 10^{-3}$ to $10^{-5}$ gauss. The heating of the nuclear spin system by this small $H_1$ is actually very striking; the temperature of the spin system is *twice* that of the lattice. The maximum values for $M_x$ and $M_y$, which occur at $\omega = \omega_0$, can be found by solving eq. (59) by use of $(H_1)_{op}$. This gives

$$
\begin{aligned}
(M_x)_{max} = (M_y)_{max} = \chi''(2H_1)_{op} &= (\frac{1}{2})\chi_0\omega_0 T_2/(T_1 T_2)^{\frac{1}{2}} \\
&= (\frac{1}{2})\chi_0 H_0(T_2/T_1)^{\frac{1}{2}} = (\frac{1}{2})M_0(T_2/T_1)^{\frac{1}{2}} \quad (68)
\end{aligned}
$$

*3.1.3. Passage Conditions.* The optimum value of $H_1$ produces a certain amount of saturation and distortion from the theoretical line shapes in Fig. 13. Saturation broadens the resonance, and from eq. (61) one finds the full width at half maximum absorption to be

$$(\delta\omega)_{\frac{1}{2}max} = (1 + \gamma^2 H_1^2 T_1 T_2)^{\frac{1}{2}} 2/T_2 \tag{69}$$

$2/T_2$ is the width of the unbroadened absorption, and so the optimum $H_1$ broadens the absorption by the factor $\sqrt{2}$. Also, the steady-state solution of the Bloch equations described above assumes that equilibrium has been attained between the rf field and the nuclear magnetization. This places a considerable restriction upon the rate at which the resonance is traversed. If the resonance is passed through too quickly, several transient effects can occur (16, 50). The static nuclear magnetization at thermal equilibrium is $M_0$, which is reduced to $M_0/(1 + \gamma^2 H_1^2 T_1 T_2)$ in the steady state. If the resonance line is entered too rapidly, the resonance will be stronger at first and then become weaker as the magnetization is reduced from $M_0$ to the steady-state value.

Another transient phenomenon, which is prominent for narrow resonances, is that known as the "relaxation wiggles." These are damped oscillations which follow the resonance when it is swept through rapidly. The effect occurs because the nuclear magnetization has not had time to follow the changing applied fields. After the resonance condition is passed, a magnetic moment persists in the $x$-$y$ plane as long as any net group of nuclei continues to precess in phase. This magnetization precesses about $H_0$, inducing a signal at the precession frequency, the amplitude decaying with the "phase memory" time, $T_2$. But once the resonance condition is passed, the precession frequency and the radiofrequency differ, and the two signals reinforce and interfere with one another, giving the low-frequency-beat signal (16). This effect is shown in Fig. 14a for the proton resonance absorption in water. The resonance was obtained by sweeping the applied magnetic field $H_0$ linearly in time. In this case, if the wiggles

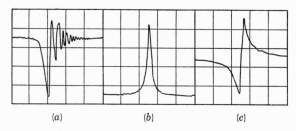

(a)　　　　(b)　　　　(c)

Fig. 14. The proton magnetic resonance observed at 17.735 Mc. (a) The absorption in a 0.01 cm.$^3$ sample of $H_2O$, showing the relaxation wiggles characteristic of narrow lines (50). The sweep rate was 5 milligauss sec.$^{-1}$; the total sweep is 10 milligauss. The relaxation pattern corresponds to a line width of 1 milligauss, which is equivalent to a $T_2$ of about 0.1 sec. (b) The resonance absorption in a 0.2 M solution of $CuCl_2$ in $H_2O$. The 25-milligauss line width is a result of the short $T_1$ and the line shape is Lorentzian. The sweep rate was 120 milligauss sec.$^{-1}$, the total sweep 600 milligauss. (c) The resonance dispersion under conditions otherwise the same as (b).

are to be eliminated, the rate of change of $H_0$ must satisfy the requirement (50)

$$dH_0/dt \leq 1/(4|\gamma|T_2{}^2) \tag{70}$$

The resonance could also be traversed at a fixed field as a function of $\nu_0$. The simple proportionality of the resonance equation $\nu_0 = \gamma H_0/2\pi$ suggests no theoretical preference for either procedure. The proportionality transforms eq. (70) directly to frequency units. It is essential, however, that either $H_0$ or $\nu_0$ be kept constant to a degree depending on the precision desired in the experiment, while the other is traversed under controlled and calibrated conditions. Both types of arrangement have been used for various purposes. But if the resonance phenomenon in question does not extend over an unusually large region of $H_0$ (or $\nu_0$), it is generally simpler to operate at fixed frequency and sweep $H_0$. Most detection systems require several frequency-sensitive units, each of which may be tuned easily to optimum for a given frequency but which would require a complex device to sweep them in synchronization. It should be mentioned that either the absorption or the dispersion mode of the resonance can be observed depending on the experimental arrangement. Figure 14 includes the two different modes for the proton resonance, observed in an aqueous solution of the paramagnetic salt, $CuCl_2$. The resonance is so broadened, because of the short $T_1$, that inhomogeneities in $H_0$ do not distort the line shapes, which agree very well with the theoretical shapes in Fig. 13. In most experiments the resonance absorption is observed rather than the dispersion, mainly because the former is usually easier to deal with from an interpretative and theoretical viewpoint.

### 3.2. Detection Systems

The subject of detection systems is extensive, and it is not intended that the present discussion be complete. The factors governing signal amplitudes and sensitivity are described in some detail, as are the general principles of the detection systems, particularly those best suited for analytical applications. A more exhaustive discussion is available elsewhere (4).

3.2.1. Signal Amplitudes and Sensitivity. In a steady-state resonance experiment the magnetization components $M_x$ and $M_y$ of eq. (59) describe a bulk magnetic moment of amplitude $2H_1[(\chi')^2 + (\chi'')^2]^{1/2}$ rotating in the $x$-$y$ plane at the angular velocity $\omega$ of the externally applied rf field. If a cylindrical coil encloses the moment, the rotation of the moment produces an oscillating magnetic flux which induces an rf voltage in the coil. Consider the axis of the coil to be in the $x$ direction, with the coil in a simple tuned circuit coupled loosely to the rf oscillator. The latter serves then as a constant current source and the system may be represented by the equivalent circuit in Fig. 15a. We wish to calculate the change in the rf voltage at the coil due to the nuclear magnetization. $M_x$ and $M_y$ are found in terms of $\chi'$ and $\chi''$ by combining eqs. (59) and (60) to obtain

$$M_x = 2H_1(\chi' \cos \omega t + \chi'' \sin \omega t)$$
$$M_y = 2H_1(-\chi' \sin \omega t + \chi'' \cos \omega t) \tag{71}$$

which are identical except for a 90° difference in phase. The magnetic induction in the coil arises from $M_x$ and is

$$B_x = 4\pi M_x = 8\pi H_1(\chi' \cos \omega t + \chi'' \sin \omega t) \tag{72}$$

The magnetic flux through the coil is, therefore,

$$\Phi_x = \zeta \Lambda B_x = 8\pi \zeta \Lambda H_1(\chi' \cos \omega t + \chi'' \sin \omega t) \tag{73}$$

where $\zeta$ is a filling factor giving the fraction of the effective coil area filled by the sample, and $\Lambda$ gives the area turns of the coil. The emf.,

$\Delta V$, induced by the nuclei may be calculated by applying Faraday's law of magnetic induction to eq. (73) and getting

$$\Delta V = -d\Phi_x/dt = -\omega 8\pi\zeta\Lambda H_1(-\chi' \sin \omega t + \chi'' \cos \omega t) \tag{74}$$

This is equivalent to a voltage generator $\Delta V$ in series with the coil in the circuit of Fig. 15a.

In the steady-state experiment an external rf voltage

$$V_0 = V_0{}^0 \cos \omega t \tag{75}$$

is *applied* to the tuned circuit, forcing a current

$$I_0 = I_0{}^0 \cos \omega t \tag{76}$$

through the coil, producing $H_1$ and thereby the rf nuclear magnetization. We wish to relate $\Delta V$ to the characteristics of the tuned circuit and

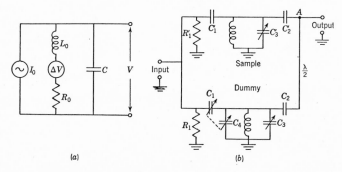

(a)                                           (b)

FIG. 15. (a) Equivalent circuit for the nuclear resonance effects. (b) Purcell-type (16) radiofrequency bridge includes a tuned circuit for the sample and a dummy tuned circuit for balancing.

to the rf voltage $V_0$ applied to it. The definition of inductance gives $L_0 I_0{}^0 = 2H_1\Lambda$, and also $I_0{}^0 R_0 = V_0{}^0$, which with the help of eq. (75) converts eq. (74) to

$$\Delta V = -4\pi\zeta \frac{\omega L_0}{R_0} (-\chi' \sin \omega t + \chi'' \cos \omega t)V_0{}^0 \tag{77}$$

$\omega L_0/R_0$ is the $Q$, or quality factor, of the circuit and the term in $\chi'$ is out of phase with $V_0$, which is $V_0{}^0 \cos \omega t$; so eq. (77) can be rewritten in explicit imaginary form as

$$\Delta V = -4\pi\zeta Q(\chi'' + i\chi')V_0 \tag{78}$$

We see that the effect of $\chi''$ is to reduce the voltage output of the circuit, corresponding to absorption as described earlier, while the imaginary term in $\chi'$ gives a phase shift which does not affect the normal rectifying detector. This derivation assumes that the fractional changes produced in the circuit parameters by the nuclear resonance are small. Also, it should be noted that the voltage developed *across* the coil is $Q$ times the voltage *applied*, but it is the latter which is used here unless otherwise specified. Before extending the analysis to include the various factors governing the signal intensity, we shall use eq. (78) to compute $\Delta V/V_0$ in a typical case.

Take a sample of $10^{-2}$ cm.$^3$ of liquid $H_2O$ at room temperature, place it in an $H_0$ of 5,000 gauss ($\omega_0/2\pi = 21.3$ Mc.), which is very slightly inhomogeneous so that the net proton $T_2$ is 1 sec., and assume the tuned circuit to have a $\zeta$ of 1 and a $Q$ of 50. With $H_1$ at its optimum value, and $\omega = \omega_0$, we have a maximum value for $\chi''$ given by eq. (61) as

$$\chi''_{max} = \chi_0\omega_0 T_2 V_c/4 \tag{79}$$

where $V_c$ is the volume of the coil taken also to be the volume of the sample. $\chi_0$ for $H_2O$ at room temperature was found in eq. (46) to be $3.2 \times 10^{-10}$ erg gauss$^{-2}$ cm.$^{-3}$, and so we find

$$(\Delta V/V_0)_{max} = -4\pi\zeta Q\chi''_{max} = -\pi\zeta Q\chi_0\omega_0 T_2 V_c \cong 0.07 \tag{80}$$

The rf voltage across the coil depends on its construction, but a typical value would be the order of $10^{-3}$ volts, giving an absorption signal of 70 $\mu$v., which is readily detectable.

The detectability of a "nuclear signal" (4, 12, 16) depends on its magnitude in comparison with the background in the circuits of random electrical fluctuations, i.e., the "noise." The ratio of the signal voltage $V_s$ to the noise voltage $V_n$ describes how readily the signal may be detected, and when $V_s/V_n$ becomes small and approaches unity the detection limit is reached. Noise is expressed most directly as a mean square voltage, and so we shall first calculate $V_s^2/V_n^2$. The series resistance $R_0$ of the sample coil in Fig. 15a is effectively a noise generator, and at a temperature $T$ the mean square voltage generated in a total frequency range $B$ is

$$(V_n^2)_{R_0} = 2R_0 kTB \tag{81}$$

Noise generated at frequencies outside the detection limits of the receiver will, of course, not influence the receiver; therefore, $B$ describes the pass band of the receiver. By *receiver* we mean all circuits past the tuned circuit containing the sample, including the display or recording equipment. The various circuits will have different band widths; the effective band width $B$ is then usually that of the "narrowest" circuit. The receiver itself will generate noise, and this is described by the noise factor $F$, which combines with the noise in the sample circuit giving the total noise

$$V_n^2 = (V_n^2)_{R_0} F = 2R_0 kTBF \tag{82}$$

The proper way to compute $V_s^2$ is influenced by the manner in which the tuned sample circuit is coupled to the detector, by the detector law, and by the manner in which the resonance is traversed. Numerical factors the order of unity account for such differences, and for simplicity we shall use $(\Delta V^2)_{Av}$ directly from eq. (80). We obtain

$$V_s^2 \equiv (\Delta V^2)_{Av} = (-4\pi\zeta Q\chi'')^2(V_0^2)_{Av} \tag{83}$$

By eq. (75) $(V_0^2)_{Av}$ is $(V_0^0)^2/2$; moreover, $H_1$ is related to the current in the coil. The magnetic energy stored in the coil may be written as either $L_0(I_0^0)^2/2$ or $V_c(2H_1)^2/8\pi$, which eliminates $(V_0^2)_{Av}$ from eq. (83) and gives upon substitution of $I_0^0 R_0 = V_0^0$ and $Q = \omega L_0/R_0$,

$$V_s^2 = 2\pi Q V_c R_0 \omega (\zeta 2 H_1 \chi'')^2 \tag{84}$$

The maximum value of $2H_1\chi''$ which occurs at $\omega = \omega_0$ is shown in eq. (68) to be $(\tfrac{1}{2})\chi_0 H_0(T_2/T_1)^{\frac{1}{2}}$. And, therefore,

$$\frac{V_s^2}{V_n^2} = \frac{\pi Q V_c \omega_0 \zeta^2 \chi_0^2 H_0^2 T_2}{4kTBFT_1} \tag{85}$$

With the value of $\chi_0$ given in eq. (45), this becomes when expressed in terms of $\nu_0$

$$\frac{V_s}{V_n} = \frac{Q^{\frac{1}{2}}V_c^{\frac{1}{2}}\zeta h^2 N\gamma I(I+1)}{6\sqrt{2}\,(kT)^{\frac{3}{2}}(BF)^{\frac{1}{2}}}\,(T_2/T_1)^{\frac{1}{2}}\nu_0^{\frac{3}{2}} \tag{86}$$

or in terms of $H_0$,

$$\frac{V_s}{V_n} = \frac{Q^{\frac{1}{2}}V_c^{\frac{1}{2}}\zeta h^2 N\gamma^{\frac{5}{2}}I(I+1)}{24(\pi kT)^{\frac{3}{2}}(BF)^{\frac{1}{2}}}\,(T_2/T_1)^{\frac{1}{2}}H_0^{\frac{3}{2}} \tag{87}$$

If two nuclear species are observed in the same apparatus at the same $\nu_0$, their relative signal to noise is given by the ratio of $N\gamma I(I+1)$ for the two species, assuming that their $(T_2/T_1)$'s are the same. Relative sensitivities at constant $\nu_0$, referred to the proton, are given in Table I for the more important isotopic species. These sensitivities assume that different samples contain the same number of nuclei; differences in isotopic abundance and concentration are thereby neglected. Similar calculations giving relative sensitivities at constant $H_0$ have been made with eq. (87), and the results are also given in Table I. In this case the circuit parameters $Q$, $V_c$, $\zeta$, $B$, and $F$ will differ somewhat for different nuclei because of the change in $\nu_0$. It is difficult to allow explicitly for these effects because they are sensitive to construction details; however, they should not change the relative sensitivities by a factor much outside limits of $\tfrac{1}{2}$ and 2.

By way of concluding this section, let us estimate the fewest protons at room temperature which can be detected under favorable conditions. This is done by setting eq. (86) or (87) equal to 1 and solving for $N$. For this calculation we take $Q = 100$, $V_c = 10^{-2}$ cm.$^3$, $\zeta = 1$, and $\nu_0 = 40$ Mc. If the resonance is observed by sweeping $H_0$ slowly through the absorption line, an effective band pass $B$ of 10 c.p.s. will reproduce the line shape; a good noise figure $F$ for the receiver is 2. Also, $T_1$ and $T_2$ are nearly equal in most liquids in homogeneous fields. With these assumptions we find $N/$cm.$^3$ to be about $5 \times 10^{18}$ protons, which is equivalent to about 0.1 mg. of $H_2O$. The sample volume assumed is $10^{-2}$ cm.$^3$, and so the actual minimum concentration of protons detectable is $5 \times 10^{20}/$cm.$^3$ or 1 gm. atom/liter. When eqs. (86) and (87) are used, the right-hand side should be multiplied by $(\frac{1}{10})^{\frac{1}{2}}$ to convert the usual c.g.s units to the proper form.

   *3.2.2. Radiofrequency Bridges and Nuclear Induction.* Although the nuclear resonance effects can be observed by placing the sample in the coil of a simple LC circuit (44) such as that just analyzed, it is usually preferable in practice to use somewhat more complex arrangements. The rf carrier voltage $V_0$ across the tuned, sample-containing circuit will be the order of $10^{-5}$ to $10^{-3}$ volts for high resolution spectra and $10^{-3}$ to 1 volt for broad lines, with the resonance absorption causing a fractional change in voltage of, say, $10^{-1}$ to $10^{-4}$. Therefore the rf amplifiers in the receiver may become saturated by the relatively high carrier voltage before the nuclear signal is amplified to a satisfactory level for detection. The way out of this difficulty is to use an arrangement—and there are several—to cancel or balance out most of the carrier voltage. This serves to cancel out to the same degree any extraneous noise from the oscillator, as well as allowing more rf amplification before detection; both factors serve to improve the sensitivity.

   Several varieties of rf bridge have been used for this purpose. A version introduced early by Purcell (16) is somewhat easier to analyze (4) descriptively than are some of the other forms (99) which are simpler in construction and operation. The Purcell bridge, as drawn in Fig. 15b, consists of two almost identical tuned LC circuits in parallel, connected with small coupling condensers and properly terminated coaxial cables to the same rf source. An additional electrical half wave length of cable is inserted somewhere in one circuit and the outputs are connected at a point $A$ and thence to the receiver. The effect of the half-wave-length line $\lambda/2$ is to reverse the phase of the voltage output at $A$ of the sample circuit compared with that of the dummy circuit, so that the voltages subtract. If the circuits were identical and tuned to $\nu_0$, there would be complete balance and cancellation at $A$ of the carrier rf, and any voltage seen by the receiver would be that induced by the nuclei. However, as stated in eqs. (77) and (78) this voltage is a mixture of the nuclear absorption and dispersion. Fortunately, the two effects can be separated and observed individually by adjusting the bridge so that it is not balanced completely and by controlling the nature of the residual imbalance.

Consider first the case where the voltage outputs at $A$ from the two halves of the bridge are exactly in phase but differ somewhat in amplitude, the case of amplitude unbalance. The voltage $v$ at $A$ is then the difference between the voltage $V_1$ from the dummy half and the voltage $V$ from the sample half. The latter is the voltage $V_0$ applied to the sample plus the $\Delta V$ of eq. (77) from the nuclei, and so

$$
\begin{aligned}
v &= V_1 - V = V_1 - (V_0 + \Delta V) \\
&= V_1{}^0 \cos \omega t - [V_0{}^0 \cos \omega t - 4\pi \zeta Q(-\chi' \sin \omega t + \chi'' \cos \omega t) V_0{}^0] \\
&= (V_1{}^0 - V_0{}^0 + 4\pi \zeta Q \chi'' V_0{}^0) \cos \omega t - 4\pi \zeta Q \chi' V_0{}^0 \sin \omega t \\
|v| &\cong (V_1{}^0 - V_0{}^0 + 4\pi \zeta Q \chi'' V_0{}^0) \cos \omega t = V_1 - V_0(1 - 4\pi \zeta Q \chi'')
\end{aligned}
\tag{88}
$$

The last step in eq. (88) depends on the fact that $v$ is a vector quantity and $\cos \omega t$ and $\sin \omega t$ represent orthogonal terms which are added vectorially. If $V_1{}^0 - V_0{}^0$ is several times larger than $4\pi \zeta Q \chi' V_0{}^0$, that is, if the residual unbalance is not too small, then the $\chi' \sin \omega t$ term serves mainly to produce a small phase shift in the voltage $v$ but leaves $|v|$, the amplitude of $v$, essentially unchanged, as shown. So in this case, as $H_0$ is swept through the resonance condition, the receiver detects $\chi''$, the absorption mode of the resonance, as given in Fig. 14b.

On the other hand, if the residual unbalance is in phase, the dispersion mode of the resonance is detected. For phase unbalance, but amplitude balance,

$$
V_1 = V_0{}^0 \cos \omega t + V_{10}{}^0 \sin \omega t
\tag{89}
$$

and this gives for $v$

$$
\begin{aligned}
v &= V_{10}{}^0 \sin \omega t + 4\pi \zeta Q(-\chi' \sin \omega t + \chi'' \cos \omega t) V_0{}^0 \\
&= (V_{10}{}^0 - 4\pi \zeta Q \chi' V_0{}^0) \sin \omega t + 4\pi \zeta Q \chi'' V_0{}^0 \cos \omega t \\
|v| &\cong (V_{10}{}^0 - 4\pi \zeta Q \chi' V_0{}^0) \sin \omega t
\end{aligned}
\tag{90}
$$

The argument for dropping the $\chi''$ term here is identical to that used in eq. (88) for $\chi'$. The dispersion mode of a proton resonance, detected by phase unbalance of an rf bridge, is shown in Fig. 14c.

A more rigorous general analysis of bridge balance can be made by use of imaginary quantities (4, 67); the results include an equation for the unwelcome intermediate line shapes which result when the bridge is unbalanced both in phase and in amplitude. If the bridge is balanced too closely, $\chi'$ and $\chi''$ will be mixed in spite of pure phase or amplitude unbalance. The permissible degree of balance depends on the maximum fractional change in $V_0$ arising from $\chi'$ or $\chi''$. If the resonance effects produce a change of 1 part in $10^3$, then the bridge could be balanced to reduce the output voltage by a factor of $10^2$ (40 db.) and still leave the nuclear signal one tenth of the output voltage. And this is a sufficiently small ratio for the approximations in eqs. (88) and (90) to be valid. Usual values of bridge balance are about 40 db.

In balancing the bridge, it is convenient to have two adjustments which control phase and amplitude independently. The phase of the output voltages from the tuned circuits in the bridge in Fig. 15b are adjusted readily by the main tuning condensers $C_3$. The amplitudes of the output voltages can be adjusted with the coupling condensers $C_1$ and/or $C_2$. However, the coupling condensers are effectively in parallel with $C_3$ via the small, impedance-matching resistor $R_1$, and so a change in $C_1$ ordinarily affects the phase as well as the amplitude balance. To avoid this, a differential condenser combination, $C_1$ and $C_4$, is used; capacitance removed from $C_1$ is added to $C_4$. In this way the phase control, $C_3$, and the amplitude control, $C_1 - C_4$, are essentially independent and the bridge can be balanced as desired in a few successive adjustments.

A somewhat different manner of balancing out the carrier rf is the crossed-coil nuclear induction system introduced by Bloch (12). In this arrangement the balance is achieved primarily by geometry. One rf coil, called the transmitter, is in a tuned circuit coupled to the oscillator, and a second coil, called the receiver coil, is mounted with its axis perpendicular to the transmitter coil; both coils are perpendicular to $H_0$ and centered at the same point. If this arrangement is geometrically perfect, the receiver coil cuts none of the magnetic flux of the transmitter coil, and so the carrier rf induces no signal in the receiver coil. But when the two coils surround a sample at resonance the rf field in the transmitting coil, taken to be along the $x$ axis, produces the rotating nuclear magnetization in the $x$-$y$ plane, as described by eq. (71). And $M_y$, the $y$ component of the nuclear magnetization, induces a voltage in the receiver coil, which lies along the $y$ axis. $M_y$ and $M_x$ differ only by a phase shift of $\pi/2$; therefore the nuclear induction voltage in the receiver coil is the same as that analyzed in such detail for $M_x$ in the preceding section, except for the same phase shift. The receiver coil is part of a tuned LC circuit which forms the input of an rf amplifier; otherwise the amplification, detection, and display systems can be the same for the bridge and nuclear induction systems.

The essential difference between the two systems is that in the bridge system one coil serves as both transmitter and receiver while in the Bloch system separate coils are used. Whether one wishes to use the nuclear induction or the resonance absorption–dispersion terminology depends somewhat on whether the macroscopic magnetization or the spectroscopic features are being emphasized. The tendency in usage is to restrict the term *nuclear induction* to those experiments conducted with a crossed-coil system and to transient phenomena in which nuclear signals are induced after the external rf field has been turned off. The choice of experimental arrangement is primarily one of experience and convenience. However, a crossed-coil system will give the relative signs of nuclear magnetic moments (74), which cannot be obtained with single-coil methods.

Complete balance of the crossed coils gives a mixture of the absorption and dispersion modes, just as in an rf bridge system. And in order to separate the two modes, there must be some "leakage" of the carrier rf to the receiver coil, with the phase and amplitude adjusted properly to give either the absorption or the dispersion. The balance conditions are the same as those used in eqs. (88) and (90) for the rf bridge. Several methods of adjusting the phase and amplitude of the leakage voltage have been used. If the receiver and transmitter coils differ from orthogonality by a small angle $\theta$, then the rf in the transmitter coil will induce a voltage in the receiver coil, which is a fraction about $\sin \theta \cong \theta$ of that in the transmitter coil. This corresponds to the amplitude adjustment in an rf bridge and can be accomplished with a micrometer screw (106) which tilts the electrical axis of one coil with respect to the other. The phase unbalance is controlled with an inductance loop in the $y$-$z$ plane, which can be rotated about the $x$ axis. An additional, fine control is provided by a "paddle" consisting of a small copper disk mounted on a Lucite rod at one end of the transmitter coil, with the plane of the disk parallel to the coil axis. The copper conductor distorts the axial symmetry of the rf field, and rotation of the rod controls the flux linkage with the receiver. The degree of bridge or leakage balance is monitored by observing the rf carrier level with a meter giving the detector current, the "S" meter in a commercial receiver.

*3.2.3. Other Methods.* In addition to the rf bridges and induction systems just described, there are detection techniques based on transient effects and also on several types of marginal oscillators. With the exception of a pseudotransient procedure described later, the transient methods do not appear to be well suited for analytical problems. In the first transient method developed (98), the radiofrequency power is applied abruptly with $H_0$ kept constant very near to or at the resonance condition. The rf is kept on at constant frequency, and a decaying beat signal between it and the nuclear magnetization is generated in a manner similar to the formation of the relaxation wiggles described in section 3.1.3. However, the nuclear magnetization determining the initial amplitude of the beat signals is more nearly $M_0$ for the pulsed rf case, and the beat signals can therefore be considerably larger than in the steady-state passage.

In a second transient method (42) the rf is applied as short intense pulses, and the resonance effects include a "Bloch decay" trailing each pulse, and separate "spin echoes" induced by the nuclei after two or more rf pulses. The echoes are a very striking effect, amusing and interesting in themselves. Studying the manner in which the echoes are formed is a good exercise in the fundamentals of magnetic resonance, and it is recommended that the reader explore the details. The amplitude of the Bloch decay and also of the echoes depends on time and can be used to evaluate $T_1$ and $T_2$. In general, the transient methods are best suited for the measurement of relaxation times. Liquid samples with complex resonance lines show characteristic beat effects in spin-echo experiments for chemically shifted components (42) and also for multiplets (43). But unless the resonance is particularly simple and symmetrical, the analysis of the spin-echo data is an order of magnitude more difficult than a direct plot of the steady-state absorption.

In the experimental arrangements thus far described the sample is placed in the coil of a tuned rf circuit which is so loosely coupled with the rf oscillator that the operation of the latter is unaffected by the nuclear resonance. In the marginal oscillator methods (83, 89) the rf coil containing the sample is actually the tank coil in the grid circuit of the rf oscillator itself. The positive feedback or regeneration of the grid circuit determines the amplitude of the rf currents in the oscillator. When the oscillator is tuned to the resonance condition, the nuclear absorption of energy decreases the feedback, and the rf amplitude decreases. In order to observe the resonance, the main magnetic field $H_0$ is usually modulated at a low audiofrequency, while $H_0$ or $\nu_0$ is swept slowly through resonance. At resonance an audiomodulation of the rf amplitude is produced, amplified, detected, and displayed on an oscilloscope or further amplified and recorded.

One of the main advantages of this arrangement is that it responds only to the nuclear absorption, avoiding the mixture of absorption and dispersion line shapes resulting from improper balance conditions. Also, the oscillator, detector, and amplifiers can be consolidated in one relatively simple circuit. The main disadvantage of the method appears to be that the lowest rf level of stable operation can still produce undesirable saturation effects. Fortunately the sensitivity of the regenerative oscillator is at a maximum at low power levels. Most standard oscillator circuits can be used as resonance detectors. The oscillator must be isolated from $H_0$, because of magnetic components and because the modulation of $H_0$ can cause spurious signals in the oscillator. And the fewer connections between the oscillator and the sample probe in the magnet gap, the simpler and less trouble will be the probe.

Several self-detecting oscillators have been employed (39). In this case audioamplification is used and the circuits are very simple. If there is radiofrequency amplification before detection, the signal-to-noise ratio is improved (73) and approaches that of the bridge and induction methods. Also, modifications have been made (104) to stabilize the oscillational level, which otherwise is unstable at low levels and changes when the frequency is changed. If the value of $\gamma^2 T_1 T_2$ is small for a sample, then larger values of $H_1$ are necessary for optimum absorption, and in this case superregenerative oscillators appear to give good results (89). But these devices are nonlinear and can distort the line shapes; moreover, the rf spectrum of the oscillator is complex. Besides the change in rf amplitude produced by the nuclear absorption, there is a displacement in the oscillator frequency by the nuclear dispersion. The usual AM detector is sufficiently broad banded that only the amplitude effects are detected. But if a narrow-band FM detector is used (39), the nuclear dispersion produces sufficient frequency modulation of a marginal oscillator to give a good plot of the dispersion curve.

The marginal oscillators have been of value primarily in spectrographs (73) to search for new resonances over wide ranges in $\nu_0$, and in various arrangements (39) to observe detailed absorption line shapes of broad resonances in solids. Also, with a calibrator circuit (104), intensity and saturation measurements can be made. The intensity measurements are probably the most useful for analytical application. It does not seem likely that a regenerative oscillator circuit could be adapted to high-resolution experiments because of the changes in radiofrequency caused by the dispersive component of the resonance. Moreover, the required frequency stability and very low oscillational levels would be difficult to obtain.

*3.2.4. Narrow-Band Systems.* In many cases the resonance absorption is too weak to detect with the broad-band receiver and display methods thus far described. A small $\gamma$, a low isotopic abundance, a weak $H_0$, and a small $T_2/T_1$ ratio, all tend to lower the signal to noise, as given in eq. (87). In solids, for instance, the proton resonance may be 10 gauss wide, the equivalent $T_2$ is $10^{-5}$ sec., and $T_1$ may be as long as 10 to 100 sec., giving a $T_2/T_1$ ratio of only about $10^{-6}$. The signal strength is proportional to $(T_2/T_1)^{1/2}$, which is less by a factor of $10^{-3}$ in the solid than in normal liquids for which $T_2$ and $T_1$ are approximately equal. For samples with short $T_2$'s, some improvement in signal strength can be had by increasing the sample size to the point where inhomogeneities in $H_0$ begin to contribute an appreciable fraction of the total line width. A more significant improvement in signal-to-noise ratio may be obtained by greatly decreasing the band width of the detection and recording system.

In the usual arrangement for narrowing the band width (4, 16) the receiver is followed by a sharply tuned audioamplifier of the phase-sensitive or lock-in variety (24, 85), which in turn feeds an integrating network of adjustable time constant. The final output of the network is observed on a sensitive meter or plotted automatically with a strip-chart recording potentiometer. The band width of the system is determined by the time constant, $\tau$, of the circuit and is approximately $1/\tau$. Typical time constants are about 1 to 100 sec., and the corresponding narrow band widths of 1 to $10^{-2}$ c.p.s. give an increase in signal to noise from 10 to 100 times that for oscilloscope display, where the band width is often about $10^3$ c.p.s.

The nuclear resonance signal is generated by modulating $H_0$ at some low audiofrequency $\nu_m$ with a set of auxiliary coils in the magnet. The particular frequency is not too important (18) so long as it does not coincide with the frequency of the A.C. power sources, which would otherwise be an overwhelming source of spurious signals. Frequencies of 25, 30, 50, and 280 c.p.s. have been used; 30 c.p.s. has an advantage in that it can be produced directly from, and locked to, the usual 60 c.p.s. A.C. by a simple multivibrator circuit. The amplitude of the field modulation is ordinarily set at some fraction of the resonance line width. $H_0$ or $\nu_0$ is then swept very slowly through the resonance condition, preferably linearly in time. Under these conditions the nuclear resonance produces a sinusoidal modulation of the rf voltage in the receiver. The magnitude of this modulation is proportional to the first derivative of the resonance line, provided that the modulation of $H_0$ is a small enough fraction of the line width (3).

The detected signal is fed into the audioamplifier via a twin-$T$ filter tuned to $\nu_m$. The phase-sensitive circuit mixes the amplified signal with a reference voltage at $\nu_m$ supplied through an adjustable phase-shifting device by the circuit modulating $H_0$. The phase-sensitive mixing circuit responds only to signals which are of the same frequency and in phase with the reference voltage, and therefore the circuit has a narrow band pass. The phase of the reference voltage is adjusted to maximize the output. A block diagram of a narrow-band spectrometer is given in Fig. 16 and the first derivative of an absorption line automatically recorded with this type of system (39) is reproduced in Fig. 17. Quantitative absorption line shapes for broad lines in solids and also very weak resonances can be obtained in this manner.

*3.2.5. Magnets.* The source of the main magnetic field is a sufficiently major and expensive part of the apparatus to warrant a separate section. Solenoids and Helmholtz coils have been used successfully for fields up to a few hundred gauss. But for most chemical applications higher fields are required and electromagnets or large permanent magnets are used.

The choice between these is dictated often by availability and experience rather than by any basic superiority of one over the other; in fact the range in quality and properties of each type of magnet is comparable to the intrinsic differences between the two types. However, if all other

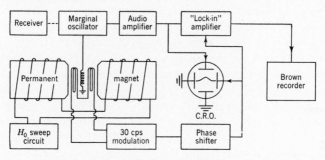

FIG. 16. Block diagram of narrow-band automatic recording spectrometer.

features are equal, there are characteristics which recommend permanent magnets for some types of experiment and electromagnets for others. The general pertinent characteristics of a magnet include the magnitude and adjustable range of the field and the gap dimensions; the homoge-

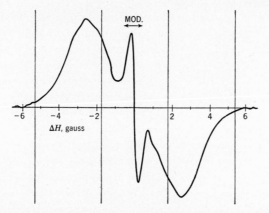

FIG. 17. The first derivative of the proton resonance absorption in $NH_4Cl$ powder at 150° C., observed with a narrow-band recording spectrometer (39) at 27.15 Mc. The sharp spike in the center is due to moisture adsorbed on the solid.

neity and stability of the field; reliability, cost and ease of operation; and the cost of the magnet and accessories and their commercial availability.

With the available permanent magnet materials the maximum fields economically obtainable in the $1\frac{1}{2}$- to 2-in. gaps required are about 7,500 gauss. Electromagnets can be built to generate considerably higher fields, up to 12,000 gauss or more. Also an electromagnet can produce a continuously adjustable field from zero to its maximum rated value, but permanent magnets are restricted to one field value which can be changed easily and reversibly only over a small range, the order of 1%, by using D.C. coils about the poles or at the gap. The current should act to increase the field to avoid irreversible demagnetization. In general, electromagnets are better suited for applications requiring very high fields or the measurement of the field dependence of phenomena.

The homogeneity of the magnetic field is determined mainly by the pole-cap material, its shape, mechanical alignment and stability, and its magnetic homogeneity. The source of the magnetic field, permanent or electromagnet, is relatively immaterial. An electromagnet shows hysteresis in the field pattern, which is different on the magnetizing cycle compared with on the demagnetizing, and at high fields saturation of the pole-cap material becomes important. A permanent magnet avoids some of these problems, but if it is not kept at constant temperature there are small changes in the field homogeneity, probably because of changes in domain structures with temperature which are not completely smoothed out by the pole caps. A primary advantage of permanent magnets is their stability. There is a reversible change in magnetization with temperature of about $-0.02\%$ per °C. which can be bothersome in high-resolution work. However, a constant temperature room or a simple thermostatted enclosure about the poles and yoke of the magnet combines with the large heat capacity of the magnet to give easily stability of 1 part in $10^7$ or better for periods of 10 min. or longer with changes from day to day of less than 1 part in $10^5$. Electromagnets have been electronically regulated to a very remarkable degree, with fluctuations limited to 1 part in $10^7$ for 10 sec., and this rating is being improved. But until an electromagnet reaches a thermal steady state there are slow drifts in field; and a great deal of electronics is required in the power supply and the regulator.

Permanent magnets have several advantages when it comes to ease of operation. They are undoubtedly much simpler and more reliable than even the best electromagnet. They do not need to be turned on or off; no power is used in their operation, nor is a cooling system necessary. As to cost, if stability and homogeneity are important, then a permanent magnet for fields up to 6,000 gauss will generally be one-half to two-thirds the price of a comparable electromagnet. The higher cost of electromagnets reflects the requirements placed upon the power supply and regulator. Electromagnets are probably being used more extensively than permanent magnets. This is mainly because electromagnets of standardized design with guaranteed stability and homogeneity are being sold commercially (101) but in the case of permanent magnets, excellent ones can be contracted for and built (49) but the design, particularly of the gap dimensions, is still an individual problem (31, 39) and the homogeneity is not specifiable. It is emphasized that good versions of both types of magnets have been employed with success in almost every variety of nuclear magnetic resonance experiment.

## 4. HIGH-RESOLUTION NMR SPECTROSCOPY

Several features distinguish high-resolution NMR spectroscopy from other branches of nuclear resonance. The main criterion is the observation of the nuclear resonance under conditions such that the finer details of the spectrum are revealed. These conditions are described first. A survey of the general results and interpretative principles thus far established follows, and a critique of the value and future of the high-resolution technique concludes the section. Questions relating to quantitative analysis are deferred to section 5.1.

### 4.1. The High-Resolution Experiment

*4.1.1. Factors Limiting Resolution.* The complex spectra in question arise from a combination of the chemical shifts and multiplet structures described in sections 2.3.1 and 2.3.2. These effects may produce resonance components separated by as little as a fraction of a milligauss or as much as a gauss or more, 1 c.p.s. to 5 kc. for protons. If the components are to be resolved, the widths of each component must be less than the separation of the components. The apparent line widths represent a combination of inherent and instrumental contributions, and care must be taken to minimize both. Inherent contributions include the direct dipole-dipole coupling, the spin-lattice relaxation, and the quadrupole effects. The dipole-dipole broadening in solids is usually several gauss, much too large to permit high-resolution experiments with solids. Chemical shifts have been measured in the resonances of the solid alkali halides (38), but these are the exception to the rule. The dipole-dipole broadening is averaged out by the molecular motions in liquids and gases, in which very narrow resonances are common. The inverse line-width parameter $T_2$ is of the order of 1 to 10 sec. for protons in most organic liquids at room temperature and the corresponding line widths of 0.3 to 0.03 c.p.s. are at present no serious limitation of resolution. The line widths in liquids are due mainly to spin-lattice relaxation, and $T_1$ increases with temperature as shown in Fig. 9 so that even narrower inherent line widths can be obtained by warming the liquid.

Samples containing paramagnetic centers will have short $T_1$'s and broadened resonance lines (16). To illustrate, the proton $T_1$ in a $10^{-2}$ molal solution of $Fe^{+3}$ in water is $10^{-2}$ sec., giving a line width of 35 c.p.s., compared with 3.6 sec. and a line width of 0.1 c.p.s. in pure water (19).

Nuclei with electric quadrupole moments have short $T_1$'s in liquids because of the quadrupole coupling effects. The iodine resonance in an aqueous solution of $I^-$ is over a gauss wide for this reason. The effects are greater in molecular compounds, and so high-resolution experiments are limited almost exclusively to nuclei with $I = \frac{1}{2}$, which have no quadrupole moments. The instrumental features influencing the resolution include the stability and homogeneity of the main magnetic field over the sample, the stability of the rf oscillator, and the conditions under which the resonance is traversed, including the broadening of the resonance by saturation effects. Experimental techniques have been

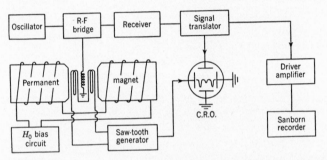

Fig. 18. Block diagram of a high-resolution NMR spectrometer equipped for oscilloscope display and automatic recording.

developed which give resolution of a milligauss or better. With special efforts this has been improved in several laboratories to 0.1 milligauss (0.4 c.p.s. for protons), which approaches the inherent line widths.

*4.1.2. High-Resolution Spectrometers.* A block diagram is sketched in Fig. 18 for a research-type spectrometer constructed and used for high-resolution experiments. An earlier version with some additional details is described elsewhere (39). The spectrometer is basically an rf bridge system but with components meeting special requirements. The oscillator should be stable to at least 1 part in $10^7$ or better for at least a minute and preferably longer. The versatility of the system is extended if the oscillator frequency is adjustable, say over a tenfold range. The one-tube circuit used in the apparatus is that of the BC-221 frequency meter and uses the same high-quality tuning condenser. An attenuator has been added so that the rf voltage across the sample coil can be adjusted to the necessary low levels between $10^{-5}$ and $10^{-2}$ volts. Direct calibration of the rf voltage in terms of $H_1$ is desirable but difficult in practice (81). Commercial oscillators, unless they are of frequency standard quality, are not very suitable.

The rf bridge is a null-$T$ type (99) with the rf coil connected by a short length of coaxial cable to the tuning elements, which are located in a brass box on top of the magnet. Good mechanical and thermal stability of the bridge is essential to prevent drifts in balance and avoid distortion of the absorption lines. Care must be taken to ensure that the probe containing the rf coil and sample is kept absolutely free of magnetic materials which would reduce the homogeneity of $H_0$. Pure aluminum seems to be generally a good material for this purpose. Cylindrical construction helps to minimize effects of differences in susceptibility of air versus probe materials. The rf coil is itself a very vulnerable spot; the wire must be of very high purity, and lengths from the same spool are not necessarily of equal quality. The coil construction is also important because a high $Q$ and a good filling factor improve the signal-to-noise ratio. Probes providing temperature control ($-100°$ to $+100°$ C.) are often useful; they should be designed to protect the pole caps from thermal contact. Also provision must be made for positioning the probe in all three dimensions, so that the field may be plotted and the sample located in the region of best homogeneity.

The main specifications for the receiver besides gain, which is no problem, include linear amplification to ensure reliable intensities and a good noise figure $F$ with a narrow band pass $B$ to provide high sensitivity. Of course, the narrower the band pass the less frequency drift can be tolerated. A variable frequency receiver is desirable for the same versatility argument as was mentioned for the oscillator; the band spread in tuning should then be large so that the frequency may be set and adjusted with good precision. The Collins Radio Co. 51J3 communications receiver is used in the apparatus here. The noise figure is exceptional for a commercial receiver, ranging from 5 at 2 Mc. to 9 at 30 Mc., and acceptable results are obtainable without benefit of the usual special low-noise-level preamplifier between rf bridge and receiver. The minimum band pass required in the receiver, display, and recording system to reproduce a complex resonance line without undue distortion is of the order of the number of resonance components divided by the sweep time in seconds. A ten-component resonance swept through in 10 sec. thus needs a band pass of at least 1 c.p.s. and should be reproduced very well by a band pass of 10 c.p.s. The audioamplifier in the receiver is not linear at such low frequencies. The signal is taken off at the detector, and any further gain requires D.C. amplifiers. The Collins receiver has a crystal filter and selectivity control with which the rf band pass can be reduced to about 200 c.p.s. This improves the signal-to-noise ratio materially, but a narrower band pass is preferable. An easy way to narrow the band pass is to put an adjustable RC integrating network just before the display and recording systems.

Almost any good D.C. oscilloscope, such as one of the Dumont 304 series, will serve to display the resonance. But there does not seem to be any completely satisfactory system now in operation for permanent recording of the spectra. Oscilloscope photography is too cumbersome for recording any sizable number of spectra, and the fastest available recording potentiometers have response times of about 1 sec. for full-scale deflection and chart speeds of 2 in./min., which are too slow. Sanborn oscillographs, model 127 recorder with a model 126 driver amplifier, have response times and chart speeds actually considerably faster than necessary; however, they suffer from several disadvantages. The paper is costly, the 5-cm. width is narrow, and of this only the center 4 cm. corresponds to linear operation of the amplifier. Moreover, the record is only semipermanent and deteriorates with handling. Yet the system is the best currently available.

For high resolution the resonance must be traversed slowly enough to avoid interference or distortion from the transient relaxation wiggles described in section 3.1.3, and this and the band pass of the receiver determine the stability needed in $\nu_0$, and in $H_0$. Early chemical shift measurements (31) used audiomodulation of $H_0$, and the transient effects restricted measurements to samples either with single or widely separated resonance lines. Slow sweep techniques were soon devised (6, 10, 31) to reduce the effects. If the transient effects are to be completely damped out, $dH_0/dt$ must satisfy eq. (70). For protons, a typical line width of 1 milligauss corresponds to a $T_2$ of 0.08 sec., and in this case the sweep rate should be of the order of 1.5 milligauss/sec. In practice somewhat faster rates can be used and this reduces the required stability. Even so, if a 5-milligauss separation between two lines is to be observed with an accuracy of 1% at a sweep rate of 5 milligauss/sec. with an $H_0$ of 5,000 gauss, both $\nu_0$ and $H_0$ should be stable to 1 part in $10^8$/sec. and the sweep itself must have an equivalent stability. It is convenient to have a sweep generator which changes $H_0$ linearly in time so that a recording system with the usual linear time base may be used. The sweep amplitude should be adjustable from a few milligauss to about 1.5 gauss and the sweep time from say $\frac{1}{5}$ sec. to 5 min. In the apparatus a pair of sweep coils is mounted about the pole caps of the magnet so as not to obstruct access to the gap or to complicate the design of the sample probe. An ampere turn per coil gives a change in $H_0$ of 0.12 gauss.

The stability requirements for the magnet are the same as for the oscillator, 1 part in $10^7$/min. or better. Also, the field inhomogeneities should be no greater than a milligauss over a sample volume of at least 0.01 cm.$^3$ Of course, a larger volume of good homogeneity will add proportionately to signal to noise. Magnets are discussed in more detail in section 3.2.5; and in the next section, techniques for improving homogeneity, along with calibration and measurement procedures. It should be mentioned that samples are usually handled in thin-walled cylindrical glass tubes with outer diameters of from 2 to 15 mm. depending on signal strength, available field homogeneity, and the resolution needed.

High-resolution NMR spectrometers are available commercially from Varian Associates (101), and it is understood that the Perkin-Elmer

FIG. 19. A complete Varian Associates high-resolution apparatus. The unit at the left is the V-4300B high-resolution n-m-r spectrometer, with its probe and spinning sample mechanism perched on the probe holder at the magnet air gap. The magnet is a model V-4012A 12-in. laboratory electromagnet; the magnet power supply and voltage regulator at the right are models V-2100 and V-2101B, respectively.

Corporation (69) is planning a commercial model; probably with a permanent magnet. A photograph of the apparatus manufactured by Varian Associates is reproduced in Fig. 19. The magnet is a carefully designed and regulated electromagnet with a guaranteed homogeneity and a maximum field of 13,500 gauss. The oscillator and receiver are fixed tuned with units available at 40 and 30 Mc. and several lower frequencies. The sample probe is based on the Bloch crossed-coil induction system and also contains the coils for sweeping $H_0$. Otherwise the *general* nature of the system is similar to the block diagram in Fig. 18. The sample probe construction presents some problems in making measurements at other than room temperature, particularly if good thermal control is needed. The stability of the magnet is good but improvement is desirable and expected. There is no doubt that the spectrometer is better than adequate for many purposes, and it is unusually good for a first commercial model, particularly in view of the numerous and rigid specifications to be met. The spectrum given in Fig. 20 is from a Varian instrument and shows the excellent signal to noise obtained.

At present, high resolution spectrometers operate at a fixed frequency with a field sweep to scan the resonance. The reasons for preferring this

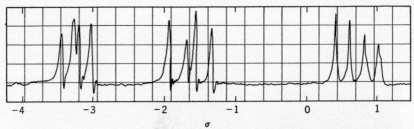

FIG. 20. The fluorine resonance absorption observed at 30 Mc. in a 0.03 cm.[3] sample of $CF_2{=}CFCl$ with a Varian Associates high-resolution spectrometer (90). $\sigma$ is defined as $10^5(H_c - H_r)/H_r$, with perfluorocyclobutane the reference compound. The sweep rate was 50 milligauss sec.[-1]; the total sweep is 420 milligauss.

arrangement in general were mentioned in section 3.1.3 on passage conditions. However, if the chemical shifts do not extend over a very wide range, it seems possible in principle to use a frequency sweep at a fixed magnetic field. In this event, the frequency sensitive elements would need to be broad banded with flat response over the frequency interval in question. This includes the rf bridge or crossed coil system, the preamplifier and the receiver. The narrow banding required to give a satisfactory signal to noise ratio could be accomplished after detection. Whether or not such a system would have any advantages over the field-sweep type is an open question.

*4.1.3. Measurement Techniques.* The actual process of obtaining useful spectral data requires several specialized techniques. A basic problem is the quantitative measurement of a chemical shift. If the shift to be measured occurs between nuclei in the same compound, or if one is interested only in "internal" fine structure, the problem is simple. The resonance is recorded or displayed under standardized, calibrated conditions and the physical separation of the different resonance components gives the desired result. But if a resonance is to be referred to some standard reference compound, the problem may be less trivial. Of course, if the sample and reference form a stable solution without shifts due to solvent-solute interaction, the method just described is used. Otherwise the reference and sample must be compared in separate sample tubes. Insertion of a small sealed tube of one sample in a larger tube of the other is an obvious trick but it produces a broadening or splitting of the resonance lines which limits the accuracy unless the assembly is rotated rapidly. These effects are discussed more fully in section 5.3 and at the end of this section.

A sample interchange method can be used if the stability of the apparatus permits. The resonance of one sample is displayed, the samples are interchanged manually, and the resonance position of the second sample is compared to that of the first. This process is repeated several times to check on the occurrence of systematic drifts and to obtain an average value of higher precision. Double sample probe and detector systems have been used (31) but are cumbersome. Good results have been obtained with a split rf coil, putting sample in one half and reference in the other (39). This requires a larger volume of homogeneous field than the sample-interchange method but gives more accurate results more easily; a small correction is needed for the difference in $H_0$ between the two halves of the coil. An ingenious modification of this procedure is to use a single sample tube with a thin diaphragm separating the sample and reference liquids, which are located in the upper and lower halves of the same rf coil (94).

The most important calibration relates some secondary parameter such as distance on the recorder paper to the corresponding change in magnetic field, although the latter may be expressed in cycles rather than gauss. An early system (31) was to amplitude modulate $\nu_0$ with an accurately known audiofrequency $\nu_a$. This produces a series of side-band frequencies $\nu_0 \pm n\nu_a$, where $n = 0,1,2 \cdots$. Separate resonances can then be picked up by tuning the bridge and receiver and adjusting $H_0$ to detect the resonance absorption at first one of these frequencies, then the next. This relates $\pm n\nu_a$ to the parameter describing the change in $H_0$. As the bridge and receiver tuning take time, this method requires high stability of $\nu_0$ and $H_0$. A simpler but related procedure is based on the frequency-field equivalence of the Larmor equation (7, 18). If $H_0$ is modulated by a small amplitude at $\nu_a$ while a normally single resonance line is observed at fixed $\nu_0$ by slowly sweeping $H_0$, the resonance now appears as a central line with satellites on either side, separated by an amount equivalent to $\nu_a$. This gives, for instance, a direct calibration on the oscilloscope or recorder chart in terms of units of $\nu_a$, or if the spectrum to be measured is simple, say with only two components, $\nu_a$ can be adjusted until the first side band from one line overlaps precisely the "fundamental" of the other line; $\nu_a$ is then the separation of the two lines (7, 48). This procedure has the advantage of being a null method of comparing the resonance positions at identically the same time.

It is convenient to have a basic calibration which is independent of display or recording-system adjustments. This is accomplished readily with a pair of coils about the poles or pole caps, for which the D.C. current equivalent to $\nu_a$ is determined by one of the modulation methods. Such a system is linear to 0.5% over field changes of the order of 10 gauss. It serves also as a means of rapidly searching for and centering upon a resonance. Chemical shifts can be measured with this system by observing the change in D.C. biasing current required to center first one resonance then a second one on an oscilloscope (39). It is noteworthy that the precision obtained in all these measurements results from measuring the change or difference directly and not measuring and subtracting the large total values. In fact, $H_0$ or $\nu_0$ need be known to only about 1 part in $10^4$ in order for it not to contribute significantly to the error in chemical shift measurements. $\nu_0$ is measured easily to this accuracy by a good commercial receiver or a simple frequency meter. The accuracy with which shifts or splittings can be measured varies with the nature of the sample and its spectrum. For proton and fluorine resonances, the error in ordinary shift measurements is less than a milligauss, while small splittings can be measured to as good as 0.1 milligauss or better.

Improvement in the homogeneity of $H_0$ over the sample increases the sensitivity and accuracy of the measurements, and several homogenization methods have been proposed and used with varying success. An inelegant and tedious method, which has nonetheless been used productively on permanent magnets, is to polish the pole faces manually, plotting the field periodically to check the results (31, 39). Another procedure (2) is to wind two spirals of wire, with taps at intervals, and place one against each pole face. The coils are used as electrical shims with the taps connected to a set of adjustable potentiometers across a D.C. source. The currents through the various segments of the coils are set to compensate the decrease in field toward the edge of the gap and are rather tricky to adjust.

Mechanical motion of the sample, such as spinning it, will expose the various nuclei to different fields and tend to average out the inhomogeneities (1, 14).* This dynamic process is described by an obvious extension of the remarks in section 2.3.3 on chemical exchange; the critical rate of motion is given by the frequency width of the inhomogeneities to be averaged. Thus a 5-milligauss inhomogeneity, 20 c.p.s. for protons, re-

* The first experiment of this type was apparently performed by Carr (18a).

quires a spinning frequency of at least 20 c.p.s. Inhomogeneities persist along the axis of spin, and good mechanical construction is essential; otherwise the spinning will increase the noise level. Moving metal parts are to be avoided in the vicinity of the rf coil; they introduce a great deal of noise, probably via eddy-current effects. The spinning frequency $\nu_s$ will sometimes appear in the form of side-band resonances such as those described just above for audiomodulation methods of calibration, for the same reason. If the magnetic field has certain types of inhomogeneity and if the sample rotates coherently, the rotation produces an audiomodulation of $H_0$. Weak sidebands of this origin occur in Fig. 11. Most spinners are driven by compressed air. In some samples the molecular motions are not fast enough to average out the broadening effects of the local dipolar magnetic fields. If such samples could be "agitated" fast enough in all three directions, the local fields would be averaged out artificially and high-resolution spectra might then be obtained. Supersonic techniques could do this, at least in principle, but no successful applications of this sort have been reported.

A different problem which arises fairly often is the disentangling of chemical shift and multiplet components in a spectrum. Observation of the spectrum at two magnetic fields differing by a ratio of say 1.25 or more will usually help. The chemical shifts, in gauss, are proportional to $H_0$, and the multiplets are not, at least as long as eq. (36) is satisfied. If $|\nu_i - \nu_j|$ is large enough so that a receiver may detect say $\nu_i$ in the presence of large rf power at $\nu_j$, then a trick (17, 93) can be used to eliminate the effects of the $A_{ij}$ coupling. The sample is exposed simultaneously to $\nu_i$ and $\nu_j$ and the resonance is observed at $\nu_i$. The rf field at $\nu_j$ causes the $j$ nuclei to precess about $H_{1j}$ at a frequency $g_j\mu_n H_{1j}/h$. But the coupling between the $i$ and $j$ nuclei depends on their relative orientation with respect to $H_0$, and so if the $j$ nuclei are "well-stirred" by the rf field, their orientation changing at a frequency $(g_j\mu_n H_{1j}/h) > A_{ij}$, the coupling is averaged out as described in section 2.3.3. Turning $\nu_j$ on at a high enough rf level collapses the multiplet in the $\nu_i$ resonance.

## 4.2. Results and Interpretative Principles

4.2.1. *Fluorine.* Fluorine compounds undoubtedly provide one of the best areas for high-resolution NMR spectroscopy. There is only one isotope, $F^{19}$, which has a spin of $\frac{1}{2}$ and so quadrupole effects need not be considered. The magnetogyric ratio is the third largest observed and therefore signal strengths are relatively very good. The small atomic volume exerts a favorable influence on the concentration of nuclei per unit volume and is partially responsible for the large nuclear signals, as is the existence of only one isotope. Fluorine forms a wide range of compounds, particularly the fluorocarbons, many of which are liquids at convenient temperatures and pressures, and other methods of analysis have some limitations and deficiencies. Moreover, the magnitudes of the chemical shifts and multiplet splittings are quite sizable, and moderate resolution of a few milligauss is sufficient for many purposes.

The binary covalent fluorides were the first sizable group of compounds whose chemical shifts were measured (31), with results demonstrating the possibility and utility of analytical applications. The fluorine chemical shifts, defined as $\delta = 10^5(H_r - H_c)/H_r$, are plotted in Fig. 21a

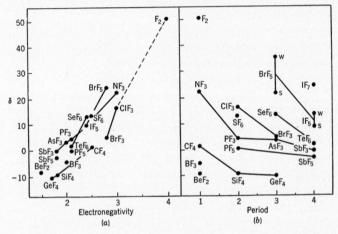

FIG. 21. The fluorine chemical shifts in the binary fluorides (31). $\delta$ is defined as $10^5(H_r - H_c)/H_r$ with $CF_3CO_2H$ the reference compound. (a) Plotted against the electronegativity of the other atomic species in the compound. (b) Plotted against the position in the periodic table of the other atomic species.

against the Pauling electronegativity of the other atom in the molecule and in Fig. 21b against the position of the other atom in the periodic table. The reference compound is arbitrarily taken as trifluoroacetic acid, $CF_3CO_2H$. The $\delta$ values range from $+50.76$ for $F_2$ to $-10.12$ for $GeF_4$. It is seen that there is a more or less linear relation between $\delta$ and the electronegativity of the atom to which the fluorine is bound.

$F_2$, which has the most covalent bond, has the largest, positive $\delta$, and $BeF_2$ and $GeF_4$, which have more ionic bonds, have the most negative $\delta$ values. This and the linear trend with electronegativity have been accounted for theoretically by a simplified version (84) of the general nuclear magnetic shielding theory (78). The starting point of the calculation is in recognizing that the diamagnetic contribution to the shielding of a fluorine nucleus differs very little in different fluorine compounds, mainly because only 2 of the 10 electrons about the fluorine nucleus participate in the chemical bonding. The resonance shifts are assigned to the second-order paramagnetism of the $2p$ valence electrons. The large instantaneous magnetic fields associated with the orbital motions of these electrons are polarized by, and therefore can add appreciably to, the static magnetic field. This effect would be zero for completely ionic $F^-$, because of the filled $L$ shell and would be largest in $F_2$, as observed.

The calculation gives the difference in shift between $F_2$ and $F^-$ to be

$$\delta(F_2) - \delta(F^-) = \sigma(F^-) - \sigma(F_2)$$
$$= (\tfrac{2}{3})(e^2h^2/4\pi^2m^2c^2)(\langle 1/r^3\rangle_{Av})_{2p}/\Delta E \qquad (91)$$
$$\cong 200 \times 10^{-5}$$

$(\langle 1/r^3\rangle_{Av})_{2p}$, the average of $1/r^3$ for the $2p$ electrons about the fluorine, is assumed to be $8.89\ a_0^3$ where $a_0$ is the Bohr radius; and $4.3$ ev. is used for $\Delta E$, the average excitation energy to the polarized electronic states contributing to the magnetic field at the fluorine nucleus. For bonds with partial ionic character $i$, the fluorine resonance will occur at an approximate fraction $i$ of the shift between $F_2$ and $F^-$. Moreover, $i$ is proportional to the electronegativity difference of the bonded atoms, which explains the general linear trend of the fluorine shifts in Fig. 21a. The $\delta$ value of 200 given in eq. (91) does not compare too badly with the observed difference of 61 between $F_2$ and $GeF_4$, allowing for the fact that the difference in ionic character of the bonds in the two compounds is more nearly 50% than the 100% assumed in the calculations.

The determination of an unknown molecular structure from a high-resolution spectrum can be considerably simpler and more direct than the sort of calculation just given. This is shown by the results for $BrF_5$ (31), the first unknown structure analyzed by these methods. The fluorine resonance of $BrF_5$ was found to have two main components with relative intensities of 4:1. The only molecular structure with four equivalent fluorines and the fifth one different is a symmetrical tetragonal pyramid with fluorines at the corners and the Br somewhere along the fourfold axis. In addition, under higher resolution, the strong line is a doublet and the weaker one is a quintuplet with an intensity distribution 1:4:6:4:1; all separations are the same, 75 c.p.s. This agrees with the multiplets predicted for the indirect spin-spin coupling of a single fluorine with a different group containing four fluorines. Confirmation of this interpretation of the spectrum was provided by the proportionality of the chemical shift in gauss, to the applied magnetic field while the multiplet separations do not change.

The study of more complicated molecules is illustrated by results obtained for a large number of substituted fluorobenzenes (33, 60). The introduction of a substituent was found to shift the fluorine resonance by an amount and direction characteristic of the substituent and its location in the molecule. The $\delta$'s, referred to fluorobenzene, produced by the commoner substituents are tabulated in Table II. These data are an interesting measure of the electronic effects of the substituents. Also it was found by observing the fluorine resonance shifts in many substituted compounds of known structure that the substituent effects are very nearly additive. This enables one, first of all, to assign particular resonance lines to particular fluorines in polyfluorobenzenes. The fluorine resonance in 2,3,5-trifluorobenzotrifluoride is reproduced in Fig. 22 and

TABLE II

*The Fluorine Chemical Shifts\* in Monosubstituted Fluorobenzenes*† (33, 60)

| Substituent | $\delta_o$ | $\delta_m$ | $\delta_p$ | Substituent | $\delta_o$ | $\delta_m$ | $\delta_p$ |
|---|---|---|---|---|---|---|---|
| Br | +0.55 | +0.24 | −0.23 | F | −2.59 | +0.31 | −0.64 |
| CH$_3$ | −0.50 | −0.09 | −0.55 | I | +1.93 | +0.26 | −0.12 |
| CH$_2$Cl | −0.54 | +0.02 | −0.07 | NH$_2$ | −2.31 | −0.02 | −1.46 |
| CHCl$_2$ | −0.51 | +0.14 | +0.25 | NHCOCH$_3$ | −1.28 | +0.10 | −0.57 |
| CHO | −0.96 | +0.10 | +0.98 | NO$_2$ | −0.56 | +0.33 | +1.08 |
| CN | +0.52 | +0.30 | +0.96 | OC$_6$H$_4$F(p) | — | −0.05 | −0.67 |
| CO$_2$H | +0.35 | +0.05 | +0.69 | OC$_2$H$_5$ | −2.17 | +0.13 | −1.15 |
| Cl | −0.27 | +0.21 | −0.24 | OH | −2.50 | +0.09 | −1.06 |

\* The shifts are referred to fluorobenzene; $\delta$ is defined as $10^5(H_r - H_c)/H_r$ and the subscripts $o$, $m$, and $p$ indicate that the substituent was ortho, meta, or para to the fluorine.

† Shifts for a few additional fluorobenzenes are given in ref. 60.

has four components, three of comparable intensity with $\delta$ values of −3.20, −1.77, and +0.07. The fourth component is about three times as intense as the others and therefore must be from the CF$_3$ group. The 3-fluorine has an ortho-F, a meta-CF$_3$, and a meta-F; so by reference to Table II, the $\delta$ of the 3-fluorine should be given as

$$\delta(\text{3-F}) = \delta(o\text{-F}) + \delta(m\text{-CF}_3) + \delta(m\text{-F}) \qquad (92)$$
$$= -2.59 + 0.28 + 0.31 = -2.00$$

This value is much closer to the line at −1.77 than to the other two; so the −1.77 line is assigned to the 3-fluorine. Similarly the +0.07 line is assigned to the 5-fluorine and, by elimination, the −3.20 line to the 2-fluorine.

An actual analytical problem of this type which was solved in the author's laboratory arose in connection with the thermal decomposition of the crude dry salt 2,5-difluorobenzene diazonium fluoborate (I), which contained NaCl (28). The originally expected product was the 2,5-difluorochlorobenzene (II) formed by a Griess-type chloride replacement of the diazonium group. However, the fluorine resonance of the initial product had three components at $-0.90$, $-0.40$, and $+0.18$ with the

N=NFBF₃ ... (I)

Cl ... (II)

F ... (III)

last one somewhat broader and several times stronger than the other two, which were of equal intensity. This showed the presence of at least two molecular species in the product. Applying the procedure of eq. (92), structure (II) should have two fluorine lines, a $\delta(2\text{-}F)$ of $-0.91$ and a

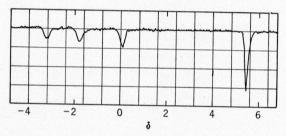

Fig. 22. The fluorine resonance absorption in a 0.01 cm.³ sample of 2,3,5-tri-fluorobenzotrifluoride at 16.682 Mc. $\delta$ is defined as $10^5(H_r - H_c)/H_r$ with fluoro-benzene the reference compound.

$\delta(5\text{-}F)$ of $-0.43$, and this accounts for the lines observed at $-0.90$ and $-0.40$. The $\delta$ values were then "computed" for all possible iso-mers of difluorochlorobenzene. For structure (III) it was found that $\delta(1\text{-}F) = +0.04$ and $\delta(5\text{-}F') = +0.07$, agreeing very well with the broadened line at $+0.18$ in the unknown. All other possible structures have predicted spectra disagreeing widely with experiment. Purification and chemical analysis of the main product confirmed that it was a difluorochlorobenzene. Moreover, the integrated absorption intensities showed that the ratio of (III) to (II) was approximately 3:1.

A considerable number of fluorine spectra have been observed for aliphatic (92) and olefinic (57) fluorocarbons, and several spectral regions are established as characteristic of particular structural groups. The pub-lished results for aliphatic fluorocarbons as well as unpublished data from the author's laboratory show that the fluorine resonances fall into three main, fairly narrow, but well-separated regions depending on the extent and type of substitution on the carbon to which the fluorine is bonded.

The first region, with δ between $-1.0$ and $+2.0$ referred to trifluoroacetic acid, includes $CF_3$—, —$CF_2$—O—, and $CF_2Cl$— groups; within this region the —$CF_2$—O— groups tend to fall at more negative positions than $CF_3$—. The second region, covering about $-4.0$ to $-6.0$, includes $> CF_2$, $> CF$—O—, and $> CFCl$ groups, while $\geqslant CF$ groups fall in the range from $-12$ to $-20$. That these separations are a more or less direct consequence of the general relationships between bond ionic character and fluorine resonance shift shows graphically in Fig. 21a. Substituents with electronegativities close to the electronegativity of carbon or with multiple bonds seem to have less characteristic effects and overlap the regions given. But in general the method is a very sensitive one for determining structures of fluorine compounds. A final point is that the multiplet splittings of the fluorine resonances can be quite extensive in the fluorocarbons (57) and often lead to complex spectra. This is suggested by the fluorine spectrum of $CF_2$=$CFCl$ reproduced in Fig. 20 from a Varian Associates recording. Restricted rotation about the C=C bond leaves the fluorines nonequivalent and accounts for the three chemically shifted groups of lines. The resonance for each fluorine has four components from the combined effects of coupling with the other two fluorines in the molecule. The chemical shifts are not much larger than the coupling constants, and so the intensities and splittings do not follow the simple rules embodied in eq. (37). The coupling constants in $CF_2$=$CFCl$ are about 50 c.p.s., which is typical of aliphatic and olefinic fluorocarbons.

*4.2.2. Hydrogen.* In some ways the proton resonance is better suited for high-resolution spectroscopy than is fluorine. The magnetic resonance of protons is usually stronger than for any other kind of nucleus. The large concentration of protons in many samples contributes to the high absorption intensities, which are due in main to the large proton magnetogyric ratio and small atomic volume. The proton $\gamma$ is only slightly smaller than that of $He^3$, the largest, which however is of little chemical interest. Protons also have the advantages associated with a spin of $\frac{1}{2}$. The chief disadvantage of protons is the smallness of the chemical shifts; the total range is of the order of $2 \times 10^{-5}$ or only a tenth of a gauss out of a total field of 5,000 gauss. The resolution required is higher than for fluorine. This may be seen by comparing the proton resonance for propionic acid in Fig. 10 with the fluorine spectrum of trifluorochloroethylene in Fig. 20; the propionic acid spectrum covers nearly the whole range of proton spectra, but the fluorine spectrum given is a small fraction of the fluorine range.

A less significant disadvantage, for most analytical applications, is the lack of as simple a correlation between the proton chemical shifts and the electronegativity of the attached atom as that found for fluorine.

Proton shifts were first observed in the binary hydrides (31), and the $\delta$ values are plotted in Fig. 23a against the Pauling electronegativity of the atom bound to the hydrogen. $\delta$ is defined as $10^5(H_r - H_c)/H_r$ with the reference compound $H_2O$ at room temperature. There is no simple linearity between $\delta$ and atomic electronegativity, in contrast to that for fluorine in Fig. 21. The proton shifts are not entirely random; the data are replotted in Fig. 23b by use of the position of the atom in the periodic table as the abscissa. It is seen that $\delta$ changes quite linearly with nuclear charge for compounds of atoms in a given period. But the slopes of the lines change systematically on going from group IV to group VII hydrides.

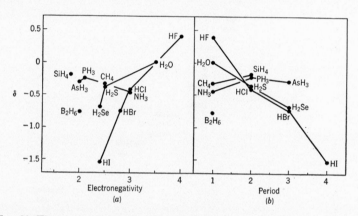

FIG. 23. The proton chemical shifts in the binary hydrides (31). $\delta$ is defined as $10^5(H_r - H_c)/H_r$ with $H_2O$ the reference compound. (a) Plotted against the electronegativity of the other atomic species in the compound. (b) Plotted against the position in the periodic table of the other atomic species.

On the other hand, there is a direct proportionality between the $\delta$ for protons in a given bond and the ionic character of that bond as it is influenced by substituents (22, 60, 61, 91). For example, the proton $\delta$ values (61) for the OH protons in $CH_3OH$, $C_6H_5OH$, and $CH_3CO_2H$ are $+0.01$, $+0.27$, and $+0.63$. The ionic character of the OH bonds, as inferred from the acidities, increases in the same order. Qualitatively, the trend is in the direction expected, for in the limiting case of a bare proton there should be no nuclear magnetic shielding and the sign of $\delta$ is defined so that this would be in the direction of positive values. The differences in the nature of the fluorine and proton shifts in the binary fluorides and hydrides are most likely a consequence of the greater importance of the diamagnetic term for protons. In fluorine compounds the bonding electrons contribute little to the diamagnetic term, but in the hydrogen compounds the bonding electrons give the most important contribution to the internal diamagnetism.

The use of high-resolution proton spectra in solving problems in the structure of organic compounds is already well advanced. A general characterization has been made (61) of the proton chemical shifts of the more common simple organic groups, and a chart summarizing the results is reproduced in Fig. 24. The chart shows that the $\delta$ regions for the various groups are distinctive enough to be of value in structural analysis even

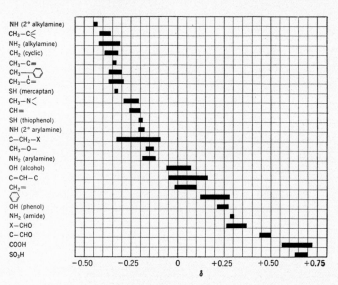

FIG. 24. Characterization chart of the proton chemical shifts in simple organic groups (61). The horizontal lines indicate the range of $\delta$-values observed for each group. $\delta$ is defined as $10^5(H_r - H_c)/H_r$ with $H_2O$ the reference compound.

though the proton shifts are very small. To be sure, there is overlapping of the absorption regions for different groups, but the groups which overlap differ from those which overlap in other spectroscopic methods, such as infrared and ultraviolet. Moreover, the location of a resonance within the range for a particular group is itself often characteristic of the neighboring groups. For instance, the wide range of $\delta$ values for $C—CH_2—X$ groups reflects the electronegativities of the many possible $X$ substituents, and the $CH_2$ group $\delta$ is directly proportional to the electronegativity of the $X$ substituent (22).

Proton-proton multiplet splittings of 5 to 10 c.p.s. often occur as a result of coupling through three bonds, such as H—C—Y—H, of protons with chemically shifted resonances. Such splittings can be useful in determining molecular structures. An example of this sort arose (45) in connection with the structure of a product from a reduction reaction (21).

The product could have had either structure (I) or (II), which differ in the position of a deuterium atom. Previous experience had shown that a

$$
\begin{array}{ccc}
\text{(phenyl)} & \text{(phenyl)} & \text{(phenyl)} \\
\text{D—C—CH}_3 & \text{H—C—CH}_2\text{D} & \text{H—C—CH}_3 \\
\text{(} p\text{-C}_6\text{H}_4\text{)} & \text{(} p\text{-C}_6\text{H}_4\text{)} & \text{(} p\text{-C}_6\text{H}_4\text{)} \\
\text{OCH}_3 & \text{OCH}_3 & \text{OCH}_3 \\
\text{(I)} & \text{(II)} & \text{(III)}
\end{array}
$$

tertiary hydrogen would split into a doublet the proton resonance of a $CH_3$ group attached to the same carbon. Moreover, the nondeutero compound (III) was available as a check.

The proton spectrum of the latter was found to consist of three main lines with relative peak intensities $7:10:21$, and $\delta$'s of $-0.40$, $-0.15$, and $+0.18$. The line at $-0.40$ is a doublet separated by about 10 c.p.s., and it is assigned as the C—$CH_3$ group resonance split by the tertiary proton. The line at $-0.15$ falls in the region given in Fig. 24 for the O—$CH_3$ group; it overlaps and obscures the weak quartet tertiary C—H line, which was found at $-0.11$ in 1,1-diphenyl ethane. The most intense line, at $+0.18$, is in the region expected for aromatic protons; it has an unresolved shoulder and so is assigned to the two benzene rings. The proton spectrum of the unknown was the same as that just described for (III) except that the line at $-0.40$ was a single sharp line instead of a doublet. It was concluded therefore that the structure of the unknown is (I), which has a D—C—$CH_3$ group, rather than (II), with H—C—$CH_2$D.

The need for a characterization chart for spectra of type compounds of known structure is certainly less for nuclear magnetic resonance than for most other spectroscopic methods. As a demonstration, consider the question of deciding which of the following five proposed structures is the correct structure of diketene.

$$
\begin{array}{ccc}
\text{CH}_3\text{COCH}=\text{C}=\text{O} & 
\begin{array}{c}\text{O}=\text{C—CH}\\[-2pt]\;\;\;|\quad\quad\|\\[-2pt]\text{H}_2\text{C—COH}\end{array} & 
\begin{array}{c}\text{O}=\text{C—CH}_2\\[-2pt]\;\;\;|\quad\quad\;|\\[-2pt]\text{H}_2\text{C—C}=\text{O}\end{array} \\
\text{(I)} & \text{(II)} & \text{(III)} \\[6pt]
\begin{array}{c}\text{CH}_3\text{—C}=\text{CH}\\[-2pt]\quad\;\;|\quad\quad|\\[-2pt]\quad\;\text{O—C}=\text{O}\end{array} & &
\begin{array}{c}\text{CH}_2=\text{C—CH}_2\\[-2pt]\quad\quad\;|\quad\quad|\\[-2pt]\quad\quad\text{O—C}=\text{O}\end{array} \\
\text{(IV)} & & \text{(V)}
\end{array}
$$

Of these structures, all but (I) and (IV) can be differentiated on the basis of number and relative intensities of the components in the proton resonance. (I) and (IV) would have two lines, relative intensities of $3:1$; (II), $2:1:1$; (III), 4; and (V), $2:2$. The proton resonance of the liquid was found (8) to have at room temperature two components of equal intensity, with $\delta$'s of 0.07 and $-0.16$. The occurrence of two equal components is in itself sufficient to prove that the liquid has structure (V), the 3-buteno-$\beta$-lactone structure, which has been shown by X rays and the broad-line proton resonance studies at low temperatures (29) to exist in the solid. The characterization chart of Fig. 24 serves to confirm the assignment; the line at $-0.07$ is close to the range for vinyl groups, and the line at $-0.16$ is about where expected for a cyclic $CH_2$ group adjacent to a $C=O$ group, which makes the C—H bonds more ionic. Under very high resolution, the two main resonance components of liquid diketene exhibit considerable fine structure, confirming the conclusions given here.

*4.2.3. Phosphorus, Nitrogen, and Other Nuclei.* Besides fluorine and hydrogen, phosphorus is the only other atomic species for which the general utility of chemical shifts and high-resolution spectra has been well established (34, 35, 70). $P^{31}$ is the sole stable isotope of phosphorus and it has a spin of $\frac{1}{2}$. But the magnetogyric ratio is of modest size, 0.4 that of the proton, and the molar volumes of the polyvalent phosphorus compounds are large; so the signal-to-noise ratio for phosphorus resonances is not nearly so good as for protons and fluorine. This is compensated to some extent by the wide range of chemical shifts, $7 \times 10^{-4}$, which is larger than that of fluorine, permitting larger samples to be used on occasion.

A number of phosphorus $\delta$ values (35), defined in the usual way as $10^5(H_r - H_c)/H_r$ and referred to aqueous $H_3PO_4$, are listed in Table III. It is seen that the shifts fall into two distinct groups, one containing the trivalent compounds and the other, the pentavalent. The $\delta$'s for the pentavalent compounds cover a relatively narrow range between $+3$ and $-2$, which is unfortunate because the majority of analytical problems concern the pentavalent compounds. The $\delta$ values for similar and homologous compounds in Table III can be interpreted by considering changes in the magnitudes and relative importance of double-bonded and ionic structures. The sign of $\delta$ corresponds to, and $\delta$ itself is a semiquantitative measure of, the changes in the electronic charge in the vicinity of the phosphorus nucleus.

The multiplet splitting produced by the indirect coupling of a phosphorus nucleus with a proton or fluorine nucleus in the same chemical bond can be as large as 1.4 kc. In fact, the first examples of structural proof by means of multiplets were in connection with the compounds phosphorous acid, $H_3PO_3$, and hypophosphorous acid, $H_3PO_3$. These acids are di- and monobasic respectively; so it has long been supposed that their structures are $HPO(OH)_2$ and $H_2PO(OH)$ with 1 and 2 hydrogens bound directly to the phosphorus. Proof of these structures was given by the phosphorus resonance (34), which is a doublet in $HPO(OH)_2$ and a triplet (1:2:1) in $H_2PO(OH)$, indicating a coupling of the phosphorus nucleus with 1 and 2 protons. The protons attached to oxygen are sufficiently isolated from the phosphorus so that their coupling is

TABLE III

*Phosphorus Nuclear Magnetic Resonance Shifts\* in Several Compounds* (35)

| Trivalent compounds | | Pentavalent compounds | |
| Formula | $\delta$ | Formula | $\delta$ |
| --- | --- | --- | --- |
| $PBr_3$ | 22.2 | $PSCl_3$ | 3.08 |
| $PCl_3$ | 21.5 | $H_2PO(OH)$ | 1.38† |
| $Cl(CH_2)_3PCl_2$ | 18.2 | $C_2H_5OPOCl_2$ | 0.64 |
| $PI_3$ | 17.8 | $HPO(OH)_2$ | 0.45† |
| $P_2I_4$ (in $CS_2$) | 17.0 | $H_3PO_4$ | 0.00 |
| $CH_3OPF_2$ | 11.1† | $POCl_2F$ | 0.00† |
| $PF_3$ | 9.7† | $POCl_3$ | −0.54 |
| $P_4S_3$ | −11.4 | $POClF_2$ | −1.48† |
| $PH_3$ | −24.1† | $F_2PO(OH)$ | −2.01† |
| $P_4$ | −45.0 | $HPF_6$ | −11.8† |
| $P_4$ (in $CS_2$) | −48.8 | | |

\* The shifts are referred to aqueous $H_3PO_4$; $\delta$ is defined as $10^5(H_r - H_c)/H_r$.

† The resonance absorption in these compounds contained multiplet structure; see ref. (34) for details.

negligible, and of course the oxygen nuclei are nonmagnetic. Similar observations and arguments demonstrated that the mono- and di-fluophosphoric acids have the structures $FPO(OH)_2$ and $F_2PO(OH)$, with the fluorines attached directly to the phosphorus. Except for the probably greater importance of the multiplets in high-resolution phosphorus spectra, the general interpretative principles are the same as for fluorine and hydrogen.

There are several other nuclear species which show more or less, but mostly less, promise in high-resolution spectroscopy. $B^{11}$, $C^{13}$ and $N^{14}$ are among these. Small chemical shifts of up to $5 \times 10^{-5}$ have been observed in the resonance of $B^{11}$ (26) and its magnetic properties are quite favorable for analytical use. It is of interest that $B^{11}$ has a small quadrupole moment of 0.03 which, however, does not prevent observation of the nuclear magnetic resonance: the magnitude of the coupling with the small quadrupole moment is reduced or eliminated by the symmetrical planar or quasitetrahedral structure of the compounds and the consequent small or negligible electric field gradient at the $B^{11}$ nucleus. $C^{13}$ has a spin of one-half and a magnetogyric ratio one-quarter that of the proton. But the low isotopic abundance of 1.1% presently restricts useful spectra to isotopically enriched samples, which would be justified in relatively few problems. In addition, little is known about the magnitudes and general nature of the $C^{13}$ chemical shifts.

$N^{14}$ forms such a wide range of important compounds that any aid in their analysis would be valuable. It is regrettable, therefore, that nature has chosen to give the $N^{14}$ nucleus a magnetogyric ratio which is less than one-tenth that of the proton. Besides the resultant very weak absorption intensities, $N^{14}$ has a spin of 1 and a small quadrupole moment of 0.02, which can broaden the resonance lines and hamper observation of them. Such broadening is apparently not too extreme because proton multiplets have been found (63) to result from proton-nitrogen coupling in $NH_3$ and $NH_4^+$. The broadening is small, perhaps for symmetry reasons similar to those of $B^{11}$ as well as because of the smallness of the quadrupole moment. The range of the $N^{14}$ resonance shifts is large (26, 75), $40 \times 10^{-5}$ between the $NH_4^+$ and $NO_3^-$ ions, and so there is some chance of developing significant NMR applications to nitrogen compounds. Such applications will probably require the use of narrow band systems, as described in section 3.2.4, in order to achieve sufficient sensitivity. Chemical shifts of resonances too weak for the usual high resolution methods have been measured (38, 76, 102) in this fashion. Some resolution is sacrificed because of the audiomodulation effects (18). If the chemical shifts are large enough, there appears to be no reason why the narrow band techniques cannot be extended and used for the structural analysis of compounds of several nuclear species of low isotopic abundance or small magnetogyric ratio, such as $C^{13}$, $O^{17}$, and $Si^{29}$ in addition to $N^{14}$.

$Li^7$, $Na^{23}$, $Al^{27}$, and a number of other metals have fairly good nuclear properties but their compounds are predominately ionic, and the chemical shifts, if any, of their solutions are determined by interionic and solvent effects. Chemical shifts have been measured for a few compounds of $Ti^{47,49}$, $V^{51}$, $Co^{59}$, $Cu^{63,65}$ (76, 102) and $Tl^{203,205}$ (37) but there do not seem to be any important analytical NMR applications for these elements.

*4.2.4. Presentation of Spectra.* The problems incidental to notation and conventions in reporting results need no elaboration. Standardization is desirable but difficult to attain. Moreover, nuclear magnetic resonance is still a fluid field, and some features are not known well enough for standardization. The American Petroleum Institute Project 44 has instituted discussions of the matter, primarily because many NMR spectra are being obtained by the petroleum industry, and a catalogue of standard spectra may be issued. General agreement exists on several features but not on others. The conventions followed in this chapter are not necessarily the best; some are definitely expedients peculiar to one laboratory. An objective summary of the problem is, however, attempted below.

Absolute values for the nuclear magnetic shielding have not been obtained directly nor is it likely that they will be in the near future. For this reason, chemical shifts are best referred to some arbitrary reference compound. Theoretical calculations have been made for $H_2$, and the results were combined with an experimental comparison of $H_2$ with other compounds to refer the proton shifts in the hydrides (31) to the bare proton. But the accuracy of present shift measurements is better than the calculations; so there seems little point in reducing the proton shifts to the theoretical zero. The choice of primary reference compounds is less unanimous.

If a compound with an extreme chemical shift is used as a zero, so that all shifts will have the same sign, then more extreme extremes will undoubtedly be discovered. A centrally located resonance may therefore be preferable. Other requirements for a primary reference are less controversial. It should be a readily available, easily handled compound with a single, sharp, intense resonance which is insensitive to differences in experimental conditions. Water is a good primary reference for proton shifts except that it has a small temperature coefficient because of hydrogen bonding effects (7); also it may dissolve enough paramagnetic ions from Pyrex glass to produce shifts of the order of a part or two in $10^7$. Benzene has been recommended because of the ease with which it can be added to hydrocarbons as an internal reference, but there are sizable solvent effects. Trifluoroacetic and phosphoric acids appear to be good references for fluorine and phosphorus shifts, but this is based on limited experience. Secondary references are convenient experimentally, and discussions of results for series of compounds may be simplified by referring shifts to the parent compound. But if this is done, the position of the secondary reference should be given with respect to a commonly used primary reference.

As usual, there is a troublesome sign convention: whether the chemical shifts should be expressed as

$$(H_c - H_r)/H_r \tag{93}$$

or as

$$(H_r - H_c)/H_r \tag{94}$$

Original usage was generally in terms of nuclear magnetic shielding, defined by the first expression. However, analyzing data for the effects of substituents in fluorobenzenes on the fluorine shifts (33) made it apparent that the sign of the nuclear magnetic shielding was reversed from the Hammett substituent constants, whose sign corresponds to the sign of the charge produced by the substituent. And this made unintelligible an already obscure discussion. The sign was accordingly reversed to eq. (94), the quantity multiplied by $10^5$ to give numbers of convenient size, and the result called $\delta$, a difference in nuclear magnetic shielding as introduced in eq. (31). This sign convention has the advantage, in a discussion of the relation between chemical shifts and electron distribution, of corresponding to the charge densities about the nuclei, at least for three species studied in detail. Thus, for fluorine the more negative $\delta$'s correspond to nuclei in bonds with greater ionic character, $F^-$. For protons attached to a given atomic species, the more positive $\delta$'s correspond to more acidic protons, $H^+$, while for phosphorus, the sign of $\delta$ correctly represent both the electronic effects of double-bond character, $P^-{=}X^+$, and of ionic character, $P^+X^-$.

On the other hand, one can think in terms of a larger number (more positive) corresponding to a greater electron density (more negative) and prefer the shielding definition. The Shell Development Laboratory uses a system of this sort, defining a shielding number as

$$100 + 10^7(H_c - H_r)/H_r \qquad (95)$$

with $H_r$ given by water as the primary reference. The 100 is added to make most shielding numbers fall in the positive range. Which sign convention is adopted eventually will depend on usage. In the meantime confusion will be reduced if the term *shielding* is used only for eq. (93) and $\delta$ for eq. (94). In any event the conventions followed should be stated and the data should be reduced to the dimensionless form of either eq. (93) or (94), rather than given as milligauss or cycles, which depend on the total field used.

In the reproduction of spectra, the abscissa will ordinarily be the main magnetic field, but the sweep direction should be such that the $\delta$ values, or shielding numbers, increase from left to right, whichever is used. Whether the resonance lines point up or down is rather trivial. Absorption spectra, such as infrared, are usually pointed down. However, if a nuclear induction apparatus is used, one can argue that the nuclei induce a signal and thus the resonance should be pointed up, even though it is observed as the absorption mode.

The multiplets arising from the indirect spin-spin coupling are best handled somewhat differently from the chemical shifts. The coupling constants have been labeled $A_{ij}$ and $J$ and are expressed most conveniently as the separation, in cycles per second, of adjacent components in a multiplet. This has the advantage that the same number applies to both of the interacting species; it is field independent and is distinct from the dimensionless units recommended for chemical shifts. In the complicated cases which arise when $A_{ij} \sim |\nu_i - \nu_j|$, there is little choice other than reproducing the entire spectrum with full experimental details.

In general, the experimental conditions which influence the appearance of a spectrum and which therefore should be given include the following, more or less in order of importance: radiofrequency or the applied magnetic field $H_r$, magnetic field sweep amplitude and period, sample size and shape and information on whether or not it was spinning, and the magnitude of $H_1$ the rf field.

*4.2.5. A Critique of the Method.* In concluding the discussion of this main analytical application of NMR, a summary of advantages and disadvantages may be worth while. The advantages are several. The method is nondestructive. Relatively small samples can be used, as little as 5 to 10 milligrams for proton or fluorine resonance. The scanning of the spectrum is fast; a complete record can be made in a minute or two. And detailed measurements require only about 15 min. The most important advantage is probably the simple relationship between the structure and composition of a sample, and the number, position and intensities of resonance lines in the spectrum. This greatly reduces the necessity for pure model compounds of known structure in order to establish the structure and/or composition of an unknown. Also, there is no overlapping of absorption by different nuclear species; it is always certain which element causes a given spectral line. Also, as described in the next section, high-resolution spectra can be used for quantitative as well as qualitative and structural analysis.

The chief disadvantage is the limited applicability. Nuclear magnetic resonance is a novel combination of simplicity and complexity. The resonance equation is undoubtedly one of the simplest spectroscopic equations. On the other hand, the interactions perturbing the resonance line shapes are numerous and often complex. So considerable experience is needed in order to make an intelligent choice of samples and experimental conditions. When NMR can be used, it is very useful, but only a limited number of nuclear species are satisfactory. The restriction of samples to liquids or high-pressure gases is unfortunate. The exchange coupling of nuclear spins often complicates the spectrum. This may make the interpretation more difficult, but it can also contribute decisively to the determination of an unknown structure. The instrumental problems are difficult but not prohibitive. Further improvements can be made in the homogeneity and stability of the main magnetic field. This would permit larger samples to be used and would extend the range of application to dilute solutions and give generally stronger signals and better results.

With improved sensitivity and linearity of the detection and recording systems, quantitative analyses would be easier.

As to the future of the field, it is unlikely that NMR spectroscopy will ever displace such generally useful physical methods as infrared or ultraviolet spectroscopy. However, NMR can give conclusive results where other methods are difficult to apply or fail. Prediction always has its dangers, but NMR spectroscopy has already been developed to the point where it is a valuable supplement to much older physical methods of analysis. Considerable improvement and wider application appear to be possible.

## 5. OTHER APPLICATIONS

The high-resolution methods just described no doubt provide the most important analytical application of NMR to chemistry. In addition there is the general question of quantitative analysis, as well as an increasing number of more or less specialized applications, which are taken up in this section.

### 5.1. Quantitative Analysis

It is implicit in the account of high-resolution spectroscopy that mixtures can be analyzed as well as molecular structures determined. For instance, the relative equilibrium amounts of the keto and enol tautomeric forms of acetylacetone have been estimated from high-resolution proton spectra (51, 59); however, the question of quantitative analysis was deferred to this section for incorporation with a more general discussion. The basic equation relating the output signal voltage to the concentration of absorbing nuclei is obtained by combining eqs. (74), (61), and (45), giving for a particular apparatus, frequency, and set of experimental conditions

$$V \propto \frac{N\gamma^2 I(I + 1)T_2 H_1}{1 + (\omega_0 - \omega)^2 T_2{}^2 + \gamma^2 H_1{}^2 T_1 T_2} \tag{96}$$

If $H_1$ is the optimum value, then

$$V_{max} \propto N\gamma I(I + 1)(T_2/T_1)^{\frac{1}{2}} \tag{97}$$

The direct proportionality of the absorption to $N$, the number of nuclei/ cm.$^3$ absorbing in a given resonance component, contrasts with the usual, exponential Beer-Lambert law for radiation absorption. This difference arises because only a small fraction ($< 10^{-2}$) of the radiation is absorbed in an NMR experiment, and so to a very good approximation the radiation intensity is constant. This direct proportionality and the use of experimental arrangements which balance out a large fraction of the applied rf make it simpler to express the absorption in arbitrary units rather than as percentage of absorption or transmission.

The dependence of the signal strength on the instrumental factors $Q$, $\zeta$, $V_c$, $B$ and $F$, most of which cannot be measured precisely, makes absolute intensity measurements very difficult. This is no great obstacle because resonances can either be measured with respect to one another in the same sample or referred to a standard, provided that the apparatus stability, linearity, and reproducibility are adequate. But the dependence of the instrumental factors on frequency leaves no practical choice other than comparisons at the same frequency. The main problem in quantitative analysis by NMR arises from the dependence of the absorption on the values of $T_1$, $T_2$ and $H_1$ through eq. (96). This can be got around by constructing an empirical calibration curve using standard known samples. Such a technique has been employed with a Varian high-resolution spectrometer to make rapid measurements of the sodium concentration in blood (90); in this case the peak absorption intensity is linear in the concentration of $Na^+$.

There are several ways of minimizing the effects of differences in relaxation times. If a large enough sample is used so that the apparent widths of the resonance lines are mainly from field inhomogeneities, differences in the natural $T_2$'s give proportionately smaller effects. This is often the case in the high-resolution spectra of liquids. But even for nuclei in the same liquid compound there will usually be sufficient differences in $T_1$ and $T_2$ to give discernible effects. Thus, the peak intensities in Fig. 22 of the four fluorine resonance components in 2,3,5-trifluorobenzotrifluoride do not follow the ideal $1:1:1:3$ ratio. Instead, the ratio is more nearly $0.6:0.7:0.9:3$. The unequal peak intensities of the three weaker lines results mainly from unresolved fine structure which makes the lines of different widths; also, the $CF_3$ line probably has a shorter $T_1$.

Another technique is to add a paramagnetic species to the sample, thereby shortening $T_1$ and reducing the differences in $T_1$ for different resonances. This has the advantage that if $T_1$ is made short enough, $T_2$ is determined mainly by $T_1$, which reduces the $T_2$ differences. Such a procedure has been used to good effect (46) in measuring the isotopic abundance ratios $H^2/H^1$ and $Li^6/Li^7$ in aqueous solution. Paramagnetic ions were added to produce a $(T_2/T_1)$ ratio of essentially unity for each magnetic nuclear species in solution. This does not necessarily mean that the actual $T_1$ and $T_2$ values are the same for the different nuclear species, because they do have different magnetic and quadrupole moments. Even so, when $H_1$ is adjusted to give the optimum signal to noise for each nuclear species at a fixed $\nu_0$, eq. (97) applies and the isotopic abundance ratio is

$$\frac{N_a}{N_b} = \frac{(V_a)_{max}}{(V_b)_{max}} \frac{\mu_b(I_b + 1)}{\mu_a(I_a + 1)} \tag{98}$$

Good results were obtained in this manner (46) for $H^2/H^1$ and for $Li^6/Li^7$. The accuracy of the lithium results is probably better than mass spectrometer values. A Varian electromagnet and variable frequency spectrometer were used in the experiments along with a narrow band phase sensitive recording system needed to improve the signal from the weak $H^2$ and $Li^6$ resonances. The narrow band system incorporated a low-frequency square wave modulation of $H_0$ with an amplitude greater than the line width, rather than the small amplitude sine wave modulation described in section 3.2.4. On sweeping $H_0$ slowly through resonance this gives the absorption curve directly rather than the derivative. The steady state condition for passing through the resonance requires that the dwell time of the square wave on the resonance be long compared with $T_1$. The peak values for the absorption curves were then used in eq. (98) to obtain the isotopic ratios.

This general procedure of adjusting to the optimum $H_1$ for each resonance and comparing the resulting peak absorption values can certainly be used in high-resolution spectra as well. The problem is somewhat simpler if the analysis involves the same nuclear species because then the $T_1$'s and the $T_2$'s are more nearly the same for different resonance components. But even so, it is difficult to establish that the $T_2/T_1$ ratios are sufficiently near unity for the resonances being compared to give the desired accuracy. Perhaps a better way is to use a large enough sample that inhomogeneities determine $T_2$, and then to reduce $H_1$ by a factor $\Delta$, say $\frac{1}{10}$ or less, from the optimum value. The important result, contained in eq. (96), is that the errors introduced by $T_1$ differences are decreased by $\Delta^2$ while the signal strength is decreased by $\Delta$. And the signal decrease is compensated partially by the larger sample size.

The experiments just described for obtaining the $Li^6/Li^7$ and $H^2/H^1$ isotopic abundance ratios require a large amount of work. Later experiments (46) have shown that, at least with $H_2O/D_2O$ mixtures, it is much easier and probably more accurate to use a high resolution apparatus operated under standardized conditions to compare the resonance peak intensities of unknowns with those of standard samples. For samples in the low concentration ranges a dilution or "spiking" technique gives increased sensitivity. Several accurately measured aliquots of the sample are taken and to each aliquot incremental amounts of the dilute species are added in pure form. The signal amplitudes of this species are measured and plotted versus the amount added. If any of the species is present in the original sample, the plot will not go through the origin, and an extrapolation of the plot to the axis representing the species added gives an intercept measuring the amount present in the original sample.

There appears to be some theoretical advantage for using the integrated total absorption $A$ rather than its peak value. In case the experiment involves only one nuclear species, integrating eq. (96) and taking the ratio of areas $A_a$ and $A_b$ for two different resonance components, we find

$$\frac{A_a}{A_b} = \frac{N_a}{N_b} \left[ \frac{1 + \gamma^2 H_{1b}{}^2 T_{1b} T_{2b}}{1 + \gamma^2 H_{1a}{}^2 T_{1a} T_{2a}} \right]^{\frac{1}{2}} \tag{99}$$

A comparison of the peak absorptions $V_a$ and $V_b$ from eq. (96) shows that the differences in $T_1$ and $T_2$ appear to a higher power and give a greater error

$$\frac{V_a}{V_a} = \frac{N_a}{N_b} \left[ \frac{1 + \gamma^2 H_{1b}{}^2 T_{1b} T_{2b}}{1 + \gamma^2 H_{1a}{}^2 T_{1a} T_{2a}} \right] \frac{T_{2a} H_{1b}}{T_{2b} H_{1a}} \tag{100}$$

To be sure, these results apply exactly only to natural Lorentzian line shapes, but they will be qualitatively true in general.

In contrast to the steady-state conditions considered above, the thermal equilibrium magnetization $M_0$ for a sample is independent of the $T_1$ and $T_2$ values. Transient methods in which the signal amplitudes depend only on the initial magnetization would avoid the difficulties associated with differences in $T_1$ and $T_2$. Moreover, $M_0$ is greater than the steady-state magnetization, and so transient, or "fast-passage," conditions will give greater signal amplitudes than the steady-state "slow-passage" experiments, and this will compensate for the noise introduced by the greater receiver-band width required to reproduce the transient signals. Insofar as is known, these features have not been utilized completely in an analytical scheme. But a pseudotransient, or "intermediate-passage," method has been developed (107) and applied very successfully for total hydrogen analysis of petroleum samples. An essential feature of the method is the use of the nuclear dispersion, rather than the absorption, which greatly reduces the dependence of signal amplitudes on $H_1$ (12).

With reference to eqs. (60) and (71), the nuclear dispersion signal is proportional to

$$\frac{\chi_0 \omega_0 H_1 (\omega_0 - \omega) T_2{}^2}{1 + (\omega_0 - \omega)^2 T_2{}^2 + \gamma^2 H_1{}^2 T_1 T_2} \tag{101}$$

when this function is plotted against $\omega$, the maximum occurs at

$$(\omega_0 - \omega) = (1/T_2)(1 + \gamma^2 H_1{}^2 T_1 T_2)^{\frac{1}{2}} \tag{102}$$

where the value is

$$\frac{\chi_0 \omega_0 H_1 T_2}{2(1 + \gamma^2 H_1{}^2 T_1 T_2)^{\frac{1}{2}}} \tag{103}$$

This expression does not decrease for large values of $H_1$, as does the absorption, but increases monotonically, and when $H_1{}^2 \gg 1/\gamma^2 T_1 T_2$, approaches the limiting value

$$(\tfrac{1}{2})\chi_0 H_0(T_2/T_1)^{1/2} \tag{104}$$

which is identical with that in eq. (68) for the absorption.

The $H_1$ levels required to approach the optimum signals are sufficiently large that the resonance widths are determined mainly by the saturation broadening. This serves, along with large sample sizes of a cubic centimeter or more, to suppress any fine structure in the resonance, which might interfere with the determination of total hydrogen. Viscous or semisolid samples are dissolved in $CS_2$ or $CCl_4$ so that $T_2/T_1$ approaches unity for all proton constituents in the sample, following the reasoning discussed for the other quantitative methods. An increase in signal to noise, which is desirable for samples of low hydrogen content, is obtained by modulation $H_0$ at an audiofrequency $\nu_m$, while passing $H_0$ through the resonance at a rate corresponding to slow passage conditions, and plotting the dispersion with a narrow band system. However, the signal amplitudes then depend on the relation of $\nu_m$ to the relaxation times, and so it is desirable to use a large enough $\nu_m$ to correspond to fast passage for all samples being analyzed. In this case, the signal amplitude is twice that for steady state conditions and more independent of the relaxation times. The requirement on $\nu_m$ for fast passage (107) is that $(2\pi\nu_m T_2)^2 \gg 1$; 80 c.p.s. is valid for $T_2$'s down to about $10^{-2}$ sec., which has been found adequate for most hydrocarbon samples.

In the measurements themselves, a calibration factor is obtained with a standard such as spectroscopic-grade $n$-hexane or toluene, in a standard test tube, dissolved in $CS_2$ or $CCl_4$ to a known proton concentration comparable with the range expected for the unknowns. The peak height from the first maximum to the first minimum of the recorded resonance signal is measured for the reference and unknown under the same operating conditions, and the ratio gives the ratio of proton concentrations. The weight percentage of hydrogen has been measured in "known" samples ranging from 6 to 16%, with a percentage standard deviation from the true value of between 1 and 2%. Asphaltic samples give values off by as much as 3 to 4% of the true value, apparently because they contain small amounts of material which do not go into true solution. But in general the method is capable of good precision and is much faster than conventional analytical procedures.

There are other NMR phenomena which might lend themselves to quantitative analysis in special cases. Some nuclear species exhibit large concentration-dependent chemical shifts (37, 58) because of interionic and solvent effects, and these shifts could be calibrated and serve for rapid and accurate quantitative analysis. A similar situation arises when fast chemical exchange occurs between two different chemical states, as described in section 2.3.3. The position of the resultant single line depends on the relative numbers of nuclei populating the two states as well as on the chemical shifts of each state (41); and in such a case a calibration curve could be constructed and applied very readily. Paramagnetic species exert a large effect on $T_1$, even in very dilute solutions. The concentration of the paramagnetic center is directly proportional to $(1/T_1)$. $T_1$ measurements could be used to determine the concentration with considerable accuracy even though $T_1$ itself is measured readily only to within about 5%.

## 5.2. Moisture Analysis

In the processing of agricultural products, the accurate and rapid determination of moisture content is a major problem. The situation is complicated by the presence of large concentrations of hydrogen in the solid, nonaqueous constituents of biological materials. However, the mobility of protons in the solid components is much less than in the aqueous phase. As a consequence, the magnetic resonance of protons in the solid remains broadened to widths of about 10 gauss, and the resonance of protons in the water is a few tenths of a gauss (86), for the reasons outlined in section 2.2.3. This is shown in Fig. 17 by the derivative of the proton absorption in a solid sample with adsorbed water. The proton resonance of the moisture is broadened from that in pure water, because the water molecules are bound more or less tightly to the solid material, which restricts the molecular reorientations.

When the proton absorption is observed in such a sample, it appears therefore as a relatively narrow, intense line from the moisture centered upon a much broader background line from the solid. The absorption from the solid is essentially constant over the small region of absorption by the moisture, and so the protons in the solid do not interfere with the moisture determination. These general features serve as the basis for two procedures which have been developed for evaluating the moisture content (88). The proton resonance itself is observed as the derivative of the absorption mode, by use of audiomodulation of $H_0$ and a narrowband recording system for improved sensitivity. In one method the peak-to-peak amplitude of the derivative for the moisture is measured under standardized conditions for known samples. This gives a calibration curve, which usually is fairly linear, for the unknowns.

The width of the proton resonance for the moisture depends on how tightly it is bound to the solid. At low moisture contents the water is bound rather tightly and may have a line width as broad as a gauss. As the percentage of water present increases, the line width decreases monotonically and may become as narrow as 0.1 gauss. An empirical calibration curve can be constructed as before (87), but the line width tends to change more slowly with concentration at higher moisture contents, where the method becomes too insensitive for use. However, this procedure does have the advantage that the measured line widths are relatively immune to changes in sensitivity and adjustment of the apparatus and to variations in the packing of the test sample.

A special instrument has been designed (65) for these measurements and probably will be commercially available (62, 69). A working model is now in use (27). The apparatus is similar to the narrow-band spectrometer for which a block diagram is given in Fig. 16. A regenerative fixed tuned oscillator (73) is used with a permanent magnet of 1240 gauss. The modulation frequency is 200 c.p.s., and $H_0$ is swept through the resonance, first up field and then back, in about a minute. The decrease in sensitivity associated with the low $H_0$ is compensated partially by the large sample volumes of about 25 cm.$^3$; and large volumes are preferred because of variations within the samples themselves. With protons and the very stable and sensitive narrow band system used, higher fields are not required to give the desired accuracy.

When the peak-to-peak amplitude of the absorption derivative is used, the precision of the results is $\pm 0.05\%$ at water contents of 11 to 14%, or $\frac{1}{2}\%$ of the measured value. However, the absolute accuracy is no better than the series of standard samples used for calibrating the instrument. Also, unless care is taken, samples will pick up enough moisture during handling to decrease the reproducibility of the measurements. Excellent results have been obtained for a wide variety of materials such as corn starches, pectin, dextrins, syrups, vegetables, and fruit. It appears that extensive use could be made of this method.

### 5.3. Bulk Magnetic Susceptibilities

If a small, thin-walled tube of a sample is placed inside a slightly larger tube which contains a liquid normally giving a single sharp resonance line, and the nuclear resonance is observed for the assembly with a high-resolution spectrometer, an amusing effect is found (82). The normally single resonance is split into a broadened U-shaped doublet. The splitting results from differences in the bulk magnetic susceptibilities of the samples and containers and is given theoretically (82) as

$$\Delta H = 4\pi H_0[(\kappa_1 - \kappa_2)(a/r)^2 + (\kappa_2 - \kappa_3)(b/r)^2] \tag{105}$$

where $a$ and $b$ are the internal and external radii of the inner glass tube, $r$ is the average radius of the annular space between the two tubes, and $\kappa_1$, $\kappa_2$, and $\kappa_3$ are the volume magnetic susceptibilities of the sample in the inner tube, of the glass, and of the liquid in the annular space. This result has been checked experimentally and forms the basis of a new and rapid method for measuring with good precision the volume susceptibilities of solids as well as liquids.

In the discussion of high-resolution experiments the effects of differences in the bulk magnetic susceptibilities were neglected, and this is certainly permissible for most nuclei in the usual diamagnetic sample. However, the chemical shifts in the proton resonances are small enough so that, if measurements are made involving separate sample tubes, the bulk susceptibility differences can be important (22). The effect of the bulk susceptibility is given by the equation

$$H - H_a = \left(\frac{4\pi}{3} - \alpha\right) \kappa H \cong \left(\frac{4\pi}{3} - \alpha\right) \kappa H_a \qquad (106)$$

where $H$ is the magnetic field in the sample, $H_a$ is the field applied to the sample, $\kappa$ is the volume susceptibility, and $\alpha$ is a demagnetization factor which is determined by the shape of the container (26). For an infinite cylinder $\alpha$ is $2\pi$, and for a sphere, $4\pi/3$. Cylindrical samples with a large length/diameter ratio are usually used, and so $\alpha = 2\pi$ is a good approximation.

This produces a shift in the resonance position of a compound with respect to a reference, in $\delta$ units of

$$\delta_\kappa = 10^5 (2\pi/3)(\kappa_c - \kappa_r) \qquad (107)$$

where $\kappa_c$ and $\kappa_r$ are the volume susceptibilities of compound and reference. The range in $\kappa$ for most of the commoner diamagnetic liquids is about $0.2 \times 10^{-6}$, and this would contribute at most the order of 0.05 to the apparent $\delta$ values. The correction can be applied if the $\kappa$'s are known. If such a correction is desirable, the $\kappa$'s can be measured very simply by the method described. Also, another NMR method for measuring bulk susceptibilities has been devised (52). It depends on observing the difference in resonance position between two samples of the same material but of different shape and with different known demagnetizing factors, $\alpha$.

### 5.4. Special Uses

Three special uses of NMR, which need only a few words to relate, are grouped here. One such special application, only indirectly of chemical interest, is the use of a variable-frequency spectrometer to measure magnetic fields. The proton resonance frequency has been measured very carefully by the National Bureau of Standards (97) in a magnetic field the precise strength of which was known independently, providing a basic calibration factor of 4.2578 kc. gauss$^{-1}$. Thus, a very accurate measurement of a magnetic field can be made by observing the proton resonance frequency in it. Commercial field meters based on this principle are available (62, 101), and several simple circuits have been described for this purpose (47, 54, 73).

The viewpoint thus far has been mainly toward the identification and quantitative measurement of discrete chemical species. An analytical application of a different sort concerns the presence and concentration of dislocations and defects in crystals, which can be described as the absence of chemical species. Many ionic crystals are cubic and contain nuclei with large quadrupole moments. If the environment of a quadrupolar nucleus has cubic symmetry, there is no electric field gradient at the nucleus, and the nuclear magnetic resonance will occur in the same fashion as described above for nuclei with $I = \frac{1}{2}$. The resonances in the solid will be broadened only by the magnetic dipolar interactions, according to eq. (24). However, if there are holes, imperfections, dislocations, or impurity atoms in the lattice, the cubic symmetry will be disrupted in the vicinity of some of the nuclei and this produces observable effects (72, 105).

In the absence of cubic symmetry, electric field gradients occur at the nuclei, and the quadrupole interactions referred to in section 2.3.5 split the nuclear magnetic resonance. If the quadrupole interactions are small, the observed effect is a broadening of the magnetic resonance. In some cases the splitting is much greater than the dipolar breadth of the resonance. The quadrupole interactions produce $2I$ components, and so if $I$ is half integral, as is often the case, a central component remains. The observed effect is thus a decrease in intensity of the resonance, which is proportional to the concentration of imperfections. The imperfections also play an important role in determining $T_1$. Applications of this sort are still in the exploratory stage, but it is clear that useful fundamental information can be obtained on such matters as impurities, work-hardening, and annealing (15, 20).

The final application to be considered is process control. Most instrumental analytical methods can be adapted for this purpose and NMR is no exception. At least one special instrument is being designed and constructed for such an application (90). Besides the usual design problems of control systems, some more are raised by the basic nature of the NMR and of its instrumentation. For instance, the necessary long-term stability will be more difficult to obtain than in infrared spectroscopy, particularly if the control requires the resolution of chemically shifted proton lines. Also, when a sample is passed continuously through the apparatus, the resonance depends on the flow rate (96), which must be adjusted so that the sample is exposed to $H_0$ and $H_1$ long enough for the proper passage conditions to be satisfied.

## ACKNOWLEDGMENT

That work described above which was conducted at the University of Illinois has been supported by a contract with the U. S. Office of Naval Research and by grants in aid from Research Corporation and E. I. du Pont de Nemours and Company. I am indebted to a number of people for some specific as well as general results not published previously; included are J. C. Buchta for his excellent aid with the electronics and J. P. Heeschen, C. H. Holm, and G. A. Williams for various measurements. I am especially grateful to J. P. Heeschen and C. H. Holm for obtaining a number of the spectra used in the figures.

## REFERENCES

1. Anderson, W. A., and Arnold, J. T., *Phys. Rev.* **94**, 497 (1954).
2. Anderson, W. A., and Arnold, J. T., *Discussions Faraday Soc.* No. **19**, 226 (1955).
3. Andrew, E. R., *Phys. Rev.* **91**, 425 (1953).
4. Andrew, E. R., "Nuclear Magnetic Resonance." Cambridge U.P., New York, 1955.
5. Andrew, E. R., and Bersohn, R., *J. Chem Phys.* **18**, 159 (1950).
6. Arnold, J. T., Dharmatti, S. S., and Packard, M. E., *J. Chem. Phys.* **19**, 507 (1951).
7. Arnold, J. T., and Packard, M. E., *J. Chem. Phys.* **19**, 1608 (1951).
8. Bader, A. L., Gutowsky, H. S., Williams, G. A., and Yankwich, P. E., unpublished data, 1954.
9. Banerjee, M. K., Das, T. P., and Saha, A. K., *Proc. Roy. Soc.* **A226**, 490 (1954).
10. Béné, G. J., Denis, P. M., and Extermann, R. C., *Compt. rend.* **231**, 1294 (1950); *Arch. sci. (Geneva)* **4**, 212 (1951).
11. Bersohn, R., and Gutowsky, H. S., *J. Chem. Phys.* **22**, 651 (1954).
12. Bloch, F., *Phys. Rev.* **70**, 460 (1946).
13. Bloch, F., *Science* **118**, 425 (1953).
14. Bloch, F., *Phys. Rev.* **94**, 496 (1954).
15. Bloembergen, N., *In* Report of the Bristol Conference on Defects in Crystalline Solids, 1954, p. 1. The Physical Society, London, 1955.
16. Bloembergen, N., Purcell, E. M., and Pound, R. V., *Phys. Rev.* **73**, 679 (1948).
17. Bloom, A. L., and Shoolery, J. N., *Phys. Rev.* **97**, 1261 (1955).
18. Burgess, J. H., and Brown, R. M., *Rev. Sci. Instr.* **23**, 334 (1952).
18a. Carr, H. Y., Ph.D Thesis, Harvard University, p. 52 (1952).
19. Chiarotti, G., Cristiani, G., and Giulotto, L., *Nuovo cimento* [10] **1**, 863 (1955).
20. Cohen, M. H., and Reif, F., *In* Report of the Bristol Conference on Defects in Crystalline Solids, 1954, p. 44. The Physical Society, London, 1955.
21. Curtin, D. Y., and Kauer, J. C., Noyes Chemical Laboratory, Urbana, Illinois, personal communication.
22. Dailey, B. P., and Shoolery, J. N., *J. Am. Chem. Soc.* **77**, 3977 (1955).
23. Dehmelt, H. G., *Am. J. Phys.* **22**, 110 (1954).
24. Dicke, R. H., *Rev. Sci. Instr.* **17**, 268 (1946).
25. Dickinson, W. C., *Phys. Rev.* **80**, 563 (1950).

26. Dickinson, W. C., *Phys. Rev.* **81**, 717 (1951).
27. Elder, A. L., Corn Products Refining Co., Argo (Cook County), Illinois, personal communication.
28. Finger, G. C., and associates, Illinois State Geological Survey, Urbana, Illinois, personal communication.
29. Ford, P. T., and Richards, R. E., *Discussions Faraday Soc.* No. **19**, 230 (1955).
30. Gutowsky, H. S., *Ann. Rev. Phys. Chem.* **5**, 333 (1954).
31. Gutowsky, H. S., and Hoffman, C. J., *J. Chem. Phys.* **19**, 1259 (1951); **20**, 200 (1952).
32. Gutowsky, H. S., Kistiakowsky, G. B., Pake, G. E., and Purcell, E. M., *J. Chem. Phys.* **17**, 972 (1949).
33. Gutowsky, H. S., McCall, D. W., McGarvey, B. R., and Meyer, L. H., *J. Am. Chem. Soc.* **74**, 4809 (1952).
34. Gutowsky, H. S., McCall, D. W., and Slichter, C. P., *J. Chem. Phys.* **21**, 279 (1953).
35. Gutowsky, H. S., and McCall, D. W., *J. Chem. Phys.* **22**, 162 (1954).
36. Gutowsky, H. S., and McGarvey, B. R., *J. Chem. Phys.* **20**, 1472 (1952).
37. Gutowsky, H. S., and McGarvey, B. R., *Phys. Rev.* **91**, 81 (1953).
38. Gutowsky, H. S., and McGarvey, B. R., *J. Chem. Phys.* **21**, 1423 (1953).
39. Gutowsky, H. S., Meyer, L. H., and McClure, R. E., *Rev. Sci. Instr.* **24**, 644 (1953).
40. Gutowsky, H. S., and Pake, G. E., *J. Chem. Phys.* **18**, 162 (1950).
41. Gutowsky, H. S., and Saika, A., *J. Chem. Phys.* **21**, 1688 (1953).
42. Hahn, E. L., *Phys. Rev.* **80**, 580 (1950).
43. Hahn, E. L., and Maxwell, D. E., *Phys. Rev.* **88**, 1070 (1952).
44. Hatton, J., and Rollin, B. V., *Proc. Roy. Soc.* **A199**, 222 (1949).
45. Heeschen, J. P., unpublished data, 1954.
46. Holder, B. E., and Klein, M. P., *Phys. Rev.* **98**, 265(A) (1955), and personal communication.
47. Hopkins, N. J., *Rev. Sci. Instr.* **20**, 401 (1949).
48. Huggins, C. H., Pimentel, G. C., and Shoolery, J. N., *J. Chem. Phys.* **23**, 1244 (1955).
49. Indiana Steel Products Co., Valparaiso, Indiana.
50. Jacobsohn, B. A., and Wangsness, R. K., *Phys. Rev.* **73**, 942 (1948).
51. Jarrett, H. S., Sadler, M. S., and Shoolery, J. N., *J. Chem. Phys.* **21**, 2092 (1953).
52. Klein, M. P., and Holder, B. E., *Phys. Rev.* **98**, 265(A) (1955).
53. Knight, W. D., *Phys. Rev.* **76**, 1259 (1949).
54. Knoebel, H. W., and Hahn, E. L., *Rev. Sci. Instr.* **22**, 904 (1951).
55. Lamb, W. E., Jr., *Phys. Rev.* **60**, 817 (1941).
56. Lloyd, J. P., and Pake, G. E., *Phys. Rev.* **94**, 579 (1954).
57. McConnell, H. M., McLean, A. D., and Reilly, C. A., *J. Chem. Phys.* **23**, 1152 (1955).
58. Masuda, Y., and Kanda, T., *J. Phys. Soc. Japan* **8**, 432 (1953); **9**, 82 (1954).
59. Meyer, L. H., unpublished data, 1953.
60. Meyer, L. H., and Gutowsky, H. S., *J. Phys. Chem.* **57**, 481 (1953).
61. Meyer, L. H., Saika, A., and Gutowsky, H. S., *J. Am. Chem. Soc.* **76**, 4567 (1953).
62. Nuclear Magnetics Corp., 154 Boylston St., Boston, Mass.
63. Ogg, R. A., Jr., *Discussions Faraday Soc.* No. **17**, 215 (1954).
64. Ogg, R. A., Jr., *Discussions Faraday Soc.* No. **19**, 239 (1955).
65. O'Meara, J. P., and Rollwitz, W. L., Southwest Research Institute, San Antonio, Texas.

66. Pake, G. E., *J. Chem. Phys.* **16**, 327 (1948).
67. Pake, G. E., *Am. J. Phys.* **18**, 438, 473 (1950).
68. Pake, G. E., and Gutowsky, H. S., *Phys. Rev.* **74**, 979 (1948).
69. Perkin-Elmer Corp., Norwalk, Conn., personal communication.
70. Peter, Brother Simon, F. S. C., *Phys. Rev.* **93**, 940(A) (1954).
71. Pound, R. V., *Phys. Rev.* **79**, 685 (1950).
72. Pound, R. V., *J. Phys. Chem.* **57**, 743 (1953).
73. Pound, R. V., and Knight, W. D., *Rev. Sci. Instr.* **21**, 219 (1950).
74. Proctor, W. G., *Phys. Rev.* **79**, 35 (1950).
75. Proctor, W. G., and Yu, F. C., *Phys. Rev.* **77**, 717 (1950).
76. Proctor, W. G., and Yu, F. C., *Phys. Rev.* **81**, 20 (1951).
77. Purcell, E. M., *Science* **107**, 433 (1948); **118**, 431 (1953).
78. Ramsey, N. F., *Phys. Rev.* **78**, 699 (1950); **86**, 243 (1952).
79. Ramsey, N. F., *Phys. Rev.* **91**, 303 (1953).
80. Ramsey, N. F., "Nuclear Moments." Wiley, New York, 1953.
81. Redfield, A. G., *Phys. Rev.* **98**, 1787 (1955).
82. Reilly, C. A., McConnell, H. M., and Meisenheimer, R. G., *Phys. Rev.* **98**, 264(A) (1955).
83. Roberts, A., *Rev. Sci. Instr.* **18**, 845 (1947).
84. Saika, A., and Slichter, C. P., *J. Chem. Phys.* **22**, 26 (1954).
85. Schuster, N. A., *Rev. Sci. Instr.* **22**, 254 (1951).
86. Shaw, T. M., and Elsken, R. H., *J. Chem. Phys.* **18**, 1113 (1950).
87. Shaw, T. M., and Elsken, R. H., *J. Chem. Phys.* **21**, 565 (1953).
88. Shaw, T. M., Elsken, R. H., and Kunsman, C. H., *J. Assoc. Offic. Agr. Chemists* **36**, 1070 (1953).
89. Sheriff, R. E., and Williams, D., *Phys. Rev.* **82**, 651 (1951).
90. Shoolery, J. N., Varian Associates, Palo Alto, Calif., personal communication.
91. Shoolery, J. N., *J. Chem. Phys.* **21**, 1899 (1953).
92. Shoolery, J. N., *Anal. Chem.* **26**, 1400 (1954).
93. Shoolery, J. N., *Discussions Faraday Soc.* No. **19**, 215 (1955).
94. Shoolery, J. N., and Alder, B. J., *J. Chem. Phys.* **23**, 805 (1955).
95. Shoolery, J. N., and Weaver, H. E., Jr., *Ann. Rev. Phys. Chem.* **6**, 433 (1955).
96. Suryan, G., *Proc. Indian Acad. Sci.* **A33**, 107 (1951).
97. Thomas, H. A., Driscoll, R. L., and Hipple, J. A., *Phys. Rev.* **78**, 787 (1950); *J. Research Natl. Bureau Standards* **44**, 569 (1950).
98. Torrey, H. C., *Phys. Rev.* **76**, 1059 (1949); **85**, 365 (1952).
99. Tuttle, W. N., *Proc. Inst. Radio Engrs.* **28**, 23 (1940).
100. Van Vleck, J. H., *Phys. Rev.* **74**, 1168 (1948).
101. Varian Associates, 611 Hansen Way, Palo Alto, Calif.
102. Walchli, H. E., A Table of Nuclear Moment Data, ORNL-1469, Oak Ridge National Laboratory, Oak Ridge, Tenn., 1953.
103. Wangsness, R. K., and Bloch, F., *Phys. Rev.* **89**, 728 (1953).
104. Watkins, G. D., and Pound, R. V., *Phys. Rev.* **82**, 342(A) (1951).
105. Watkins, G. D., and Pound, R. V., *Phys. Rev.* **89**, 658 (1953).
106. Weaver, H. E., Jr., *Phys. Rev.* **89**, 923 (1953).
107. Williams, R. B., Pittsburgh Conference on Analytical Chemistry and Applied Spectroscopy March, 1955, and personal communication.

# Fluorescent X-Ray Spectrometric Analysis

By

GEORGE L. CLARK

*Department of Chemistry, University of Illinois, Urbana, Illinois*

Analytical chemistry since 1950 has witnessed the resurrection and regeneration of a surprising number of techniques long known but relatively little used because of inherent experimental limitations. One of the most striking examples of rebirth and progress is analysis by fluorescent X-ray spectrometry. Here is a method which had to wait for forty years for the development of instrumentation which would realize its potentialities and assure its practical usefulness. Now it is the subject of symposia, of a mounting flood of scientific papers, and of inquiry and discussion wherever there is concern with the best of modern analytical procedures. On the basis of critical test and solid achievement, it has taken an assured and permanent place alongside classical and well-established instrumental techniques such as optical emission and absorption spectrographic analyses. This coming of age was made possible by vast improvements, which will be considered in the light of the historical background.

## 1. THE DEVELOPMENT OF X-RAY EMISSION SPECTROMETRY

Röntgen, who discovered X rays on November 8, 1895, in his experiments with cathode rays, made every effort to produce a spectrum of a beam of X rays, assuming that these invisible rays belonged in the same electromagnetic spectrum with visible light, ultraviolet, infrared, and Hertzian or radio waves. His logical experiments designed to disperse a beam by refraction by prisms and diffraction by ruled gratings were unsuccessful because of failure to recognize that the refractive index was less than 1 by a quantity of the order of 0.000001 and that diffraction by the grating required that the beam have an exceedingly small grazing angle of incidence. Thus from 1895 to 1912 there was no method of X-ray spectrometry and the nature of X radiation remained mysterious. By absorption measurements of X-ray beams, Barkla in 1905 found evidences of discontinuities in such properties, as if under proper conditions of excitation the energy of emission was distributed in groups instead of continuously. As a matter of fact he devised the nomenclature used to this day, namely, $K$, $L$, $M$, $N$, $O$, $P$ series by analogy with series in the optical spectrum of hydrogen. But, of course, these absorption measurements did not permit resolution of characteristic spectral emission lines or absorption edges. It was the experiment in 1912 by von Laue and his associates, Friedrich and Knipping, proving that all crystals are three-dimensional diffraction gratings for X rays, and the subsequent derivation of the Bragg law, $n\lambda = 2d \sin \theta$ (where $n$ is an integer, the order of the spectrum; $\lambda$ is the wave length of a ray reflected (or diffracted) by a set of planes in a crystal of spacing $d$, at an angle of incidence $\theta$), which opened the way for the construction of a crystal spectrometer. It was put to use by the Braggs, Moseley, Siegbahn, and many others, to resolve X-ray beams into spectra with emission lines characteristic of the chemical element serving as the target in the X-ray tube. Of course the von Laue experiment proved the electromagnetic nature of X rays, even though it was not until after 1920 that refraction by prisms and diffraction by ruled gratings were successfully proved. The Bragg ionization spectrometer consisted of a central movable table upon which the crystal could be mounted on a rotating arm, the position of which could also be read on a scale. It was soon clearly understood that when a target was bombarded by a stream of electrons in an evacuated bulb, the electrons were stopped by the target atoms and their kinetic energy transformed by a process involving the inner electrons in the atoms, into X radiation. Further, it was apparent that at all voltages on the X-ray tube X rays were generated which had a continuous, or "white," spectrum, independent of the atomic number of the target but that above certain critical voltages radiation was generated which gave sharp lines (or peaks on the spectra plotted from spectrometer readings), in series already designated by Barkla, with the letters $K$ (for groups of four principal lines with the shortest wave lengths generated at the highest critical voltage), $L$, the next longer group of about 20 lines, and the still longer $M$, $N$, $O$, and $P$ series. These were emission lines and series, characteristic of the chemical elements in the continuous progression of atomic numbers whose significance for the first time was proved by Moseley with a Bragg spectrometer. So began the accurate measurement of the wave lengths of these X-ray lines (and associated characteristic absorption edges) as a means of spectrometric identification of any unknown sample thereafter which could be pasted on a target and bombarded with electrons in the X-ray tube. The values of these characteristic wave lengths of $K$ and $L$ series lines for almost all the chemical elements are tabulated in readily available handbooks and are not repeated in this chapter.

There were immediate advantages of X ray in comparison with optical spectra: (1) the far greater simplicity such as four (two are close doublets) principal $K$ lines for iron, in comparison with hundreds of lines in the arc of spark spectrum; (2) the identical appearances of the series for all elements except the lightest, and the continuous and systematic variation of wave lengths with atomic number instead of a periodic relationship as for optical spectra. X-ray spectra and the Moseley law became the basis for proof of discovery of new chemical elements and for the derivation first of the Bohr theory and then of the modern vector model theory of the structure of atoms from hydrogen, number 1, up to element 101. The analytical chemist, of course, had at his command a new and powerful method of qualitative and quantitative analysis, supplementing or superseding optical spectrography. However, there were inherent shortcomings which militated against widespread adoption and use in analytical laboratories; these shortcomings resided chiefly in the difficulties of preparing a target material from the unknown in a demountable tube, of providing a reliable source of electrons from a cold or hot cathode, and of laboriously pumping the tubes to requisite high vacua. Physicists were willing to undergo such difficulties in order to measure wave lengths and derive theories of atomic structures, but chemists except in rare instances were unwilling to install and use such equipment when other less troublesome analytical methods were available.

## 2. FLUORESCENT X-RAY SPECTROMETRY AND ITS EARLY DIFFICULTIES

Soon after the first primary spectra of beams excited by electrons in an X-ray tube were observed with the spectrometer, it was found that secondary fluorescent X rays were excited in any material irradiated with beams of primary X rays and that the spectra of these fluorescent X rays were identical in wave lengths and relative intensities with those excited when the specimen is bombarded with electrons. Hence the characteristic emission spectrum is generated either by electron or X-ray photon excitation. The advantage was obvious of being able to irradiate any sample as a massive solid, powder, or liquid with a permanent sealed-off source of primary X rays and then to analyze the fluorescent beam with the crystal spectrometer. Beginning in 1923, Hevesy, Coster, and others investigated in detail the possibilities of fluorescent X-ray spectroscopy as a means of qualitative and quantitative analysis, and Hevesy's book still stands as a classic (16). However, there was one apparently insuperable obstacle in the way of analytical usage—the extremely low intensity of the fluorescent rays, which made photographic exposures prohibitively long and fell below or at the very limit of sensitivity of the ionization chamber, which provides no amplification of ionization current resulting from ionization of gas molecules in the chamber. And so for forty years analysis by fluorescent X-ray spectrometry was known as a potentially powerful but practically useless method.

The relative inefficiency of the fluorescence mechanism is demonstrated in recent measurements under the best conditions with the most modern high-intensity X-ray tubes with beryllium windows as primary source (26). For example, the intensity of fluorescent radiation from a copper radiator as a function of the voltage on a tungsten-target tube supplying primary rays is about 0.01 that of the tungsten rays, measured respectively at 5 cm. from the radiator and 20 cm. from the target. Today this secondary radiation is sufficiently intense for many applications such as microradiography. But for spectroscopic purposes must be added the fact that only a very small fraction of the total energy impinging upon the crystal in the spectrometer is diffracted and appears in the spectrum.

### 3. IMPROVEMENTS IN TECHNIQUES AND INSTRUMENTATION

#### 3.1. X-Ray Tubes

In the face of such a discouraging prospect, three nearly simultaneous pathways of improvement were, and still are being, followed. The convergence of these developments in equipment and techniques has resulted in a success beyond all expectations, with the end not in sight.

The first of these contributing factors was the design and construction of X-ray tubes with beryllium-foil windows, such as the Machlett AEG-50 (operating in air) and OEG-50 (oil-immersed) tubes, which produce primary X rays of intensity measured in millions of roentgens instead of the tens from earlier tubes. Consequently the intensity of excited fluorescent rays is amplified in proportion.

### 3.2. Compact X-Ray Sources Utilizing β-Ray Excitation

In 1954 a "pocket-sized" X-ray generator long dreamed of became an accomplished fact in experiments by L. Reiffel of the Armour Research Foundation. Radioactive isotopes which are β emitters, such as strontium-90–yttrium-90 (half-life 25 years with a monoenergetic β of 2.2 mev.), are placed in a small cavity with lead-foil walls which serve as target for the generation of lead K rays primarily. These in turn may serve as primary rays to excite secondary fluorescent rays in any adjacent specimen. Or, of course, the unknown may serve as the target directly for the β rays without the intermediate steps of generating characteristic lead rays. Preliminary results have been very promising.

### 3.3. Detectors

The second factor was the perfection of the now familiar devices for detecting and measuring intensity of ionizing radiations, namely Geiger, proportional, and scintillation counters, all made possible by the great upsurge in electronics. It is not intended in this chapter to review the design and operation of these detectors since texts, papers, and manufacturers' directions adequately describe them. Special attention, however, is directed to the paper "Basic Theory and Fundamentals of Fluorescent X-Ray Spectrographic Analysis" by Friedman, Birks, and Brooks of the U.S. Naval Research Laboratory (13). Suffice it to say that ionization chambers, proportional and Geiger-counter tubes, consisting of a wire anode and sheet-metal cathode enclosed in a glass envelope containing gas, differ essentially in the voltage across the electrodes. In the ionization chamber, which along with photographic blackening had to serve as detector and dosimeter of X rays for thirty-five years, this voltage is low and the amplification factor is 1, that is, a 1:1 ratio of gas ions to X-ray photons. When used on the Bragg spectrometer, the ionization chamber was insufficiently sensitive for fluorescent spectral analysis. Over a range of a few hundred volts, the proportional counter operates by means of ionization avalanches, which may mean an amplification ratio of $10^6$. At a sufficiently high voltage (usually 1100 to 1200 volts) the 1:1 correspondence between avalanches and primary ionization gives way to a new process, the excitation of short-wave-length ultraviolet light which travels throughout the entire volume of gas and permits gas gains of $10^{10}$ in the Geiger counter. It combines high-quantum efficiency, simple construction, large signal amplitude, excellent stability, and very low background. It is limited to maximum counting rates of the order of several thousand per second. The proportional counter is capable of responding to very high counting rates, but this is accomplished at a great sacrifice in internal gains, and so high external pulse amplification is necessary. In combination with a pulse amplitude analyzer it provides resolution sufficient to separate the $K\alpha$ lines of neighboring elements. The scintillation counter (employing alkali halide crystals containing thallium ions, or organic crystals such as anthracene, or even solutions such as terphenyl in xylol, together with multiplier phototubes to evaluate intensity of the light scintillations) is comparable to the Geiger counter in signal output and to the proportional counter in ability to count at a high rate. The signal-to-noise ratio is poor compared with that of the Geiger counter for soft X rays, but much superior to both types of gas-filled tubes for hard X rays. The scintillation counter provides spectral resolutions by means of pulse amplitude discrimination which is inferior to that of the proportional counter. However, rapid progress is being made continuously in research on this newest type of counter, which actually is resurrected from the old spinthariscope of 1896 (19, second reference).

### 3.4. The Design of Fluorescent X-Ray Spectrometers for Quantitative Analysis

For quantitative analysis, the accuracy of a determination depends on the square root of the total number of counts measured (19, 20); for a standard deviation of 1% it is necessary to take 10,000 counts. It is obviously desirable to obtain these counts in the shortest time possible and therefore the optimum analyzing system is one designed to give the greatest X-ray intensity without sacrificing necessary resolution. The *intensity* is controlled by the exciting radiation, the geometric arrangement, the size and diffracting power of the analyzing crystal, and the efficiency of the counter components. The *resolution* is controlled by the perfection of the analyzing crystal and by the divergence allowed by slits or collimators defining the X-ray beam. This intensive study of the optics of the spectrometer is the third of the details of instrumentation which have contributed to the success of this method.

As an example may be cited the study by Birks, Brooks, and Friedman (7) of reflection from a flat crystal, transmission through a curved crystal, reflection from a curved crystal, and double-crystal reflection. Figure 1 illustrates diagrammatically the first of these methods. Primary radiation from the X-ray tube strikes the specimen, which may be in the form of a solid, a powder, or a liquid. The fluorescent radiation emerging in all directions is collimated into a parallel beam of polychromatic radiation which strikes the analyzing crystal and is spread out into a spectrum in accordance with the Bragg law.

A great deal of attention has been devoted not only to the focusing effects of bent crystals but the design of the collimating devices (7a). These may be simple slits used from the time of the original Bragg spectrometer; Soller slits, a series of narrowly spaced parallel metal sheets which provides collimation for a much larger amount of the fluorescent radiation; or collimations made from a bundle of nickel tubings. Studies have also been made with optical flats or with lead-glass capillary tubes in

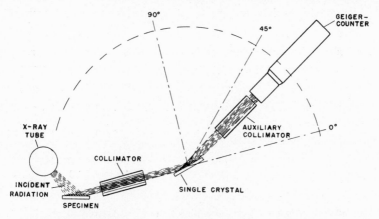

FIG. 1. Basic geometry of single crystal spectrometer.

which totally reflected beams at grazing angles are transmitted with high intensity. These are satisfactory for X-ray diffraction analysis of crystals, but not for spectrometric analysis since the constitution of the beam may be changed by selective removal of some components.

The second method, transmission through a curved crystal (such as mica in the General Electric spectrometer), requires no collimator ahead of the crystal, which selects radiation of wave length $\lambda$ and focuses it at a slit in front of the detector. The crystal is bent to a radius equal to the diameter of the focusing circle upon which the detector slit is located. As the crystal is rotated through the angle $\theta$ the detector is rotated through $2\theta$. In order to keep the distance from crystal to detector, $L$, constant, the bending radius of the crystal $R$ is changed automatically with $\theta$ to satisfy the equation $L = R \sin \theta$.

In the third method the crystal has a fixed curvature $R$ and reflects rather than transmits the beam. A slit located on the focusing circle defines a point source of X rays; its distance $l$, rather than the crystal radius, must change with rotation of the crystal to satisfy $l = R \sin \theta$. In this case no slit is required in front of the detector since only one wave length will be diffracted at a given setting of the crystal. The crystal is bent to radius $R$ and then ground to $R/2$ so that the surface lies exactly on the focusing circle. In order to keep $l$ within 5 to 15 cm. as $\theta$ is changed to cover the whole range of wave lengths it is best to have several crystals of diffracting curvature $R$.

The fourth, or double-spectrometer, method involves no collimators or curved crystals. Fluorescent rays from the specimen strike the first crystal and a range of wave lengths will be diffracted for any setting of it,

TABLE I

| Method | Crystal | Order | Slit size or collimator | Intensity counts per second | Line breadth $2\theta$ | Relative resolution |
|---|---|---|---|---|---|---|
| 1. Flat crystal, reflection | NaCl | 1 | 1.8°, 4-in. col. | 7450 | 2° | 24 |
| | | 1 | 0.45°, 16-in. col. | 1640 | 0.6° | 7.2 |
| 2. Curved crystal, transmission | Mica | 1 | 0.3° divergence | 2100 | 0.6° | 3.3 |
| 3. Curved crystal, reflection | NaCl | 1 | 0.25° | 60,000 | 0.5° | 6.0 |
| | | 2 | 0.25° | 10,000 | 1.0° | 5.3 |
| | | 2 | 0.6° | 600 | 0.15° | 0.8 |
| 4. Double crystal, reflection | NaCl | 1 | no collimation | 1480 | 0.5° | 6.0 |

while only one wave length will satisfy the Bragg equation for a particular setting of the second crystal, which with the detector analyzes the beam of rather limited range coming from the first crystal. The comparison of results from the four types of analyzers studied at the Naval Research Laboratory are summarized in Table I for the copper $K\alpha$ fluorescent ray excited by a tungsten-target tube operated at 50 kv., 20 ma.

This table shows that method 3, reflection from a bent rock-salt crystal, gives by far the greatest intensity, but lower resolution than curved mica (method 2). The latter is recommended for qualitative analysis and the former for quantitative. However, a tenfold increase in intensity is gained with Soller slits from flat crystals (method 1) and is not to be disregarded.

### 3.5. The Choice of Crystal Analyzers

Many crystals have been tried as analyzers, especially for the flat-crystal technique. Sodium chloride is most frequently used though lithium fluoride and aluminum give somewhat greater intensities; curved aluminum crystals have been successfully used instead of mica. The primary concern is with the range of wave lengths to be measured. No particular complications are involved in elements titanium (atomic number 22) to uranium (atomic number 92) as the characteristic rays may have air paths without serious absorption. In the range magnesium (atomic number 12), which has a $K\alpha$ wave length of 9.889 Å. to titanium (22) with a $K\alpha_1$ wave length of 2.74841 Å., the vacuum- or helium-tunnel spectrometer must be employed together with special precautions in collimation, focusing, thinner windows for Geiger tubes, sample preparations, and choice of analyzing crystal. For magnesium (12), aluminum (13), and silicon (14) gypsum has given greatest intensity, and for phosphorus (15) to titanium (22), potassium iodide and potassium chloride crystals give appreciably better intensity. Birks (2) has presented the requirements of an apparatus for vacuum X-ray fluorescence analysis of light elements.

### 3.6. A New Miniature Spectrograph

Birks has also designed a miniature fluorescent X-ray spectrograph for recording spectra from a standard and unknown specimen side by side on photographic film in exposures of about 30 min. The whole unit is about the size of an ordinary powder-diffraction camera and may be mounted on any standard X-ray diffraction equipment (3). The crystal arrangement is unique in that it permits whole spectra to be recorded without any moving parts. A thin crystal slab in fixed position diffracts a narrow bundle of radiation of each wave length from planes parallel to the narrow edge of the crystal. The diffracting region limits resolution and eliminates the need for any collimating device, although a limiting edge acting as a half slit may be moved in to limit the region of diffraction by a thick crystal. Fluorescent radiation of wave length $\lambda_1$, emerging from only one region of the specimen could be diffracted by the crystal while $\lambda_2$ must emerge from a different region to provide the correct angle of incidence, $\theta_2$, on the same set of planes. With the fixed crystal the angular measure on the film is in terms of $\theta$ instead of the usual diffraction angle $2\theta$; hence a 90° arc covers the complete spectrum. With this very simple miniature spectrograph it is possible to detect 2% manganese in an iron matrix and less than 0.5% manganese in aluminum. Resolution is good enough to separate manganese $K\alpha$ rays at 2.10 Å. from chromium $K\beta$ at 2.08 Å.

### 3.7. Differential Analyses at Controlled Voltages

Even with the relative simplicity of X-ray spectra some complications still remain in overlapping lines, effects of characteristic absorption edges where several elements may be present in the sample such that one fluorescent ray will excite another and thus lead to difficulties in quantitative analysis. In order to excite fluorescent radiation, for example the $K$ series, it is necessary that the primary beam be generated at or above a critical voltage $V$ defined by $V = hc/e\lambda_{Kabs}$ where $\lambda_{Kabs}$ is the wave length of the $K$ absorption edge of the fluorescent element and $h$, $c$, and $e$ are the usual constants, or $V = 12400/\lambda_{Kabs}$. It is obvious that by careful control of $V$ for the primary beam the $K$ or $L$ series lines of elements in a mixture can be generated separately or in groups at will and thus produce improved stepwise resolution and simplification of interpretation. Thus far no comprehensive tests of this differential technique have been published, but it is certain that rapid progress will be made especially for complex mixtures and with the aid of multichannel spectrometers (see section 5).

### 4. Quantitative Analyses from Line Intensities and Intensity Ratios with Internal Standards

For quantitative analysis of mixtures by fluorescent X-ray spectrometry it is obvious that the relationship between intensity, measured photographically or with a Geiger counter, and amount of element sought must be established. As is familiar practice in optical spectrography the usual procedure is to set up calibration curves for intensity versus amount of element present from known standards. In most cases the ratio of the intensity of a characteristic line (such as $K\alpha$) for the element being analyzed to that of a line in the same range of wave lengths for a known element serving as an internal standard is plotted as a function of composition from standard homogeneous samples of known composition. For example, Clark and Terford (12) prepared a calibration curve for analysis of iron in dusts from known mixtures of iron and nickel and plotted the ratios $I(FeK\alpha)/I(NiK\alpha)$ against percentage of iron.

A considerable number of theoretical and experimental investigations has been made for the Geiger counter, one of the most thorough being that of Sherman (27). Because of the polychromatic nature of the X-ray beam the rigorous correlation is complicated since the analytical curves are hyperbolas. But linear approximations are generally satisfactory for practical use and Sherman shows that the intensity of the fluorescent beam of an element in a binary mixture, measured by the time $T$ for a fixed count, is linearly proportional to the intensity of the fluorescent beam from the free element and the ratio of concentrations of the elements; or $T$ (mixture) = const. $\times T$ (free element) + const. $(C_1/C_2)$, where $C_2$ is the concentration of the element sought. For multicomponent systems it is generally simpler to determine a calibration curve empirically. Because the intensity from a given element is affected mainly by the amount of element present and to only a minor extent by the matrix, oftentimes the standards need not be especially close to the unknown in composition or even contain all the same elements. However, special precautions have to be taken, for example, in the analysis for chromium of high-speed steels containing tungsten or molybdenum, for the standard must contain within $\pm 1\%$ of the same amount of these heavier elements. This means that absorption is of great importance in causing deviations, defined as the difference between the atomic percentage present of an element in a sample $U$ and the atomic percentage calculated from the equation

$$(\%)_U = \text{(corrected counts per second)}_U / \text{(corrected counts per second)}_S \cdot (\%)_S$$

where the standard $S$ is the pure element. The incident beam may be absorbed (the penetration of X rays in a sample may be 200 times greater than that of electrons in primary excitation) or the characteristic line being used may be absorbed or it may be strengthened owing to absorption of a characteristic line generated in the matrix. The deviations then can be dealt with by (1) selecting standards virtually identical in composition with unknowns, as noted above, or (2) using calculations employing only a few coefficients measured in elements or unknown mixtures such as binary mixtures of iron with copper, which may serve for iron in zinc or iron in nickel or (3) using calculations from known properties. The first of course is safest but most laborious. Among other alternatives Noakes (22) devised a method for stainless steel, involving the use of absorption-enhancement coefficients determined experimentally by means of the equation

$$I(\lambda_A) = I_1 e^{\sum_{i=1}^{n} k_i x_i t}$$

where $I(\lambda_A)$ is the measured intensity of a line, $I_1$ the intensity of a virtual source at depth $t$ below the surface, $k_i = $ the linear absorption-enhancement (negative absorption) coefficient for element $i$, $x_i$ is the weight fraction of element $i$.

## 5. Multichannel Recording

One of the greatest aids to improved speed and accuracy in optical spectroscopy was the development by Applied Research Laboratories, Glendale, Cal. of the Quantometer, or multichannel recording, which involves the ratio system of unknown to known standards. It was quite logical to extend the same techniques to fluorescent X-ray analysis by means of Geiger tubes. Actually two systems are involved, the dispersive multichannel and the nondispersive utilizing filters (15). The latter, diagrammatically represented in Fig. 2, may be illustrated by the analysis of an aluminum alloy containing zinc, copper, and magnesium. The non-dispersive analyzer is set up for analysis of zinc and copper. A filter of 0.0045-in. copper sheet was used in the zinc channel (to a Geiger counter) to absorb radiation shorter than 1.4 Å. but transmitting copper and zinc $K$ radiation. A filter of 0.0030-in. nickel sheet is used in the copper channel to absorb the zinc $K$ radiation. A third channel has an external standard and a 0.0030-in. copper filter. Working curves were made from alloy with varying copper and fixed zinc and with varying zinc and fixed copper. Two channel ratios are recorded and each corrected by an amount depending on the reading on the other. Nondispersive recording has the

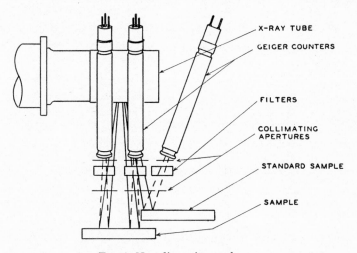

FIG. 2. Non-dispersive analyzer.

advantage of much higher intensities than dispersive, in which flat aluminum crystals are so arranged as to pick off two to eight characteristic rays of elements in the sample. The electronic circuit of course is designed so that the ratios of integrated intensity of each channel to the standard channel are recorded.

## 6. APPLICATIONS

### 6.1. Major Constituents

6.1.1. Alloys. In the analysis for elements present in amount from several per cent up to 100 per cent, fluorescence analysis has the greatest advantage over optical spectrographic analysis. Values correct to a fraction of 1% for counting times less than 1 min. are commonly obtained in spite of some of the complications of calibration. A number of papers have been devoted to analysis of alloys. Invariably the fluorescent method is more rapid, more accurate, and more economical in terms of man-hours than spectrochemical or wet-chemical methods. Among these are routine analyses of high-temperature steel for chromium, cobalt, iron, molybdenum, and nickel (9, 18) as shown in Fig. 3. Several practical metallurgical applications in the research laboratories of one of the large steel companies are reported by Koh and Caugherty (17).

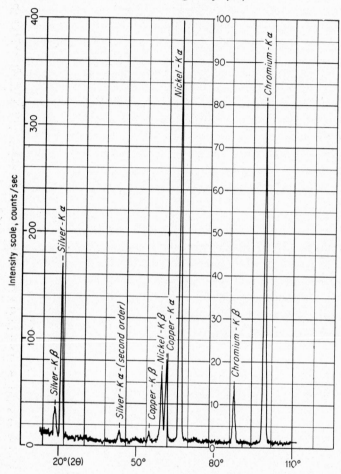

FIG. 3. Chart recording of characteristic x-ray lines from a typical high temperature alloy.

*6.1.2. Analysis of Surface Films.* In view of the fact that the minimum effective thickness of a metallic element to produce maximum fluorescent yield is very low, the analysis is an excellent means of observing chemical change on or near the surface, thus supplementing the electron diffraction method (26). This has been applied to the study of oxide films formed on alloys at elevated temperatures. Thus in iron-chromium alloys there is an impoverished chromium content in layers next to the oxide-film boundary, then a chromium-rich layer next to the unoxidized metal. For substitutional solid solutions diffraction patterns alone may be insufficient for identification since crystal spacings may not be changed; the fluorescence analysis, of course, will detect all elements present. For example, a bromine extract from type-347 stainless steel gave a diffraction pattern only for columbium carbide; the fluorescence spectrum showed chromium, iron, nickel, tungsten, and bromine besides columbium (17).

*6.1.3. Minerals.* The fluorescent X-ray spectrograph is being widely used by the Bureau of Mines for analyzing a variety of minerals and ores ranging from high-purity minerals to low-grade ores, including mineral-dressing products obtained in the beneficiation of such ores. Examples are selenium in pyrite (bromine forms a good standard for selenium and vice versa) and sulfur and thorium in monazite; perhaps most exhaustively studied are the analyses of hafnium-zirconium and niobium-tantalum systems in ores (4, 10, 11, 21), for which chemical analyses are extremely difficult, requiring from 5 to 15 days. Examples from the field of ceramics are given by Patrick (23); and barite by Gulbranson (13a).

*6.1.4. Iron in Dusts.* While the analysis by means of X-ray diffraction of mining and foundry dusts for crystalline $\alpha$-quartz, which is responsible for the serious pathological lung condition silicosis, has been in successful use for several years, nothing has been done to devise a method of analysis of such dusts for iron, which may be responsible for the lung condition known as siderosis, supposedly benign but actually capable of developing into nodules and simulating the appearance of silicosis in diagnostic lung radiographs. Since the iron in dusts is not indicated in diffraction patterns owing to amorphous conditions, it has been necessary to resort to very laborious and inaccurate chemical analyses. Clark and Terford (12) found the fluorescent spectral analyses remarkably successful in the analyses of dusts from all parts of a large steel foundry. With the same samples the same basic Geiger unit was used as a diffractometer to determine quartz quantitatively by diffraction and as a spectrometer to determine iron. Powdered nickel served satisfactorily as an internal standard for both. A strictly linear working calibration curve of $I_{FeK\alpha}/I_{NiK\alpha}$ against percentage of iron holds up to the maximum amount of iron found in any dust, about 30%. For a large number of dusts collected in various areas the amounts of silica and of iron vary inversely.

### 6.2. Minor Constituents

As the amount of a constituent undergoing analysis decreases it is evident that for maintaining accuracy the counting times must be increased. Under these conditions linear calibration curves can be obtained and a wide range of useful analyses made, with potential applications to many medical and biological problems. Some reported analyses are:

Iron in the hemoglobin of blood (average 12 mg./100 ml.), compared with the usual color match of a diluted blood sample with color standards. The accuracy is ±5%, which is improved by the use of samples larger than 0.3 ml. (5). Urinalysis is another application.

Lead and bromine in gasoline (8) with liquid samples. The $L\alpha$ line of lead at 1.17 Å. and the $K\alpha$ line of bromine (present in ethyl fluid as ethylene dibromide) are used. Geiger counts of 1 min. on the peak of the lead line gave a probable error of ±0.06 ml./gal. in a content of 4 ml. of tetraethyllead/gal. of gasoline, and for bromine ±0.16 ml./gal. in 1.8 ml. of ethylene dibromide/gal. of gasoline. This analysis is particularly interesting since it has been compared most favorably with chemical methods, polarography, and X-ray absorption photometry. Fluorescence analysis has the great advantage that variation in the gasoline base stock or presence of additives such as chlorine have negligible effects. The method has been further critically studied as to the matrix effect and improved so that an average error of ±0.026 ml./gal. is achieved in times as short as 5 min. per sample (18). Vanadium and nickel in residual fuels and charging stocks may be similarly analyzed (12a).

Sulfur in oil is a similar analysis, although here the vacuum spectrometer is used for element 16. To avoid use of a liquid the oil is mixed with 10% of lithium stearate to form a grease (2).

Uranium and thorium in ores and in aqueous solutions. Calibration curves have been prepared for these important analyses. X-ray absorption methods have been widely used on the solutions themselves but the results are subject to interferences. In the presence of lead the accuracy is within 5% for a counting time of 30 sec. (1, 6, 10a, 16a, 25a).

Nickel flashings on porcelain enamels (23). Nickel deposits ranging from 0.015 to 0.070 g./sq. ft. have been easily determined.

### 6.3. Microanalyses

It has been a matter of interest to discover how well fluorescent X-ray spectral analyses can compete with optical spectroscopy in detecting trace amounts of elements. Though techniques are improving the analyses have not yet been adapted for detecting traces in parts per million, but in parts per 10,000. By a technique resembling that of the familiar spot test, Pfeiffer and Zemany of the General Electric Laboratory (25) have shown that 15.6 counts/sec. above background of $ZnK\alpha$ radiation per microgram on filter paper could be measured. A counting time of only 2 min. is required to detect $\frac{1}{30}$ μg. of zinc. Absorption effects are eliminated in such thin samples as 1 $\mu$g. of zinc spread over 1 sq. cm. is only 3 atoms, or 10 Å., thick. The same technique is successfully used for determinations of microquantities of vanadium, copper, iron, silver, bromine, gold, and lead. Exceptionally promising is the microanalysis of thin sections of biological tissue (14). By means of comparison between the intensity of a given spectral line from the specimens and the intensity of the same line from a similar specimen with a known quantity of element per unit of surface, the unknown is evaluated. In the development of the technique in 1944 the curved crystal was used to focus the secondary radiation to a true monochromatic image of the specimen. Distinct zinc peaks were produced with only 0.2$\gamma$ of zinc in the area of a thin microtome section of pancreas 200$\mu$ thick and a similar amount of iron in a spleen section 80$\mu$ thick.

### 6.4. Measurement of Plating Thickness

Fluorescent X-ray spectroscopy has found one of its best practical applications in the determination of plating thickness. Where, for example, silver-plated copper is excited the fluorescent copper rays could be partly absorbed by the silver plating. A measurement of this reduction in intensity, or of the Ag$K\alpha$ intensity leads to a direct measurement of thickness. Calibration curves may be calculated directly from known absorption coefficients for single plating layers. Families of curves may be found for double or more plating layers. The application of this technique to tin plating on steel has been adopted by the industry recently and is in perhaps the largest scale use of any of the applications (1a, 24).

REFERENCES

1. Adler, I., and Axelrod, J. M., *Anal. Chem.* **27**, 1002 (1955).
1a. Beeghly, H. F., *J. Electrochem. Soc.* **97**, 152 (1952).
2. Birks, L. S., *Rev. Sci. Inst.* **22**, 891 (1951).
3. Birks, L. S., and Brooks, E. J., *Anal. Chem.* **27**, 1147 (1955).
4. Birks, L. S., and Brooks, E. J., *Anal. Chem.* **22**, 1017 (1950).
5. Birks, L. S., and Brooks, E. J., *Naval Research Lab. Rept.* **3867** (1951).
6. Birks, L. S., and Brooks, E. J., *Anal. Chem.* **23**, 707 (1951).
7. Birks, L. S., Brooks, E. J., and Friedman, H., *Anal. Chem.* **25**, 692 (1953).
7a. Birks, L. S., and Brooks, E. J., *Anal. Chem.* **27**, 437 (1955).
8. Birks, L. S., Brooks, E. J., Friedman, H., and Roe, J., *Anal. Chem.* **22**, 1208 (1950).
9. Brissey, R. M., Liebhafsky, H. A., and Pfeiffer, H. G., Symposium on Fluorescent X-Ray Spectrographic Analysis. *Am. Soc. Testing Materials Spec. Tech. Publ.* **No. 157**, 43 (1953).
10. Campbell, W. J., and Carl, H. F., *Anal. Chem.* **26**, 800 (1954).
10a. Campbell, W. J., and Carl, H. F., *Anal. Chem.* **27**, 1884 (1955).
11. Carl, H. F., and Campbell, W. J., *Am. Soc. Testing Materials Spec. Tech. Publ.* **No. 157**, 63 (1953).
12. Clark, G. L., and Terford, H. C., *Anal. Chem.* **26**, 1416 (1954).
12a. Davis, E. N., and Haeck, B. C., *Anal. Chem.* **27**, 1880 (1955).

13. Friedman, H., Birks, L. S., and Brooks, E. J., *Am. Soc. Testing Materials Spec. Tech. Publ.* **No. 157,** 3 (1953).

13a. Gulbranson, L. B., *Anal. Chem.* **27,** 1181 (1955). (Barite.)

14. Hamos, L. von, and Engstrom, A., *Acta Radiol.* **25,** 325 (1944).

15. Hasler, M. F., and Kemp, J. W., *Am. Soc. Testing Materials Spec. Tech. Publ.* **No. 157,** 34 (1953).

16. Hevesy, G. von, "Chemical Analysis by X-Rays and its Applications." McGraw-Hill, New York, 1932.

16a. King, A. G., and Dunton, P., *Science* **122,** 72 (1955).

17. Koh, P. K., and Caugherty, B., *J. Appl. Phys.* **23,** 427, 698 (1952).

18. Lamb, F. W., Niebylski, L. M., and Kiefer, E. W., *Anal. Chem.* **27,** 129 (1955).

19. Liebhafsky, H. A., *Anal. Chem.* **26,** 26 (1954); **28,** 583 (1956).

20. Liebhafsky, H. A., Pfeiffer, H. G., and Zemany, P. D., *Anal. Chem.* **27,** 1257 (1955).

21. Mortimore, D. M., and Romans, P. A., *J. Opt. Soc. Amer.* **42,** 673 (1952); *Norelco Reptr.* **1,** 107 (1954).

22. Noakes, G. E., *Am. Soc. Testing Materials Spec. Tech. Publ.* **No. 157,** 57 (1953).

23. Patrick R. F., *J. Am. Ceramic Soc.* **35,** 189 (1952).

24. Pelissier, G. E., *Elec. Mfg.* **49,** 124 (1952).

25. Pfeiffer, H. G., and Zemany, P. D., private communication.

25a. Pish, G., and Huffman, A. A., *Anal. Chem.* **27,** 1875 (1955).

26. Rhodin, T. N., *Anal. Chem.* **27,** 1857 (1955).

26a. Rogers, T. H., *J. Appl. Phys.* **23,** 881 (1952).

27. Sherman, J., *Am. Soc. Testing Materials Spec. Tech. Publ.* **No. 157,** 27 (1953).

# Analytical Distillation

By

WALTER J. PODBIELNIAK AND SEATON T. PRESTON

*Podbielniak, Inc., Chicago, Illinois*

## 1. INTRODUCTION

Distillation for the purpose of analysis, or *analytical distillation*, bears roughly the same relation to general distillation in the laboratory as quantitative to qualitative chemical analysis. As in qualitative chemical analysis, it is often possible to obtain a degree of separation and an approximate indication of the quantity of certain components present by the simplest apparatus and procedures. Thus, a simple flask, heated with a gas burner, with suitable side-arm take-off, water condenser, and collecting graduate, suffices for many routine industrial specification tests. This apparatus is not adequate, however, for separation of individual components in complex mixtures, as coke-oven light oil and coal tar products, petroleum and its fractions, or the products of most organic chemical reactions. The accurate determination by distillation of the composition of even such a simple mixture as benzene and toluene requires a fairly efficient fractionating column and suitable control of heat input and ratio of reflux returned to column vs. distillate rate. Petroleum and its fractions challenge the resolving capacity of the most highly developed analytical fractional distillation devices.

The evolution of laboratory distillation from the use of the "indented tube," Le Bel, Glinsky, and other crude columns as described by Young

(46), without adequate reflux and with up to 50 redistillations required to separate isopentane from $n$-pentane, to present-day 100-plate columns and automatic controls has been a gradual process. Development has been spurred on by the great need of the petroleum industry for rapid and effective analysis of its hydrocarbon materials, too similar chemically and too complex for effective separation by most other available methods. The basic form of apparatus for analytical distillation was developed from the theory and practice established by industrial alcohol rectification. Leslie, one of the pioneers in this development, described early forms of apparatus (12), which included insulated columns, random packed with vapor-liquid contacting particles, with provisions for controlling heat input and reflux ratio. Fenske and his associates (6–9, 40) exhaustively investigated performance of column packings and contributed extensively to theory. Podbielniak (20–23) developed apparatus and methods for distillation analysis of mixtures having components which can be made to boil below room temperature, including methane to octane. A. and E. Rose (33–35) contributed to developments in theory and also wrote comprehensive and authoritative monographs and reviews on the entire subject of laboratory distillation.

With the availability of precisely controlled apparatus with columns of separating effectiveness up to 400 plates even the mystery of crude petroleum has to a large extent been unfolded (36, 37). Analytical distillation of natural gas and gasoline, light oil, solvents, and other distillable mixtures has become indispensable to both research and production. Obviously, the apparatus, instrumentation, and technique required will vary greatly according to the difficulty of separation encountered and accuracy required. It is the objective of this chapter to present the basic working theory underlying all apparatus for analysis by distillation; to describe the best available packings, columns and apparatus; and to guide the selection of apparatus and technique for specific applications.

## 2. General Discussion of Analytical Distillation

### 2.1. Division into Low- and High-Temperature Fractionation

The term *high temperature* is applied to the familiar type of laboratory distillation where the sample is liquid at room temperature and the distillates are collected in liquid form, usually although not always at room temperature, either at atmospheric or at reduced pressure. Most of the applications of analytical distillation fall into this category, principally because there are more compounds and more complex mixtures to be separated in the high- than in the low boiling-point range.

For the analysis by low-temperature distillation of normally gaseous or highly volatile liquid samples, such as natural gas and gasoline, special apparatus and methods had to be developed. These include the use of special semimicro vacuum-jacketed columns utilizing liquid nitrogen to condense and reflux components in the boiling-point range of $-190°$ C. to room temperature at atmospheric or reduced pressure. The division into low- and high-temperature distillation is a practical one, because the handling and sampling of materials to be analyzed, the general methods of collecting and measuring distillates, and the methods of column pressure and reflux cooling control are and must be entirely different for the two cases.

### 2.2. Distinctive Features, Advantages and Limitations

Both low- and high-temperature fractionation apparatus share the following characteristics, which can conveniently be stated generally here.

2.2.1. *Components Determined Consecutively.* Components are evaluated and/or physically separated in the order of their ascending boiling points. One component after another is physically separated from its boiling-point neighbor, distilled away from the scene of action, etc., until the entire mixture is distilled. As components of distant boiling points have little interfering effect on the currently proceeding separation at the top (or bottom) end of the column, the number of components present (if adequately separated in boiling point and of adequate amount) has little effect on results, except on time of distillation; in this instance the method differs from most other analytical methods.

2.2.2. *Components Separated Physically.* In application to complex mixtures such as high boiling fractions from petroleum, the characteristic of analytical distillation of actually separating the unchanged components physically is of inestimable value. It makes possible checks on purity of single-component distillates and further differentiation of "cuts" by other more selective methods when distillation alone is unable to effect separation into chemical individuals.

2.2.3. *Miniature of Commercial Plant Practice.* Since the large-scale processing of petroleum and other complex mixtures is accomplished largely by fractional distillation, the characteristics of which resemble those of analytical distillation, the latter serves in effect as a micro pilot plant as well as an analytical method.

Both the industrial and analytical operations are similarly affected by the presence of water or insoluble material and the occurrence of hydrates or azeotropes.

2.2.4. *Basic Simplicity of Principle and Operation.* Although the apparatus, instrumentation, and procedures necessarily grow complex as the analytical requirements increase, analytical distillation apparatus is basically simple and requires little calibration or calculation; the sample is separated into distillates which can be separately collected, measured, tested, and observed.

*2.2.5. Limitations.* The main limitations of analytical distillation are that it is cumbersome and lengthy for single-component determination; inapplicable or inaccurate for systems having small boiling-point (vapor-pressure ratio) differences between the components; limited when components of interest occur in too small quantity, relative to column holdup, for reasonable sample size; inapplicable to systems containing insoluble components, such as water, hydrates, and so forth, which must be removed prior to distillation; interfered with by components forming no liquid phase at ordinary pressures, such as acetylene, carbon dioxide, etc. (interference stopped by increase in pressure but removal of such components usually more desirable); limited to components boiling above the boiling point of the refrigerant used, usually liquid nitrogen, and which can be distilled without thermal decomposition.

## 2.3. Basic Apparatus and Technique

Analytical distillation requires in one form or another certain basic apparatus components and involves to a greater or lesser degree certain important variables of operation. They are summarized below to present a unified and objective concept of the general methods.

### a. Basic Apparatus Components

1. Distilling flask.
2. Source of heat to distilling flask.
3. Fractionating column proper.
4. Column packing.
5. Column insulation.
6. Condenser to supply reflux.
7. Reflux head to control reflux ratio. (6 and 7 are frequently combined.)
8. Means for indicating or recording boiling point (or other distinctive property) of distillate.
9. Column pressure control.
10. Distillate receivers.
11. Means for measuring distillate quantity.

### b. Basic Operational Variables

1. Control of heat input (and thereby of column loading).
2. Control of reflux ratio (and thereby distillate rate or vice versa).
3. Observation (visual or automatic) of accumulating distillate quantity as a function of its boiling point.

Discontinuous functions concerned in analytical distillation that should also be mentioned are entering the sample, bringing column to equilibrium, physically separating fractions, and withdrawing the residue.

Some of the apparatus components mentioned need not be complex, and means of controlling the operational variables can at times be very simple. Effective analytical distillation requires in any case, however, a reasonably well-insulated fractionating column of at least 10 to 20 plates; either a sensitive thermometer or thermocouple for continuous determination of changing distillate identity; accurate graduates or other means to collect and measure distillate; and reasonably effective means for controlling heat input to operate column at optimum capacity and for adjusting reflux ratio to make possible the desired separations. With less than these, quantitative analytical separations are rarely possible.

### 2.4. General Field of Application

Taken together, low- and high-temperature analytical distillations embrace the extreme range of all "distillable" mixtures from methane (B.P. $-161°$ C.) to heavy petroleum fractions (B.P. $300°$ C. at 5 mm. Hg abs.), subject to the limitations of the method discussed above. Because of its great versatility, the method should be considered in problems of separation or analysis of liquids or liquefiable gases, at least for primary separation. In general, the full potentialities of analytical distillation have not been exploited, perhaps from lack of knowledge of the capabilities of available effective apparatus and realization of its high "resolving power" when properly used.

### 3. Essential Theoretical Basis

The theory of analytical distillation is highly complicated, primarily because none of the usual simplifying assumptions of text-book distillation theory, namely, adiabatic column, zero holdup, and constant conditions and concentrations, may be used in a consideration of batch analytical distillations. A limited discussion of applicable theory with suitable reservations is, however, presented here, applicable to both low- and high-temperature distillation.

The separation by distillation of two or more components of a liquid or liquefied gas mixture is made possible by the fact that the composition of the vapor phase above the liquid, at equilibrium, is usually richer in the more volatile component. The ease with which two or more components may be separated varies directly with this difference in composition. Fractional distillation, i.e., distillation with return of some condensed vapor or reflux to the column, multiplies greatly the separation attainable in a single vaporization step.

### 3.1. Vapor-Liquid Equilibrium in Mixtures

*3.1.1. Vapor-Liquid–Equilibrium Diagrams.* It follows from the fore-going that a knowledge of vapor-liquid equilibria is essential to any study of distillation. The results of computed or experimental determinations of vapor-liquid–equilibrium compositions are generally presented graphically in the form of (*a*) temperature-composition diagrams, and (*b*) *x-y* diagrams.

The temperature-composition diagram of a typical miscible binary system is shown in Fig. 1. The dew-point and bubble-point curves

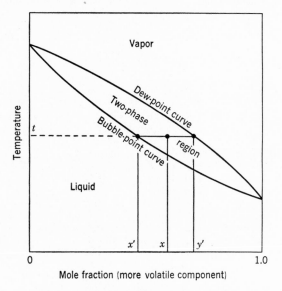

FIG. 1. Temperature-composition diagram.

separate the areas corresponding to liquid, vapor, and the two phases in equilibrium. To illustrate the use of this diagram, a mixture of composition *x* when brought to temperature *t* will separate into a vapor phase of composition *y′* and a liquid of composition *x′*. The difference between *x′* and *y′* indicates the enrichment of the vapor accomplished by a single partial vaporization.

The *x-y* diagram shown in Fig. 2 depicts the relationship between vapor and liquid composition, without reference to temperature. The difficulty of separation of a mixture is directly related to the proximity of this curve to the 45° diagonal; thus when the *x-y* curve touches or intersects this diagonal there is no difference in composition of the two phases and no separation can be accomplished.

*3.1.2. Concept of Relative Volatility.* The tendency of a component to escape from the liquid to the vapor phase is indicated by its volatility, which is defined as the ratio of the concentration of the particular component in the vapor phase to its concentration in the liquid phase, or

$$\text{Volatility} = y_a/x_a$$

The ease with which two components may be separated is directly

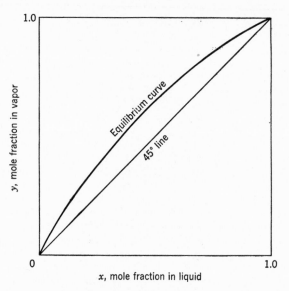

FIG. 2. $x - y$ diagram. Relation between liquid $(x)$ and vapor mole fraction of the more volatile component.

related to the relative volatility, generally designated by $\alpha$, of the two components, or

$$\text{Relative volatility of } a \text{ to } b = \alpha_{ab} = \frac{y_a/x_a}{y_b/x_b} = \frac{y_a x_b}{y_b x_a}$$

For liquids which form ideal solutions the foregoing relationship simplifies to the ratio of vapor pressures at the same temperature, or

$$\alpha_{ab} = \frac{p_a}{p_b}$$

The shape of vapor-liquid equilibrium curves corresponding to various constant values of $\alpha$ are shown in Fig. 3.

The volatility of component $a$ in a mixture may be described as the partial vapor pressure, divided by the concentration in the liquid, or

$$v_a = \bar{p}_a/x_a$$

In an ideal mixture $v_a$ will be equal to the vapor pressure, $p_a$, of the pure material and for nonideal mixtures the volatility will be abnormally high or low according to the deviation of the actual partial pressure from that calculated from Raoult's law. The volatility of a component is then related to the vapor pressure by means of the activity coefficient, $\gamma$, or

$$v_a = p_a\gamma_a$$

*3.1.3. Anomalous Vapor-Liquid Equilibria.* Occasionally mixtures are encountered in analytical distillation which fail to follow the usual pattern of vapor-liquid behavior.

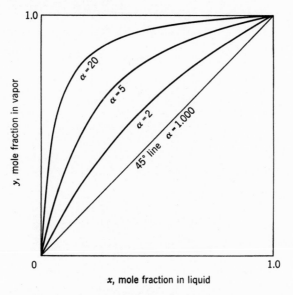

FIG. 3. Equilibrium curves corresponding to values of constant relative volatility for the more volatile component.

Mixtures containing carbon dioxide and acetylene encountered in low-temperature analytical distillation are frequently treated for removal of these compounds because the transition between vapor and solid phase occurs without the formation of a liquid phase at ordinary pressures.

Systems which exhibit a maximum or minimum constant boiling-point mixture (azeotrope) require special techniques for separation. Some of these special techniques are

1. Dehydration where water is one component of the azeotrope.

2. Addition of a third component to form a different azeotrope which permits the removal of the desired component either as distillate or bottom product. Examples of this form of separation include the addition of

benzene or ether to ethyl alcohol–water mixtures to obtain absolute ethyl alcohol as a bottom product.

3. Separate distillations at two or more pressures. A change in distillation pressure will generally shift the composition of the azeotrope and may even make the system nonazeotropic. Mixtures of methanol and acetone form an azeotrope at all pressures between 200 and 15,000 mm. Hg abs. Below 200 mm. the mixture is nonazeotropic with methanol as the more volatile component and above 15,000 mm. the mixture is nonazeotropic with acetone as the more volatile component (2).

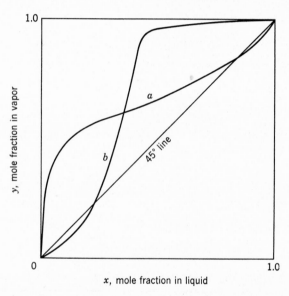

Fig. 4. $x - y$ diagrams for the more volatile components of typical azeotropes. a. Minimum boiling point azeotrope $C_2H_5OH$-$H_2O$; b. Maximum boiling point azeotrope $HCl$-$H_2O$.

The $x$-$y$ curve ($a$) of Fig. 4 for the ethyl alcohol-water system is typical of those exhibiting a minimum boiling point. A typical curve for a maximum boiling point mixture, such as the HCl-water system is shown as curve $b$.

*3.1.4. Separation by Simple Vaporization and Condensation.* The simplest way to utilize the enrichment effect occurring when a liquid mixture is partially vaporized is to heat the original liquid phase under pressure and then discharge it into a "flash" chamber, to form two phases in substantial equilibrium, as shown in the temperature-composition diagram, Fig. 1. This procedure is used industrially, but not in the laboratory.

The next simplest way is to vaporize a liquid sample differentially, without reflux, and under substantial equilibrium conditions between the liquid and its vapor. This has been done exactly experimentally (19) and is approximated by the usual Engler distillation or other simple distillations from a side-arm–equipped distilling flask without provisions for reflux. In this method the separation of components is poor, even when boiling points are 20° C. or more apart. In the special case of distilling low-boiling hydrocarbons, methane to pentanes, from bulb to bulb at near liquid air temperatures and at very low pressures, fairly good separations and analyses were obtained up to the butane fraction (41). The Raleigh equation

$$\ln S = \int \frac{dx_s}{x_d - x_s}$$

where $S$ = total moles in still
    $x_s$ = mole fraction of more volatile component in still
    $x_d$ = mole fraction of more volatile component in distillate

enables the computation of the entire course of composition change for an ideal (i.e., observing ideal-solution laws) binary mixture. Incidentally, this process and equation work equally well, in reverse, i.e., starting with the sample in all-vapor phase and chilling it gradually to remove differential amounts of the condensate thus formed. As far as is known, this process has not found laboratory use.

Partial vaporization (or condensation) has, however, one unique advantage over the otherwise superior countercurrent reflux process to be described: its action is independent of the amount of liquid or of time (except as time is required to chill the vapor or warm the liquid). Thus a partial differential condenser, on top of a rectifying column, can serve to sharpen separation quite appreciably over the best that even a very effective column can accomplish, since the resolution of the column is limited by its liquid holdup. This effect is very important in low-temperature analytical distillation.

For close-boiling compounds, the separation attainable from a single vaporization step is highly inadequate. Accordingly, a more effective procedure is generally used, as described in section 3.2, in that some of the vapor first produced is condensed and sent back countercurrently as a solvent or reflux. The use of reflux modifies the separation process, and when effected in a long contacting passageway, as a packed column, greatly improves the separation.

### 3.2. The Fractional Distillation Process

3.2.1. *McCabe-Thiele Graphical Method.* The relationship of vapor-liquid equilibrium compositions, theoretical plates, and reflux ratio to the separation which can be effected by fractional distillation may be shown by the analytical and graphical method derived by McCabe and Thiele (13). A typical batch-fractionating column is shown diagrammatically in Fig. 5. By making a material balance around the top half

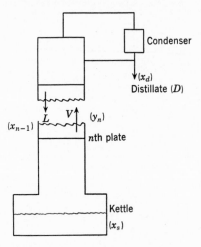

FIG. 5. Diagrammatic flow in distillation column. Composition of various streams shown in parentheses.

of this column, assuming (a) that the latent heat of vaporization is independent of composition and temperature, (b) constant molal overflow, and (c) steady-state conditions, one can derive the following relationship:

$$y_n = \left(\frac{L}{V}\right) x_{n-1} + \left(\frac{D}{V}\right) x_d$$

where $y_n$ = mole fraction of more volatile component (MVC), in vapor leaving the $n$th plate

$x_{n-1}$ = mole fraction of MVC in liquid leaving $n$-1st plate

$x_d$ = mole fraction of MVC in distillate

$L$ = moles of liquid flowing down column

$V$ = moles of vapor rising in column

$D$ = moles of distillate leaving column

This relationship when plotted on an $x$-$y$ diagram is the operating line for a distillation column. The slope of the operating line $m$ is related to the reflux ratio as shown below:

$$m = \frac{R}{R+1}$$

where $R$ = reflux ratio = ratio of liquid returned to column, $L$, to distillate, $D$, removed from column.

The operating line represents the locus of points corresponding to the composition of passing liquid and vapor streams. The graphical presentation of the McCabe-Thiele method is given in Fig. 6. Starting at the point on the 45° diagonal corresponding to $x_d$, the composition of the vapor leaving the first (top) plate is given by $y_1$. The composition of the liquid leaving the first plate, assumed to be in equilibrium with the vapor leaving the same plate, is given by $x_1$, the abscissa of the intersection of $y_1$ with the equilibrium curve. The composition of the vapor passing liquid $x_1$ is given by the ordinate of the intersection of $x_1$ and the operating line.

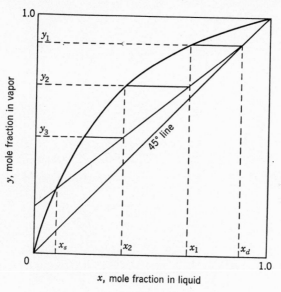

FIG. 6. McCabe-Thiele graphic method.

Each similar step represents one theoretical plate. It should be noted that regardless of the number of theoretical plates available a product purity corresponding to $x_d$ cannot be obtained, with the operating conditions as indicated, when the kettle composition falls below $x_S$.

For any given binary system of fixed relative volatility, the relationship among kettle composition, product composition, reflux ratio, and theoretical plates can be shown by means of a McCabe-Thiele diagram. Consider the system shown in Fig. 6, with a desired distillate composition of $x_d$, to be obtained from a kettle charge of composition $x_S$. This separation can be effected with the minimum reflux ratio as computed from the slope of the operating line which intersects the diagonal at $x_d$ and the equilibrium curve at $x_S$. The use of minimum reflux ratio to accomplish this separation would require an infinite number of theoretical

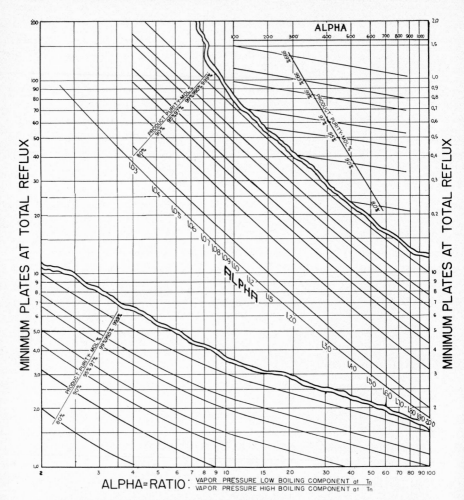

FIG. 7. Relation between minimum plates, product purity, and $\alpha$ for binary mixtures with 50–50 mole % kettle composition.

NOTE: This same chart may be used to compute plates required to effect composition change from indicated product purities to kettle compositions lower than 50–50% as follows: 1. Compute plates required from 50–50 to desired product purity in indicated manner. 2. Compute additional plates required to effect composition change from 50–50 to desired kettle composition expressed in mole % higher boiling component. 3. Add plates derived from steps 1 and 2 above to yield total required plates.

TABLE I

Ease of Separation by Distillation of the Low-Boiling Hydrocarbons

| Binary hydrocarbon mixture | Boiling point at 760 mm., °C | Ratio of vapor pressure α at midway B.P. of two components | Plates required at total reflux for 99.5 mole % overhead from 50% MVC in kettle | Plates required at total reflux for 99.5 mole % overhead from 10% low-boiling component in kettle | Minimum reflux ratio for 100 mole %* overhead from 50% MVC in kettle | Minimum reflux ratio for 100 mole %* overhead from 10% low-boiling component in kettle |
|---|---|---|---|---|---|---|
| Methane-ethylene† | (−161.4)(−103.9) | 61.2 | 1.32 | 1.82 | 0.03 | 0.164 |
| Methane-ethane‡ | (−161.4)(−89.3) | 107 | 1.14 | 1.60 | 0.018 | 0.093 |
| Ethylene-ethane | (−103.9)(−89.3) | 2.3 | 6.5 | 9.2 | 1.60 | 7.95 |
| Ethane-propene | (−89.3)(−47.7) | 8.1 | 2.52 | 3.57 | 0.27 | 1.4 |
| Ethane-propane | (−89.3)(−44.1) | 9.3 | 2.38 | 3.36 | 0.23 | 1.2 |
| Propene-propane | (−47.7)(−44.1) | 1.3 | 20.2 | 28.6 | 6.65 | 33.0 |
| Propane-isobutane | (−44.1)(−13.4) | 3.3 | 4.6 | 6.5 | 0.89 | 4.5 |
| Isobutane-butane | (−11.7)(−0.5) | 1.5 | 13.0 | 18.4 | 3.99 | 20.0 |
| Isobutane-isobutene | (−11.7)(−6.7) | 1.20 | 28.8 | 40.8 | 10.0 | 50.0 |
| Isobutene-butene | (−6.7)(−6.3) | 1.03 | 176.0 | 249.0 | 65.5 | 328.0 |
| 1-butene-N-butane | (−6.3)(−0.5) | 1.23 | 25.5 | 36.0 | 8.98 | 43.5 |
| Butane-isopentane | (−0.5)(27.95) | 2.8 | 5.3 | 7.5 | 1.16 | 5.8 |
| Isopentane-N-pentane | (27.95)(36.06) | 1.33 | 18.6 | 26.3 | 6.25 | 30.1 |
| Pentane-hexane | (36.06)(69.0) | 3.0 | 4.9 | 6.95 | 1.04 | 5.25 |
| Pentane-diisopropyl | (36.06)(58.1) | 2.15 | 7.0 | 9.9 | 1.75 | 8.7 |

* Minimum reflux ratio (at infinite plates) is relatively insensitive to small changes in desired overhead purity especially for low α's and small concentrations of low-boiling components in kettle.

† α at B.P. of methane = 185.

‡ α at B.P. of methane = 642.

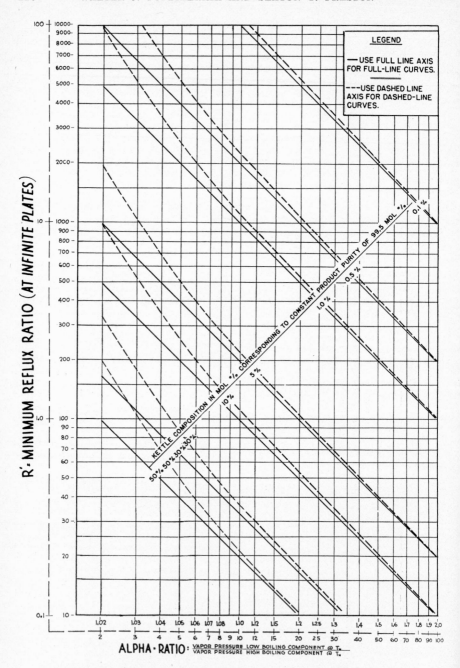

FIG. 8. Relation between minimum reflux, $\alpha$, and composition of kettle for

plates to effect the separation. The minimum number of theoretical plates required to effect the separation corresponds to operation of the column at total reflux, i.e., $R = \infty$, and $m = 1.0$. The operating line in this case coincides with the 45° diagonal and the number of theoretical plates may be determined graphically from a diagram such as Fig. 7.

*3.2.2. Graphical Summary.* The relationships between the several variables as computed by the methods of McCabe and Thiele, Fenske, or Underwood are shown in Figs. 7 and 8. Figure 7 gives the minimum number of theoretical plates required to obtain a fixed distillate composition from a 50–50 mole % kettle composition, as a function of the relative volatility of the particular vapor-liquid system. Figure 8 gives the minimum reflux ratio required to obtain a 99.5% distillate composition from various kettle concentrations, as a function of the relative volatility of the system.

If one knows the number of theoretical plates in a particular distillation column and the relative volatility of the mixture to be separated, Fig. 8 provides a guide as to how to vary the reflux ratio with changing kettle concentration to secure the desired overhead purity.

*3.2.3. Ease of Separation.* The ease with which two components may be separated by distillation is summarized in Table I, which gives the relative volatility of various systems and the theoretical plates required to produce a product purity of 99.5% from a 50–50 kettle composition. The table also presents the plates required to produce a 99.5% pure distillate from a 10% MVC kettle composition and the minimum reflux ratio required to produce 100% MVC as distillate from kettle compositions of 50% and 10% MVC.

### 3.3. Other Factors Influencing Design and Operation of Distillation Equipment

*3.3.1. Effect of Material Holdup in Column.* The presence of column holdup has a significant effect on the separation which can be obtained. It is generally agreed that low column holdup is the preferred condition (33). The two principal effects of column holdup are that (1) high holdup is not compatible with sharp separations and (2) the ratio of holdup to

---

binary mixtures with constant overhead purity of 99.5 mole %.

Minimum reflux is relatively insensitive to small changes in product purity even when these are near 100%. To compute the approximate change in minimum reflux for other product purities than 99.5 mole % multiply minimum reflux, as obtained from chart, by the ratio of desired product purity to 99.5 mole %, times a correction factor varying as follows: (a) 0.88 for 50% in kettle; (b) 0.95 for 30% in kettle; (c) 0.965 for 5% in kettle; and (d) 0.998 for 0.1% in kettle.

charge determines the fraction of the charge which cannot be recovered as distillate without special techniques such as the use of chasers, etc.

The efficiency of packings is frequently compared by means of an efficiency factor $A$, which is defined as

$$A = \frac{\text{throughput}}{\text{holdup/plate}}$$

which emphasizes the importance of column holdup.

*3.3.2. Time to Reach Equilibrium.* Following the charging of a sample to a distillation column, the column must be brought to both thermal and phase equilibrium before distillate is removed. The time required to reach phase equilibrium is related to the net rate of transfer of the more volatile component from the still liquid to the column. The approach to equilibrium is brought about by simultaneous transfer of both heat and mass between the liquid and vapor phases within the column. The time to reach thermal equilibrium is related to the heat capacity of the column, the packing, and, to a lesser extent, the column jacket. The heat capacity of these parts creates a resistance to rapid changes in temperature, thereby influencing the time required for the transition between plateaus.

*3.3.3. Effect of Heat Transfer to or from Column.* The usual discussions of distillation theory are generally based on the assumption that the column is operated adiabatically. The loss of heat from a column causes condensation of ascending vapor with a resulting increase in the reflux ratio. Equal insulation over the length of a column being assumed, the heat lost to the surroundings will be greater at the bottom of the column, owing to the higher temperature prevailing in this section. As a result the liquid traffic in the lower part of the column will be high and will limit the vapor velocity, boil-up rate, and in general the speed of distillation. Experimentally it has been possible to improve the separating efficiency of a column by distributing the condenser load over a considerable portion (or all) of the column, i.e., transferring heat from the entire column to the coolant, with greater heat removal at the top of the column and lesser at the bottom. In this mode of operations the less volatile component in the ascending vapor may be partially eliminated from the vapor by fractional condensation caused by heat transfer through the column wall.

Superheating the top of a column (as in the case of a low-temperature column with a defective vacuum jacket) will raise the boiling point and lower the purity of overhead distillate. However, within certain limits, supercooling the *top* part and superheating the *lower* part of a column, will tend to accentuate both temperature and concentration gradient, hence improve separation.

## 4. Low-Temperature Analytical Distillation

### 4.1. Definition and Scope of Application

Low-temperature analytical distillation is used for the analysis of gases and volatile liquids which may be made to boil below room temperature. Low-temperature analytical distillation differs from high-temperature distillation not only in the boiling-point range it covers, but also because the separated components are collected and measured in the vapor rather than liquid phase, and column pressure is maintained at any desired level by a closed system which controls reflux cooling and distillate removal.

TABLE II

*Substances Frequently Separated by Low-Temperature Distillation*

| | B.P. @ 760 mm., °C. | | B.P. @ 760 mm., °C. |
|---|---|---|---|
| Methane | −161.49 | Hexane | +68.74 |
| Ethylene | −103.71 | Trifluoromethane | −82.2 |
| Ethane | −88.63 | Fluoromethane | −78.2 |
| Propylene | −47.7 | Ammonia | −33.3 |
| Propane | −42.07 | Freon 12—dichloro- | |
| Propadiene (Allene) | −34.5 | difluoromethane | −30 |
| Isobutane | −11.73 | Methyl chloride | −23.7 |
| Isobutylene | −6.90 | Freon 21—dichloro- | |
| 1-Butene | −6.26* | fluoromethane | +8.9 |
| 1,3-Butadiene | −4.41* | Freon 114—dichloro- | |
| Butane | −0.50 | tetrafluoroethane | +3.55 |
| 2-Butene (trans) | +0.88* | Genetron 101—di- | |
| 2-Butene (cis) | +3.72* | fluorochloroethane | −9.2 |
| Neopentane | +9.50 | Genetron 100—1, | |
| Isopentane | +27.85 | 1 difluoroethane | −24.7 |
| Pentane | +36.07 | Vinyl chloride | −13.9 |

* Not usually separated as a pure component by distillation. Separated as part of a fraction subjected to additional analytical methods such as chemical absorption or infrared spectroscopy.

A comprehensive list of gases and volatile liquids which are susceptible to separation and analysis by low-temperature distillation has been compiled by A. and E. Rose (33). The components most frequently encountered in the petroleum, petrochemical, and chemical industries which are successfully analyzed by low-temperature distillation are listed in Table II.

### 4.2. Development of Apparatus and Method

The need for a method of analyzing products and plant streams in the natural gasoline industry led between 1925 and 1930 to the development of low-temperature analytical fractionation (18). Advances in the status of the equipment and method made between 1930 and 1940 included (a) the development of high-efficiency packings as required to separate close boiling components (24), (b) improvements in the column insulation through the use of better vacuum jackets with metal radiation reflectors (21), and (c) the development of automatic devices for controlling and recording a distillation.

Developments between 1940 and 1950 consisted principally of improvements in the automatic control devices and in the design of the fractionating column and kettle.

Since 1950 improvement in the apparatus and method has received considerable impetus by virtue of the cooperative testing program, seminars, and analysts' training school sponsored by the Natural Gasoline Association of America (14, 15). Recent improvements include (a) the use of thermal-conductivity measurements to identify the components in the column distillate and (b) a method of controlling the rate of distillate removal which is based upon the concentration gradient existing in the top of the packing (29).

## 4.3. Essentials of Apparatus Design

Distillation at temperatures approaching the boiling point of nitrogen requires the use of highly efficient column insulation. Heat leakage into the column from the surroundings may be shown to influence adversely the separation which can be effected. Heat transfer from the surroundings to the vapor leaving the kettle superheats the vapor entering the column, causing a reduction in separation accomplished by the lower section of the packing. To minimize these effects the column and kettle shown in Fig. 9 are generally supported within a vacuum jacket which includes a polished-metal radiation shield.

The distillate from a low-temperature distillation column is removed as a vapor, collected in calibrated, evacuated receivers, and measured by observation of the pressure rise within a receiver. The components removed from the top of the column are identified by measurements of the temperature within the reflux section of the column (probably dewpoint temperature) or by measurements of the thermal conductivity of the vapor.

The low-temperature distillation apparatus has been highly automatized. Of particular importance are the means of regulating column pressure by controlling the reflux cooling and removal of distillate. The rate of distillate removal, at constant input of kettle heat, is inversely related to reflux ratio. The distillation-rate valve is automatically controlled to increase reflux ratio as a "break" is approached, i.e., as kettle concentration of the most volatile component approaches zero.

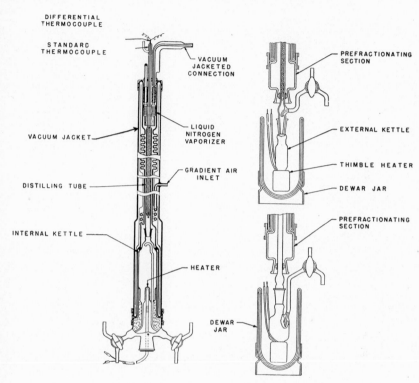

FIG. 9. Column assembly with various kettle designs.

### 4.4. Typical Apparatus and Results

*4.4.1. Semiautomatic Distillation Equipment.* Low-temperature distillation equipment is generally classified according to the degree of automation, as manual, semiautomatic, and automatic. The simplest (30) present form of the apparatus is the Heli-Robot, shown diagrammatically in Fig. 10, with which reflux cooling and column pressure are automatically controlled, although all other operating variables are controlled manually. The Semi-Robot automatically records distillate volume vs. column overhead temperature, all other operations except distillation rate also being controlled automatically. The automatic controls provided on this apparatus minimize the attention required of the operator (28).

*4.4.2. Automatic Distillation Equipment.* Automatic devices have been developed and incorporated in the design of the apparatus to:

1. Standardize operating techniques by minimizing human variables (27).

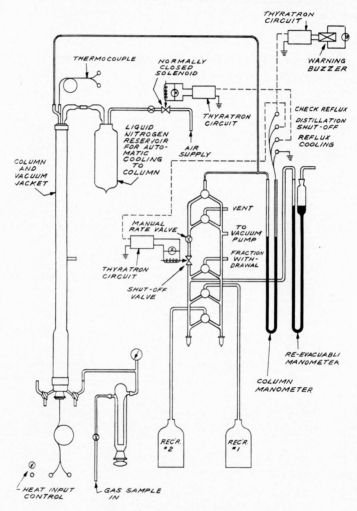

FIG. 10. Heli-Robot diagram.

2. Reduce analyst's time required per analysis.

3. Provide permanent records of analytical distillations.

The Hyd-Robot has for several years been the standard automatic apparatus used by laboratories requiring frequent analyses of gases and volatile liquids. This apparatus automatically reduces distillate rate, thus increasing reflux ratio to counteract the tendency of the column overhead temperature to rise with an approaching higher boiling component. The use of this control device, with other automatic features, reduces the operator's required attention sufficiently to enable one analyst to operate two units, thereby simultaneously analyzing two samples.

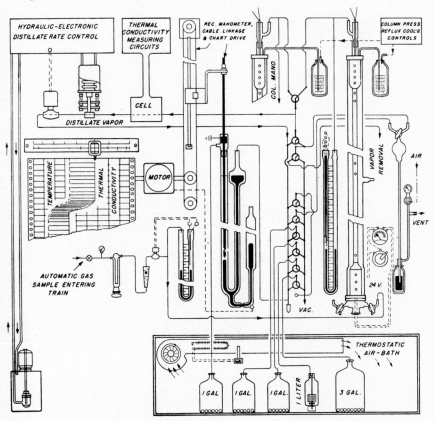

FIG. 11. Schematic diagram of Thermocon.

The most recently developed apparatus for low-temperature distillation, the Thermocon, records distillate volume vs. both the column overhead temperature and the thermal conductivity of the distillate. The use of two distinct physical properties to identify distillate materially improves the delineation of the distillation curve. The Thermocon permits the analysis of smaller samples with a substantial reduction in distillation time, owing to the smaller quantity of gas required for identification by thermal conductivity measurements.

The Thermocon, shown in Figs. 11 and 12, incorporates a unique method of controlling the distillation rate, which is based on the temperature difference or concentration gradient existing in the uppermost section of the packing. A differential thermocouple (upper junction at top of packing, lower junction 3 in. below top) is used to sense the approach of a higher boiling component.

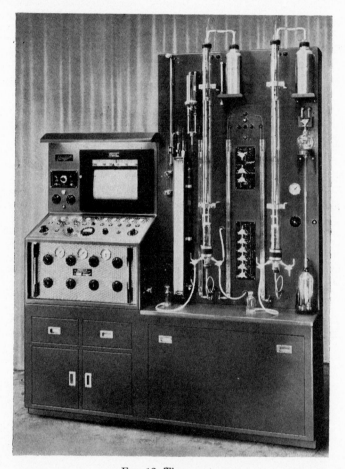

FIG. 12. Thermocon.

*4.4.3. Typical Analysis Chart and Results.* The results of a low-temperature distillation are generally obtained as a continuous record of the composition of the distillate vs. volume of distillate. A typical distillation chart as obtained during the analysis of a refinery-cracked gas on a Thermocon is shown in Fig. 13. The boiling-point temperature is used primarily for identification purposes while the thermal con-

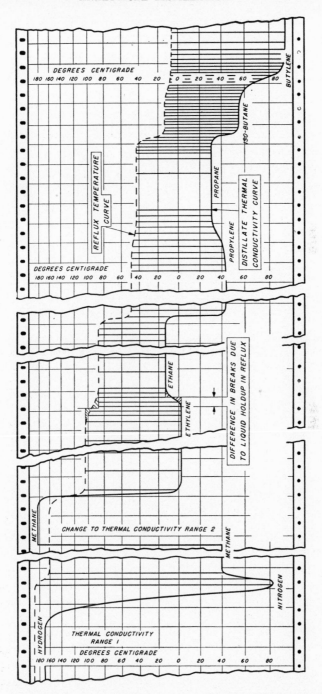

FIG. 13. Typical Thermocon distillation curve. Cracked refinery gas sample.

ductivity curve is used to locate accurately the "breaks" between components. The spacing of the pen-swings from one curve to the other on the chart represent constant time intervals, hence a narrowing of this spacing indicates reduced distillate rate (due to action of automatic rate control) as when approaching a "break."

TABLE III

*Results Submitted on N.G.A.A. Analytical Survey*

| N.G.A.A. Liquid Sample 6 Synthetic composition, mole % | Lab. 66 | Lab. 58A | Lab. 36 | Lab. 18A | Lab. 25B | Lab. 58B |
|---|---|---|---|---|---|---|
| Propane | 4.07 | 3.83 | 4.05 | 3.92 | 4.06 | 3.52 | 3.88 |
| Isobutane | 13.05 | 13.05 | 13.24 | 13.15 | 12.63 | 13.05 | 13.25 |
| n-Butane | 30.80 | 30.95 | 30.83 | 30.70 | 31.02 | 30.79 | 31.16 |
| Isopentane | 11.08 | 11.03 | 11.24 | 11.28 | 10.99 | 11.37 | 10.72 |
| n-Pentane | 12.93 | 13.07 | 12.57 | 12.72 | 13.14 | 13.03 | 12.94 |
| Hexanes + | 28.07 | 28.07 | 28.07 | 28.23 | 28.16 | 28.24 | 28.05 |
| Avg. deviation/component | 0.097 | 0.123 | 0.153 | 0.157 | 0.170 | 0.190 |

| N.G.A.A. Gas Sample 1 Statistically derived true composition | Lab. 41 | Lab. 66 | Lab. 105 | Lab. 20 |
|---|---|---|---|---|
| Nitrogen | 12.99 | 12.86 | 13.51 | 13.00 | 13.36 |
| Methane | 75.03 | 75.19 | 74.46 | 75.01 | 74.60 |
| Ethane | 6.31 | 6.31 | 6.30 | 6.38 | 6.45 |
| Propane | 3.67 | 3.66 | 3.68 | 3.75 | 3.67 |
| Isobutane | 0.44 | 0.43 | 0.43 | 0.43 | 0.50 |
| n-Butane | 1.00 | 1.00 | 0.98 | 0.93 | 0.93 |
| Isopentane | 0.18 | 0.20 | 0.24 | ..... | 0.20 |
| n-Pentane | 0.19 | 0.18 | 0.20 | 0.50 | 0.17 |
| Hexanes + | 0.18 | 0.17 | 0.20 | ..... | 0.12 |
| Avg. deviation/component* (6 components) | 0.012 | 0.032 | 0.045 | 0.062 |

*Computed on the basis of 6 components with methane and nitrogen combined and the isopentane and heavier as one fraction.

*4.4.4. Attainable Accuracy and Time Required for Analysis.* The accuracy which can be attained in the analysis of carefully prepared hydrocarbon mixtures has been determined from the results of the cooperative testing program sponsored by the Natural Gasoline Association of America (14, 15). The liquid samples used for this program were prepared by blending pure hydrocarbons by use of the procedure described by Tooke (3). The results submitted by several of the eighty-five or more participating laboratories are given in Table III. These results were obtained by means of equipment maintained in good condition and by conscientious attention to all operating techniques.

The time required for an analysis depends on the accuracy required, complexity of the sample, and type of equipment used. A three-component liquefied petroleum gas sample may be analyzed in 1 to 2 hr. with an accuracy comparable to that shown for N.G.A.A. liquid sample 6. A gas sample of the type shown in Table III generally requires 3 to 6 hr. for analysis.

*4.4.5. Low-Temperature Distillation in Combination with Other Methods of Analysis.* Low-temperature distillation is frequently employed to separate fractions, of a complex mixture, for subsequent analysis by other methods such as chemical absorption and mass or infrared spectroscopy.

Combining distillation analysis with another method will avoid the limitations inherent in both methods. The inability to separate by distillation (in a reasonable time) close boiling components, as found in a butane-butene fraction of a refinery product, may be circumvented by separating the fraction from the remainder of the sample by distillation and analyzing the desired fraction by any of several methods. Infrared spectroscopy has been found particularly useful to meet this limitation of distillation. On the other hand, separation of the original sample into fractions avoids a serious limitation of the infrared method, namely that of interference caused by components in the $C_3$ or $C_5$ fraction. The chemical-absorption methods are useful to establish the concentration of unsaturated hydrocarbons and other soluble gases such as carbon dioxide but cannot be used to distinguish the various saturated hydrocarbons.

The mass spectrometer, although frequently used alone, may also be used to advantage in combination with analytical distillation. The heavy fraction (pentanes and heavier) of natural gas, natural gasoline, or refinery plant streams is composed of a large variety of components, knowledge of the individual concentration of which, is of little value to the manufacturer or user. It is therefore customary to determine only the total quantity (concentration) of the heavy fraction present. When used alone, the mass spectrometer is limited in the determination of the components of high molecular weight, and requires the estimation of an average molecular weight of the heavy fraction in order to report the concentration of this fraction. When separated by distillation, the heavy fraction may be determined as a measured liquid or vapor quantity and is available for further evaluation by determination of its gravity, molecular weight, concentration of aromatics and naphthenes, etc., as required by the intended use of the analytical results.

A number of the combined methods of analysis have been compiled and published under the sponsorship of the Office of Rubber Reserve (3).

## 5. High-Temperature Analytical Distillation

### 5.1. Definition and Scope of Application

The essential differences between low- and high-temperature analytical distillation have already been explained. The high-temperature distillation apparatus is in general not intended to handle samples, or distillates boiling below room temperature at atmospheric pressure. Its distillate flow connections are designed to permit the gravity flow of liquid distillate into graduated receivers for measurement.

The substances which may be distilled by high-temperature analytical distillation extend in boiling point from slightly below room temperature at atmospheric pressure to a temperature of approximately 350° C. at 1 mm. Hg abs. They are so numerous that whereas a list of some 200 substances covers those which could be analyzed by low-temperature distillation, no similar list is feasible for high-temperature operations.

Industries based on the following basic materials are the principal users of high-temperature analytical distillation:

Crude petroleum and its fractions: motor fuels, solvents, gas oils, lubes, etc.

Petrochemicals: aromatics, aldehydes, ketones, glycols, etc.

Destructive wood distillation products: acetone, acetaldehyde and their homologues, acetic and higher acids and esters, alcohols, etc.

Fermentation products: acetone, ethanol, isopropanol, butanol, isoamyl alcohol, etc.

Coal-tar products and chemical derivatives: light oil, tar acids, benzol, toluene, phenol, cresols, xylenes, etc.

Chemicals: methylamine and homologues, nitrobenzene, aniline, dyestuff intermediates, chloroform, halogenated compounds, etc.

In these and other industries analytical distillation may be used for routine material evaluation, plant- and equipment-control uses, plant design, or in product development and research investigations.

### 5.2. Apparatus Design and Selection as Related to Application

The selection of the proper equipment for a given application of high-temperature analytical distillation is a complex problem. The following factors must be considered in making any choice.

5.2.1. Column Requirements. a. Separating Ability. The theoretical plates and reflux ratio required to effect a given separation have a significant influence on the design or selection of equipment. Table IV, computed for typical cases of binary mixtures, is intended to permit the approximation of the number of plates and reflux ratio to be used for any given separation.

The relation between distillate purity occurring when the kettle concentration is as used in the table, and the average purity of the distillate, is complicated (26) depending on the specific composition, actual course of distillation, column holdup, etc. However, the 90, 96, and 99% values taken do correspond loosely with analytical accuracies of the order of ±5, ±2–3, and ±0.5–1.0%, respectively.

TABLE IV

*Theoretical Plate and Reflux Ratio Requirements*

| Boiling-point difference, °C. | Relative volatility ($\alpha$)* | Distillate purity reqd.† | Min. theor. plates reqd.‡ | Actual plates reqd.¶ | Min. theor. reflux ratio reqd. | Actual reflux ratio reqd.¶ |
|---|---|---|---|---|---|---|
|  |  | 90 | 7.2 | 13 | 10.3 | 11 |
| 20 | 1.71 | 96 | 9.0 | 16 | 11.1 | 12 |
|  |  | 99 | 11.6 | 20 | 15.1 | 19 |
|  |  | 90 | 15.2 | 27 | 24.8 | 27 |
| 10 | 1.31 | 96 | 18.9 | 34 | 26.7 | 29 |
|  |  | 99 | 24.2 | 41 | 27.7 | 35 |
|  |  | 90 | 30.4 | 55 | 52.3 | 58 |
| 5 | 1.15 | 96 | 37.4 | 67 | 56.4 | 62 |
|  |  | 99 | 47.6 | 81 | 58.3 | 73 |
|  |  | 90 | 64 | 115 | 113 | 124 |
| 2.5 | 1.07 | 96 | 78 | 140 | 122 | 134 |
|  |  | 99 | 99 | 168 | 126 | 156 |

* Relative volatility computed from boiling point difference by use of Trouton's rule and the approximate Clapeyron equation.

† At 10 mole % more volatile component in kettle—a useful reference point.

‡ Calculated from Fenske's equation.

¶ Computed from theoretical values by empirical rules.

The actual plate value derived for a particular case, with the aid of Table IV, can be used to select a suitable packing of known height equivalent to a theoretical plate and to compute the required column length.

Experimentally it has been found (26) that a substantial excess of column plates over either the minimum theoretical or actual required plate number coacts with column holdup to decrease the necessary reflux ratio, sometimes to a value below the theoretical minimum. Therefore, it seems practical to err on the side of excess packing height, even to 50% and more.

*b.* CAPACITY. The capacity (throughput) required of a column is equal to the rate of product removal multiplied by the reflux ratio plus one. The kettle capacity is fixed by the size of the sample to be distilled. The sample size also influences the selection of column diameter, since the ratio of column holdup to total sample must be small. The column capacity is decreased when operated at reduced pressure in an amount equal to the square root of the ratio of the pressures. Column pressure drop increases at reduced pressure and may influence the choice of type of packing and size of column. Thermal decomposition of all or part of the sample may limit the maximum permissible operating temperature and consequently determine the operating pressure.

c. INSULATION. The column insulation required is directly related to the operating temperature. For separation of components boiling at a temperature closely approximating the room temperature, a minimum of insulation is sufficient, but a distillation of components at temperatures as high as 350° C. requires the use of a highly efficient vacuum jacket with radiation reflectors. Heat leakage from the column to the surroundings, caused by insufficient insulation, may be eliminated by the use of controlled heaters located around the column within a suitable jacket.

5.2.2. Component Identification. The separated components are identified by measurements of their boiling point as they appear at the top of the column. When close boiling substances are being distilled without complete separation, valuable information concerning the composition of the mixture can be obtained by the measurement of some other and more definitive physical property of the collected fractions. Measurements of refractive index have been especially useful in establishing the concentration of certain types of components, such as aromatics in hydrocarbon mixture. Measurements of other physical properties, such as density, dielectric constant, thermal conductivity, etc., have also been used to establish or confirm the identity of substances separated by distillation.

5.2.3. Distillate Collection and Measuring System. The capacity of the distillate collection system must be consistent with the column throughput and sample size. The calibrations required on the measuring burettes are determined by the accuracy required. The selection or design of a distillate collection and measuring system requires special consideration if (a) numerous small fractions are to be collected for subsequent tests, (b) distillation is to be conducted at subatmospheric pressures, (c) distillate contains substances melting above ambient temperatures, and (d) distillate contains substances boiling below ambient temperatures. Observations of distillate volume and identity must be synchronized to establish the concentration of each component.

5.2.4. Automation. Automatic control and/or recording of various operating functions may be used to (a) reduce operator attention required,

(b) standardize operating techniques, and (c) provide permanent records of distillations. The choice and design of automatic controls must be determined by the nature of distillations to be made, frequency of analysis, and other requirements of the particular laboratory.

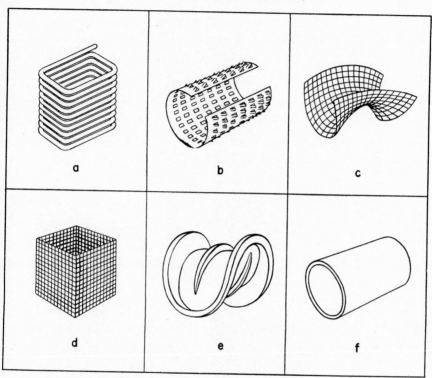

FIG. 14a. Particle type packings. (a) Heli-Pak; precision formed and spaced rectangular wire coils, in several sizes. (b) Protruded; curved shapes of thin metal perforated with jagged holes. (c) McMahon; saddle-shaped from wire screen. (d) Octa-Pak; rectangular open cylinders from wire screen. (e) Berl Saddle; saddle-shaped, usually of ceramic material, in many sizes. (f) Raschig Ring; ring type, of metal or ceramic, in many sizes.

### 5.3. Basic Apparatus Components

*5.3.1. Column Packings.* Since in distillation it is the column packing which by its repeated contacting of ascending vapor and descending condensate accomplishes the actual separation of components, it is the most important component of the apparatus. Packing has been developed in a variety of forms (16) (Fig. 14) ranging from a series of concentric glass tubes to precision die-formed patterns such as Stedman, Heli-Grid, McMahon, Protruded, Heli-Pak, and Octa-Pak packings. Table V lists

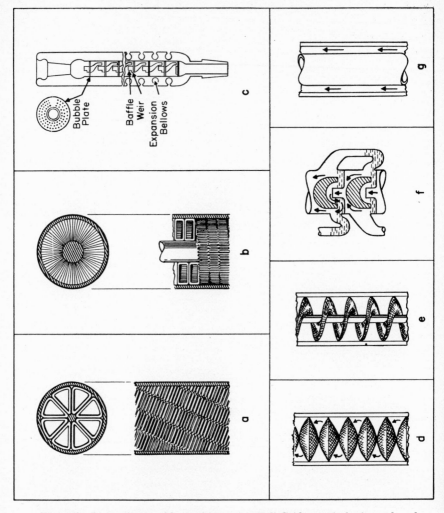

Fig. 14b. Integral assembly packings. (a) Heli-Grid; precisely formed and spaced wire coil assembly. Assembly of sector-section coils twisted around central core. (b) Heli-Grid; precisely formed and spaced wire coil assembly. Staircase assembly of rectangular section coils around central core; single or multiple layers. (c) Oldershaw; all-glass perforated tray type with down-spouters. (d) Stedman; precisely formed wire screen cones, with suitable perforations for vapor flow. (e) Lecky-Ewell; wire screen staircase type around a central core. (f) Bruun; all-glass miniature of bubble-tray tower. (g) Concentric Tube; all-glass column depending on narrow annular space between two tubes for vapor-liquid contact.

TABLE V

*Typical Performance Characteristics of Various Column Packings*
Data at 750 mm. Hg

| Packing | Column Diam. in inches | Length in inches | Through-put ml./hour | H.E.T.P. in inches | Hold-up (ml.)/plate | % Free space | Efficiency factor | References |
|---|---|---|---|---|---|---|---|---|
| ¼-inch Raschig rings (carbon) | 2 | 114 | 3500 4100 | 5.7 6.0 | — — | 60 | — — | 6 |
| ¼-inch Berl saddle (porcelain) | 1 | 42 | 2000 | 4.7 | 4.3 | 57 | 450 | 16 |
| ³⁄₃₂-inch Single turn helices stainless steel (Fenske) | 1 | 105 | 510 1015 | 0.8 1.0 | 1.2 1.6 | 80 | 425 630 | 43a |
| ¼-inch Mc-Mahon stainless steel (100 × 100 mesh) | ¾ | 32 | 540 1580 | 0.97 1.43 | 1.15 2.1 | 93 | 470 750 | 38a |
| 0.16-inch × 0.16-inch Protruded nickel | 1 | 40 | 1500 2120 | 1.37 1.26 | 1.95 1.95 | 93 | 770 980 | 33 |
| 0.24-inch × 0.24-inch Protruded nickel | 2 | 100 | 6060 11280 | 2.0 2.1 | 15.0 17.3 | 95 | 405 650 | 3a |
| Heli-Pak 0.090 × 0.175 × 0.175 inches | 2 | 36 | 1980 6000 | 0.7 1.0 | 2.19 4.64 | 87 | 905 1293 | 24 |
| Heli-Pak 0.050 × 0.100 × 0.100 inches | 1 | 36 | 480 1440 | 0.4 0.6 | 0.54 1.02 | 84 | 890 1410 | 24 |
| Heli-Pak 0.035 × 0.070 × 0.070 inches | 0.5 | 36 | 210 300 | 0.3 0.4 | 0.25 0.29 | 80 | 840 1034 | 24 |
| Octa-Pak 0.200 × 0.200 inches stainless steel | 2 | 36 | 6000 10000 | 2.5 3.0 | — — | 96 | — — | 24 |
| Heli-Grid (Nichrome) | 0.53 | 36 | 120 300 | 0.3 0.53 | 0.10 0.23 | 80 | 1200 1300 | 24 1a |
| Heli-Grid (Nichrome) | 1 | 36 | 500 1500 | 0.4 0.7 | 0.36 0.76 | 80 | 1390 1970 | 24 1a, 16 |

the packings in general use which are classed as high efficiency. According to Westhaver (42), the best of these packings crowd the theoretical limit of H.E.T.P. (height for equivalent theoretical plate) so closely that in their use difference in vertical height is no longer a determining factor.

For analytical purposes, therefore, the efficiency factor (24) is a better measure of usefulness of a packing, since it distinguishes between two columns of the same plate number and boil-up rate capacity but of different total holdup. The greater the efficiency factor, the more suitable the packing for analytical distillation. Note that H.E.T.P. vanishes in this concept and that the efficiency factor is at least theoretically independent of packed height and varies slowly with packed diameter (owing to increasing liquid channeling effect in larger diameters).

The particle type packings in Table V are improvements on the original Raschig rings but retain the advantage of relatively low cost; can be adapted to various column diameters and easily removed and replaced; are expendable; and some forms have low H.E.T.P. and high efficiency factor. Diameter of packing particles should be no greater than $\frac{1}{8}$ of column diameter to ensure good vapor-liquid distribution. The "integral" packings, as the Heli-Grid, Stedman, and Concentric Tube, are designed and constructed as a unit, preformed to fit in the column with close clearance, and to some extent actually are superior to particle packings in both H.E.T.P. and efficiency factors, with relative freedom from liquid channeling.

The concentric tube, being all glass, can be used for distillation of chlorinated and other corrosive mixtures which are detrimental to metallic materials. This same advantage plus large capacity and steady operation is possessed by the perforated glass plate type of column.

The spinning-band type of column (Fig. 15) is unique for its very low holdup and pressure drop, combined with high plates, when made in the smaller (5 to 6 mm.) diameters (4, 17, 45). The spinning-band column, owing to the mechanics of the rotating band, magnetic coupling, variable-speed motor, etc., requires more operational technique than the conventional packed column. A spinning-band column should not be selected for applications when a stationary type of packing will be adequate.

Summarizing, the data on the packings in Table V afford at least a rough comparison and basis for selection of packing for a specific application. Costs of packings will have to be obtained from manufacturers or supply houses, as indicated. An exhaustive comparison of all known packings is given by Glazebrook and Williams (11).

*5.3.2. Column Insulation.* To minimize heat losses various types of insulation are being used depending on temperature range and fractionating requirements. **Common forms are double-tube air jacket, glass, cotton, magnesia, asbestos, etc.**

The development of the glass vacuum jacket greatly improved insulating effectiveness, especially with chemically deposited silver coatings. The relative insulating power of various means of insulations is shown in Fig. 16 (21). Roughly, the heat loss through (a) double-tube glass air jacket, (b) unsilvered evacuated glass jacket, and (c)

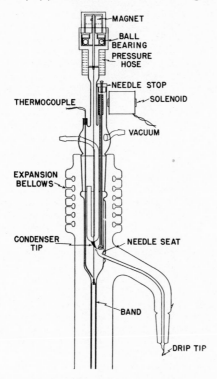

FIG. 15. Spinning band column.

silvered evacuated glass jacket is in the ratio of 25:5:1. At interior temperatures ranging from 150° to 350° C., chemically deposited silver coatings tend to vaporize and do not sufficiently reflect radiant heat. Multiple, thin, highly polished shields suitably supported and spaced within the vacuum space overcome these difficulties and make possible vacuum jackets which are practically perfect insulators at even 350° C., except for thermal conduction around seals at column ends. This last type of column, including a double flexible glass tubing coil, which compensates for differential expansion of the inside column tube, is illustrated in the Hyper-Cal design (Fig. 17).

At one time heated air blown from the bottom through a double-glass tube air-jacket was used to approximate column temperature gradient and thus to minimize heat transfer. This proved to be very crude and unsatisfactory; however, an arrangement is often used, in lieu of an efficient vacuum jacket, whereby sectional electric resistance wire heaters are placed between layers of insulation and the current to these heaters is varied independently in each section through suitable controls to

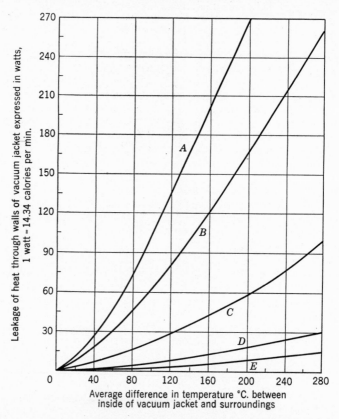

FIG. 16. Thermal insulation effectiveness of column vacuum jackets. A. Plain air jacket, inner tube 30 mm. i.d. outer tube 45 mm. o.d.; B. same jacket as in A but annular space of tube filled with mineral wool insulation; C. vacuum jacket silvered solid, except for ¼″ to ⁵⁄₁₆″ clear strip running lengthwise on both sides for visibility; D. double reflector suitably perforated for visibility; E. same type vacuum jacket as in D but of improved construction.

maintain only a very small temperature difference across the insulation layer next to the column, as determined by differential thermocouples (8, 39). This arrangement can be used to minimize the average heat loss through each section, but a recently applied continuously pumped all-metal multiple-reflector type of vacuum jacket appears to be free from residual heat loss and requires no controls (43). Either of these two

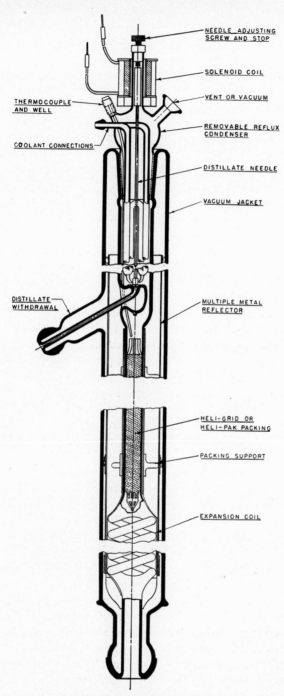

NEEDLE ADJUSTING
SCREW AND STOP

SOLENOID COIL

VENT OR VACUUM

THERMOCOUPLE
AND WELL

REMOVABLE REFLUX
CONDENSER

COOLANT CONNECTIONS

DISTILLATE NEEDLE

VACUUM JACKET

DISTILLATE
WITHDRAWAL

MULTIPLE METAL
REFLECTOR

HELI-GRID OR
HELI-PAK PACKING

PACKING SUPPORT

EXPANSION COIL

FIG. 17. Hyper-Cal column assembly.
437

arrangements would be used for large-diameter metal columns where the use of glass is prohibited, because of mechanical strength, fabrication problems, etc.

Heat losses have a significant effect on reflux ratio especially at reduced pressure operation when throughput is decreased. Excessive heat losses can prevent a considerable portion of the vapors from reaching the condenser and thus increase the reflux ratio beyond the predetermined optimum value.

*5.3.3. Distilling Flasks.* Glass kettles ranging from 10 ml. to 22 liters are used for distillation work. Selection of a suitable kettle is based mainly on column distilling capacity.

When small-diameter columns are operated at reduced pressures, the throughput is so low that any heat unbalance due to excess heat leakage at the kettle upsets column equilibrium. The usual procedure is to place the small kettle in a Dewar jar and wrap the mouth with glass wool. Improved insulating effectiveness can be obtained with a vacuum-jacketed kettle. However, the high cost of vacuum-jacketed kettles has limited their use mainly to research investigations.

The ordinary round-bottom kettle is usually satisfactory for most distillations. The usual modifications comprise a charging stopcock, a well for thermometer or thermocouple, a pressure-drop manometer connection, an entering capillary nozzle or glass frit "sparger" when it is desired to enter a fine stream of nitrogen to preclude bumping, and, sometimes, a connection for an internal direct resistance wire heater. In recent years the glass- or quartz-fiber electric heating mantle, for use with such flasks, has been highly developed and is preferred as a heating means over all other devices. The kettle is attached to the bottom column outlet by means of either a taper or spherical ground joint. Although many commercially available ground joints are not vacuum tight, a properly ground joint of either type can be entirely satisfactory for distillation work when used with a suitable lubricant. For high-temperature work, the spherical joint has the important advantage of being free from "freezing." However, a spherical joint must be properly lubricated and clamped, either with suitable spring clamps or with a spring-loaded device under the distilling kettle. Otherwise, it may break either from excess pressure or leak vapors during distillation, owing to expansion of parts.

*5.3.4. Reflux Cooling and Ratio-Controlling Heads.* The dual function of a column reflux head is to condense vapor leaving the top of the column and to divide the resulting condensate into product and column reflux, according to the reflux ratio desired. To accomplish this objective more or less satisfactorily, the technical literature can supply a large number of different reflux head designs. No one simple reflux head design combines the advantages of both partial and total condensing types, defined as follows:

*a.* PARTIAL CONDENSING. In this type of head the vapor is differentially condensed while ascending, with cooling rate controlled to obtain the desired ratio between the uncondensed vapor leaving the column proper (to be condensed into product, usually in another condenser) and the condensate returned to the packing as reflux.

This type of head can be very simple and has the least holdup possible above the thermocouple or other distillate-identifying device; thus it enables the sharpest possible "breaks" between components. For simpler distillations, where the analyst is willing to watch the cooling-rate adjustment constantly, in order to control his product rate and reflux ratio with any degree of exactness, this head is ideal. It should be noted that in the low-temperature analytical distillation apparatus, where the distillate vapor withdrawal and column pressure are automatically controlled, the partial condensing principle is used to great advantage (see section 4.3).

*b.* TOTAL CONDENSING. In this type of head all the vapor rising from the column is condensed, a condenser of considerable overcapacity, capable of condensing the maximum vapor load of column, being used. The condensate is divided into product and reflux by a stopcock, weir, or intermittent product-bumping device. Coolant rate need not be closely controlled, as atmospheric air, or other noncondensable gas above the "condensation ring" of the condenser, automatically maintains column pressure equal to atmosphere or other operating pressures.

The stopcock or valve method of withdrawing product at a desired constant rate can be satisfactory, especially for larger flows, and in any case demands far less frequent readjustment attention than the coolant flow to a partial condensing head. In order to obtain completely automatic operation the intermittent time cycle method of product withdrawal has been developed in several available designs. Control of reflux ratio by means of a cyclic timer does not necessarily imply that the reflux ratio is the same as the time interval. This is due partially to heat leakage. To be able precisely to control all distillation functions, efficient insulation is of prime importance. For precise distillations in the temperature ranges 100°–300° C. adiabatic operation and electrical windings or vacuum jacketing are essential. Removable reflux heads have the disadvantage of heat leakage at the end seals, where large volumes of glass are concentrated, resulting in erratic reflux ratio. This is usually overcome by an integral vacuum-jacketed head design. It should be borne in mind that every total condensing head has an inherently large holdup of liquid and vapor above the thermometer or thermocouple. To minimize the ratio of error, a larger sample must be taken than would be required for the same separation and accuracy with a partial condensing head. Ordinarily the increased time for a larger sample is compensated by the automaticity of the total condensing type of head.

5.3.5. *Distillate Identification.* The identity of separated components at the top of the column is usually indicated by boiling-point measurements with a thermometer or preferably with a small-diameter thermocouple. Advantages of a thermocouple are shorter length and less surface area, which minimizes lag and condensate holdup, thus increasing sharpness of separation.

The inherent difficulty in using either a thermometer or thermocouple for indicating boiling point is that of providing the proper bubble point and thermal equilibrium conditions without a large liquid holdup of varying and uncertain amount above the sensing point. This difficulty must be appreciated, and the resulting displacement error in comparing distillate identity with its collected and measured amount must be minimized by experimentation with thermocouple placement, by calibration with mixtures of known composition, and by use of sufficiently large samples. Thermal conductivity and dielectric constant, measured in the liquid phase, can be used to supplement boiling-point measurement but so far is used by only a few investigators (29, 31, 44).

5.3.6. *Distillate Collection and Measurement.* The simplest way to collect and measure distillate is to distill into a long graduated burette and note visually and record cumulative distillate quantity against boiling point frequently enough to delineate a useful distillation curve. This procedure may be made automatic by use of a photocell or electronic pickup to follow the rising distillate level in the burette, simultaneously and proportionally unrolling a strip chart, on which the boiling point is also traced (32). Such devices are not commercially available.

Alternatively, or at the same time (by collecting each fraction in a burette as above, etc.), the distillate can be collected in discrete fractions, usually although not necessarily, of uniform volume or weight, and the fractions identified by determining their individual refractive indices, densities, etc., or by redistillation in a small column. If a sufficient number of fractions are collected (say 5% cuts) then this procedure, while laborious, gives much more information (for example, the concentration of aromatics or unsaturates in hydrocarbon mixtures) than boiling point alone.

Automatic fraction-collection apparatus have been developed for atmospheric pressure only by several laboratories (4, 10, 38), but are not commercially available, except for the Technikon intended for chromatographic fractions.

## 5.4. Typical Apparatus and Results

*5.4.1. Typical Apparatus.* The individual laboratory worker frequently constructs his own distillation apparatus assembled from such packings, as described here, either a simple insulated or air-jacketed column, or a purchased vacuum-jacketed column, and other standard or homemade components, mountings, and instrumentation. In such cases complete diversity prevails, according to the specific requirements and the individual preferences of the analyst.

There is a need for commercially available completely engineered analytical distillation apparatus of maximum versatility, ready to use with minimum setup time and experimentation, with optional instruments and automatic controls to relieve the demand on skill and time of analyst. Relatively few concerns offer such apparatus in this specialized field.

Figure 18 is a photograph of the Hyper-Cal (29a) automatic, recording distillation apparatus, with fully vacuum-jacketed column and reflux head, in a wide range of column types and sizes, with automatic reflux ratio, heat input vacuum, and other controls designed for greatest practical versatility and efficiency.

*5.4.2. Testing of Column Efficiency.* The separating or resolving power of a column is obviously its most important characteristic, usually measured by H.E.T.P. The actual determination of H.E.T.P. requires knowledge of all factors affecting column separation and an exacting experimental procedure, as follows:

1. A test mixture is required, consisting of two close-boiling components (as normal heptane-methylcyclohexane) preferably exhibiting an ideal vapor-liquid equilibrium diagram. Any impurities likely to interfere with the fractionating characteristics of the mixture must be meticulously removed, usually by distilling and taking heart cuts of the pure components before blending. Even with ideal vapor-liquid equilibrium diagrams, different test mixtures may yield considerably different H.E.T.P. values on the same column. Obviously the mixture should be readily analyzable as by refractive index.

2. H.E.T.P. determinations are normally made at total reflux or zero product from the analyses of top and bottom column compositions. Application of H.E.T.P. values thus obtained to finite reflux ratio distillation may be done by suitable computation. Experimentally, a product stream of say $\frac{1}{10}$ of the column boilup rate may be continuously returned to kettle, and the separation thus obtained may be measured, but this procedure does *not* determine H.E.T.P. as usually defined.

3. The "column" to be tested necessarily comprises the packing, surrounding insulation, reflux head, flask and heater, each of these components affecting both separation and H.E.T.P. determination. Particularly, gain or loss of heat from the column through the insulation

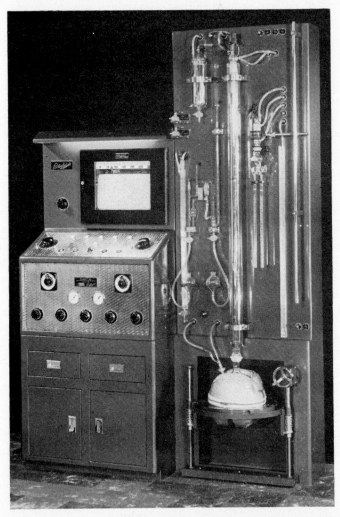

Fig. 18. Podbielniak Hyper-Cal automatic recording distillation apparatus.

vitally affects separation. Most of the results reported on H.E.T.P.'s in the literature, without efficient vacuum jackets, are likely to be in considerable error from this cause. Actually, it is possible to decrease H.E.T.P. considerably, by manipulating column temperature gradient, at total reflux, even beyond the best performance of fully vacuum-jacketed columns.

4. H.E.T.P. will vary widely with boilup rate, with distillation pressure, and according to whether or not packing is "pre-flooded" before distillation. Usually the H.E.T.P. vs. boilup rate curve is obtained from the lowest practical to the flood-point capacity.

5. For every H.E.T.P. vs. boilup rate point, and after every change in operating conditions, the column must be given time to reach complete equilibrium (i.e., the point where no further change in distillate composition occurs with time), before the distillate is sampled or analyzed. This may take hours, when testing packings of 50 or more theoretical plates.

For further details on column testing, the reader is referred to the paper by Ward (40a).

*5.4.3. Combined Use of Distillation and Other Methods.* As pointed out in section 2.2.5, distillation cannot separate components the boiling points of which are very close or which show no change in concentration upon varporization. For such components supplementary tests by other methods are required.

In most cases, narrow-cut distillation fractions are subjected to chemical tests, as for determining acidity or iodine number of vegetable oils, or refractive index measurements to determine aromatics, or to infrared and other spectroscopic tests, the application of which is greatly facilitated by the primary separations possible through distillation. Recently, another powerful analytical tool has become available for this purpose, vapor phase chromatography (29a) which requires liquid samples of only about 0.01 cc., is extremely rapid (5 to 30 minutes for a determination), and can be adjusted to accomplish the separations of close-boilers, azeotropes, etc., not possible by distillation. Unlike most spectroscopic methods, vapor phase chromatography requires only very simple calibration, apparatus, and operation.

It may also be expedient to separate the sample *before* distillation into compounds of different chemical *types*, as into paraffins, cyclics, aromatics, and olefinics, by preliminary adsorption or liquid phase chromatography (12a). This preliminary sorting greatly facilitates the problem of separating the resulting usually non-azeotropic and simplified sample portions, by efficient distillation.

Finally, full boiling point range samples as crude petroleum containing volatile hydrocarbons including methane and ethane, requires, among other things, a splitting into low-boiling portion, say methane to pentanes inclusive, which is best handled by low-temperature distillation, and the residue, subject to normal high-temperature distillation. In both cases, vapor phase chromatography can be a valuable companion analytical method, especially with cracked olefin containing samples.

### 5.5. Special Distillation Techniques

Besides ordinary batch distillation, which is the only type of high-temperature distillation discussed thus far, other variants of analytical distillations may be used.

5.5.1. *Azeotropic Distillation.* Azeotropes usually interfere with analytical distillations. Occasionally, however, they are formed deliberately. For example, a straight-run petroleum fraction boiling at the temperature of toluene cannot be separated by usual distillation. Addition of acetonitrile causes formation of an azeotrope with toluene allowing an almost quantitative separation of toluene.

5.5.2. *Extractive Distillation.* Extractive distillation is a form of distillation where a solvent is added to the material being distilled to create a nonideal solution. Since the partial pressures of components over a nonideal solution differ from those predicted by Raoult's law the ease of separation is changed, generally enabling better separation. The solvent selected normally boils at a much higher temperature than the components being distilled, and so the components can be easily recovered by fractional distillation. The improved separation effected by this method is exemplified by the addition of aniline as a solvent to a mixture of normal heptane and methyl-cyclohexane. The number of theoretical plates required to effect a given separation is reduced by 75%.

5.5.3. *Amplified Distillation.* For the determination of components present in trace quantities which would be lost in column holdup during ordinary distillation, Bailey (1) added a quantity of a substance of practically the same boiling point separable by chemical or other means from the trace component. Fractionation then removed the trace component with the added substance in a sizable fraction in which the trace component could be accurately determined. This technique has been used to determine traces of isopentane in pentane.

5.5.4. *Continuous Distillation.* An analytical distillation process can be set up entirely analogous to commercial continuous distillation in which the feed is introduced continuously near the middle of a column. A low holdup flask reboiler is used at the bottom, and products are taken off continuously at top and bottom. Standard laboratory column components, plus a column provided with a feed inlet and a "flash" reboiler at the bottom, can be combined to distill a mixture into two products continuously.

5.5.5. *Column Temperature Gradient Analysis.* In the usual meaning of the word, this is not a distillation process at all, as no distillate leaves the top of the column. The column is a special one (25) with provisions for determining the temperatures existing throughout the length of the column. In general, an amount of sample is taken just sufficient to fill the holdup of the packing. With constant heat input and column pressure, the sample will separate into fractions forming a concentration and temperature gradient within the column, simulating the usual distillation curve, thus supplying a fairly accurate analysis. The advantages of the method are simplicity, complete automaticity, very short time to reach substantial equilibrium, and the final calculable temperature-gradient curve.

REFERENCES

1. Bailey, J. R., U. S. Patent 2,231,241, February 11, 1941.
1a. Brandt, P. L., Perkins, R. B., and Halverson, L. K., *Oil and Gas J.* No. 31, 86–90 (1946).
2. Britton, E. C., Nutting, H. S., and Horsley, L. H., U. S. Patent 2,324,255, July 13, 1943.
3. Burke, O. W., Jr., Starr, C. E., Jr., and Tuemmler, F. D., "Light Hydrocarbon Analysis." Reinhold, New York, 1951.
3a. Cannon, M. R., *Ind. Eng. Chem.* **41**, 1953 (1949).
4. Dixon, O. G., and Ronnebeck, H. R., *J. Soc. Chem. Ind.* **69**, 202 (1950).
5. Feldman, J., Svedi, A., Connell, S., and Orchin, M., *Ind. Eng. Chem.* **45**, 214 (1953).
6. Fenske, M. R., Lawroski, S., and Tongberg, C. O., *Ind. Eng. Chem.* **30**, 297 (1938).
7. Fenske, M. R., Tongberg, C. O., Quiggle, D., and Cryder, D. S., *Ind. Eng. Chem.* **28**, 644 (1936).
8. Fenske, M. R., Quiggle, D., and Tongberg, C. O., *Ind. Eng. Chem.* **24**, 408 (1932).
9. Fenske, M. R., Quiggle, D., and Tongberg, C. O., *Ind. Eng. Chem.* **26**, 1169 (1934).
10. Galstaun, L. S., Harrison, R. D., Keever, E. R., and Risso, L., Paper presented before 124th meeting of American Chemical Society, Chicago, September, 1953.
11. Glazebrook, A. L., and Williams, F. E., "Technique of Organic Chemistry." Vol. IV, Chapter II, Interscience, New York, 1951.
12. Leslie, E. H., "Motor Fuels, Their Production and Technology." Reinhold, New York, 1923.
12a. Mair, B. J., Montjar, M. J., and Rossini, F. D., *Anal. Chem.* **28**, No. 1, 56 (1956).
13. McCabe, W. L., and Thiele, E. W., *Ind. Eng. Chem.* **17**, 605 (1925).
14. Miller, A. J., *Petroleum Engr.* **21**, No. 7, C-40 (1949).
15. Miller, A. J., *Petroleum Engr.* **24**, No. 9, C-31 (1952).
16. Myles, M., Feldman, J., Wender, I., and Orchin, M., *Ind. Eng. Chem.* **43**, 1452 (1951).
17. Nerheim, A. G., and Dinerstein, R. A., Paper presented before American Petroleum Institute 20th Midyear Meeting of Refining Division, St. Louis, May 9, 1955.
18. Podbielniak, W. J., Ph. D. Thesis, University of Michigan (1928).
19. Podbielniak, W. J., and Brown, G. G., *Ind. Eng. Chem.* **21**, 773 (1929).
20. Podbielniak, W. J., *Ind. Eng. Chem. Anal. Ed.* **3**, 177 (1931).
21. Podbielniak, W. J., *Ind. Eng. Chem. Anal. Ed.* **5**, 119 (1933).
22. Podbielniak, W. J., *Ind. Eng. Chem. Anal. Ed.* **5**, 135 (1933).
23. Podbielniak, W. J., *Ind. Eng. Chem. Anal. Ed.* **5**, 172 (1933).

24. Podbielniak, W. J., *Ind. Eng. Chem. Anal. Ed.* **13**, 639 (1941).
25. Podbielniak, W. J., U. S. Patent 2,377,900, June 12, 1945.
26. Podbielniak, W. J., *Petroleum Refiner* **30**, No. 4, 85 (1951).
27. Podbielniak, W. J., *Petroleum Refiner* **30**, No. 5, 145 (1951).
28. Podbielniak, W. J., Paper on LTDA of Liquefied Petroleum Gases delivered at Symposium on Methods for Testing Liquefied Petroleum Gases, St. Louis, September, 1954, sponsored by N.G.A.A., A.S.T.M., Committee D-2 and D-3, and C.N.G.A.
29. Podbielniak, W. J., and Preston, S. T., *Petroleum Engr.* **27**, C-17 (1955).
29a. Podbielniak, W. J., and Preston, S. T., *Petroleum Refiner* **34**, No. 11, 165 (1955).
30. Preston, S. T., and Podbielniak, W. J., *Petroleum Refiner* **33**, No. 4, 132 (1954).
31. Preston, S. T., *J. Eng. Ind. Research* **11**, 14 Summer (1952).
32. Rolfson, F. B., Penther, C. J., and Pompeo, D. J., *Anal. Chem.* **20**, 1014 (1948).
33. Rose, A., and Rose, E., "Technique of Organic Chemistry," Vol. IV, Chapters I, IV, Interscience, New York, 1951.
34. Rose, A., and Rose, E., "Distillation Literature, Index and Abstracts, 1941-1945." Applied Science Lab., State College, Pa., 1948.
35. Rose, A., and Rose, E., "Distillation Literature, Index and Abstracts, 1946-1952." Applied Science Lab., State College, Pa., 1953.
36. Rossini, F. D., Mair, B. J., and Streiff, A. J., "Hydrocarbons from Petroleum." Reinhold, New York, 1953.
37. Rossini, F. D., and Willingham, C. B., Proceedings American Petroleum Institute 26th Annual Meeting, Section III (Refining), Chicago, November 11-14 (1946).
38. Smith, V. C., Glazebrook, A. L., Begeman, C. R., and Lovell, W. G., *Ind. Eng. Chem. Anal. Ed.* **17**, 47 (1945).
38a. Struck, R. T., and Kinney, C. R., *Ind. Eng. Chem.* **42**, No. 1, 77 (1950).
39. Todd, F., *Ind. Eng. Chem. Anal. Ed.* **17**, 175 (1945).
40. Tongberg, C. O., Quiggle, D., and Fenske, M. R., *Ind. Eng. Chem.* **26**, 1213 (1934).
40a. Ward, C. C., Technical Paper 600, Bureau of Mines (1939).
41. Ward, E. C., *Ind. Eng. Chem. Anal. Ed.* **10**, 169 (1938).
42. Westhaver, J. W., *Ind. Eng. Chem.* **34**, 126 (1942).
43. Weedman, J. A., and Dodge, B. F., *Ind. Eng. Chem.* **39**, 734 (1947).
43a. Whitmore, F. C., Fenske, M. R., Quiggle, D., Bernstein, H., Carney, T. P., Lawroski, S., Popkin, A. H., Wagner R. B., Wheeler, W. R., and Whitaker, J. S., *J. Am. Chem. Soc.* **62**, 795 (1940).
44. Wilson, L. H., Paper presented before American Chemical Society, New York Metropolitan section (1955).
45. Winters, J. C., and Dinerstein, R. A., *Anal. Chem.* **27**, 546 (1955).
46. Young, S., "Distillation Principles and Processes." Macmillan, New York, 1922.

# Neutron Spectroscopy and Neutron Interactions in Chemical Analysis

By

T. I. TAYLOR AND W. W. HAVENS, JR.

*Chemistry and Physics Departments, Columbia University, New York, New York*

## 1. INTRODUCTION

Since the discovery of neutrons (42) their interactions have played an important role in the study of nuclear properties. These interactions are now being applied to many other problems of physics and chemistry. Several of these are particularly valuable as aids to chemical analyses, identifications, and structure determinations. Among the measurements that can be applied to problems of chemical analysis are the following:

1. Transmission of thermal neutrons
2. Transmission at selected energies
3. Resonance absorption and scattering
4. Absorption in a flux of neutrons
5. Radioactivation
6. Tracers and isotope dilution
7. Neutron diffraction

Before the techniques of using these methods are discussed, a summary of the properties, sources, and methods of detecting neutrons will be given. Procedures for selecting neutrons of known energies or wave lengths will also be reviewed because of the importance of neutron spectroscopy and neutron diffraction.

## 2. SUMMARY OF PROPERTIES AND INTERACTIONS OF NEUTRONS

A detailed discussion of the properties and interactions of neutrons can be found in many texts on nuclear physics (54, 79, 103, 118, 188). A brief summary is given in Table I.

## 3. NEUTRON SOURCES

One of the most important factors that determine the extent to which neutrons are applied to problems of chemical analysis is the availability of suitable sources. The increasing number (28) of research reactors with high neutron fluxes will broaden the application of neutron interactions. Progress has also been made in the development of various types of high-voltage machines for production of neutrons (81, 86) in the laboratory. Lower intensity radioactive sources will also find some uses. A summary of a few typical sources is given in Table II.

In practically all sources the neutrons are liberated at rather high energies (0.1 to 10 Mev.) as a result of the nuclear reactions listed in Table II. Slow neutrons are usually required for applications to chemical analysis; consequently the fast neutrons must be slowed down. This is done by allowing them to pass through layers of materials containing certain of the lighter elements such as hydrogen (in paraffin or water),

## TABLE I

*Summary of Properties and Interactions of Neutrons*

| Property | Data |
|---|---|
| General | Mass, 1.00898; charge, 0; spin $\frac{1}{2}$; half-life 10–12 min., statistics, Fermi-Dirac |
| Sources | See Table II |
| Wave length, energy, and velocity conversions | $\lambda = h/mv = h/\sqrt{2mE}$ <br> $\lambda(\text{Å.}) = 3.96 \times 10^3/v(\text{meters/sec.}) = 0.286/\sqrt{E(\text{ev.})} = 3.96 \times 10^{-3}t$ <br> $t(\mu \text{ sec./meter}) = 1/v(\text{meters/sec.}) \times 10^6 = 253\lambda(\text{Å.})$ <br> $\qquad\qquad\qquad\qquad\qquad\qquad = 72.3/\sqrt{E(\text{ev.})}$ <br> $E(\text{ev.}) = 5.226 \times 10^{-9}v^2(\text{meters/sec.}) = 5226/t^2 = 0.0818/\lambda^2(\text{Å.})$ <br> $v(\text{meters/sec.}) = 10^6/t = 1.383 \times 10^4\sqrt{E(\text{ev.})} = 3.96 \times 10^3/\lambda(\text{Å.})$ <br> $\lambda$ = wave length, cm.; $\lambda(\text{Å.})$ = wave length in Å. units; $h$ = Planck's constant, $6.624 \times 10^{-27}$ erg. sec.; $m$ = mass of neutron in g.; $v$ = velocity, cm./sec.; $v(\text{meters/sec.})$ = velocity in meters per second; $E$ = kinetic energy in ergs = $\frac{1}{2}mv^2$; $E(\text{ev.})$ = kinetic energy in electron volts*; $t$ = time of flight in microseconds per meter. |
| Diffraction by crystals | At $E = 1$ ev., $\lambda = 0.286$ Å.; at $E = 0.026$ ev., $\lambda = 1.8$ Å.; Wave length in this energy range is of the order of distance between atomic planes in crystals. Bragg diffraction occurs: $n\lambda = 2d \sin \theta$ where $n$ = order of reflection, $d$ = distance between atomic planes, and $\theta$ = angle of incidence with plane of atoms. |
| Interaction with matter | Pass through matter much more readily than charged particles. Practically no ionization produced. <br> Fast neutrons knock protons from hydrogen-containing material. <br> Prolonged irradiation may change color, thermal conductivity, or electrical conductivity. <br> Bonds may be broken with decomposition of molecules. <br> Owing to their magnetic moment, slow neutrons interact with electron magnetic moment of paramagnetic and ferromagnetic atoms. |
| Detection | Fast neutrons: recoil protons and nuclear reactions. <br> *Example:* <br> $Si^{28}(n,p)Al^{28} \xrightarrow[\text{2.3 min., 3.0 Mev.}]{\beta^-} Si^{28}$ <br> Slow neutrons: radioactivation of foils of In, Mn, Au, Ag, Rh, etc. <br> *Example:* <br> $Mn^{55}(n,\gamma)Mn^{56} \xrightarrow[\text{1.59 h, 2.8 Mev.}]{\beta^-} Fe^{56}$ <br> Counters lined with B or Li or proportional counters filled with $B^{10}F_3$. |

TABLE I. (*Continued*)

| Property | Data |
|---|---|
| | *Example:* $$B^{10} + n \rightarrow Li^7 + \alpha$$ $$Li^6 + n \rightarrow H^3 + \alpha$$ Fission *Example:* $U^{235} + n \rightarrow$ high energy fission fragments Photographic plates containing elements that become radioactive by interaction with neutrons. Scintillation counters arranged to detect $\gamma$ rays emitted when neutrons are absorbed or to detect other nuclear reactions caused by neutrons. |
| Scattering process, $(n,n)$ reactions | Elastic nuclear scattering; inelastic nuclear scattering; resonant nuclear scattering; coherent crystal scattering (diffraction); ferromagnetic scattering; paramagnetic scattering; inelastic molecular scattering; neutron-electron scattering. |
| Absorption process | The neutron is retained by nucleus and a photon or other particle is emitted: $(n,\gamma)$, $(n,p)$ $(n,\alpha)$. Also $(n,2n)$ and $(n, \text{fission})$. |

* One electron volt is the energy acquired by an electron when it is accelerated by a potential difference of 1 volt. The electron acquires an energy of $E = Ve = 4.802 \times 10^{-10}/299.8 = 1.602 \times 10^{-12}$ erg and a velocity given by

$$E = \tfrac{1}{2}mv^2 \text{ or } v = \sqrt{2E/m} = \sqrt{(2)(1.602 \times 10^{-12})/9.107 \times 10^{-28}} = 5.931 \times 10^7 \text{ cm./sec.}$$

Per mole of electrons, the energy would be

$(1.602 \times 10^{-12})(6.023 \times 10^{23}) = 9.648 \times 10^{11}$ ergs/mole $= 96,480$ Joules/mole $= 23,055$ cal./mole

A neutron with an energy equivalent to one electron volt would have an energy of $1.602 \times 10^{-12}$ ergs and a velocity of $v = \sqrt{(2)(1.602 \times 10^{-12})(6.023 \times 10^{23})/1.00898} = 1.383 \times 10^6$ cm./sec. or $1.383 \times 10^4$ meters/sec.

beryllium, or carbon. The slowing down results from a billiard-ball-type of collision in which the neutrons lose a part of their kinetic energy to the light element and cascade in a short time to lower energies. A 2-Mev. neutron, for example, will be slowed down to the thermal energies (0.026 ev.) of molecules, on the average, in about 18 collisions with hydrogen, 80 with helium, 110 with carbon, and over 2,000 with lead or uranium. About 5 cm. of paraffin is sufficient for slowing down the fast neutrons.

The result of the slowing-down process is a flux of slow neutrons that diffuses through the material and emerges with an energy distribution corresponding approximately to the Maxwell-Boltzmann distribution for a temperature somewhat higher than the temperature of the slowing-down material. A high-energy component that varies with the source of the neutrons is also present. A typical energy or wave-length distribution of slow neutrons produced in this way is illustrated in Fig. 1 for a cyclotron source (173) and in Fig. 2 for the distribution from a nuclear reactor

## TABLE II
### *Typical Neutron Sources*

| Name and place | Date | Moderator | Coolant | Power, kw. | Flux, $n$/cm.$^2$/sec. |
|---|---|---|---|---|---|
| **A. Nuclear Research Reactors ($U^{235},n,f$) Normal Uranium (28)** | | | | | |
| CP-1, Chicago | 1942 | Graphite | Air | 0.1 | $4 \times 10^6$ |
| CP-2, Argonne | 1943 | Graphite | Air | 0.2 | $1 \times 10^8$ |
| X-10, Oak Ridge | 1943 | Graphite | Air | 4000 | $1 \times 10^{12}$ |
| CP-3, Argonne | 1944 | $D_2O$ | $D_2O$ | 300 | $1 \times 10^{12}$ |
| NRX, Canada | 1947 | $D_2O$ | $H_2O$ | 40,000 | $7 \times 10^{13}$ |
| GLEEP, England | 1947 | Graphite | Air | 100 | $3 \times 10^{10}$ |
| ZOE, France | 1948 | $D_2O$ | $D_2O$ | 10 | $3 \times 10^{10}$ |
| BEPO, England | 1948 | Graphite | Air | 4000 | $1 \times 10^{12}$ |
| BNL, Brookhaven | 1950 | Graphite | Air | 28,000 | $5 \times 10^{12}$ |
| JEEP, Norway | 1951 | $D_2O$ | $D_2O$ | 300 | $1 \times 10^{12}$ |
| P-2, France | 1952 | $D_2O$ | $N_2$ gas | 1500 | $4 \times 10^{12}$ |
| SLEEP, Sweden | 1954 | $D_2O$ | $D_2O$ | 300 | $1 \times 10^{12}$ |
| **B. Nuclear Research Reactors ($U^{235},n,f$) Enriched Uranium** | | | | | |
| LOPO, Los Alamos | 1944 | — | Conduction | 0.001 | — |
| HYPO, Los Alamos | 1944 | $H_2O$ | $H_2O$ | 6 | $10^{11}$ |
| LITR, Oak Ridge | 1950 | $H_2O$ | $H_2O$ | 2000 | $10^{13}$ |
| CP-3', Argonne | 1950 | $D_2O$ | $D_2O$ | 300 | $4 \times 10^{12}$ |
| SUPO, Los Alamos | 1951 | $H_2O$ | $H_2O$ | 45 | $2 \times 10^{12}$ |
| Swimming pool, Oak Ridge | 1951 | $H_2O$ | $H_2O$ | 100 | $1 \times 10^{12}$ |
| MTR, Arco, Idaho | 1952 | $H_2O$ | $H_2O$ | 43,000 | $5 \times 10^{14}$ |
| NCRR, Raleigh, N.C. | 1953 | $H_2O$ | $H_2O$ | 10 | $4 \times 10^{11}$ |
| CP-5, Argonne | 1954 | $D_2O$ | $D_2O$ | 1000 | $2 \times 10^{13}$ |

### C. Typical Radioactive Sources (5, 224)

| Type | Reaction | Half-life | Neutron emission $n$/curie/sec. |
|---|---|---|---|
| Plutonium 239-beryllium | $Be^9(\alpha,n)C^{12}$ | 24,400 years | $1.4 \times 10^7$ |
| Radium-beryllium | $Be^9(\alpha,n)C^{12}$ | 1622 years | $1.3 \times 10^7$ |
| Radium-boron | $B^{11}(\alpha,n)N^{14}$ | 1622 years | $5.0 \times 10^6$ |
| Radium D-beryllium | $Be^9(\alpha,n)C^{12}$ | 22 years | $2.6 \times 10^6$ |
| Polonium-beryllium | $Be^9(\alpha,n)C^{12}$ | 138 days | $2.6 \times 10^6$ |
| Radium-beryllium | $Ra,Be^9(\gamma,n)Be^8$ | 1622 years | $0.2 \times 10^6$ |
| Antimony-beryllium | $Sb^{124},Be^9(\gamma,n)Be^8$ | 60 days | $3.2 \times 10^6$ |
| Sodium-heavy water | $Na^{24},D^2(\gamma,n)H^1$ | 14.8 hours | $2.5 \times 10^6$ |
| Yttrium-beryllium | $Y^{88},Be^9(\gamma,n)Be^8$ | 105 days | $1.7 \times 10^6$ |
| Lanthanum-beryllium | $La^{140},Be(\gamma,n)Be^8$ | 40 hours | $0.06 \times 10^6$ |
| Plutonium 240 | Spontaneous fission | 6600 years | $4.7 \times 10^3$ |

TABLE II. (*Continued*)

D. Typical Pulsed Particle Accelerators (86)

| Type | Particle-target, voltage, current in pulse | $\tau_s$, $\tau_D$, $T$ $\mu$sec. | Distance, channels, resolutions | Neutrons per sec. in burst |
|---|---|---|---|---|
| Synchrocyclotron, Columbia, 170″ | H-W, 380 Mev., 300 ma. | 0.05, (1–256), 16, 667 | 35 meters, 256, 0.014 $\mu$sec./ meter | $>10^{17}$ |
| Cyclotron, Brookhaven, 60″ | D-Be, 21 Mev., 1.2 ma. | 1.2, (0.5–512), (512–32, 728) | 4.3 meters, 64, 0.2 $\mu$sec./ meter | $3 \times 10^{14}$ |
| Cyclotron, Columbia, 36″ | D-Be, 8 Mev., 3 ma. | (0.5–512), (0.5–512), ($\overline{5}$12–32, 728) | 6 meters, 64, 0.33 $\mu$sec./ meter | $6 \times 10^{13}$ |
| Van de Graaff, Oak Ridge | D-Li, 2.5 Mev., 50 $\mu$a. | $<$0.01, $<$0.01, 2 | 0.8 meters, 100, 0.013 $\mu$sec./ meter | $5 \times 10^8$ |
| Electron accelerator, Yale | e-Be, 6 Mev., 125 ma. | (0.1–2), (0.1–2), 10,000 | 5 or 15 meters, 500, 0.4 $\mu$sec./ meter | $3 \times 10^{13}$ |
| Betatron, General Electric | e-U, 80 Mev., 30 ma. | 0.1, 0.2, 16,667 | 7 or 20 meters, 200, 0.01 $\mu$sec./meter | $>10^{15}$ |
| Pulse transformer, Columbia | D-ZrT, 0.4 Mev., 10 ma. | 1, 5–512, $10^4$–$10^5$ | 3 meters, 64, 0.5 $\mu$sec./ meter | $3 \times 10^{12}$ |
| Linear accelerator, Harwell | e-U, 14 Mev., 25 ma. | 0.2, (0.2–400), 2500 | 3 to 55 meters, (100, 40,170) (0.15–0.004 $\mu$sec./meter) | $4 \times 10^{14}$ |

E. Typical Particle Accelerators, Continuous

| Type | Particle and target | Voltage, current | Neutrons/sec. | Approx. flux in moderator |
|---|---|---|---|---|
| Cyclotron | $Be^9(d,n)B^{10}$ | 8 Mev., 1 ma. | $3 \times 10^{13}$ | $1 \times 10^{11}$ |
| Van de Graaff | $Be^9(d,n)B^{10}$ | 1 Mev., 10 $\mu$a. | $1 \times 10^9$ | $1 \times 10^7$ |
| Van de Graaff | $Be^9(d,n)B^{10}$ | 2 Mev., 50 $\mu$a. | $1 \times 10^{10}$ | $5 \times 10^8$ |
| Cockroft-Walton | $T(d,n)He^4$ | 250 kev., 100 $\mu$a. | $1 \times 10^9$ | $1 \times 10^8$ |
| Pulse transformer | $T(d,n)He^4$ | 400 kev., 60 cycle, 1 $\mu\alpha$ (avg.) | $1 \times 10^8$ | $1 \times 10^6$ |
| Betatron | $e(U,\gamma\text{-}n)$ | 80 Mev., 60 cycle, 3 $\mu\alpha$ (avg.) | $2 \times 10^{10}$ | $1 \times 10^8$ |

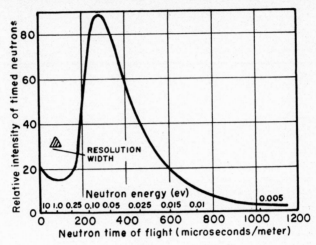

FIG. 1. Distribution of slow neutrons from a paraffin source (6.2 cm. thick in a ¼-in.-thick plywood box) used with the Columbia University cyclotron.

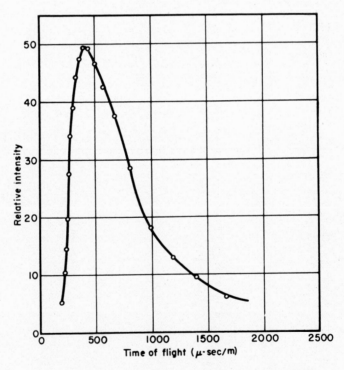

FIG. 2. Distribution of neutrons in a beam from a reactor.

(180). Further discussions of some of the neutron sources will be given in later sections.

In some of the applications that will be described later, slow neutrons with a rather broad energy distribution are useful. However, if the interactions at a particular energy or wave length are to be used for a chemical analysis, it is necessary to select a narrow energy band by means of suitable spectrometers, velocity selectors, filters, or selective detectors.

## 4. CROSS SECTIONS FOR NEUTRON INTERACTIONS

The magnitude of neutron interactions is usually expressed in terms of *cross sections*. The unit is the barn ($1 \times 10^{-24}$ sq. cm.), which is of the order of physical area of nuclei. Cross sections for many reactions can be measured by transmission experiments as discussed in the following.

When an essentially unidirectional beam of neutrons is incident on a sample of material, some of the neutrons pass through unaffected, and the

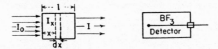

FIG. 3. Determination of neutron cross sections by transmission measurements: $I_0$ = initial neutron intensity; $I_x$ = neutron intensity at $x$; $l$ = thickness of sample.

others are either absorbed or scattered from the beam as a result of neutron interactions. This attenuation of the neutron beam can be determined in a suitable experimental arrangement, shown diagrammatically in Fig. 3. The fractional decrease in intensity $dI/I_x$ of a neutron beam in passing through a layer $dx$ (Fig. 3) is equal to the ratio of the effective area of the nuclei in the layer to the total area of the layer. The effective area presented by the nuclei is given by the total effective cross section $\sigma_t$ of each nucleus times the number of nuclei in the layer, or $\sigma_t n A dx$, where $n$ is the number of nuclei per cubic centimeter and $A$ is the area.

Hence

$$dI/I_x = -\sigma_t n A \, dx/A = -\sigma_t n \, dx$$

from which

$$I = I_0 e^{-\sigma_t n l} \text{ or } \ln I_0/I = \sigma_t n l \qquad (4.1)$$

where $I_0$ is the initial intensity of the neutron beam, and $I$ is the intensity after it has passed through the sample of thickness $l$. Hence the total cross section per nucleus in square centimeters can be calculated from the results of transmission measurements by using eq. (4.1) in the form

$$\sigma_t = \frac{1}{nl} \ln \frac{I_0}{I} = \frac{1}{nl} \ln \frac{1}{T} = \frac{1}{nl} 2.303 \log \frac{1}{T} \qquad (4.2)$$

As the number of atoms per cubic centimeter is given by $\rho N/M$, where $M$ is the atomic weight, $\rho$ is the density, and $N$ is Avogadro's number,

$$\sigma_t = \frac{M}{\rho Nl} \ln \frac{I_0}{I} = \frac{M}{\mu N} \ln \frac{I_0}{I},$$
$$= \frac{2.303M}{\mu N} \log \frac{I_0}{I} = \frac{2.303M}{\mu N} \log \frac{1}{T} \qquad (4.3)$$

in which $\mu$ is the grams per square centimeter of the nuclei in the path of the neutron beam and $T$ is the transmission. The cross section obtained from eq. (4.3) is that for the element when $M$ and $\mu$ refer to the element as a whole rather than to a particular isotope. Thus, in sections 4–10, $\sigma$ will refer to the cross section of the element. However, in sections 11–14 where we shall be more concerned with the interactions of a particular isotope of an element, $\sigma$ will refer to the cross section of the isotope, in which case, the cross section of the element will be $\alpha\sigma$ where $\alpha$ is the atom fraction or abundance of the isotope.

The cross section obtained in this way is the total cross section for all processes that tend to deflect the neutrons from their straight line of flight. Neutron and charged-particle scattering measurements, the life-time energy relationship in heavy-charged-particle emitters, and the transition energies of mirror nuclei indicate that the actual physical radius of an element of mass number $A$ is given approximately by $1.43 \times 10^{-13} \times A^{1/3}$. For an element of mass number of about 125, the radius of the nucleus would be $7.15 \times 10^{-13}$ cm., or a cross section of about $1.6 \times 10^{-24}$ cm.$^2$ (1.6 barns). Cross sections for neutrons may vary from this value up to over 3,400,000 barns for xenon-135 at a neutron velocity corresponding to an energy of about 0.082 ev.; that is, the cross section of this nucleus at certain energies is many thousands of times larger than its actual physical cross section. Since the observed cross sections depend so markedly upon the velocity of the neutrons, it becomes necessary to examine more closely the processes that contribute to the cross section.

## 5. NATURE OF NEUTRON INTERACTIONS

One of the generally adopted views of nuclear interactions is based upon Bohr's (26) idea of the compound nucleus, as illustrated in Fig. 4. On the basis of this picture, a neutron that comes close enough to a nucleus to interact with it actually unites with it to form a compound nucleus. This new nucleus, excited by both the kinetic and the binding energy of the neutron with the nucleus (8–9 Mev.), may change to a more stable state in any one of a variety of ways. The relative probabilities for the different possible reactions are usually described in terms of *reaction widths*, $\Gamma_x$. The total cross section $\sigma_t$ obtained from transmission measurements is the sum of the cross sections for all the absorption and scattering

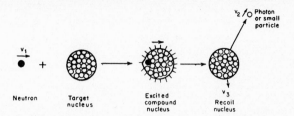

FIG. 4. Schematic representation of the interaction of a neutron with a nucleus.

interactions summarized in Tables I and III. Thus the total cross section for transmission of crystals for slow neutrons will be given by

$$\sigma_{\text{total}} = \sigma_a + \sigma_{\text{el}} + \sigma_{\text{inel}} + \sigma_{\text{coh}} + \sigma_D + \sigma_m + \cdots \tag{5.1}$$

in which the terms refer respectively to cross sections arising from absorption, elastic, inelastic, coherent Bragg scattering, diffuse or incoherent effects, magnetic effects, etc.

TABLE III

*Types of Neutron Interactions*

| $\sigma_t$ | $=$ | $\sigma_a$ | $+$ | $\sigma_s$ |
|---|---|---|---|---|

| Total = | $\left\{\begin{array}{l}\textit{Absorption processes}\\ n,\gamma \\ n,p \\ n,\alpha \\ n,d \\ \text{Also} \\ n,2n \\ n,\text{fission}\end{array}\right.$ | $+$ | $\left\{\begin{array}{l}\textit{Scattering processes}\\ \text{Elastic nuclear scattering}\\ \text{Inelastic nuclear scattering}\\ \text{Resonant nuclear scattering}\\ \text{Coherent crystal (diffraction)}\\ \text{Ferromagnetic scattering}\\ \text{Paramagnetic scattering}\\ \text{Inelastic molecular scattering}\\ \text{Neutron-electron scattering}\end{array}\right.$ |
|---|---|---|---|

## 5.1. Absorption

Except for a few of the lighter elements, the most probable absorption reaction for slow neutrons is the $(n,\gamma)$ reaction, in which the incident neutron is retained by the nucleus and a photon $(\gamma)$ is emitted. This reaction is sometimes called *radiative capture*, because the $\gamma$ ray is emitted from the compound nucleus very shortly after it is formed (about $10^{-14}$ sec.). The atomic number does not change in this process, but the mass number increases by one unit. If the isotope does not normally exist in nature, it will be radioactive. The properties of many of the radioactive isotopes formed in this way are suitable for chemical analysis by the radioactivation method. Such isotopes are also valuable as tracers in many types of research.

## 5.2. Scattering

When a neutron rather than another particle is emitted from the compound nucleus, scattering results and the process is called an $(n,n)$ reaction. For most of these reactions neutrons are emitted nearly isotropically from the compound nuclei, and consequently very few of them reach the detector if good geometry is maintained. For good geometry the incident neutron beam should be essentially parallel, and the detector should be sufficiently distant from the sample so that it subtends only a negligible solid angle.

Scattering may be inelastic if a part of the kinetic energy is lost by a fast neutron in exciting the nucleus to higher energy levels. Slow neutrons may also be involved in inelastic molecular collisions when a part of their kinetic energy is used up in breaking bonds or in exciting higher vibrational and rotational energy states of molecules or crystals.

Elastic-type collisions occur when the kinetic energy of the neutron and nucleus remains constant, and the interaction may be treated as a billiard-ball type of collision. This is the main process by which fast neutrons are slowed down by the lighter elements.

## 5.3. Neutron Diffraction

When the energy or wave length of the neutron is decreased to the thermal region where the associated wave length is of the order of the distance between atoms in crystals, diffraction effects occur (13) in accordance with the Bragg relation, $n\lambda = 2d \sin \theta$. With a heterogeneous beam of neutrons Laue patterns may be obtained; whereas with a monoenergetic or monochromatic beam powder patterns can be taken with a neutron spectrometer. The intensity of the coherently scattered neutrons depends upon scattering from nuclei, but X-ray scattering involves the electrons of the atoms and therefore depends markedly upon the atomic weight of the element. Neutron scattering, on the other hand, is about as intense for the nuclei of light atoms as for heavy atoms. For example, the relative coherent-scattering cross sections in barns for a few elements are H = 1.8, D = 5.4, O = 4.2, Na = 1.5, Cu = 7.3, Bi = 9.0. This makes possible the determination of the position of hydrogen in crystals by neutron diffraction where it would not be possible by X-ray diffraction. If the absorption cross section is large for one or more of the elements in a crystal, the intensity of the beam may be reduced so much that neutron diffraction will not be very useful.

Differences between neutron diffraction and X-ray diffraction also occur with respect to *diffuse-scattering* effects that arise from such causes as differences in the *scattering amplitude* and the *spin* of the isotopes of the element. Some elements, such as $H^1$, $Li^6$, Ti, and Mn, scatter neutrons with a *phase* opposite to that of D, $Li^7$, and most other elements (228). Consequently the amplitude of the scattered wave from planes in crystals containing nuclei of opposite scattering phase will be reduced. This effect is useful in certain structure problems, particularly those involving hydrogen, where both the hydrogen and deuterium compounds can be studied.

When the energy of the neutrons is reduced to a value such that the wave length is equal to $2d$ for the first Bragg reflection, no coherent crystal scattering will occur. Neutrons of longer wave length can then readily pass through the crystals. This effect has been used to obtain neutron beams of long wave length by filtering through BeO (57). With such a filter, neutrons with wave lengths less than about 4.66 Å. are scattered from the beam. The residual cross section for the longer wave lengths is then caused by absorption, inelastic molecular effects, crystal imperfections, spin, isotope, temperature effects, etc. In addition, paramagnetic (80, 103, 182) and ferromagnetic substances have an additional effect caused by the interaction of the nuclear magnetic moment of the neutron and the electron magnetic moment of the unpaired electrons. Paramagnetic scattering becomes important only at the lower energies (long wave lengths).

## 6. Variations in Cross Sections with Neutron Energy

Marked variations exist in the cross sections for neutron interactions as the velocity of the neutron is changed. At high energies (1 Mev.), where the wave length of the neutron is of the same order of magnitude as the radius of the nucleus ($\lambda \approx R$), the effective total cross section is roughly twice the geometric size of the nucleus, or $2\pi r^2$ as measured by other methods, i.e., from 1 to $10 \times 10^{-24}$ cm.$^2$ (1–10 barns). In this high-energy region the principal processes involve particle emissions, primarily scattering [$(n,n)$ reactions]. However, there are some $(n,p)$ and $(n,\alpha)$ reactions. As the energy of the neutrons is decreased, the cross section increases approximately as $1/v$, as illustrated in Fig. 5.

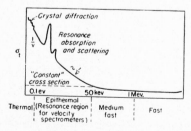

Fig. 5. General variation of the cross section with neutron energy.

## 6.1. Resonance Absorption and Scattering

Many of the isotopes show regions of resonance absorption and scattering where a marked increase in cross section occurs at definite neutron energies (Fig. 5). One or more of these resonances exist for many nuclei. The fact that they occur at specific neutron energies may serve as an indication of the presence or absence of a particular nuclear species in an unknown sample. Furthermore, the large cross section at resonance is useful in quantitative determinations of a limited number of elements, some of which can be determined chemically only with difficulty. Examples will be given in a later section.

The shape of the cross-section curve as a function of energy is given by the Breit-Wigner one-level formula (18, 22, 32), which can be broken up into four parts: (a) resonance capture, (b) resonance scattering, (c) potential scattering, and (d) interference between potential and resonant scattering. In the vicinity of a resonance the most important terms are the resonance capture and resonance-scattering terms. The potential scattering is independent of energy and is the free-atom cross section. The interference term is usually small compared with the resonance terms.

The capture cross section at an energy $E$ (electron volts) in the region of a resonance for an $(n,\gamma)$ reaction is

$$\sigma_{(n,\gamma)} = \frac{\lambda_0 \lambda}{4\pi} \frac{g \Gamma_n \Gamma_\gamma}{(E - E_0)^2 + (\Gamma/2)^2} \tag{6.1}$$

where $\lambda$ is the wave length ($\lambda = h/mv$) of the incident neutron; $E_0$ is the energy of the neutron at exact resonance; $g = (2J + 1)/2(2I + 1)$ is the statistical weight factor for the reaction where $I$ is the spin of the initial nucleus and $J$ is the spin of the compound nucleus; $\Gamma_n$ is the partial width for neutron scattering at $E_0$; $\Gamma_\gamma$ is the partial width for neutron capture; $\Gamma = \Gamma_n + \Gamma_\gamma$ is the full width of the resonance at half the maximum value $\sigma_{0(n,\gamma)}$; $E$ is the energy of the incident neutron; and $\lambda_0$ is the wave length of the neutron at exact resonance.

At exact resonance the capture cross section is

$$\sigma_{0(n,\gamma)} = \frac{2.6 \times 10^6}{E_0} g \frac{\Gamma_n \Gamma_\gamma}{\Gamma^2} \quad \text{(in barns)} \tag{6.2}$$

where all energies are measured in electron volts.

## 6.2. Resonance Absorption

In most cases for the very low energy resonances in the heavier elements, $\Gamma_n$ is less than $\Gamma_\gamma$ by a factor of 10 to 100, so that $\Gamma_\gamma \cong \Gamma$

and the maximum possible cross section for resonance absorption is $\sigma_0 = (\lambda_0{}^2/\pi)g(\Gamma_n/\Gamma)$. Since $\Gamma_n$ varies as the velocity $v$ or as $\sqrt{E}$, the cross section $\sigma_{(E)}$ for an energy $E$ other than the resonance energy can be obtained by bringing eq. (6.1) into the following form:

$$\sigma_{(n,\gamma)} = \left(\frac{E_0}{E}\right)^{\frac{1}{2}} \frac{\sigma_0 \Gamma^2}{4(E - E_0)^2 + \Gamma^2} \tag{6.3}$$

At energies low compared with $E_0$, eq. (6.3) shows that $\sigma_{(E)}$ is proportional to $1/\sqrt{E}$ or to $1/v$. This is the well-known $1/v$ law. Examples are $Rh^{103}$, $In^{115}$, and $Au^{197}$, in which $\Gamma_\gamma$ is about ten times $\Gamma_n$.

### 6.3. Resonance Scattering

The resonant scattering term (22) in the Breit-Wigner formula is given by

$$\sigma_{\text{res}}(n,n) = \frac{\lambda_0{}^2}{4\pi} g \frac{\Gamma_n{}^2}{(E - E_0)^2 + (\Gamma/2)^2} \tag{6.4}$$

which at the resonance energy gives the maximum scattering as

$$\sigma_0(n,n) = \frac{\lambda_0{}^2}{\pi} g \left(\frac{\Gamma_n}{\Gamma}\right)^2 \tag{6.5}$$

There are cases of levels such as Mn and Co in which the levels are predominantly scattering for $\Gamma_n \approx 10$ ev. and $\Gamma_\gamma \approx 0.1$ ev.

In the very light nuclei $\Gamma_n \gg \Gamma_\gamma$. For heavier nuclei for the low energy resonances $\Gamma_\gamma$ is usually much larger than $\Gamma_n$. However, there are many cases in the intermediate and heavy nuclei where $\Gamma_n \approx \Gamma_\gamma$. In this case the resonance term in the Breit-Wigner formula is made up of both resonance capture and resonance scattering which, by neglecting the variation in the $\sqrt{E_0/E}$ term over the region of the resonance, can be combined to give the formula

$$\sigma_{\text{res}} = \frac{\lambda_0{}^2}{4\pi} g \frac{\Gamma_n \Gamma}{(E - E_0)^2 + (\Gamma/2)^2} \tag{6.6}$$

A few nuclei, such as $Br^{79}$, $Br^{81}$, $Pd^{108}$, $Sm^{152}$, $Hf^{178}$, and $W^{186}$ appear to have levels in which $\Gamma_\gamma \approx \Gamma_n$.

### 6.4. The 1/v Region

At neutron energies somewhat below the first resonance but above that corresponding to the Bragg cutoff, the cross section for scattering varies as $(\lambda_0{}^2/\pi) \times g(\Gamma_n{}^2/4E_0{}^2)$, in which all the terms are constants so that the scattering cross section should be quite constant. Hence, the total cross section $[\sigma_{\text{total}} = \sigma_{\text{capture }(n,\gamma)} + \sigma_{\text{scattering }(n,n)}]$ in the $1/v$ region is made up of a constant scattering term plus a capture term that varies as $1/v$ or as $1/\sqrt{E}$. Thus the cross section in this region can be expressed by an equation of the form $\sigma_{(E)} = a + b/v$ or $\sigma_{(E)} = a + c/\sqrt{E}$. The magnitudes of the scattering cross sections, as well as the slopes of the $1/v$ curves, differ for a number of the elements (Table IV and Fig. 6). Consequently, a method of analysis of certain simple binary systems can be based upon the transmission at two different neutron velocities. This

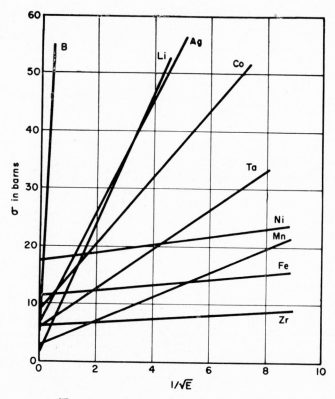

FIG. 6. The $1/\sqrt{E}$ or $1/v$ variation in cross sections for a number of elements.

method would give adequate results only in cases where the $1/v$ slopes and the scattering cross sections are markedly different for the elements in the sample. At energies below the Bragg cutoff the constant term decreases from $a$ to $a'$ because all but the small incoherent and diffuse scattering is lost so that $\sigma_{(E)} = a' + c/\sqrt{E}$.

### 6.5. Molecular Effects

In the case of the lighter elements, such as hydrogen and deuterium, chemical binding effects become significant below energies of 1 ev.

### TABLE IV
*Constants for the Equation $\sigma = a + c/\sqrt{E}$* *

| Z | Element | a | c |
|---|---------|-----|------|
| 1 | H | 20.4 | 0.053† |
| 1 | D | 7.0 | <.001† |
| 2 | He | 0.8 | <.001 |
| 3 | Li | 1.4 | 11.3 |
| 4 | Be | 6.1 | <.001 |
| 5 | B | 4 | 119 |
| 6 | C | 4.8 | <.001 |
| 7 | N | 10 | 0.30 |
| 8 | O | 3.8 | <.001 |
| 9 | F | 3.6 | <.002 |
| 10 | Ne | 2.5 | 0.44 |
| 11 | Na | 3.1 | 0.08 |
| 12 | Mg | 3.4 | 0.10 |
| 13 | Al | 1.4 | 0.04 |
| 14 | Si | 2.2 | 0.02 |
| 15 | P | 3.4 | 0.03 |
| 16 | S | 1.1 | 0.08 |
| 17 | Cl | 16 | 4.99† |
| 18 | A | 0.86 | 0.98 |
| 19 | K | 2.1 | 0.31 |
| 20 | Ca | 3 | 0.068 |
| 22 | Ti | 4.2 | 0.88 |
| 23 | V | 5 | 0.81 |
| 24 | Cr | 4.1 | 0.46 |
| 25 | Mn | 2.9 | 2.09 |
| 26 | Fe | 11.4 | 0.40 |
| 27 | Co | 8.9 | 5.85 |
| 28 | Ni | 17.5 | 0.73 |
| 29 | Cu | 7.8 | 0.58 |
| 30 | Zn | 4 | 0.17 |
| 31 | Ga | 4.8 | 0.44 |
| 32 | Ge | 8.8 | 0.37 |
| 33 | As | 7.8 | 0.65 |
| 34 | Se | 7.8 | 1.86 |
| 35 | Br | 5.9 | 1.04 |
| 36 | Kr | 7.2 | 4.43 |
| 37 | Rb | 5.4 | 0.011 |
| 38 | Sr | 9.8 | 0.18 |
| 39 | Y | 3 | 0.22 |
| 40 | Zr | 6.2 | 0.28 |
| 41 | Cb | 6.5 | 0.17 |
| 42 | Mo | 6.0 | 0.40 |
| 44 | Ru | 6.5 | 0.40 |
| 45 | Rh | 5.5 | 23.7 |

TABLE IV. (*Continued*)

Constants for the Equation $\sigma = a + c/\sqrt{E}$*

| Z | Element | $a$ | $c$ |
|---|---------|-----|-----|
| 46 | Pd | 4.7 | 1.27 |
| 47 | Ag | 6.4 | 9.8 |
| 49 | In | | 30.02† |
| 50 | Sn | 4.8 | 0.09 |
| 51 | Sb | 4.1 | 0.87 |
| 52 | Te | 4.4 | 0.71 |
| 53 | I | 3.7 | 1.06 |
| 54 | Xe | 4.3 | 5.53† |
| 55 | Cs | 6.9 | 4.6 |
| 56 | Ba | 7 | 0.19 |
| 57 | La | 9.2 | 1.41 |
| 58 | Ce | 2.8 | 0.11 |
| 59 | Pr | 3.9 | 1.78 |
| 60 | Nd | 15.8 | 7.27 |
| 73 | Ta | 5.9 | 3.37 |
| 74 | W | 5.6 | 3.03 |
| 76 | Os | 14.9 | 2.32 |
| 78 | Pt | 11.9 | 1.28 |
| 79 | Au | 9.8 | 15.48 |
| 80 | Hg | 1.7 | 11.5† |
| 81 | Tl | 9.9 | 0.52 |
| 82 | Pb | 11.3 | 0.027 |
| 83 | Bi | 9.3 | 0.005 |
| 92 | U | 9.0 | 1.21† |

\* The constant $a$ is the free atom scattering cross section calculated from the bound atom cross sections (106). The absorption coefficient $c$ was calculated from the thermal-absorption cross section.

† The absorption cross sections of these elements do not strictly follow the $1/v$ or $1/\sqrt{E}$ relationship.

Actually the scattering is proportional to the square of the reduced mass of the neutron and the scatterer (18, 55). If the hydrogen atom is free, the reduced mass $\mu \cong 0.5$. However, when hydrogen is bound in heavy molecules such as paraffin, the reduced mass will be $\mu \cong 1$. Consequently the ratio of the cross section of the free hydrogen atoms to a rigidly bound one is approximately $(1/0.5)^2 = 4$; or, in general, the cross section $\sigma_b$ for a rigidly bound nucleus of mass $A$ relative to the cross section $\sigma_f$ of the same nucleus in a free state will be given by $\sigma_b = \sigma_f[(A + 1)/A]^2$.

When the energy of the neutron is considerably higher than the vibrational energy of the C-H bond in paraffin (i.e., $E \gg h\nu \approx 0.4$ ev.), H may be separated from the molecule, and the cross section for hydrogen is what would be expected for free hydrogen atoms. At energies of the order of $h\nu$, however, the neutron can lose energy to the vibration of the hydrogen atom or other groups in the molecule. In this case the hydrogen atom is essentially bound, and the cross section increases to about four times that at the higher energies. Experiments show (9, 146, 218), in fact, that the cross section for hydrogen bound in a salt hydride does increase from about 20 barns in the region of 10–1 ev. to about 80 barns at low energies or long wave lengths (Fig. 7). For gaseous molecules such as the hydrocarbons or for liquids and solids such as water, polyethylene, or paraffin, the cross section is considerably larger than 80 barns at the very low energies. This arises because of interactions due to translation and other molecular motions of the molecules. Differences in the cross

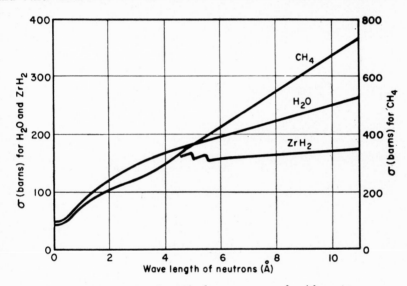

Fig. 7. Variation in cross section of hydrogen compounds with neutron energy.

sections of hydrogen containing compounds as a function of neutron energy will serve as a tool in studying the nature of the chemical binding and molecular motions as well as in chemical analyses. Specific applications of the transmission of thermal neutrons to the determination of hydrogen will be given in later sections.

## 7. Neutron Spectrometers for Selection of Neutrons of Known Energies

A number of methods of selecting neutrons for measurements as a function of wave length or energy are available (103). Sometimes it is desired to select neutrons of a narrow wave-length band; at other times a broad band of known distribution will be suitable for the measurements.

## 7.1. *Mechanical Velocity Selectors and Choppers*

One of the first methods of selecting a narrow energy band of neutrons employed a mechanical velocity selector and was used by Dunning *et al.* (51) in conjunction with a radium-beryllium source. Other types of mechanical velocity selectors (103) have been designed since that time for operation in different regions of the slow-neutron-distribution curve (see p. 454). The general principle of the mechanical chopper, when used as a neutron spectrometer, is illustrated in Fig. 8. It was designed by Fermi and his co-workers (33, 56) for use with the nuclear reactor. A rotating cylinder of alternate thin laminations of aluminum and cadmium is placed next to the graphite thermal neutron column. Neutrons can pass through the cylinder only when the direction of the layers is parallel to the beam. The mirror rotates with the cylinder, and the reflected light

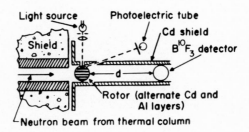

FIG. 8. Schematic diagram of a mechanical velocity selector, or "chopper."

activates the photoelectric tube, which in turn activates the BF₃ neutron counter. By adjusting the position of the mirror, the photoelectric tube and time delay circuits, the counter can be activated at time $t$ after the neutrons have passed through the cylinder. Thus only those neutrons are counted whose velocity is equal to $d/t$. An absorber can then be placed in the beam, and the transmission of neutrons through it for this velocity can be measured. The time $t$ can then be changed, and the transmission can be measured at other velocities. This method is useful to about 0.2 ev., where the resolution becomes poor because the speed at which the cylinder can be rotated is limited.

The mechanical velocity selectors of the type described by Selove (109) and Seidel, Hughes, and Palevsky (195) represent significant improvements for the higher energy neutrons (up to 1 to 5 kev.). These "fast choppers" provide mechanical interruptions of the neutron beam by means of a long narrow channel in a suitable rotor. The one used at Argonne (190) is illustrated in Fig. 9. Six 0.010- by 1-in. slots are cut in the 16-in. steel rotor, which is mounted on the axis of the neutron beam.

A stator with similar slots is in line with the rotor. For each revolution of the rotor its six slots are aligned with the six slots of the stator for a very short time depending on the speed of rotation. At 10,000 r.p.m. the burst time is about 4 μsec. During the times when the shutter is closed, the length of steel in the rotor reduces the intensity of the neutrons by $10^{-4}$. This is necessary because the time of the neutron burst is short compared with the time between bursts. With crystal-oscillator controlled-timing circuits the delay time between the burst and the beginning of the counting can be varied over wide limits. Also the length of time that the pulses from the detector are fed successively to 56 scalers is variable. Thus for each burst of neutrons, the intensity at 56 different velocities is measured starting with a velocity corresponding to those arriving at the delay time. For a 2-ev. neutron, $t = 72.3/\sqrt{2} = 51$ μsec./meter,

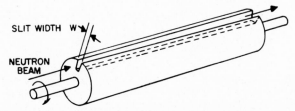

SLIT WIDTH W

NEUTRON BEAM

FIG. 9. Principle of the Argonne "fast chopper" for the higher energy neutrons.

or for a 20-meter path, the delay time would be 1020 μsec. If the channel time is 2 μsec., the time of flight of the neutrons detected by the last scaler is $1020 + 56 \times 2 = 1132$ μsec.

A "fast chopper" of somewhat different design has been built at Brookhaven National Laboratories (195). It is a rotor with plastic slits designed to run at 15,000 r.p.m. and to give a burst time of 0.5 μsec. At 20 meters with a channel time of 0.5 μsec., a resolution of 0.05 μsec./meter corresponding to a velocity resolution of 1% is obtained for 200 ev. neutrons (5 μsec./meter).

Improved designs of mechanical choppers for neutrons of thermal and subthermal energies have also been built. "Slow choppers" for this region are similar to the fast choppers but somewhat simpler because the burst times are of the order of 10 to 20 μsec. and thin cadmium rather than thick plastic or steel can be used.

The application of mechanical velocity selectors to measurements of total cross sections as a function of energy will be discussed later. Since the beam contains all energies, activation cross sections as a function of energy cannot be made as can be done with crystal spectrometers. The small size of sample needed for the "fast chopper" has an advantage over the pulsed cylotron in this respect.

## 7.2. Crystal Spectrometers

Crystal spectrometers for selection of neutrons of a narrow energy-band or wave-length range are based on the wave properties of neutrons (29, 30, 229). The general arrangement of the equipment as illustrated in Fig. 10 is very similar to that used for X-ray spectrometers.

Neutrons from a nuclear reactor are collimated so that a parallel beam of neutrons hits the surface of a crystal such as lithium fluoride. Maxima in the diffraction pattern occur in such a way that the Bragg relation $n\lambda = (nh)/(mv) = 2d \sin \theta$ is satisfied (Table I). Neutrons of a given energy can be obtained by setting the crystal and detector at the appropriate angle with respect to the neutron beam. Thus, if the (100) planes

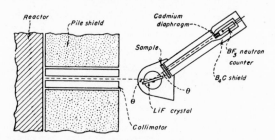

FIG. 10. Schematic diagram of a single-crystal neutron spectrometer.

of LiF in which $d = 2.005$ Å. are set such that $\theta = 20°$, then the velocity of the neutrons impinging upon the detector can be calculated in the following manner for a first-order reflection:

$$v = \frac{nh}{m\,2d \sin \theta} = \frac{(1)(6.62) \times 10^{-27}}{(1.67 \times 10^{-24})(4.01 \times 10^{-8})(0.342)} = 2.88 \times 10^5 \text{ cm./sec.} \quad (7.1)$$

which corresponds to an energy in electron volts of

$$E = \frac{\frac{1}{2}mv^2}{e} = \frac{(0.5)(1.67 \times 10^{-24})(2.88 \times 10^5)^2(300)}{(4.80 \times 10^{-10})} = 0.043 \text{ ev.} \quad (7.2)$$

or to a wave length of $\lambda = 0.286/\sqrt{E} = 1.38 \times 10^{-8}$ cm., or 1.38 Å. Second-order reflection at 0.69 Å. (0.172 ev.) is much weaker in intensity (see Fig. 2) and corrections can be made for those that do contaminate the beam.

For neutrons of wave length greater than 4 Å., sheets of mica (spacing 9.95 Å.) have been employed (72, 73, 97) in conjunction with filters of Be and BeO. When 6 to 8 in. of beryllium metal is placed in a beam of neutrons from the nuclear reactor practically all the high-energy neutrons as well as the slow ones with wave lengths below 4 Å. are scattered from the beam. If the beryllium filter is cooled to liquid nitrogen temperatures, over 90% of the neutrons with wave lengths greater than 4 Å. pass through the filter (see Fig. 11). This beryllium filter is used for wave lengths between 4 and 6 Å. For wave lengths greater than 8 Å. beryllium alone is not effective because the second-order reflections of 4 Å. and greater readily pass through the beryllium. The use of 4 in. of beryllium and 10 in. of beryllium oxide scatters neutrons of wave length shorter than 4.66 Å. from the beam. This filter gives relatively pure beams up to

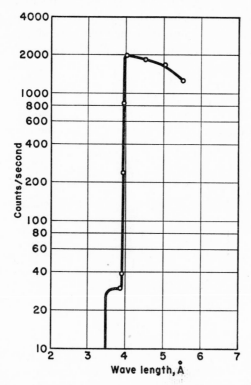

FIG. 11. Effect of a beryllium filter on the intensity of neutrons as a function of wave length.

8.75 Å; for example, the transmission of the filter for 6.6-Å. neutrons is about 0.96, for the second-order 3.3-Å. neutrons it is about $10^{-10}$, and for third and higher orders about $10^{-8}$. The addition of 2 in. of microcrystalline bismuth reduces the background for measurements between 8.25 and 8.75 Å. For wave lengths longer than 8.75 Å. a high-transmission mechanical monochromator (see p. 482) in conjunction with the mica crystal is used to cut out the higher orders.

To measure the transmission of a sample at a given velocity, the intensity of the beam is measured, first without the sample present and then with the sample between the crystal and the detector. Background readings are obtained with the crystal set 1° from $\theta$. The angle of incidence, $\theta$, can then be changed to obtain the transmission at other neutron energies from 0.0001 to 10 ev. At the higher energies the angle of incidence is very small, and at lower energies the higher order reflections interfere. One important advantage of the crystal spectrometer is that the beam is essentially monoenergetic; that is, the only neutrons that pass through the sample are those that have the energy given by the Bragg equation. Consequently, by measurement of the activation of the sample, the cross section of certain isotopes can be determined for specific neutron energies.

### 7.3. Pulsed Accelerators

Block diagrams showing the general principles of the modulated cyclotron velocity selector (4, 14, 87, 173) are given in Figs. 12 and 13. Modulation of the ion-accelerating potential in the source of a cyclotron

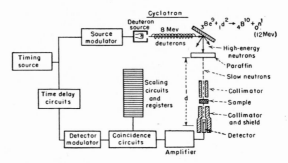

Fig. 12. Block diagram of a pulsed cyclotron velocity selector.

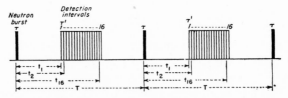

Fig. 13. Principle of a time-of-flight velocity selector.

causes short bursts of deuterons to hit a beryllium target. This produces fast neutrons for short periods of $\tau$ $\mu$sec. (variable from 2 to 1024 $\mu$sec. in the Columbia University neutron spectrometer). After being slowed down in paraffin, they travel toward the detector placed at a distance $d$ (6 meters) from the source. The neutrons arriving at the detector after $t_1$ $\mu$sec. (except for a small correction for the time necessary to accelerate the deuterons and to slow down the neutrons) are counted for a period of $\tau'$ $\mu$sec. This period is usually the same as the time of the neutron burst.

The time of flight of this group of neutrons is then $t_1/d$ $\mu$sec./meter or their velocity is $d/t_1$. At the end of this first detection interval, a second coincidence unit is turned on for $\tau'$ $\mu$sec. to count the neutrons arriving after a time of $t_2$ $\mu$sec. In this way a total of 64 scaling units count the neutrons arriving at the detector during each of the 64 successive detection intervals of $\tau'$ $\mu$sec. each.

After a time $T$—which may be 1024 $\mu$sec., for example—another burst of neutrons is produced, and the neutrons are again counted at each detection interval. The time between bursts can be adjusted in steps from 256 to 32,768 $\mu$sec., and the detection may be started at any delay time $t_1$ after the start of the burst. Also both the duration of the burst $\tau$ and of the detection interval $\tau'$ can be varied from 2 to 1024 $\mu$sec. With this

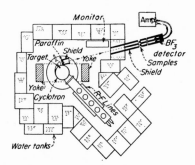

Fig. 14. General arrangement of a pulsed cyclotron, paraffin moderator, flight path, sample, and detectors.

system, the number of neutrons arriving at the detector as a function of time can be determined in any desired range of neutron energies from 0.001 to 10,000 ev. The resolution function is approximately triangular and constant for a specified setting of the apparatus when measured on the time-of-flight basis.

The general arrangement of the cyclotron is shown diagrammatically in Fig. 14. Neutrons emerging from the paraffin source are collimated by thick shields of boron carbide. They then pass through the sample and into the detector, which consists of a proportional counter 10 cm. long and 5.0 cm. in diameter, filled with 50 cm. of $BF_3$ enriched in $B^{10}$. Actually two channels with associated detectors, circuits, and scaling units are provided. Alternating the container plus sample with an identical empty container between the two channels yields duplicate determinations of the transmission. An average of the values obtained in this way improves the accuracy of the transmission measurements by reducing the effects of fluctuations in the intensity of the neutron beam. The effects of fluctuations are also minimized by counting the neutrons arriving at the counters for equal amounts of total neutron production rather than for equal intervals of time. A uranium fission chamber placed within the cyclotron enclosure is used for this purpose. Detailed discussion of the operation of the cyclotron velocity selector is given in papers by Rainwater, Havens, Wu, Dunning, and their associates (174).

A 60-in. cyclotron at Brookhaven National Laboratories operates similarly to the Columbia 36-in. cyclotron described above. It accelerates a 1.2 ma. pulsed beam of deuterons to 21 Mev. when they hit a beryllium target giving a peak neutron intensity of $3 \times 10^{14}$ in the burst compared with $6 \times 10^{13}$ for the 36-in. cyclotron. Instead of a $B^{10}F_3$ neutron detector there is used in certain types of measurements a circular disk of the sample material at the detector position to detect by use of sodium iodide crystals the $\gamma$ rays emitted when the neutron is captured. The intensity of the $\gamma$ rays without and then with the material in the sample position gives data for calculating some characteristics of the resonance levels.

The 170-in. Columbia University synchrocyclotron operating at 380 Mev. with 300 ma. of protons in the pulse at a tungsten target gives more than $10^{17}$ neutrons/sec. peak intensity in the burst. The duration of the pulse at the source is $\tau_s = 0.05$ $\mu$sec. with 16,667 $\mu$sec. between bursts; detector on time, $\tau' = 0.1$ to 256 $\mu$sec.; 128 channels; source to detector $= 35$ meters; best resolution attained $= 0.003$ $\mu$sec./meter or $dt/t = \frac{1}{1000}$, whichever is greater. With this resolution, using an $(n,\gamma)$ detector as described above for the Brookhaven cyclotron as well as an additional absorber before the detector to determine transmission of the sample, one can measure rather narrowly spaced resonance absorption peaks. Thus the 40.38- and 41.56-ev. resonances in silver are well resolved. The separation of the previously reported single resonance in tantalum at 76.9 ev. into three resonances at 76.39, 77.25, and 78.35 ev. illustrates the resolution that can be obtained with this apparatus.

Van de Graaff accelerators can also be used for pulsed sources of neutrons (58, 86, 88, 139, 208). For example, at Oak Ridge National Laboratories 50 $\mu$a. of 2.5 Mev. protons hitting on a lithium target gives peak intensity of $5 \times 10^8$ neutrons/sec. in pulses 0.01 $\mu$sec. in duration. Rapid repetition at 2 $\mu$sec. between pulses can be used since slow neutrons are not produced. This spectrometer compares favorably in intensity and resolution with others in the 1- to 40-kev. region which use monochromatic neutrons from thin targets.

A small pulse tranformer accelerator has been designed and tested at Columbia University (86) for a laboratory source of neutrons. It accelerates 100-ma. pulses of deuterons to 0.4 Mev., which then hit a zirconium-tritium target to give a peak intensity of $3 \times 10^{12}$ neutrons/sec. Pulses 1 $\mu$sec. long and $10^4$ to $10^5$ $\mu$sec. apart can be produced and measured with a 64-channel analyzer for 5 to 512 $\mu$sec. per channel.

Electron accelerators (44) represented by the Harwell linear electron accelerator (226), the Yale linear electron accelerator (187), and the General Electric betatron can easily be used for pulsed sources of neutrons. When a 3.2-Mev., 100-ma. beam of electrons hits a target such as lead, high-energy $\gamma$ rays are produced. A $(\gamma,n)$ reaction with $D_2O$ or Be then produces $3 \times 10^{12}$ neutrons/sec. in 2-$\mu$sec. pulses (44). Increasing the energy of the electrons above 10 Mev. allows the use of one target for the production of both the $\gamma$ rays from the electrons and the neutrons from the $\gamma$ rays. The existence of very large $(\gamma,n)$ resonances above 10 Mev. in many nuclei makes this possible. Thus, with 35 ma. of electron current at 13 Mev. about $10^{14}$ neutrons are produced per second during the burst when the electrons strike a thick uranium target. Similarly when the General Electric betatron (62) accelerates 30 ma. of electrons to 100 Mev., a 0.1-$\mu$sec. burst of over $10^{15}$ neutrons per second is produced by bombardment of a uranium target. The Yale electron linear accelerator (187) has been modified to operate at 10 Mev. with an electron current of 100 ma. to give about $10^{14}$ neutrons per second in the pulse.

Of course the difficulty with most of these pulsed accelerators is that they are too expensive in original cost and operation to serve as a routine analytical instrument. Other methods can in general be used more cheaply. However as time goes on in this nuclear age, the chemist may at times be as concerned with particular nuclei as with chemical elements. Neutron spectrometers capable of good resolution and high intensity may then warrant application to practical chemical analysis. With the development of smaller laboratory machines, such as Van de Graaff accelerators, pulse transformers, and small cyclotrons as well as simpler timing and analyzer circuits, pulsed accelerator attachments will undoubtedly find many useful applications.

## 8. Other Methods of Selecting Neutrons for Interactions

### 8.1. Fast Neutrons from Thermal Neutrons

When uranium is placed in a beam of thermal neutrons from a reactor, as illustrated in Fig. 15, each slow neutron absorbed gives more than two fast neutrons as a result of fission. Hughes, Spatz, and Goldstein (64, 105, 107) used this method to measure cross sections for fission-energy neutrons. Activation of a foil or thin sample of the material in the thermal beam before it hits the uranium plate ($I_{foil}$) and of a second foil or thin sample covered with cadmium and placed behind the uranium plate ($I_{\text{Cd-foil}}$) gives data for calculating the cross section for fission energy neutrons:

$$\sigma = \frac{\sigma_{th}}{R} \frac{I_{\text{Cd-foil}}}{I_{\text{foil}} - I_{\text{Cd-foil}}} \tag{8.1}$$

Here $\sigma_{th}$ is the known activation cross section for thermal neutrons and $R$ is the ratio of fast to slow neutrons at the uranium plate. Since these cross sections are small, direct-transmission measurements may not be too useful for analytical determinations. However, the fast neutrons, especially if the irradiation is carried out inside a uranium fuel element or inside $U^{235}$ metal within the nuclear reactor, can produce $(n,p)$ and $(n,\alpha)$ reactions (103) for preparation of tracers or activation analysis. For example, $P^{32}$ is produced by the $(n,p)$ reaction $S^{32}(n,p)P^{32}$. Fast neutrons also find use in the study of the effect of dislocations of atoms in solid-state studies.

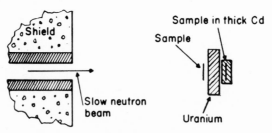

Fig. 15. Uranium converter for obtaining fast neutrons from thermal neutrons.

The reaction $T(d,n)He^4$, as previously discussed, is used to produce neutrons in particle accelerators when deuteron beams with energies of about 200 kev. hit a target of tritium combined with zirconium. The neutrons produced have an energy of about 14 Mev. Deuterium bombarded by tritons, $D(t,n)He^4$, is the same reaction and can be produced in a nuclear reactor with slow neutrons as follows. When LiOD, as a slurry in heavy water (2), is placed in a flux of slow neutrons, the reaction $Li^6(n,\alpha)H^3$ occurs. The tritons with 2.73-Mev. energy hit the deuterium to yield 14-Mev. neutrons. Similarly the use of LiF gives neutrons by the reaction $Li(t,n)$ but the energy is lower than for the reaction of tritons with deuterium.

Thermal neutrons from nuclear reactors can be used to produce radio-isotopes for photoneutron sources which give nearly monoenergetic neutrons. The energies produced range from 30 kev. for the 60-day $Sb^{124}$, $Be(\gamma,n)$ source to 830 kev. for the 14.8-hr. $Na^{24}$, $Be(\gamma,n)$ (224). Other similar photoneutron sources are the $\gamma$ emitters, $Na^{24}$, $Mn^{56}$, $Ca^{72}$, and $La^{140}$ mixed with $D_2O$ or Be. Cross sections of a number of nuclei for the 30-kev. neutrons from an $Sb^{124}$-Be source have been measured (108).

When such a source is surrounded by a moderator such as paraffin, slow neutrons are obtained. Such moderated photoneutron sources will in general be more useful for chemical purposes than the higher energy ones. The analytical application of the production of neutrons by radioactivation of samples containing certain elements will be discussed in a later section.

### 8.2. Resonance Detectors

Resonance detectors (71, 219) combined with suitable filters may at times be conveniently employed to measure transmissions of samples at the resonance energy of the detector. For example, the transmission of a substance for neutrons with an energy of 1.46 ev. (the resonance-absorp-energy for indium) can be measured by use of cadmium-covered indium

TABLE V

*Characteristics of Resonance Detectors and Filters*

| Element | $E_0$, resonance energy (ev.) | $a\sigma_0$ Calculated (barns) | $\sigma_t$ Max. observed at $E_0$ | Energy of other smaller resonances (ev.) (See Table VII) |
|---------|------|--------|--------|-----------------------------|
| Gd | 0.030 | 49,400 | 42,000 | 2.0, 2.6, 6.4, 7.7 |
| Sm | 0.096 | 18,000 | 16,000 | 0.87, 3.45, 4.9, 8.2 |
| Cd | 0.178 | 7,660 | 7,200 | 18, 27, 66 |
| Eu | 0.461 | 13,400 | 11,000 | 0.327, 1.06, 1.76, 2.46, 3.34 |
| Rh | 1.26 | 7,540 | 4,500 | |
| In | 1.458 | 41,900 | 30,000 | 3.86, 4.71, 9.10, 12.1 |
| Re | 2.18 | 6,430 | 3,500 | 4.40, 5.9, 7.2 |
| Te | 2.33 | 662 | 450 | 8.3, 25 |
| Tm | 3.92 | 72,800 | 16,500 | 14.4, 17.6, 29.1, 35.2 |
| Ta | 4.28 | 27,600 | 13,000 | 10.38, 13.95, 20.5, 24.1 |
| Au | 4.91 | 37,000 | 30,000 | 61.5 |
| Ag | 5.2 | 16,700 | 12,500 | 16.6, 30.9, 40.8, 42.4 |
| Cs | 5.9 | 10,700 | 2,600 | 22.6, 47.8, 83.1 |
| U | 6.70 | 22,900 | 7,000 | 21.0, 26.9 |
| W | 19.2 | 30,000 | 14,500 | 4.15, 7.8, 22, 28 |
| Co | 132 | 9,850 | 7,000 | 475 |
| Mn | 337 | 3,860 | 2,000 | 1010, 2400 |
| Na | 2900 | 448 | 300 | |

foil as a detector. The radioactivity induced in the foil with the sample in the beam, divided by the radioactivity induced in the foil with the sample out of the beam, gives the transmission of the sample at this energy. Other resonance detectors besides indium are listed in Table V.

If more than one activation resonance is present in the detector, then one or another of the levels can be discriminated against by use of the proper boron or cadmium filter. Although this method has certain limitations, it can be useful in determining the transmission at a particular energy when a velocity selector is not available. Cross sections for indium resonance neutrons have been tabulated by Marshall (140) and by Hanstein (82) and can be used for the determination of composition in appropriate samples.

Resonance detectors are particularly useful for quantitive determination of the element of the detector. By use of a cadmium-filtered beam of neutrons, the ratio of the activity induced in a thin (0.1 mg./cm.² or less) indium foil with a sample containing indium in the beam, to the activity when the sample is out of the beam gives a sensitive method for the determination of indium. Other resonance detectors can be used for self-indication in a similar manner.

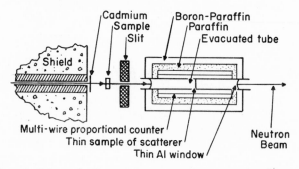

FIG. 16. Schematic diagram for a resonance-scattering detector.

Resonance-scattering detectors can also be used to determine transmissions for neutrons of the resonance energy or for self-indication (158). A beam of cadmium-filtered, i.e., epi-$C$, neutrons passes into a Langsdorf counter containing a thin foil of a resonance scatterer such as manganese. This counter is an evacuated tube surrounded by an annular $B^{10}F_3$ proportional neutron counter, as illustrated in Fig. 16. It is surrounded by paraffin to scatter and reflect neutrons scattered by the detector foil back into the counter. Those neutrons that are not scattered by the foil are either absorbed or pass out the end of the evacuated tube and thus do not contribute to the counting rate. Neutrons of the energy corresponding to the scattering resonance (337 ev. for Mn) are strongly scattered, and, after being slowed down in the paraffin, many of them are reflected back into the $B^{10}F_3$ counter, where they are absorbed and counted. The high efficiency of the cylindrical geometry and the fact that the high intensity of other neutrons in the beam does not result in a high background make this a useful analytical method. Thus transmission of a sample for 337-ev. neutrons with good resolution can readily be determined.

When the above mentioned arrangement is used with samples containing manganese, strong self-indication results and relatively small quantities of manganese can be determined. It has been estimated (158), for example, that 0.10% Mn can be determined to ±0.02% Mn. Cobalt with a scattering resonance at 132 ev. can also be used in a similar manner. The method is limited by the fact that there are not many elements with large scattering resonances in the low energy region.

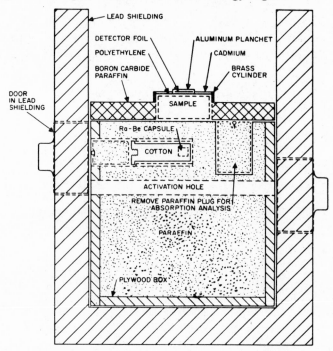

FIG. 17. Arrangement of a 0.5-curie Ra-Be neutron source illustrating the use of a resonance detector. A 4-in. wall of lead bricks and a $\frac{1}{16}$-in. sheet of cadmium are used for protection against radiation.

If a sensitive $\gamma$-ray detector such as a scintillation counter surrounds a thin foil of a resonance absorber in an arrangement such as described above, the prompt $\gamma$ rays emitted can be used as a measure of the intensity of the resonance-energy neutrons. Transmission of samples for this energy can then be measured and compared with standards for analysis. Samples containing the same element as the detector foil could be analyzed most effectively. Alternatively a sample containing a resonance absorber could be placed in the foil position. A determination of the intensity of the $\gamma$-rays emitted as compared to suitable standards can serve as a method of analysis.

A radium-beryllium source with which these detectors may be used in a laboratory is illustrated in Fig. 17. Neutron sources of this or other types (Table II) can be arranged for transmission experiments using either the radioactivation of foils or $BF_3$ counters. Samples can also be introduced for radioactivation analysis. Results obtained with this source will be described later.

### 8.3. Resonance Filters

If a beam of neutrons from a reactor or other source is available, resonance filters can be used to obtain cross sections at definite energies. The experimental arrangement is illustrated in Fig. 18. With the cadmium

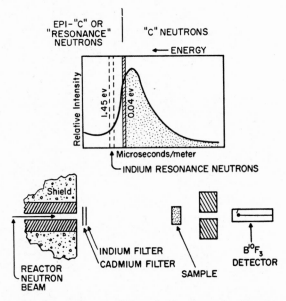

FIG. 18. Illustration of the use of filters in the determination of cross sections for neutrons of known energies or energy ranges.

remaining in the beam all the time, to remove low-energy neutrons, the "indium difference" is obtained with the sample out of the beam by subtracting the intensity with the indium filter in the beam from that with the indium filter out of the beam. This gives the intensity of the indium resonance neutrons, called the "open" or "sample-out" intensity. This indium difference is taken again with the sample in the beam. Then the transmission is

$$T = \frac{\text{(indium difference)}_{\text{sample in}}}{\text{(indium difference)}_{\text{sample out}}} \qquad (8.2)$$

The thickness of the cadmium should be sufficient (0.020 to 0.030 in.) to remove thermal neutrons without removing too many resonance neutrons, and the indium filter should not be greater than about 0.02 g./cm.$^2$; otherwise resonances at other energies will significantly affect the results.

### 8.4. Cadmium and Boron Filters

For certain analyses, particularly those in which the sample contains elements that have resonance peaks near the thermal region, it may be advantageous to change the energy distribution of the beam with appropriate filters. Cadmium filters can, for example, be used to obtain the transmission for neutrons below 0.4 ev. As cadmium has a strong absorption resonance at 0.178 ev., a thickness of about 0.6 mm. removes practically all neutrons with energies below 0.4 ev. The neutrons not transmitted by such cadmium filters are called $c$ neutrons.

By making measurements with and without a cadmium filter, one can obtain transmissions for neutrons with energies above and below the cadmium cutoff. Four measurements are required:

1. Open-beam intensity $I_0$
2. Intensity with the sample in the beam, $I_{sample}$
3. Intensity with the cadmium filter in the beam, $I_{Cd}$
4. Intensity with both cadmium filter and the sample in the beam, $I_{Cd+sample}$

The transmission $T_c$ for the $c$ neutrons is

$$T_c = \frac{(I_{sample} - I_{Cd+sample})}{(I_0 - I_{Cd})} = \frac{(\text{Cd-difference})_{sample\ in}}{(\text{Cd-difference})_{sample\ out}} \tag{8.3}$$

and the transmission $T_{ec}$ for the neutrons with energies above the cadmium cutoff, i.e., epi-$c$ neutrons, is given by

$$T_{ec} = \frac{I_{Cd+sample}}{I_{Cd}} \tag{8.4}$$

These transmission values can then be used as will be described later for determining the composition of the sample.

Another filtering material that has been particularly useful in neutron measurements is boron, because the cross section is known to be directly proportional to $1/v$ or to $1/\sqrt{E}$. By means of boron filters of different thicknesses, the energy distribution of the neutron beam can be changed. The thicker the boron filter, the higher the average energy of the neutron beam. In this way the cross section of a sample for different average energy distributions may be determined.

By use of a cadmium filter (0.03 to 0.04 g./cm.$^2$ Cd) and a boron filter (0.2 to 0.3 g./cm.$^2$ of B), the transmission of a sample for a group of neutrons primarily in the 0.5 to 10-ev. range can be obtained. The cadmium is left in the beam at all times and the difference between the intensity with the boron filter out and in the beam is obtained, i.e., the "boron difference" for cadmium-filtered neutrons. This is then repeated with the sample in the beam. The transmission is then

$$T = \frac{(I_{Cd} - I_{Cd+B})_{\text{sample in}}}{(I_{Cd} - I_{Cd+B})_{\text{sample out}}} \tag{8.5}$$

An analytical method based on such measurements would be useful for a substance of high-free-atom-scattering cross section in a material that has low scattering and no strong resonances in this region. A quantity of an element with strong resonances in the 0.5- to 10-ev. range might also be estimated in favorable cases by comparison with suitable standards. Resonance-scattering detectors can be used for transmission at higher energies as described previously (p. 476).

Boron filters are also useful in determining resonance energies in certain cases (134) as an aid in identification of a resonance absorber. This is done as follows. With 0.030 in. of Cd permanently in the beam to remove neutrons with energies below about 0.4 ev., a thin sample of material such as gold is placed in the beam. The activation of the gold foil is then measured with successive thicknesses of boron in front of the sample. From the slope of a plot of the log of the activity of the foil against the thickness of the boron, the cross section of boron, $\sigma_r$, for gold resonance neutrons is calculated. With the known cross section, $\sigma_{th}$ of boron at thermal energies ( 0.025 ev.) and the $1/\sqrt{E}$ variation in cross section with energy, the resonance energy is

$$E_r = E_{th} \times \frac{\sigma_{th}^2}{\sigma_r^2}$$

This method gives reasonably good values for resonance energies where single resonances are involved. If two resonances are present, the plot referred to above will have two straight-line portions. This filter method does not have the flexibility, resolution, or accuracy of the methods employing spectrometers or velocity selectors.

### 8.5. Use of Polycrystalline Filters for Long-Wave-Length Neutrons

When a beam of neutrons passes through a polycrystalline material consisting of many small grains oriented in all directions, scattering from the beam will occur whenever Bragg's equation, $n\lambda = 2d \sin \theta$, is satisfied (Fig. 19). As there are many crystals, any one set of planes will be oriented at many angles; also there are a number of different spacings, $d$, between planes. Consequently, if the sample is thick enough, there is a high probability that neutrons of all wave lengths less than $2d_{max}$ will be scattered from the beam. Here $d_{max}$ is the largest spacing between crystal planes. When these planes are perpendicular to the direction of neutron motion, sin $\theta = 1$ and $\lambda_{max} = 2d_{max}$. In other words most of the neutrons with a wave length greater than twice the distance between the crystal planes with greatest $d$ will readily pass through the crystal without being scattered.

Materials such as graphite ($\lambda_{max} = 6.70$ Å.), beryllium ($\lambda_{max} = 3.95$ Å.), beryllium oxide ($\lambda_{max} = 4.66$ Å.), or bismuth ($\lambda_{max} = 6.8$ Å.), which have low-absorption cross sections for neutrons, can serve as filters. The beam passing through such filters contains neutrons of all wave lengths greater than $\lambda_{max}$. Although the beam is not monochromatic, there is a sharp cutoff on the short-wave-length side, as illustrated in Fig. 11. The use of such filters in conjunction with the crystal monochromator or the slow chopper has already been mentioned. If such monochromators are

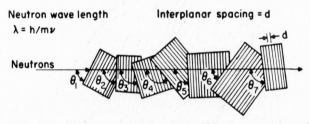

Fig. 19. Polycrystalline filter. Neutrons are incident on successive microcrystals at angles $\theta_1$, $\theta_2$, $\theta_3$, etc. If the wave length and $\theta_i$ are such that $\lambda = 2d \sin \theta_i$, the neutron will be scattered from the beam. Those with $\lambda > 2d$ will pass through undiminished in intensity except for absorption, nuclear-incoherent, and lattice-vibration effects.

not available, transmission measurements for groups of long-wave-length neutrons can still be made using such filters. These may be of value in chemical analysis when it is desired to eliminate some of the crystalline effects that might arise in a series of samples. Thus measurements with a filter consisting of 4 in. of beryllium and 10 in. of beryllium oxide in the beam would aid in those cases where Bragg reflections fall below 4.66 Å., etc.

### 8.6. Mechanical Monochromators

Several mechanical monochromators have been built (47) to obtain slow neutrons of a known wave length. In principle they consist of a series of cadmium-covered disks containing slots and mounted in a shaft parallel to the neutron beam. Others have spiral grooves on a large shaft (Fig. 20). As the shaft rotates, only those neutrons with velocities correct for the speed of rotation and the pitch of the slots will pass through the monochrometer. While the resolution and intensity is not so favorable as with the slow chopper, such monochromators do have the advantage of giving neutrons of one particular velocity or wave-length band. These are particularly useful for activation measurements as a function of wave length.

For many transmission measurements good resolution will not be needed, and this will make it possible to obtain greater intensity. Rough mechanical monochromators will also be useful to cut out higher orders of reflected neutrons with crystal spectrometers. Such a selector has been designed by Dr. Norman Holt (97) and constructed by Brookhaven

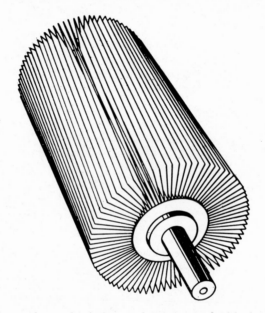

FIG. 20. Rotor of a mechanical monochromator used with the crystal spectrometer to allow passage of first order but not second or higher orders.

National Laboratories for use with the crystal spectrometer in use by Floyd Gould and the authors for cross-section measurements at long wave lengths. It was designed to have a high transmission (about 85%) and a broad-wave-length resolution of about 70%. That is, if its speed is set so that the center of its range is 9.0 Å., then neutrons in the range 9.0 ± 3.2 Å. will pass through the monochrometer. The mica crystal of the spectrometer selects a narrow band in this wave-length range. A beryllium filter removes all the high-energy neutrons and the monochrometer removes the second-order 4.5-Å. neutrons. This monochrometer is particularly valuable, as it is difficult to obtain filter systems for use with a crystal spectrometer at wave lengths greater than about 9 Å.

From the discussions in this section it can be seen that the interaction of neutrons with materials may be measured over a very wide range of energies ($10^6$ to $10^{-4}$ ev.), velocities, or wave lengths. Not all these regions appear to be useful as yet for chemical analyses, but the means of measuring the effects have been developed in case they should be useful for one purpose or another.

## 9. Use of Thermal Neutron Beams

### 9.1. Distribution of Neutrons in a Thermal Beam

When neutrons are in equilibrium with the atoms that have slowed them down, they have a Maxwellian velocity distribution (see p. 454) given by (103, 121)

$$dn = \frac{4n}{\sqrt{\pi} v_0^3} v^2 e^{-\frac{v^2}{v_0^2}} dv \tag{9.1}$$

Here $dn$ is the number of neutrons per cubic centimeter in the velocity range $dv$ at velocity $v$ cm./sec., $n$ is the number of neutrons per cubic centimeter, and $v_0$ is the most probable velocity as given by $\frac{1}{2} m v_0^2 = kT$. At room temperature (20° C.), $v_0 = 2200$ m./sec., $\lambda = 1.8$ Å. or a kinetic energy $= 0.0253$ ev. The average velocity is greater than the most probable velocity by $2/\sqrt{\pi} = 1.128$, as can be shown by integration of the foregoing equation. The average neutron kinetic energy is $\frac{3}{2} kT$ and the root-mean-square velocity is $\sqrt{\frac{3}{2}} v_0$.

Equation (9.1) refers to numbers of neutrons per cubic centimeter in a given velocity range. However, for a beam of neutrons from a moderator, it is the flux ($nv$) that is of interest. The flux distribution in the beam is the same as that in the moderator and can be obtained by multiplying both sides of the equation by the velocity $v$. The most probable flux is then found by differentiation to be at a velocity $\sqrt{\frac{3}{2}} v_0 = 1.22 v_0$, that is, at a slightly higher velocity than the most probable velocity in the Maxwell distribution. If the detector is a $BF_3$ counter whose response to neutrons varies as $1/v$, then the counting rate will follow the Maxwell velocity distribution rather than the flux distribution. The total counting rate will then be given by

$$R = C \int v^2 e^{-\frac{v^2}{v_0^2}} dv \tag{9.2}$$

rather than the integral of the flux. Here $R$ is the counting rate and $C$ is a constant.

It can be seen from the foregoing discussion that transmission measurements with a beam of thermal neutrons, while it does not give measurements at a specific velocity, does give results for neutrons of a known distribution of velocities. Depending on the place in a reactor from which the neutrons are taken, or on the thickness of a paraffin moderator used with a particle accelerator, the thermal neutron beam will contain appreciable numbers of high-energy neutrons (frequently called resonance neutrons). The ratio of those neutrons passing a 0.030-in. cadmium sheet to the total beam is a measure of the number of neutrons with energies higher than about 0.4 ev. This "cadmium ratio" varies (103) from about 1 in 30 (3%) for neutrons taken from the lattice of a thermal reactor to about 1 in 3000 (0.03%) for neutrons taken from the best position in the reflector when measured with a 1/v detector such as a BF$_3$ counter or by activation of 1/v foils.

### 9.2. The Cadmium or c Neutrons of a Thermal Beam

When a thermal neutron beam is used for transmission measurements, the effects of the higher energy neutrons are usually eliminated by taking a cadmium difference for both the sample-in and the sample-out measurements. When a cadmium sheet about 0.030 in. thick is placed in the beam, only those neutrons with energies greater than about 0.4 ev. pass and affect the counter. This count rate is subtracted from the count rate without the cadmium to give the cadmium-difference neutrons, which are frequently called c neutrons (p. 478). The ratio of the cadmium difference with the sample in the beam to that without the sample in the beam gives the transmission of the sample for thermal neutrons with energies from 0 to 0.4 ev. Many of the early cross sections of the elements for thermal neutrons were determined in this way (51). Such measurements can now be used in certain cases to be described in the following sections for analytical determinations.

Some complications arise in the use of a beam with a rather wide spread of energies. Neutrons are removed from a beam as a result of both absorption and scattering. For samples which have large absorption effects compared with scattering, the sample thickness will affect the results. There is a preferential absorption of the slower neutrons because of the 1/v relationship. Increasing the thickness of the sample will tend to remove more of the slower neutrons, and so the beam contains more of the faster neutrons as it passes through the sample. This "hardening" of the beam makes it necessary to apply a correction, which can be done with the aid of the "Bethe hardening curve" (18, 103). For very thin samples (with scattering subtracted) the ratio $(\sigma_{exp}/\sigma_{v_0})$ of observed absorption cross section for a pure material to that at the most probable velocity (2200 m./sec., 0.025 ev.) is $2/\sqrt{\pi}$, or 1.128; that is, the observed cross section for a beam of thermal neutrons will be 1.128 times that listed for 0.025 ev. in the tables. Since the accuracy for thin samples of high transmission is not good (p. 529), thicker samples with transmissions from 10 to 50% are usually used. At 50% transmission, the foregoing ratio is very nearly 1, and the observed cross section is that for the most probable velocity (2200 m./sec., 0.025 ev.). For 10% transmission, the ratio of $\sigma_{exp}$ to $\sigma_{v_0}$ is only about 0.95. Thus the effect is not large except for very low transmissions arising from absorption. When the scattering is large compared with absorption, the hardening of the beam will be even smaller. Crystalline compounds of elements with low-absorption cross sections may have relatively high scattering owing to diffraction effects (p. 480). Compounds containing hydrogen also have relatively large scattering effects.

When thermal neutron beams are used for chemical determinations many of the complications referred to in the above-mentioned treatment can be obviated by use of standards with compositions and physical characteristics similar to the unknown samples.

### 9.3. Total Cross Sections of the Elements for Thermal Neutrons

In general, any element that has a high cross section can be determined if it is in a matrix or on a base material that has a relatively lower cross section. A partial list of elements with high cross sections in the thermal region is given in Table VI. The values are total cross sections (absorption plus scattering) for a neutron energy of 0.025 ev. They have been estimated from data reported in the literature, primarily from compilations such as the ones by Way et al. (225) and the compilation of the A. E. C. cross-section committee (106).

### 9.4. Analysis by Transmission of Thermal Neutrons Beams

It is possible in certain cases to use a thermal neutron beam without filters or without taking a cadmium difference, provided that the cross sections of the elements of interest are first measured with the particular beam. Alternatively a calibration curve with samples of known composition can be constructed as described later. To make an analysis by transmission measurements, the intensity of the beam is measured, first without the sample in the beam ($I_0$) and then with the sample in the beam ($I$). This gives the transmission $T = I/I_0$. As shown previously, the number of atoms in the beam is related to the transmission by the equation

$$- \ln T = \Sigma_i n_i' \sigma_i \tag{9.3}$$

where $n_i'$ is the number of atoms of $i$th kind per square centimeter and $\sigma_i$ is the cross section of the $i$th atom in square centimeters.

If the cross section and the amount of one element are such that they cause practically all the decrease in the intensity of the neutron beam,

## TABLE VI

*Total Thermal Cross Sections of the Elements*

| Atomic No. | Element | $\sigma_{abs}$ | $\bar{\sigma}_s$ | $\sigma_t$ |
|---|---|---|---|---|
| 1 | H | 0.33 | 38 | 38.3 |
| 1 | D | 0.0005 | 7.0 | 7.0 |
| 2 | He | — | 0.8 | 0.8 |
| 3 | Li | 71.0 | 1.4 | 72.4 |
| 4 | Be | 0.010 | 7 | 7.0 |
| 5 | B | 755 | 4 | 759 |
| 6 | C | 0.0032 | 4.8 | 4.8 |
| 7 | N | 1.88 | 10 | 11.9 |
| 8 | O | <0.0002 | 4.2 | 4.2 |
| 9 | F | <0.001 | 3.9 | 3.9 |
| 10 | Ne | <2.8 | 2.4 | 5.2 |
| 11 | Na | 0.505 | 4.0 | 4.5 |
| 12 | Mg | 0.063 | 3.6 | 3.7 |
| 13 | Al | 0.230 | 1.4 | 1.6 |
| 14 | Si | 0.13 | 1.7 | 1.8 |
| 15 | P | 0.19 | 5 | 5.2 |
| 16 | S | 0.49 | 1.1 | 1.6 |
| 17 | Cl | 31.6 | 16 | 47.6 |
| 18 | A | 0.62 | 1.5 | 2.1 |
| 19 | K | 1.97 | 1.5 | 3.5 |
| 20 | Ca | 0.43 | | |
| 21 | Sc | 24.0 | 24 | 48.0 |
| 22 | Ti | 5.6 | 4 | 9.6 |
| 23 | V | 5.1 | 5 | 10.1 |
| 24 | Cr | 2.9 | 3.0 | 5.9 |
| 25 | Mn | 13.2 | 2.3 | 15.5 |
| 26 | Fe | 2.53 | 11.0 | 13.5 |
| 27 | Co | 37.0 | 7 | 44.0 |
| 28 | Ni | 4.6 | 17.5 | 22.1 |
| 29 | Cu | 3.69 | 7.2 | 10.9 |
| 30 | Zn | 1.06 | 3.6 | 4.7 |
| 31 | Ga | 2.77 | 4 | 6.8 |
| 32 | Ge | 2.35 | 3 | 5.4 |
| 33 | As | 4.1 | 6 | 10.1 |
| 34 | Se | 11.8 | 11 | 22.8 |
| 35 | Br | 6.6 | 6 | 12.6 |
| 36 | Kr | 28 | 7.2 | 35.2 |
| 37 | Rb | 0.70 | 12 | 12.7 |
| 38 | Sr | 1.16 | 10 | 11.2 |
| 39 | Y | 1.38 | 3 | 4.4 |
| 40 | Zr | 0.180 | 8 | 8.2 |
| 41 | Nb | 1.1 | 5 | 6.1 |
| 42 | Mo | 2.5 | 7 | 9.5 |
| 43 | Tc | 100 | | |

TABLE VI. (*Continued*)

| Atomic No. | Element | $\sigma_{abs}$ | $\bar{\sigma}_s$ | $\sigma_T$ |
|---|---|---|---|---|
| 44 | Ru | 2.46 | 6 | 8.46 |
| 45 | Rh | 150 | 5 | 155 |
| 46 | Pd | 8.0 | 3.6 | 11.6 |
| 47 | Ag | 62 | 6 | 68 |
| 48 | Cd | 2550 | 7 | 2557 |
| 49 | In | 190 | 2.2 | 192 |
| 50 | Sn | 0.60 | 4 | 4.60 |
| 51 | Sb | 5.5 | 4.3 | 9.8 |
| 52 | Te | 4.5 | 5 | 9.5 |
| 53 | I | 6.7 | 3.6 | 10.3 |
| 54 | Xe | 35 | 4.3 | 39.3 |
| 55 | Cs | 29.0 | 20.0 | 49.0 |
| 56 | Ba | 1.17 | 8 | 9.17 |
| 57 | La | 8.9 | 15 | 23.9 |
| 58 | Ce | 0.70 | 9 | 9.70 |
| 59 | Pr | 11.2 | | |
| 60 | Nd | 46 | | |
| 62 | Sm | 5500 | | |
| 63 | Eu | 4600 | 8 | 4608 |
| 64 | Gd | 46,000 | | |
| 65 | Tb | 44 | | |
| 66 | Dy | 1100 | 100 | 1200 |
| 67 | Ho | 64 | | |
| 68 | Er | 166 | 15 | 181 |
| 69 | Tm | 118 | | |
| 70 | Yb | 36 | 12 | 48 |
| 71 | Lu | 108 | | |
| 72 | Hf | 105 | 8 | 113 |
| 73 | Ta | 21.3 | 5 | 26.3 |
| 74 | W | 19.2 | 5.1 | 24.3 |
| 75 | Re | 84 | 14 | 98 |
| 76 | Os | 14.7 | 11 | 25.7 |
| 77 | Ir | 430 | | |
| 78 | Pt | 8.1 | 10 | 18.1 |
| 79 | Au | 98.0 | 9.3 | 107.3 |
| 80 | Hg | 380 | 20 | 400 |
| 81 | Tl | 3.3 | 14 | 17.3 |
| 82 | Pb | 0.170 | 11 | 11.2 |
| 83 | Bi | 0.032 | 9 | 9.03 |
| 89 | Ac | 510 | | |
| 90 | Th | 7 | 12.6 | 19.6 |
| 92 | U | 7.68 | | |
| 92 | U$^{235}$ | 687 | 10 | 697 |
| 93 | Np$^{237}$ | 170 | | |
| 94 | Pu$^{239}$ | 1065 | 9.6 | 1075 |

then the effect of the other elements can be neglected, and the number of atoms of the elements per square centimeter is given by

$$n' = -\frac{\ln T}{\sigma} = -\frac{2.303 \log T}{\sigma} \tag{9.4}$$

or

$$\mu = \frac{(-\ln T)M}{N\sigma} = \frac{2.303M \log 1/T}{N\sigma} \tag{9.5}$$

where $\mu$ is the grams/square centimeter of the element, $M$ is its atomic weight, and $N$ is Avogadro's number. The percentage of the element is then given by

$$\% \text{ of element} = \mu/G \times 100 \tag{9.6}$$

where $G$ is the total grams/square centimeter of the element and the matrix in which it occurs.

Binary mixtures in which one element has a greater cross section than the other can be analyzed if the cross sections of the two elements are known. In this case it is necessary to know both the thickness and the density of the sample to give the total grams of material per square centimeter. For such a mixture

$$2.303 \log 1/T = (n_A'\sigma_A + n_B'\sigma_B) = \frac{\mu_A N}{M_A}\sigma_A + \frac{\mu_B N}{M_B}\sigma_B \tag{9.7}$$

$\mu_A$ and $\mu_B$ are the grams/square centimeter of substances $A$ and $B$; $M_A$ and $M_B$ are their respective atomic or molecular weights. As the total grams/square centimeter of the sample is $G = \mu_A + \mu_B$, the $\mu_B = G - \mu_A$. Substitution in the equation above gives

$$2.303 \log 1/T = \mu_A \frac{N}{M_A}\sigma_A + (G - \mu_A)\frac{N}{M_B}\sigma_B \tag{9.8}$$
$$= \mu_A K_A + (G - \mu_A)K_B \tag{9.9}$$

where $K_A = N\sigma_A/M_A$ and $K_B = N\sigma_B/M_B$. Since $T$, $G$, and the constants $K_A$ and $K_B$ are known, $\mu_A$ may be calculated. Then

$$\% \text{ of } A = \frac{\mu_A}{G} \times 100$$

### 9.5. Approximate Equations for an Impurity

If a relatively high-cross-section impurity is present in a sample, its percentage can be estimated by determining the transmission and calculating the apparent cross section of the principal component. The difference between the cross section of the pure material $\sigma_A$ and that calculated with the impurity present $\sigma_c$ can then be related to the percentage of impurity (209). Thus, if there are $n_i'$ molecules per square centimeter of an impurity with $n_A'$ molecules per square centimeter of a given sample, the measured transmission is given by

$$T = e^{-(n_i'\sigma_i + n_A'\sigma_A)} \tag{9.10}$$

where $\sigma_i$ and $\sigma_A$ are the cross sections of the impurity and the sample. Then

$$\log 1/T = n_A'\sigma_A + n_i'\sigma_i \tag{9.11}$$

The cross section $\sigma_c$ calculated for the major component on the assumption that no impurity is present is given by

$$\sigma_c = \frac{\log 1/T}{n_c'} \tag{9.12}$$

or

$$\log 1/T = n_c'\sigma_c \tag{9.13}$$

where $T$ is the measured transmission. The number of atoms or molecules $n_c'$ is calculated from the measured grams per square centimeter $\mu$ assuming no impurity present, i.e., $n_c' = \mu N/M_A$. Since the total grams per square centimeter is $\mu = \mu_A + \mu_i$,

$$n_c'M_A/N = n_A'M_A/N + n_i'M_i/N \tag{9.14}$$

If the concentration and molecular weight of the impurity are such that $n_i'M_i$ is small compared to $n_A'M_A$ eq. (9.14) shows that $n_c' \approx n_A'$. From eq. (9.11) and (9.13)

$$n_c'\sigma_c = n_A'\sigma_A + n_i'\sigma_i \tag{9.15}$$

which, on substituting $n_c'$ for $n_A'$ and rearranging the terms, gives $n_i'\sigma_i = n_c'(\sigma_c - \sigma_A)$

or

$$n_i = \frac{n_c'\Delta\sigma}{\sigma_i} \tag{9.16}$$

Here $\Delta\sigma$ is the difference between the known cross section of the major component $A$ and that calculated from eq. (9.12). Substituting $\mu_i N/M_i$ for $n_i'$ and $\mu N/M_A$ for $n_c'$ gives

$$P_i = \frac{\mu_i}{\mu} = \frac{\Delta\sigma M_i}{\sigma_i M_A} \tag{9.17}$$

which is the weight fraction $P_i$ of the impurity. Thus from the increase in calculated cross section as compared with that of the pure material, the percentage of a known impurity can be estimated.

## 9.6. Analysis with c Neutrons

In order to define a thermal beam more closely, cadmium filters are used to correct for the effects of the higher energy (resonance) neutrons in the beam. The procedure for doing this has already been described (p. 479) in which the cadmium difference is obtained with the sample in and out of the beam. The transmission thus obtained is used in the fore-going equations. The cross sections used are those for cadmium-difference neutrons (p. 484).

### 9.7. Comparison with Standards

Instead of direct calculations based on the known cross section of the elements, it may be advantageous in many cases to prepare standards containing known concentrations of the element in a matrix similar to that of the unknown. Then from a plot of log $1/T$ vs. $\mu$, the value of $\mu$ for the unknown can be read. Alternatively, if the sample is the appropri-ate type, the addition technique can be used. When the transmission of the unknown sample has been obtained, the measurement can be repeated after more known amounts of the element being determined are added. Using the linear relationship of log $1/T$ vs. $\mu$, one can calculate the amount of the element initially present. This is the addition technique often used in other methods of analysis.

### 9.8. Examples of Possible Analyses

Reference to Tables IV and VI indicates the possibility of a number of analyses by simple transmission measurements with thermal neutrons such as cadmium in alloys with lead, bismuth, and tin; thickness of elec-troplated films of such elements as gold, silver, rhodium, cadmium, manganese, etc., on a base material of low cross section; hafnium in zirconium, indium in tin, tantalum in niobium; certain rare earths; hydrogen combined with, or dissolved in, metals; hydrogen in organic compounds; water in compounds that do not contain other combined hydrogen; etc.

### 9.9. Determination of Hydrogen by Thermal Neutron Transmission

An interesting application of the transmission of thermal neutrons was the determination of hydrogen in fluorocarbon polymers $(CF_2)_x$ by Burger and Rainwater (37) using the Columbia University cyclotron. Measurements were made with an empty cell, the unknown sample, and a standard sample of nearly the same composition as the unknown. Then, from the transmission measurements and the weight per square centi-meter, the percentage of fluorine atoms replaced by H atoms relative to a standard could be calculated, as illustrated in the following example.

If there are $n'$ $(CF_2)$ units per square centimeter of a pure fluoro-carbon in a sample and one assumes the cross sections of carbon and fluorine to be 4.8 and 4 barns, respectively, the transmission is given by

$$2.303 \log 1/T = n'(\sigma_c + 2\sigma_F)$$
$$= n' \times 12.8 \times 10^{-24} \tag{9.18}$$

If the mass per square centimeter is $\mu$ and the molecular weight is 50, the number of ($CF_2$) per square centimeter, $n' = \mu \times (6.02 \times 10^{23})/50$. Substitutions for the $n'$ in the foregoing equation gives

$$\frac{2.303 \log 1/T}{\mu} = \frac{12.8 \times 10^{-24} \times 6.02 \times 10^{23}}{50} \tag{9.19}$$
$$= 0.154$$

If a fraction $x$ of the fluorine atoms in fluorocarbon ($CF_2$)$_x$ is replaced by hydrogen atoms, then

$$\begin{aligned}
2.303 \log 1/T &= n'[\sigma_c + 2(1 - x)\sigma_F + 2x\sigma_H] \\
&= n'[4.8 + 8 - 8x + 60x] \times 10^{-24} \\
&= n'[12.8 + 52x] \times 10^{-24}
\end{aligned} \tag{9.20}$$

The number of units per square centimeter is

$$n' = \frac{\mu \times 6.02 \times 10^{23}}{50 - 38x + 2x} \tag{9.21}$$

Substitution gives

$$\frac{2.303 \log 1/T}{\mu} = 0.602 \left(\frac{12.8 + 52x}{50 - 36x}\right) \tag{9.22}$$
$$\cong 0.154(1 + 4.8x)$$

That is, the value of the total cross section increases by $4.8x$ when a fraction $x$ of the fluorine atoms is replaced by hydrogen atoms, provided that the grams per square centimeter remain the same.

From the ratio of the effective cross sections per unit weight per square centimeter of the sample as compared to the standard, the fraction $x$ of hydrogen atoms replacing fluorine atoms can be solved from

$$\frac{\left(\dfrac{2.303 \log 1/T}{\mu}\right)_{\text{sample}}}{\left(\dfrac{2.303 \log 1/T}{\mu}\right)_{\text{standard}}} - 1 = 4.8x \tag{9.23}$$

Using samples of about 10 g./cm.$^2$ determined to within 0.2–0.3% and counting times sufficient to give 40,000 counts, one can determine the ratio of the transmissions to within about 1% uncertainty. This corresponds to about 2 parts per 1000 in the uncertainty in the replacement of F by H. In a typical case, for example, the value of $2.303 \log 1/T/\mu$ for the standard was 0.1413, and that for the sample was 0.1480.

Hence, from the equation above, $0.0475 = 4.8x$, and $x = 0.0099$, or 9.9 fluorine atoms per 1000 replaced by hydrogen atoms.

The percentage of water or hydrogen in metals or in inorganic or organic compounds can be determined in a similar manner. If one wants to find out how much hydrogen there is in a sample of iron, the transmission can be determined. Then, by heating and evacuation, the hydrogen can be removed and the transmission redetermined.

If, for example, the transmission of the iron sample containing the hydrogen is $T$ and the transmission after removal of the hydrogen is $T'$ then

$$2.303 \log 1/T = n_{Fe}'\sigma_{Fe} + n_H'\sigma_H \tag{9.24}$$
$$2.303 \log 1/T' = n_{Fe}'\sigma_{Fe} \tag{9.25}$$

Subtracting,

$$2.303 \log (T'/T) = n_H'\sigma_H \tag{9.26}$$

Assume that the transmission increased from 10.0 to 10.5% when the hydrogen was removed, an easily measurable change; then

$$n_H' = \frac{0.049}{60 \times 10^{-24}} = 8.2 \times 10^{20} \text{ atoms per cm.}^2 \tag{9.27}$$

This is $(8.2 \times 10^{20})/(6.02 \times 10^{23}) = 1.35 \times 10^{-3}$ moles/cm.$^2$ or 1.36 mg. of H/cm.$^2$

The weight of iron required to give a transmission of 10.5% is

$$n_{Fe}' = \frac{2.303 \log 1/T}{\sigma_{Fe}} = \frac{2.25}{13 \times 10^{-24}} = 1.73 \times 10^{23} \text{ atoms/cm.}^2 \tag{9.28}$$

or $(1.73 \times 10^{23})/(6.02 \times 10^{23}) = 0.287$ mole/cm.$^2$ This is 16.0 g./cm.$^2$, or a piece about 2.1 cm. thick. The percentage by weight of hydrogen in such a sample would be $0.00136 \times 100/16.0 = 0.0085\%$ H by weight. Thus it can be seen that the method is reasonably sensitive, but the size of sample required for low percentages of hydrogen is rather large. The size of sample would be smaller if the transmission measurements were done at a wave length beyond the Bragg cutoff for iron at 4 Å. Here the cross section of hydrogen is greater. Also that of iron is smaller because the coherent scattering is lost and there remains only the absorption, incoherent nuclear, and lattice vibration-scattering cross sections. Such measurements could be made simply by putting a beryllium plus beryllium oxide filter (p. 469) in the thermal neutron beam. The only neutrons that pass are those with wave lengths greater than 4.7 Å.

Hydrides such as those of Ti, Zr, Pd, the alkaline earths, etc., have been studied at long wave length by use of a crystal spectrometer (74) and are more favorable cases than the illustration above.

To determine hydrogen in organic compounds, the compound can be dissolved in carbon disulfide, a fluorocarbon, or other solvent that does not contain hydrogen. The intensity $I$ of the neutron beam with the solvent plus sample divided by the intensity $I_0$ of the beam with the solvent alone gives the transmission of the sample. About 45 mg./cm.$^2$ of hydrogen would be required to give a transmission of 20%, which, if determined to 1%, would give the hydrogen content of the compound to within about 5 parts in 1000.

Instead of determining hydrogen by transmission of a thermal neutron beam or $c$ neutrons, it is sometimes advantageous to determine the transmission as a function of energy and to extrapolate to high energies as will be described later (p. 501).

## 10. ANALYSIS BY TRANSMISSION AT SELECTED VELOCITIES

Frequently it is desirable to select narrow energy bands of neutrons rather than those represented by a thermalized beam, $c$ neutrons, or all long-wave-length neutrons passing a filter such as BeO. Mechanical choppers, pulsed accelerators, crystal spectrometers, or mechanical monochrometers can be used for this purpose as explained in previous sections. Also resonance detectors, self-indicating detectors, or combinations of filters are useful. The general principles and procedures for measuring the transmission using such methods have already been discussed. Examples of possible applications will be given here.

### 10.1. Analysis at Selected Energies in the Epithermal Region

At energies somewhat above thermal (0.025 ev.), that is, from 0.4 ev. and higher, a number of differences from thermal beams exist. This is sometimes referred to as the resonance region, where marked increases in neutron absorption and scattering occur at definite energies, giving rise to peaks in the cross-section curves. The use of these resonance peaks will be discussed fully in a subsequent section.

The transmission of a whole epithermal group of neutrons can be measured by use of a cadmium filter 0.03 in. thick as explained previously (p. 480). This may have some advantages in analyzing for an element with a number of large resonances in the low-energy region, particularly when it is in the presence of elements with few or high energy resonances. For example, transmission measurements or activation measurements in this region may be useful in special cases for determination of such elements as the rare earths, indium, rhodium, rhenium, iridium, hafnium, gold, silver, uranium, bromine, antimony, tantalum, etc. However, in some cases the samples available may not be large enough for application of the method.

In the thermal neutron region some complications arise in transmission measurements because of coherent crystalline effects. If these interfere, measurements can be made with cadmium filters or at even higher energies (0.5 to 10 ev.) by use of a 0.2 g./cm.$^2$ boron filter (p. 480). For example, an element with a large scattering cross section in the presence of others with low scattering and absorption might be determined with the epi-cadmium group of neutrons or the boron-filtered neutrons. If resonances interfere, a suitable narrower band obtained with a crystal spectrometer or chopper can be used. Some elements with relatively high-scattering cross sections include H, Fe, Ni, Se, Tl, and Rb, as indicated by the constant $a$ term in Table IV. Since hydrogen has a relatively high-scattering cross section, measurements with epithermal neutrons may at times be used to advantage where crystalline-diffraction effects might otherwise interfere.

### 10.2. Analysis with Long-Wave-Length or Low-Energy Neutrons

Diffraction effects that sometimes interfere in the thermal region can be obviated by use of neutrons at wave lengths greater than the last Bragg cutoff. In some cases useful analyses or measurements can be made with a group of neutrons that pass a given filter. Thus practically all the

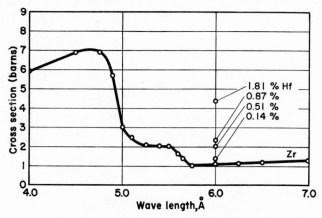

Fig. 21. Cross section of zirconium as a function of wave length and the effect of hafnium at a wave length beyond the Bragg cut-off (6 Å.).

neutrons from a thermal beam that pass an 8-in. beryllium filter have wave lengths greater than 4 Å. (0.0052 ev.). Those passing through a filter of 4-in. Be and 10-in. BeO have wave lengths larger than 4.7 Å. and those through a graphite filter greater than 6.7 Å.

The use of a crystal spectrometer in conjunction with these filters will allow the selection of narrower bands, as described previously. Thus analytical determinations with these long-wave-length neutrons will probably find application for cases where coherent scattering is large and crystal effects interfere. For example, if hafnium is the principal high-cross-section impurity in zirconium, the concentration can be determined by neutron transmission at wave lengths beyond the Bragg cutoff of zirconium. The following data taken at 6 Å. on a crystal monochromator will illustrate the foregoing applications. Figure 21 shows the cross section of a nearly pure sample of Zr (74) as a function of neutron wave length.

At a wave length of 6 Å. the coherent scattering has been lost and the cross section drops to 1.14 barns. Four other samples gave values of log $1/T/G$ of (a) 0.00400, (b) 0.00581, (c) 0.00666, and (d) 0.01255, compared to 0.00325 for the purest sample, where $G$ is the total grams per square centimeter of the sample. These values correspond to calculated cross sections of 1.39, 2.06, 2.34, and 4.38 barns respectively, compared with 1.14 barns for the first sample, which contained only 0.03% Hf as determined by resonance absorption (p. 531).

If one assumes that the impurity giving rise to the increased cross section is all due to hafnium, then the equations given previously (p. 488) can be used in the following form to calculate the percentage of hafnium:

$$\log 1/T = \mu_A \frac{N\sigma_A}{2.303 M_A} + \mu_B \frac{N\sigma_B}{2.303 M_B} \tag{10.1}$$

$$= \mu_A K_A + \mu_B K_B \tag{10.2}$$

Since for a binary mixture $G = \mu_A + \mu_B$, or $\mu_A = (G - \mu_B)$

$$\log 1/T = (G - \mu_B)K_A + \mu_B K_B \tag{10.3}$$

$$= G K_A - \mu_B K_A + \mu_B K_B \tag{10.4}$$

or

$$\frac{\log 1/T}{G} = K_A + \frac{\mu_B}{G}(K_B - K_A) \tag{10.5}$$

In these equations $\mu$, $\sigma$, and $M$ are the grams per square centimeter, the cross section in square centimeters, and the atomic weight respectively for the element represented in the subscript; $N$ is Avogadro's number; and $G$ is the total grams per square centimeter of the sample. From the measured value of $1/T$ and $G$ the value of $\mu_B$ can be calculated since $K_A$ and $K_B$ are constants. Then, $(\mu_B/G) \times 100$ is the percentage of $B$ in the sample.

Differences between samples 1 and 2 can also be calculated if their respective values of log $1/T/G$ are known. Thus

$$\log \frac{1}{T_1}\bigg/G_1 = K_A + \frac{\mu_{B_1}}{G_1}(K_B - K_A) \tag{10.6}$$

$$\log \frac{1}{T_2}\bigg/G_2 = K_A + \frac{\mu_{B_2}}{G_2}(K_B - K_A) \tag{10.7}$$

Subtracting the first equation from the second gives

$$\log \frac{1}{T_2}\bigg/G_2 - \log \frac{1}{T_1}\bigg/G_1 = (K_B - K_A)\left(\frac{\mu_{B_2}}{G_2} - \frac{\mu_{B_1}}{G_1}\right) \tag{10.8}$$

As the last term is the difference in the weight fraction of $B$ in the two samples,

$$\Delta P = \frac{\mu_{B_2}}{G_2} - \frac{\mu_{B_1}}{G_1} = \frac{\log \dfrac{1}{T_2}\bigg/G_2 - \log \dfrac{1}{T}\bigg/G_1}{(K_B - K_A)} \tag{10.9}$$

When multiplied by 100 this gives the difference in percentage of $B$ in the two samples. With $\log 1/T = GK_A + \mu_B(K_B - K_A)$ used for two different samples,

$$\log 1/T_2 - \log 1/T_1 = \log (T_1/T_2)$$
$$= K_A(G_2 - G_1) + (K_B - K_A)(\mu_{B2} - \mu_{B1}) \quad (10.10)$$

This equation is more convenient if the difference in grams per square centimeter ($\mu_{B2} - \mu_{B1}$) is desired for $B$ in the samples of $A$.

For zirconium sample (c) mentioned above, $\log 1/T/G = 0.0066$, and

$$K_{Zr} = \frac{(0.6023 \times 10^{24})(1.14 \times 10^{-24})}{(2.303)(91.22)} = 0.00327 \quad (10.11)$$

$$K_{Hf} = \frac{(0.6023 \times 10^{24})(0.350 \times 10^{-24})}{(2.303)(178.6)} = 0.512 \quad (10.12)$$

then from

$$\log 1/T/G = K_{Zr} + \frac{\mu_{Hf}}{G} (K_{Hf} - K_{Zr}) \quad (10.13)$$

$$0.00666 = 0.00327 + \left(\frac{\mu_{Hf}}{G}\right) 0.509 \quad (10.14)$$

$$\frac{\mu_{Hf}}{G} = \frac{0.00339}{0.509} = 0.0067, \text{ or } 0.67\% \quad (10.15)$$

Alternatively the percentage of these small amounts of impurity can be calculated by eq. (9.17).

$$P = \frac{\Delta\sigma M_i}{\sigma_i M_A} = \frac{(2.34 - 1.14)(178.6)}{(350)(91.2)} = 0.0067, \text{ or } 0.67\% \quad (10.16)$$

The values calculated for the other samples are (a) 0.14, (b) 0.51 and (c) 1.81%. One difficulty is that there is no assurance that the decrease in transmission is due to hafnium alone. All that can be determined from these transmission measurements is that neutrons are absorbed and scattered from the sample as though the calculated amounts of hafnium were present. If there is good evidence from other sources that hafnium is the principal neutron-absorbing impurity, then the calculated values will have more meaning. In this respect, resonance absorption and activation analysis are more positive because they can be used not only to determine but to identify the hafnium. On the other hand, the transmission measurement is more rapid, but it suffers from the fact that large samples are needed as compared with those for spectrographic or activation methods. For the analysis described above, samples from 15 to 50 g./cm.² were used and the entrance slits to the counter of the neutron spectrometer were about ⅛ in. wide by 2 in. long. In cases where samples this large are available, such transmission measurements will find some useful applications.

A similar series (74) of measurements was made at 6 Å. on a series of samples of tin containing known percentages of indium from 0.01 to

0.5%. A plot of $\Delta\sigma$, the difference between the calculated values of the cross section of tin in the purest sample and that calculated for the other samples, against the percentage of indium, gave a working curve for use with unknown samples. Using the known cross section for indium and the experimental value of 0.65 barn for $\Delta\sigma$, one can calculate the percentage of indium in a sample known to contain 0.10% to be 0.099. Thus, one can either use standards with a working curve or calculate the composition by use of known cross sections.

A further illustration (74) is the determination of the mole fraction of $H_2O$ in samples of $D_2O$. The transmissions of a series of samples containing from 3 to 40 mole% $H_2O$ were determined in standard 1.00-cm. quartz optical cells that had a neutron transmission of 96.6%. One can use the usual equation

$$\log 1/T = k_1 C_1 l + k_2 C_2 l \tag{10.17}$$

where $k_1$ and $k_2$ are constants, $C_1$ and $C_2$ are the mole fractions of $H_2O$ and $D_2O$ respectively, and $l$ is the path length of the cells. The value of $k_2$ for the $D_2O$ was 0.3365. By use of samples of known mole fractions of $H_2O$ the value $k_1$ was calculated from the foregoing equation rearranged to

$$k_1 = \frac{\log 1/T - k_2 C_2}{C_1} \tag{10.18}$$

The average for several samples was 2.990. Then with $k_1$ and $k_2$ known and since $C_2 = (1 - C_1)$,

$$\log 1/T = C_1(k_1 - k_2) + k_2 \tag{10.19}$$

and

$$C_1 = \frac{\log 1/T - k_2}{(k_1 - k_2)} \tag{10.20}$$

An unknown sample was found to have a value of $\log 1/T = 0.4178$, from which

$$C_1 = \frac{0.4178 - 0.3365}{(2.990 - 0.3365)} = 0.0306, \text{ or } 3.06 \text{ mole}\% \ H_2O$$

Similar methods are applicable to the determination of other suitable substances in solution.

### 10.3. Other Applications of Long-Wave-Length Neutrons

Transmission measurements with long-wave-length neutrons find numerous important applications to other problems in chemistry and solid-state physics (103). These include studies of inelastic scattering by energy exchanges with lattice vibrations of crystals; disorder due to random distribution of isotopes with different scattering cross sections or nuclear spins; absorption cross sections from the $1/v$ relationship beyond the Bragg cutoff; small angle scattering from microcrystalline substances;

molecular motion and chemical binding effects with hydrogen; paramagnetic, ferrimagnetic, and ferromagnetic properties; refraction, reflection, and polarization of neutrons; etc.

It is interesting to note (38, 104) that reflection of neutrons from a liquid surface may be useful in determining the ratio of hydrogen to carbon in certain hydrocarbons. Reflection at very small angles from such mirror surfaces is determined by the coherent scattering amplitudes of the atoms, and the critical glancing angle $\theta_c$ is

$$\theta_c = \lambda \sqrt{Na/\pi} \qquad (10.21)$$

where $\lambda$ is the neutron wave length, $N$ is the number of nuclei per cubic centimeter, and $a$ is the average coherent scattering amplitude. The amplitude for carbon is positive and 1.5 times greater than the negative amplitude of hydrogen. The angle of incidence required to reflect neutrons of a given wave length is therefore sensitive to the carbon-hydrogen ratio. Thus when this ratio is 1.5, the value of $a$ will be zero and $\theta_c$ will be zero. For ratios greater than 1.5 the beam will be reflected upward from the surface and for those less than this, it will be reflected into the liquid. Consequently such measurements would be most useful for carbon-hydrogen ratios greater than 1.5.

*10.4. Use of Resonance Detectors, Resonance Filters, and Self-Indication*

The general principles and procedures for determining transmission of neutron beams by these methods have been given in previous sections (pp. 475 and 478). If the cross sections are known for the wave lengths selected by these procedures, the concentration of certain components can be calculated in favorable cases. The methods are similar to those illustrated above. In other cases it may be necessary to prepare samples of known composition and to plot suitable curves.

It is not always necessary to use collimated beams of neutrons for an analytical procedure involving neutron absorption. Measurements in a flux of neutrons such as inside a nuclear reactor or in a moderator surrounding a neutron source can frequently be used. Such measurements usually involve the activation of suitable foils or thin samples of elements listed in Table V. For example, when a thin foil of indium is placed at a given position in a constant flux of neutrons for a fixed time, it becomes radioactive (see section 13) owing to the absorption of neutrons. If a similar foil is surrounded by a sample containing a neutron-absorbing element and placed in the flux at the same position for the same length of time, the activity of this foil is lower. The ratio of the activities induced in the two foils is a measure of the quantity of neutron absorbers in the sample. By calibration with suitable standards quantitative determinations can be made for samples of unknown amounts of the absorber.

The foregoing procedure utilizes the whole spectrum of neutron energies in the flux, modified somewhat by the presence of the sample and detector foil. By the use of appropriate filters different energy groups of neutrons can sometimes be used to advantage for selectivity with respect to the substances in the sample. For example, if the indium foil is wrapped with 0.03-in. cadmium foil, only neutrons with energies greater than about 0.6 ev. will cause the activation of the foil as the lower energy neutrons are practically completely absorbed by the cadmium. As indium has a peak cross section of about 30,000 barns at its resonance of 1.46 ev., most of the activity will be due to neutrons near this energy. Thus, if the previous experiment is done with the foil wrapped in such a cadmium filter, the ratio of activities will be a measure of these higher energy neutrons absorbed by the sample. Such an arrangement would be particularly useful in determining indium in tin for example.

By combining the results of the two sets of measurements described above the effect of the sample on the thermal neutrons in a flux can be determined. Thus the difference in activation between the bare and cadmium-covered foil is the cadmium difference discussed previously (p. 479). Other detectors and filters can be used in a similar manner.

Although a uniform flux of neutrons is desirable for the experiments described above, it is possible to use arrangements part way between a flux and a beam, as illustrated in Fig. 17. By means of a 0.5-curie radium-beryllium source, the activity induced in indium foils as a self-detector was determined for several samples of tin containing known percentages of indium. Measurements were made with bare foils and with the foils surrounded by $\frac{1}{32}$ cadmium to remove the thermal neutrons and thereby favor the selectivity of neutron absorption in the indium rather than the tin. After a 54 min. exposure (half-saturation for indium) the counting rate of the foils was determined with a thin-end window counter. The 54-min. half-life $T_{\frac{1}{2}}$ of indium-115 and the time $t_2$ between activation and counting was used to calculate (p. 546) the half-saturation activity $A_{\frac{1}{2}}$ from the equation

$$A_{t_2} = A_{(\frac{1}{2})} e^{-\dfrac{0.693 t_2}{T_{\frac{1}{2}}}} \tag{10.22}$$

An empirical working curve as shown in Fig. 22 was used to relate the average counting rate of bare identical foils to the percentage of indium in the samples. Standard deviations of the counting rates were $\pm 1\%$. Other plots involving the transmission $T$ or log $1/T$ could also be used. The selectivity gained by using cadmium around the detector foil can be seen from the ratios of the counts/minute in the sample with 0.5% indium to the counts/minute in the purest tin sample. For the bare foil this was 0.77 and for the covered foil it was 0.54. However, the counting rate is lower, but higher intensity neutron sources would improve the precision of the determination.

Other similar measurements were made to determine the thickness of electroplated gold films using gold and manganese foils as detectors. By use of higher intensity laboratory neutron sources, small accelerators,

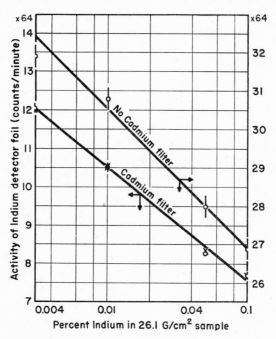

Fig. 22. Empirical working curve for converting measured activity in an indium detector foil to percentage of indium in tin.

pulsed generators, small cyclotrons, or research reactors that are becoming more generally available, such determinations will find a number of useful applications.

### 10.5. Use of Variation in Transmission or Cross Sections with Neutron Energy

In a previous section (p. 461) it was shown that the cross section of a substance between the diffraction and resonance-energy regions varied as $\sigma(v) = a + b/v$, $\sigma(E) = a + c/\sqrt{E}$, $\sigma(\lambda) = a + d\lambda$, or as $\sigma(t) = a + et$ in which $v$, $E$, $\lambda$, and $t$ refer to velocity, energy, wave length, and time of flight of the neutrons respectively. The high-energy intercept of the straight line as shown in Fig. 23 gives the constant $a$ which is principally the sum of the free-atom-scattering cross sections of the elements in the molecule. The presence of an impurity with a high-scattering cross section will raise this intercept. The increase in this

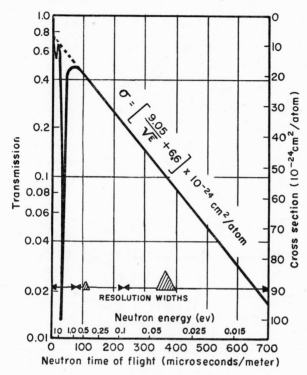

FIG. 23. Cross section of silver as a function of neutron time of flight showing the $1/v$ and resonance effects. The intercept at zero time of flight, i.e., at high energy, gives the free atom-scattering cross section and the slope gives the absorption coefficient.

extrapolated cross section $\Delta\sigma$ over that known for the pure material can be used to calculate the fraction of impurity from eq. (9.17):

$$P_i = \frac{\Delta\sigma M_i}{\sigma_i M_A} \tag{10.23}$$

This method is particularly useful in the determination of hydrogen since it has a high free-atom-scattering cross section of about 20.4 barns.

This procedure has been applied to estimating the maximum percentage of hydrogen (or water) that could be present in some samples of manganous oxide and manganous fluoride used in the study of paramagnetic scattering of neutrons (182, 210). The high-energy intercept in the case of manganous oxide was 5.6 ± 0.2 barns and that calculated from the known values for manganese and oxygen was 5.5 ± 0.1. It is concluded, therefore, that hydrogen if present could not contribute more than about 0.2 barn, which corresponds to

$$P_i = \frac{(0.2)}{22} \frac{(1)}{(70.93)} = 0.00013, \text{ or } 0.013\% \text{ H} \qquad (10.24)$$

or since the scattering for oxygen is 4 barns, and two hydrogens are present in water,

$$P_i = \frac{(0.2)}{(48)} \frac{(18)}{(70.93)} = 0.00053, \text{ or } 0.053\% \text{ H}_2\text{O} \qquad (10.25)$$

If the measurements are made at long wave lengths, the method is more sensitive, as illustrated by the following example (209). The cross section of sodium fluoride as a function of wave length is shown in Fig. 24.

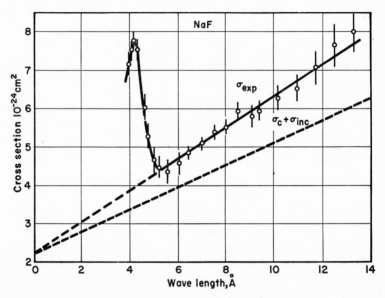

FIG. 24. Cross section of a sodium fluoride sample as a function of neutron wave length. An intercept close to that corresponding to the incoherent scattering of the atoms demonstrates the absence of significant quantities of water.

Beyond the Bragg cutoff for such a crystalline material, the coherent scattering is lost and there remains the $1/v$ absorption, incoherent scattering, and inelastic scattering from lattice vibrations and molecular motion. Both the absorption and the inelastic scattering vary as $1/v$ but the incoherent scattering arising from nuclear-spin interactions and randomness of isotopes of different scattering amplitudes is independent of wave length. Thus extrapolation of the straight line beyond the Bragg cutoff for sodium fluoride should give a zero wave-length intercept equal to the incoherent-scattering cross sections of the constituent elements, although this is not always the case for certain paramagnetic materials or hydrogen compounds.

It was of interest to estimate the maximum quantity of water that could be present in this sample. A difficulty arises in that the cross section of hydrogen at energies below about 0.4 ev. is not linear with wave length, but depends upon its binding and molecular motion (Fig. 7). However, for water above about 4 Å. the cross section follows a roughly linear variation given by $\sigma = 123 + 12.5\lambda$. That is, the zero wave-length intercept would be about 123. The intercept for the sodium fluoride is within 0.2 barn of the sum of the incoherent-scattering cross sections of sodium and fluorine. The maximum percentage of water is then

$$P_i = \frac{(\Delta\sigma)}{\sigma_i} \frac{(M_i)}{M_A} = \frac{(0.2)}{(123)} \frac{(18)}{(42)} = 0.0007, \text{ or } 0.07\% \tag{10.26}$$

These examples show how it is possible at times to learn something about the chemical composition from a series of measurements made for another purpose. Such considerations often eliminate the need for further analyses.

If the constants $a$ and $c$ in the expression $\sigma = a + c/\sqrt{E}$ are appreciably different for the elements in a sample, measurements of the thickness and of the transmission at two different energies can give some information on the composition. For a sample of a thickness of $x$ cm., when the transmission is measured at two different energies $E'$ and $E''$, the following equations apply:

$$n_A\sigma_A' + n_B\sigma_B' = \frac{2.303 \log 1/T'}{x} \tag{10.27}$$

$$n_A\sigma_A'' + n_B\sigma_B'' = \frac{2.303 \log 1/T''}{x} \tag{10.28}$$

Here $n_A$ and $n_B$ are the number of atoms per cubic centimeter, $\sigma_A'$ and $\sigma_B'$ are the cross sections in square centimeters at one energy, $\sigma_A''$ and $\sigma_B''$ are the cross sections at a second energy, and $T'$ and $T''$ are the transmissions at the two energies. As $x$, the cross sections, and the transmissions are known, the equations can be solved for $n_A$ and $n_B$.

For a sample consisting of two elements the composition can be expressed in weight per cent from the fact that the density of the sample in grams per cubic centimeter is given by

$$d = \frac{n_A M_A}{N} + \frac{n_B M_B}{N} \tag{10.29}$$

Then

$$\%A = \frac{n_A M_A \times 100}{n_A M_A + n_B M_B} \tag{10.30}$$

where $M_A$ and $M_B$ are the atomic weights of $A$ and $B$ respectively and $N$ is Avogadro's number.

A consideration of the determination of manganese in iron will illustrate the requirements of the method. The equations for the cross sections of manganese and iron in the $1/v$ region at energies above the Bragg cutoff are

$$\sigma_{Fe} = 11.4 + 0.40/\sqrt{E} \tag{10.31}$$
$$\sigma_{Mn} = 2.90 + 2.09/\sqrt{E} \tag{10.32}$$

Suppose the transmission for a 2.0-cm.-thick sample was found to be $T' = 0.181$ at 10 ev. and $T'' = 0.136$ at 0.1 ev. The cross sections for Fe at 10 ev. and at 0.1 ev. are respectively 11.5 and 12.7 barns; for Mn they are respectively 3.56 and 9.52 barns (1 barn $= 10^{-24}$ cm².). Substitution of these values in the foregoing equations gives

$$11.5n_{Fe} + 3.56n_{Mn} = \frac{1.71}{2} \times 10^{24} \tag{10.33}$$

$$12.7n_{Fe} + 9.52n_{Mn} = \frac{1.99}{2} \times 10^{24} \tag{10.34}$$

Solution of these gives $n_{Fe} = 7.12 \times 10^{22}$ atoms/cc. and $n_{Mn} = 0.95 \times 10^{22}$ atoms/cc., or 11.8 atom % Mn. This may be converted to weight per cent as described above.

Assuming that the transmissions were measured to $\pm 0.01$, the error in the foregoing example might be as high as $\pm 4\%$. To obtain greater precision it would be necessary to measure the transmissions more accurately or at energies more widely spaced. Other systems in which there is a greater difference in the constants $a$ and $c$, particularly the scattering term, would be more favorable. Although this method has limited application and accuracy, it may find specific applications where the thickness of a sample can be measured readily but the weight or density would be more difficult. Alternatively, for a single material with a high value of $c$, the thickness can be calculated from measurements of $T$ at two energies.

## 11. ANALYSIS BY RESONANCE ABSORPTION AND SCATTERING OF NEUTRONS

### 11.1. Use of Neutron Resonances

As pointed out previously (p. 460), many of the elements exhibit marked increases in cross section at certain neutron energies. These neutron-absorption and -scattering resonances are characteristic of a particular nucleus and therefore can be used to analyze for the presence of that nucleus. The cross section vs. energy curve for tantalum shown in Fig. 25 is typical of the experimental results obtained for many of the elements. As shown in this curve, the lowest energy large-absorption

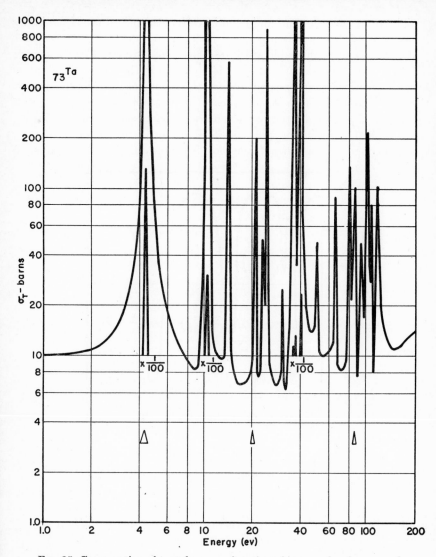

Fig. 25. Cross section of tantalum as a function of energy showing a number of its resonances.

resonance occurs in tantalum at 4.28 ev. This can be used not only to indicate the presence of tantalum but also to measure quantitatively the amount of tantalum in a sample that contains no elements with interfering resonances. It is, for example, useful in determining the percentage of tantalum in a sample of niobium. Similar curves have been obtained and compiled for many of the elements (106).

The resonance energies and effective strengths of the resonances for a large number of isotopes are given in Table VII. The quantities $\alpha\sigma_0\Gamma$ and $\alpha\sigma_0\Gamma^2$ given in the table are those most closely related to the experimentally measurable quantities. The term $\alpha$ is the abundance (atom fraction) of the isotope responsible for the resonance. In the determination of the amount of an *element* present in a sample, the observed effect will depend on this quantity, $\alpha$, as neutron resonances are due to a particular isotope. The resonance parameters given in the neutron-cross-section compilation (106) are in a form most suitable for a nuclear physicist

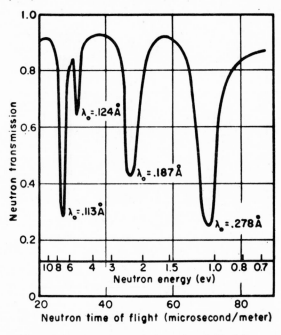

Fig. 26. Neutron-transmission curve for hafnium.

attempting to compare a nuclear theory with experiment. These resonance parameters are determined from the experimental results only after extensive analysis. The quantities given in Table VII are related [see eq. (6.6)] to the resonance parameters by the equations

$$\alpha\sigma_0\Gamma = \frac{2.6 \times 10^6}{E_0}\,\alpha g \Gamma_n$$

and

$$\alpha\sigma_0\Gamma^2 = \frac{2.6 \times 10^6}{E_0}\,\alpha g \Gamma_n \Gamma$$ (11.1)

where the terms in the formula have the same meaning as given in section 6-1.

Those elements with large resonances can be detected qualitatively and determined quantitatively in the absence of other elements that have interfering resonances. Some knowledge about the composition of the sample is, therefore, advantageous before one uses the resonance method described here. In general, resonances for the lighter elements occur at relatively high energies where some of the velocity selectors described previously do not have sufficient resolution. However, among the heavier elements a number of analyses appear to be feasible, such as Ta in Nb; Hf in Zr; In in Sn; Mn in Al or Fe; Co or Mn in steels; certain rare-earth elements; thicknesses of films or electroplates of Ag, Au, Rh, or Cd, etc.

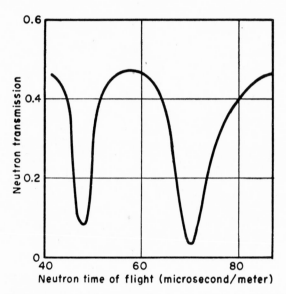

FIG. 27. Neutron-transmission curve for a sample of zirconium containing hafnium.

The analysis can be done by preparing an empirical working curve from a series of standards, just as is done in analysis by light absorption. Alternatively, if the constants for the resonance are known, the quantity of the elements in the sample can be calculated from a single curve. In Fig. 26 the transmission as a function of neutron energy is given for a sample containing 160 mg./cm.$^2$ of hafnium. A section of a similar curve is given in Fig. 27 for a sample of zirconium, 16.3 g./cm.$^2$ It is obvious from these curves that the resonances in the zirconium sample occur at about 47 and 70 μsec./meter, or 2.36 and 1.08 ev., the same as resonances in the sample of hafnium. Resonance absorption at these energies are characteristic of the hafnium isotopes and can be used as a qualitative

## TABLE VII
### Lower Energy Neutron Resonances of the Elements
(Other higher energy resonances may be found in reference (106))

| Element | Isotope and abundance $a$ (%) | $E_0$ | $a\sigma_0\Gamma$ barns-ev. | $g$ | $a\sigma_0\Gamma^2$ barns-ev.$^2$ | $\Gamma_\gamma$ volts | $\Gamma_n$ volts | Calculated $a\sigma_0$ at $E_0$, barns | Observed $\sigma$, at $E_0$, barns |
|---|---|---|---|---|---|---|---|---|---|
| $_{11}$Na | Na$^{23}$(100) | 2,900 | $1.08 \times 10^5$ | — | $2.58 \times 10^7$ | $\Gamma_\gamma \ll \Gamma_n$ | 240 | 448 | 300 |
| $_{21}$Sc | Sc$^{45}$(100) | 3,400 | — | — | — | — | — | — | 44 |
|  | — | 4,400 | — | — | — | — | — | — | 100 |
| $_{22}$Ti | — | 3,200 | — | — | — | — | — | — | 17 |
|  | — | 18,000 | — | — | — | — | — | — | 100 |
| $_{23}$V | — | 165 | — | — | — | — | — | — | 12.5 |
|  | — | 1,040 | — | — | — | — | — | — | 9.5 |
|  | — | 4,200 | — | — | — | — | — | — | 200 |
| $_{24}$Cr | — | 4,300 | — | — | — | — | — | — | 27 |
| $_{25}$Mn | Mn$^{55}$(100) | 337 | $8.49 \times 10^4$ | — | $1.87 \times 10^6$ | $\Gamma_\gamma \ll \Gamma_n$ | 22 | 3,860 | 2,000 |
|  | — | 1,010 | — | — | — | — | — | — | 250 |
|  | — | 2,400 | — | — | — | — | — | — | 550 |
| $_{26}$Fe | — | 810 | — | — | — | — | — | — | 7 |
| $_{27}$Co | Co$^{59}$(100) | 132 | $4.83 \times 10^4$ | — | $2.37 \times 10^5$ | $\Gamma_\gamma \ll \Gamma_n$ | 4.9 | 9,850 | 7,000 |
|  | — | 475 | — | — | — | — | — | — | 54 |

| | | | | | | | | | | | |
|---|---|---|---|---|---|---|---|---|---|---|---|
| $_{28}$Ni | Ni$^{62}$(3.66) | 4,200 | — | $1.47 \times 10^4$ | — | $1.91 \times 10^7$ | | 1300 | — | 11.3 | 30 |
| $_{29}$Cu | Cu$^{65}$(30.9) | 240 | — | — | — | — | — | — | — | — | 12 |
| | Cu$^{63}$(69.1) | 450 | — | — | — | — | — | — | — | — | 22 |
| | Cu$^{65}$ | 2,010 | — | | | | | | | | 42 |
| $_{30}$Zn | Zn$^{67}$(4.11) | 225 | — | $0.309 \times 10^3$ | — | $0.401 \times 10^3$ | $\Gamma_\gamma \ll \Gamma_n$ | 1.3 | — | 237 | 30 |
| | Zn$^{67}$ | 455 | — | $1.53 \times 10^3$ | — | $19.8 \times 10^3$ | $\Gamma_\gamma \ll \Gamma_n$ | 13 | — | 117 | 42 |
| | Zn$^{68}$(18.56) | 530 | — | $4.57 \times 10^3$ | — | $45.7 \times 10^3$ | $\Gamma_\gamma \ll \Gamma_n$ | 10 | — | 457 | 140 |
| | Zn$^{64}$(48.89) | 2,750 | — | $16.2 \times 10^3$ | — | $1131 \times 10^3$ | $\Gamma_\gamma \ll \Gamma_n$ | 70 | — | 231 | 59 |
| $_{31}$Ga | — | 94 | — | — | — | — | — | — | — | — | 16 |
| | — | 125 | — | — | — | — | — | — | — | — | 14 |
| | — | 290 | — | — | — | — | — | — | — | — | 52 |
| | — | 390 | — | — | — | — | — | — | — | — | 41 |
| $_{32}$Ge | — | 105 | — | — | — | — | — | — | — | — | 105 |
| | — | 335 | — | — | — | — | — | — | — | — | 24 |
| | — | 490 | — | — | — | — | — | — | — | — | 17.5 |
| $_{33}$As | As$^{75}$(100) | 47 | — | — | — | — | — | — | — | — | 950 |
| | — | 92 | — | — | — | — | — | — | — | — | 68 |
| | — | 250 | — | — | — | — | — | — | — | — | 33 |
| $_{34}$Se | — | 27 | — | — | — | — | — | — | — | — | 94 |
| | — | 210 | — | — | — | — | — | — | — | — | 31 |
| | — | 270 | — | — | — | — | — | — | — | — | 31 |
| $_{35}$Br | — | 36 | — | — | — | — | — | — | — | — | 29 |
| | — | 54 | — | — | — | — | — | — | — | — | 14 |
| | — | 105 | — | — | — | — | — | — | — | — | 12 |
| | — | 135 | — | — | — | — | — | — | — | — | 14 |

## TABLE VII. (Continued)

| Element | Isotope and abundance $a$ (%) | $E_0$ | $a\sigma_0\Gamma$ barns-ev. | $g$ | $a\sigma_0\Gamma^2$ barns-ev.² | $\Gamma_\gamma$ volts | $\Gamma_n$ volts | Calculated $a\sigma_0$ at $E_0$, barns | Observed $\sigma_t$ at $E_0$, barns |
|---|---|---|---|---|---|---|---|---|---|
| $_{37}$Rb | — | 5,400 | — | — | — | — | — | — | 14 |
| $_{38}$Sr | — | 3.6 | — | — | — | — | — | — | 78 |
| $_{39}$Y | $Y^{89}$(100) | 30,000 | — | — | — | — | — | — | 10 |
| $_{40}$Zr | $Zr^{91}$(11.23) | 295 | — | — | — | — | — | — | 15.5 |
| | — | 680 | — | — | — | — | — | — | 7.8 |
| $_{41}$Nb | $Nb^{93}$(100) | 36 | — | — | — | — | — | — | 14 |
| | — | 43 | — | — | — | — | — | — | 8.8 |
| | — | 94 | — | — | — | — | — | — | 10.5 |
| | — | 105 | — | — | — | — | — | — | 9.8 |
| $_{42}$Mo | $Mo^{95}$(15.70) | 45 | 922 | $\frac{7}{12}$ | 354 | 0.210 | 0.174 | 2,400 | 880 |
| | $Mo^{97}$(9.45) | 71.5 | 33 | $\frac{7}{12}$ | 11.5 | 0.330 | 0.017 | 96 | 26 |
| | $Mo^{96}$(16.50) | 133 | 644 | 1 | 296 | 0.260 | 0.200 | 1,400 | 260 |
| | $Mo^{95}$ | 162 | 20.0 | $\frac{7}{12}$ | 45 | (0.210) | 0.014 | 89 | 11 |
| $_{43}$Tc | $Tc^{99}$(100) | 2.2 | — | — | — | — | — | — | 50 |
| | — | 5.6 | — | — | — | — | — | — | 360 |
| | — | 21 | — | — | — | — | — | — | 115 |
| $_{44}$Ru | — | 9.7 | — | — | — | — | — | — | 22 |
| | — | 15 | — | — | — | — | — | — | 16.5 |
| | — | 24 | — | — | — | — | — | — | 13 |
| | — | 40 | — | — | — | — | — | — | 10 |

| | | 1.26 | 1,180 | 3/4 | 183 | 0.155 | 0.00076 | 7,540 | 4,500 |
|---|---|---|---|---|---|---|---|---|---|
| 45Rh | Rh$^{103}$(100) | 13 | — | — | — | — | — | — | 32 |
| 46Pd | | 26 | — | — | — | — | — | — | 14 |
| | | 34 | — | — | — | — | — | — | 147 |
| 47Ag | Ag$^{109}$(48.65) | 5.2 | 2,490 | 3/4 | 371 | 0.136 | 0.0134 | 16,700 | 12,500 |
| | Ag$^{107}$(51.35) | 16.6 | 291 | 3/4 | 50.8 | 0.170 | 0.0048 | 1,660 | 640 |
| | Ag$^{109}$ | 30.9 | 337 | 3/4 | 37.4 | 0.100 | 0.011 | 3,040 | 85 |
| | Ag$^{109}$ | 40.8 | 186 | 3/4 | 20.1 | (0.100) | 0.008 | 1,720 | 190 |
| | Ag$^{107}$ | 42.4 | 213 | 3/4 | 38.1 | (0.170) | 0.009 | 1,190 | 245 |
| | Ag$^{107}$ | 45.4 | 26.5 | 3/4 | 4.5 | (0.170) | 0.0012 | 155 | 22 |
| | Ag$^{107}$ | 52.2 | 653 | 3/4 | 101 | 0.120 | 0.034 | 4,240 | 485 |
| 48Cd | Cd$^{113}$(12.26) | 0.178 | 873 | 3/4 | 99.5 | 0.113 | 0.00065 | 7,660 | 7,200 |
| | | 18 | — | — | — | — | — | — | 7 |
| | | 27 | — | — | — | — | — | — | 34 |
| | | 66 | — | — | — | — | — | — | 13 |
| | | 89 | — | — | — | — | — | — | 36 |
| 49In | In$^{115}$(95.77) | 1.458 | 3,160 | 11/20 | 238 | 0.072 | 0.00336 | 41,900 | 30,000 |
| | In$^{115}$ | 3.86 | 113 | 11/20 | 9.2 | 0.081 | 0.00032 | 1,390 | 820 |
| | In$^{113}$(4.23) | 4.71 | 1.34 | 11/20 | 0.11 | 0.080 | 0.000104 | 17 | 16 |
| | In$^{115}$ | 9.10 | 261 | 11/20 | 21.3 | 0.080 | 0.00173 | 3,190 | 950 |
| | In$^{115}$ | 12.1 | 12 | 11/20 | 1.7 | 0.140 | 0.000106 | 86 | 47 |
| | In$^{113}$ | 14.7 | 31.7 | 11/20 | 2.1 | 0.060 | 0.0077 | 468 | 94 |
| | In$^{113}$ | 21.7 | 12.2 | 11/20 | 0.79 | 0.060 | 0.0044 | 190 | 28 |
| | In$^{115}$ | 23.0 | 59.5 | 11/20 | 8.4 | (0.140) | 0.001 | 422 | 105 |
| 50Sn | Sn$^{117}$(7.57) | 39.4 | 20.3 | 3/4 | 2.26 | 0.106 | 0.0054 | 182 | 20 |
| | Sn$^{118}$(24.01) | 46.3 | 9.4 | 1 | 1.04 | 0.110 | 0.0007 | 85 | 12 |
| | Sn$^{124}$(5.98) | 62.5 | 29.9 | 1 | 3.65 | 0.110 | 0.012 | 245 | 7.6 |
| | Sn$^{112}$(0.95) | 96.5 | 21.8 | 1 | 4.26 | 0.110 | 0.085 | 112 | 9.6 |
| | Sn$^{116}$(14.24) | 112 | 192 | 1 | 32.2 | 0.110 | 0.058 | 1,140 | 63 |

TABLE VII. (Continued)

| Element | Isotope and abundance $a$ (%) | $E_0$ | $a\sigma_0\Gamma$ barns-ev. | $g$ | $a\sigma_0\Gamma^2$ barns-ev.² | $\Gamma_\gamma$ volts | $\Gamma_n$ volts | Calculated $a\sigma_0$ at $E_0$, barns | Observed $\sigma_t$ at $E_0$, barns |
|---|---|---|---|---|---|---|---|---|---|
| $_{51}$Sb | Sb$^{121}$(57.25) | 6.2 | — | — | — | — | — | — | 1,400 |
| | Sb$^{121}$ | 15.5 | — | — | — | — | — | — | 780 |
| | Sb$^{123}$(42.75) | 21.5 | — | — | — | — | — | — | 1,250 |
| | Sb$^{121}$ | 29.5 | — | — | — | — | — | — | 137 |
| $_{52}$Te | Te$^{123}$(0.87) | 2.33 | 75.7 | ¾ | 8.7 | 0.104 | 0.0104 | 662 | 450 |
| | Te$^{125}$(6.99) | 8.3 | — | — | — | — | — | — | 5.2 |
| | Te$^{125}$ | 25 | — | — | — | — | — | — | 11 |
| $_{53}$I | I$^{127}$(100) | 20.5 | 118 | $\frac{7}{12}$ | 12.0 | 0.100 | 0.0016 | 1,160 | 100 |
| | | 31.4 | 1,010 | $\frac{7}{12}$ | 123 | (0.100) | 0.021 | 8,380 | 155 |
| | | 37.7 | 1,610 | $\frac{7}{12}$ | 225 | (0.100) | 0.040 | 11,500 | 180 |
| | | 46.0 | 726 | $\frac{7}{12}$ | 88.6 | (0.100) | 0.022 | 5,950 | 90 |
| $_{54}$Xe | | 9.1 | — | — | — | — | — | — | 500 |
| | | 14.0 | — | — | — | — | — | — | 1,850 |
| $_{54}$Xe$^{135}$ | Xe$^{135}$ | 0.082 | — | — | — | — | — | — | 3.4 × 10$^6$ |
| $_{55}$Cs | Cs$^{133}$(100) | 5.9 | 1,290 | $\frac{9}{16}$ | 155 | 0.115 | 0.0052 | 10,700 | 2,600 |
| | | 22.6 | 427 | $\frac{9}{16}$ | 54.1 | 0.120 | 0.0066 | 3,370 | 585 |
| | | 47.8 | 582 | $\frac{9}{16}$ | 92.5 | 0.140 | 0.019 | 3,660 | 275 |
| | | 83.1 | 158 | $\frac{9}{16}$ | 23.5 | (0.140) | 0.009 | 1,060 | 29 |
| | | 94.8 | 293 | $\frac{9}{16}$ | 46.5 | (0.140) | 0.019 | 1,840 | 68 |

| | | | | | | | | | |
|---|---|---|---|---|---|---|---|---|---|
| ₅₆Ba | Ba¹³⁵(5.59) | 24.5 | — | — | — | — | — | — | 39 |
| | Ba¹³⁵ | 81 | — | — | — | — | — | — | 78 |
| | Ba¹³⁵ | 85 | — | — | — | — | — | — | 38 |
| | — | 103 | — | — | — | — | — | — | 53 |
| ₅₇La | — | 72 | — | — | — | — | — | — | 175 |
| ₅₈Ce | — | 6,600 | — | — | — | — | — | — | 5 |
| ₅₉Pr | Pr¹⁴¹(100) | 85 | — | — | — | — | — | — | 39 |
| | — | 220 | — | — | — | — | — | — | 440 |
| | — | 240 | — | — | — | — | — | — | 320 |
| | — | 360 | — | — | — | — | — | — | 220 |
| | — | 530 | — | — | — | — | — | — | 75 |
| ₆₀Nd | Nd¹⁴⁵(8.3) | 4.4 | — | — | — | — | — | — | 170 |
| | Nd¹⁴⁵ | 43 | — | — | — | — | — | — | 145 |
| | Nd¹⁴³(12.2) | 57 | — | — | — | — | — | — | 36 |
| ₆₂Sm | Sm¹⁴⁹(13.84) | 0.096 | 1,180 | $\frac{9}{16}$ | 77.4 | 0.065 | 0.00056 | 18,000 | 16,000 |
| | Sm¹⁴⁹ | 0.87 | — | — | — | — | — | — | 2,200 |
| | Sm¹⁴⁷(15.07) | 3.45 | — | — | — | — | — | — | 530 |
| | Sm¹⁴⁹ | 4.9 | — | — | — | — | — | — | 500 |
| | Sm¹⁵²(26.63) | 8.2 | — | — | — | — | — | — | 15,000 |
| ₆₃Eu | Eu¹⁵¹(47.77) | 0.327 | 195 | $\frac{7}{2}$ | 13.7 | 0.070 | 0.000088 | 2,780 | 3,500 |
| | Eu¹⁵¹ | 0.461 | 1,260 | $\frac{7}{2}$ | 118 | 0.093 | 0.0008 | 13,400 | 11,000 |
| | Eu¹⁵¹ | 1.06 | 185 | $\frac{7}{2}$ | 17.4 | 0.094 | 0.00027 | 1,960 | 1,600 |
| | Eu¹⁵³(52.23) | 1.76 | 31.5 | $\frac{7}{2}$ | 2.8 | 0.090 | 0.00007 | 350 | 280 |
| | Eu¹⁵³ | 2.46 | 579 | $\frac{7}{2}$ | 53.2 | (0.090) | 0.0018 | 6,310 | 2,900 |
| | Eu¹⁵¹ | 3.34 | 735 | $\frac{7}{2}$ | 716 | (0.094) | 0.0034 | 7,550 | 3,000 |

TABLE VII. (Continued)

| Element | Isotope and abundance a (%) | $E_0$ | $a\sigma_0\Gamma$ barns-ev. | $g$ | $a\sigma_0\Gamma^2$ barns-ev.² | $\Gamma_\gamma$ volts | $\Gamma_n$ volts | Calculated $a\sigma_0$ at $E_0$, barns | Observed $\sigma_t$ at $E_0$, barns |
|---|---|---|---|---|---|---|---|---|---|
| 64Gd | Gd¹⁵⁷(15.68) | 0.030 | 4,970 | 9/16 | 501 | 0.100 | 0.00065 | 49,400 | 42,000 |
|  |  | 2.0 | — | — | — | — | — | — | 310 |
|  |  | 2.6 | — | — | — | — | — | — | 1,000 |
|  |  | 6.4 | — | — | — | — | — | — | 240 |
|  |  | 7.7 | — | — | — | — | — | — | 68 |
| 65Tb | Tb¹⁵⁹(100) | 3.35 | 209 | 5/8 | 18.9 | 0.090 | 0.00043 | 2,310 | 1,050 |
|  |  | 4.99 | 17.9 | 5/8 | 1.6 | (0.090) | 0.000055 | 200 | 110 |
|  |  | 11.1 | 1,350 | 5/8 | 134 | (0.090) | 0.0092 | 13,600 | 2,400 |
|  |  | 14.4 | 61 | 5/8 | 5.5 | (0.090) | 0.00054 | 673 | 76 |
| 66Dy |  | 1.75 | — | — | — | — | — | — | 1,000 |
|  |  | 2.7 | — | — | — | — | — | — | 500 |
|  |  | 3.7 | — | — | — | — | — | — | 780 |
|  |  | 4.4 | — | — | — | — | — | — | 480 |
|  |  | 5.4 | — | — | — | — | — | — | 7,200 |
| 67Ho | Ho¹⁶⁵(100) | 3.92 | 934 | 9/16 | 86.4 | 0.090 | 0.0025 | 10,100 | 5,100 |
|  |  | 12.8 | 1,490 | 9/16 | 154 | (0.090) | 0.0131 | 14,500 | 2,600 |
|  |  | 18.2 | 74 | 9/16 | 13.4 | 0.180 | 0.00092 | 409 | 105 |
|  |  | 21.3 | 50.1 | 9/16 | 9.0 | (0.180) | 0.00073 | 277 | 64 |
| 68Er |  | 0.47 | — | — | — | — | — | — | 2,700 |
|  |  | 0.58 | — | — | — | — | — | — | 1,850 |
|  |  | 6.1 | — | — | — | — | — | — | 710 |
|  |  | 8.0 | — | — | — | — | — | — | 54 |
|  |  | 9.5 | — | — | — | — | — | — | 280 |

| | | | | | | | | | |
|---|---|---|---|---|---|---|---|---|---|
| $_{69}$Tm | Tm$^{169}$(100) | 3.92 | 5,970 | ¾ | 490 | 0.070 | 0.012 | 72,800 | 16,500 |
| | — | 14.4 | 771 | ¾ | 62.3 | 0.075 | 0.0057 | 9,560 | 1,100 |
| | — | 17.6 | 355 | ¾ | 23.5 | 0.063 | 0.0032 | 5,360 | 550 |
| | — | 29.1 | 24.8 | ¾ | 1.6 | (0.063) | 0.00037 | 391 | 27 |
| | — | 35.2 | 721 | ¾ | 88.6 | 0.110 | 0.013 | 5,860 | 360 |
| $_{70}$Yb | Yb$^{168}$(0.14) | 0.597 | 20.2 | 1 | 1.48 | 0.070 | 0.0033 | 275 | 170 |
| | — | 4.6 | — | — | — | — | — | — | 72 |
| | — | 8.2 | — | — | — | — | — | — | 230 |
| | — | 13.5 | — | — | — | — | — | — | 93 |
| | — | 18 | — | — | — | — | — | — | 128 |
| $_{71}$Lu | Lu$^{176}$(2.60) | 0.14 | — | — | — | — | — | — | 360 |
| | Lu$^{176}$ | 1.6 | — | — | — | — | — | — | 120 |
| | — | 2.6 | — | — | — | — | — | — | 870 |
| | — | 4.7 | — | — | — | — | — | — | 700 |
| | — | 5.2 | — | — | — | — | — | — | 1,800 |
| $_{72}$Hf | Hf$^{177}$(18.39) | 1.08 | 596 | ¾ | 26.7 | 0.043 | 0.0018 | 13,300 | 5,000 |
| | Hf$^{177}$ | 2.36 | 791 | ¾ | 54.0 | 0.063 | 0.0052 | 11,600 | 5,800 |
| | — | 5.3 | — | — | — | — | — | — | 270 |
| | {Hf$^{179}$(13.78) | 5.69 | 198 | ¾ | 12.7 | 0.060 | 0.0042 | 3,090 | 1,150 |
| | {Hf$^{177}$ | 5.9 | 310 | ¾ | 21.1 | 0.063 | 0.0051 | 4,550 | |
| | Hf$^{177}$ | 6.6 | 600 | ¾ | 33 | 0.044 | 0.011 | 10,900 | 1,500 |
| | Hf$^{178}$(27.02) | 7.8 | 4,410 | 1 | 481 | 0.060 | 0.049 | 40,500 | 10,000 |
| $_{73}$Ta | Ta$^{181}$(100) | 4.28 | 1,470 | 9/16 | 78.4 | 0.049 | 0.0043 | 27,600 | 13,000 |
| | — | 10.38 | 637 | 9/16 | 34.1 | 0.049 | 0.0045 | 11,900 | 3,000 |
| | — | 13.95 | 115 | 9/16 | 5.9 | 0.050 | 0.0011 | 2,260 | 580 |
| | — | 20.5 | 78.7 | 9/16 | 4.1 | 0.051 | 0.0011 | 1,151 | 200 |
| | — | 24.1 | 425 | 9/16 | 24.2 | 0.050 | 0.007 | 7,450 | 900 |

TABLE VII. (*Continued*)

| Element | Isotope and abundance $a$ (%) | $E_0$ | $a\sigma_0\Gamma$ barns-ev. | $g$ | $a\sigma_0\Gamma^2$ barns-ev.² | $\Gamma_\gamma$ volts | $\Gamma_n$ volts | Calculated $a\sigma_0$ at $E_0$, barns | Observed $\sigma_t$ at $E_0$, barns |
|---|---|---|---|---|---|---|---|---|---|
| $_{74}$W | W$^{182}$(26.4) | 4.15 | 182 | 1 | 12.9 | 0.070 | 0.0011 | 2,560 | 115 |
| | W$^{183}$(14.4) | 7.8 | 75.8 | 3/4 | 4.7 | 0.060 | 0.0021 | 1,220 | 47 |
| | W$^{186}$(28.4) | 19.2 | 9,600 | 1 | 3070 | 0.070 | 0.250 | 30,000 | 14,500 |
| | W$^{182}$ | 22 | — | — | — | — | — | — | 3,500 |
| | W$^{183}$ | 28 | — | — | — | — | — | — | 525 |
| $_{75}$Re | Re$^{185}$(37.07) | 2.18 | 593 | 7/12 | 54.8 | 0.090 | 0.0023 | 6,430 | 3,500 |
| | Re$^{187}$(62.93) | 4.40 | 117 | 7/12 | 10.6 | 0.090 | 0.00054 | 1,290 | 390 |
| | Re$^{185}$ | 5.9 | — | — | — | — | — | — | 88 |
| | Re$^{185}$ | 7.2 | — | — | — | — | — | — | 245 |
| $_{76}$Os | — | 6.5 | — | — | — | — | — | — | 37 |
| | — | 8.8 | — | — | — | — | — | — | 47 |
| | — | 19.5 | — | — | — | — | — | — | 23.5 |
| $_{77}$Ir | Ir$^{191}$(38.5) | 0.66 | — | — | — | — | — | — | 4,800 |
| | Ir$^{193}$(61.5) | 1.3 | — | — | — | — | — | — | 5,700 |
| | — | 5.4 | — | — | — | — | — | — | 5,200 |
| | — | 6.1 | — | — | — | — | — | — | 360 |
| | — | 8.7 | — | — | — | — | — | — | 135 |
| $_{78}$Pt | Pt$^{195}$(33.7) | 12 | — | — | — | — | — | — | 2,000 |
| | Pt$^{195}$ | 19 | — | — | — | — | — | — | 660 |
| | Pt$^{195}$ | 67 | — | — | — | — | — | — | 700 |
| | Pt$^{198}$(7.2) | 96 | — | — | — | — | — | — | 300 |
| $_{79}$Au | Au$^{197}$(100) | 4.91 | 5,170 | 5/8 | 721 | 0.124 | 0.0156 | 37,000 | 30,000 |
| | — | 61.5 | 2,910 | 5/8 | 819 | 0.170 | 0.110 | 10,400 | 500 |
| | — | 80.2 | 303 | 5/8 | 56.1 | (0.170) | 0.015 | 1,640 | 28 |

| | | | | | | | | | |
|---|---|---|---|---|---|---|---|---|---|
| $_{80}$Hg | $Hg^{198}$(10.02) | 23.3 | 64.8 | 1 | 9.8 | 0.145 | 0.0058 | 430 | 150 |
| | $Hg^{199}$(16.84) | 34.0 | 754 | ¾ | 247 | 0.250 | 0.078 | 2,300 | 510 |
| | | 43 | — | — | — | — | — | — | 32 |
| $_{81}$Tl | $Tl^{203}$(29.50) | 240 | — | — | — | — | — | — | 430 |
| | — | 1,300 | — | — | — | — | — | — | 17.5 |
| $_{82}$Pb | — | 20,000 | — | — | — | — | — | — | 10.8 |
| | — | 29,000 | — | — | — | — | — | — | 11.3 |
| | — | 47,000 | — | — | — | — | — | — | 13.3 |
| $_{83}$Bi | — | 810 | — | — | — | — | — | — | 58 |
| | — | 2,300 | — | — | — | — | — | — | 37.5 |
| | — | 13,000 | — | — | — | — | — | — | 24 |
| $_{90}$Th | $Th^{232}$(100) | 22.0 | 236 | 1 | 7.57 | 0.030 | 0.002 | 7,390 | 550 |
| | — | 23.7 | 404 | 1 | 13.6 | (0.030) | 0.0037 | 12,000 | 720 |
| | — | 59.6 | 196 | 1 | 6.77 | (0.030) | 0.0045 | 5,690 | 150 |
| | — | 70.1 | 1,480 | 1 | 104 | (0.030) | 0.040 | 21,200 | 420 |
| $_{92}$U | $U^{235}$(0.714) | 0.29 | 0.149 | 9/16 | 0.00447 | 0.031 | $4 \times 10^{-6}$ | 4.7 | — |
| | — | 1.12 | 0.149 | 9/16 | 0.00224 | 0.015 | $15 \times 10^{-6}$ | 10 | — |
| | — | 2.04 | 0.0410 | 9/16 | 0.00111 | 0.027 | $8 \times 10^{-6}$ | 1.5 | — |
| | — | 2.86 | 0.0146 | 9/16 | 0.00039 | 0.027 | $4 \times 10^{-6}$ | 0.54 | — |
| | — | 3.17 | 0.079 | 9/16 | 0.0024 | 0.030 | $24 \times 10^{-6}$ | 2.6 | — |
| | — | 3.60 | 0.145 | 9/16 | 0.0058 | 0.040 | $50 \times 10^{-6}$ | 3.6 | — |
| | — | 4.85 | 0.112 | 9/16 | 0.0045 | 0.040 | $52 \times 10^{-6}$ | 2.8 | — |
| | $U^{234}$(0.0057) | 5.10 | 0.131 | 1 | 0.0031 | 0.019 | 0.0045 | 0.51 | — |
| | $U^{238}$(99.3) | 6.70 | 584 | 1 | 14.9 | 0.024 | 0.00152 | 22,900 | 7,000 |
| | — | 21.0 | 1,090 | 1 | 37.1 | 0.025 | 0.0089 | 32,300 | 5,500 |
| | — | 26.9 | 2,270 | 1 | 140 | 0.029 | 0.0325 | 36,900 | 4,700 |

## TABLE VII. (Continued)

*Summary of Neutron Resonances of the Elements (0 to 10 ev.) in Order of Energy*
*($w$ = 0 to 100 barns; $m$ = 100 to 1000 barns; $s$ = > 1000 barns)*

| 0 to 3 ev. | | 3 to 6 ev. | | 6 to 10 ev. | |
|---|---|---|---|---|---|
| $Gd^{157}$ | 0.030$s$ | $U^{235}$ | 3.17$w$ | Eu | 6.03$m$ |
| $Xe^{135}$ | 0.082$s$ | $Eu^{151}$ | 3.34$s$ | Er | 6.1$m$ |
| $Sm^{149}$ | 0.096$s$ | $Tb^{159}$ | 3.35$s$ | Ir | 6.1$m$ |
| $Lu^{176}$ | 0.14$m$ | $Sm^{147}$ | 3.45$m$ | Lu | 6.2$w$ |
| $Cd^{113}$ | 0.178$s$ | $U^{235}$ | 3.6$w$ | $Sb^{121}$ | 6.2$s$ |
| $U^{235}$ | 0.29$w$ | Sr | 3.6$w$ | $U^{235}$ | 6.2$w$ |
| $Eu^{151}$ | 0.327$s$ | Dy | 3.7$m$ | Eu | 6.25$m$ |
| $Eu^{151}$ | 0.461$s$ | $Eu^{153}$ | 3.84$s$ | Gd | 6.4$m$ |
| Er | 0.47$s$ | $In^{115}$ | 3.86$s$ | $U^{235}$ | 6.4$w$ |
| Er | 0.58$s$ | $Ho^{165}$ | 3.92$s$ | Os | 6.5$w$ |
| $Yb^{168}$ | 0.597$m$ | $Tm^{169}$ | 3.92$s$ | $Hf^{177}$ | 6.6$s$ |
| $Ir^{191}$ | 0.66$s$ | $W^{182}$ | 4.15$m$ | $U^{238}$ | 6.70$s$ |
| $Sm^{149}$ | 0.87$s$ | $Ta^{181}$ | 4.28$s$ | $U^{235}$ | 7.1$w$ |
| $Eu^{151}$ | 1.06$s$ | Dy | 4.4$m$ | $Re^{187}$ | 7.2$m$ |
| $Hf^{177}$ | 1.08$s$ | $Nd^{145}$ | 4.4$m$ | $Eu^{151}$ | 7.24$s$ |
| $U^{235}$ | 1.12$w$ | $Re^{187}$ | 4.4$m$ | Gd | 7.7$w$ |
| $Rh^{103}$ | 1.26$s$ | Yb | 4.6$w$ | $Hf^{178}$ | 7.8$s$ |
| $Ir^{193}$ | 1.3$s$ | Lu | 4.7$m$ | $W^{183}$ | 7.8$w$ |
| $In^{115}$ | 1.46$s$ | $In^{113}$ | 4.71$w$ | Dy | 7.9$m$ |
| $Lu^{176}$ | 1.6$m$ | Eu | 4.83$w$ | Er | 8.0$w$ |
| Dy | 1.75$s$ | $U^{235}$ | 4.85$w$ | $Sm^{152}$ | 8.2$s$ |
| $Eu^{153}$ | 1.76$m$ | $Sm^{149}$ | 4.9$m$ | Yb | 8.2$m$ |
| Gd | 2.0$m$ | $Au^{197}$ | 4.91$s$ | $Te^{125}$ | 8.3$w$ |
| $U^{235}$ | 2.04$w$ | $Tb^{159}$ | 4.99$m$ | Ir | 8.7$m$ |
| $Re^{185}$ | 2.18$s$ | $Ag^{109}$ | 5.1$s$ | $U^{235}$ | 8.8$w$ |
| Tc | 2.2$w$ | $U^{234}$ | 5.1$w$ | $Hf^{177}$ | 8.8$m$ |
| $Te^{123}$ | 2.33$m$ | Lu | 5.2$s$ | Os | 8.8$w$ |
| $Hf^{177}$ | 2.36$s$ | Hf | 5.3$m$ | Eu | 8.9$s$ |
| $Eu^{153}$ | 2.46$s$ | $U^{235}$ | 5.4$w$ | $In^{115}$ | 9.1$s$ |
| Gd | 2.6$s$ | Dy | 5.4$s$ | Xe | 9.1$m$ |
| Lu | 2.6$m$ | Ir | 5.4$s$ | $U^{235}$ | 9.3$w$ |
| Dy | 2.7$m$ | Eu | 5.47$m$ | Er | 9.5$m$ |
| $Eu^{151}$ | 2.73$m$ | Tc | 5.6$m$ | Ru | 9.7$w$ |
| $U^{235}$ | 2.86$w$ | $Hf^{179}$ | 5.69$s$ | $U^{235}$ | 9.8$w$ |
| | | $Hf^{177}$ | 5.9$s$ | Lu | 9.8$w$ |
| | | $Cs^{133}$ | 5.9$s$ | | |
| | | $Re^{185}$ | 5.9$w$ | | |
| | | $U^{235}$ | 5.9$w$ | | |

identification of this element. The following treatment will show how these resonance dips in the transmission curves can be used for quantitative estimation once the appropriate constants are known for the element.

### 11.2. Resonance-Transmission Curves

When the energy of the neutron is not near the resonant energy of any of the isotopes present, the cross section is approximately $4\pi R^2$ where $R$ is the nuclear radius. This cross section varies between 2 and 11 barns for practically all elements. When the energy of the neutron approaches the resonant energy, the cross section increases very rapidly. In some cases, for example $Xe^{135}$, it is as high as $3.4 \times 10^6$ barns at $E_0$. This rapid increase in cross section in the vicinity of a resonance causes the resonant dip in the transmission curve.

In the transmission curve for a sample of material, the observed transmission near a resonance can be divided into two parts: (a) the part which varies slowly with energy and (b) the part which is due to resonance absorption and scattering and varies rapidly with energy. The part of the transmission which varies slowly with energy can be determined by drawing the best straight line through the experimental points some distance from the center of the resonance. This transmission is called the "background" transmission for this particular resonance.

It is obvious from the transmission curve of zirconium with the hafnium impurity that the hafnium transmission dip recovers to the background transmission of approximately 0.49. A derived resonance-transmission curve for the hafnium in this sample of zirconium can be obtained by dividing the observed transmission curve by the background transmission. This derived transmission curve is the one used for the quantitative estimation of an element.

### 11.3. Effect of Resolution Width

To obtain the quantity of an element from its resonance transmission curve, one must consider the method by which the data are obtained.

In the modulated cyclotron velocity selector, as described above, there is approximately uniform production of neutrons for a time $\tau$ and detection of the neutrons for an interval of time $\tau'$ (p. 470). Suppose for simplicity (usually applied in practice) that we let $\tau = \tau'$. Then neutrons having times of flight between $t_1 - \tau$ and $t_1 + \tau$ will be detected and recorded. The probability that the particle having a time of flight $t$ between $t_1 - \tau$ and $t_1 + \tau$ being detected will be proportional to the sum of area of the production pulse and the detection pulse overlapping at the time $t$. Therefore, the probability of a particle of time of flight $t$ being detected will be zero at $t = t_1 - \tau$, increase linearly until $t = t_1$, and then decrease linearly to zero at $t = t_1 + \tau$.

The probability of detection can be represented mathematically by a distribution function expressed by the following relations:

$$\Phi(t,\tau) = 0 \text{ for } t < (t_1 - \tau) \tag{11.2}$$
$$\Phi(t,\tau) = 1/\tau^2[t - (t_1 - \tau)] \text{ for } (t_1 - \tau) < t < t_1 \tag{11.3}$$
$$\Phi(t,\tau) = 1/\tau^2[(t_1 + \tau) - t] \text{ for } t_1 < t < (t_1 + \tau) \tag{11.4}$$
$$\Phi(t,\tau) = 0 \text{ for } t > (t_1 + \tau) \tag{11.5}$$

This distribution function is usually called the *resolution function* or *resolution width* of the apparatus. The relation of the resolution function of the apparatus to "cyclotron on time" and "detector on time" is given in Fig. 28.

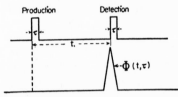

Fig. 28. Resolution function $\phi(u)$ showing its relation to cyclotron on time and detector on time.

If the constants for the Breit-Wigner formula (p. 460) are known, a calculated value for the transmission, $T_c$, of the sample for neutrons of energy $E$ can be obtained from the equation

$$T_c = e^{-n'\sigma(E)} \tag{11.6}$$

Here $n'$ is the number of atoms per square centimeter of the absorbing isotope and $\sigma(E)$ is the cross section of the isotope at the energy $E$ as given by the Breit-Wigner formula. This, however, is not the curve that is observed experimentally, because the apparatus does not have infinitely sharp resolution. To match the experimental curve, it is necessary to include the effect of the resolution width of the apparatus.

The actual observed transmission at an energy $E$ is given by

$$T = \int_{-b}^{+b} \phi(u) T_c(E + u) \, du \tag{11.7}$$

where $\phi(u)$ is the smearing function representing the resolution width of the apparatus on the energy basis and $b$ is the half width of the resolution function.

The observed transmission at a particular energy in the vicinity of a resonance can be quite different from the calculated transmission of the sample at this point. Therefore, the observed transmission value at the minimum of the transmission dip is not a reliable measure of the amount of the resonance absorber. This problem is similar to that encountered in optical spectroscopy, where the resolution width of the spectrometer is much wider than the absorption line.

## 11.4. Area of the Derived Resonance Dip

The difficulty noted can be circumvented by considering the integrated effect of the resonance over the energy range where it is effective. Let us define a quantity $A_E$ which is given by the expression

$$A_E = \int_{E_1}^{E_2} (1 - T)\, dE \tag{11.8}$$

where $E_1$ is less than $E_0$ and $E_2$ is greater than $E_0$. The quantity $A_E$ represents the area between the observed resonance transmission curve and unity transmission and is proportional to what we shall call the *strength of the resonance level*.

Substituting the expression for the experimental transmission into this formula gives

$$A_E = \int_{E_1}^{E_2} \left[ 1 - \int_{-b}^{+b} \varphi(u) T_c(E + u)\, du \right] dE \tag{11.9}$$

If (1) $\varphi(u)$ is a symmetrical normalized function, that is

$$\int_{-b}^{+b} \varphi(u)\, du = 1 \tag{11.10}$$

(2) $(E_2 - E_1) \gg b$, (3) there is negligible difference between the odd derivatives of $T_c(E)$ at the limits of the integration, then the integral may be written as

$$A_E = \int_{E_1}^{E_2} [1 - T_c(E)]\, dE \tag{11.11}$$

If we also assume that $E_0 \gg \Gamma$ (as it is in most cases), then the term $(E_0/E)^{1/2}$ is approximately unity over the energy range where $\sigma$ is very large. The function $[1 - T_c(E)]$ then becomes a function that has a value different from zero in a small energy range compared with the range of integration. Therefore, we can let the limits of the integration go from $-\infty$ to $+\infty$ without changing the value of this integral appreciably.

If we also further simplify the expression for $A_E$ by changing the variable $E$ such that $x = [2(E - E_0)]/\Gamma$, the quantity $A_E$ is given by

$$A_E = \frac{\Gamma}{2} \int_{-\infty}^{\infty} (1 - e^{\frac{-n'\sigma_0}{1+x^2}})\, dx \tag{11.12}$$

This integral cannot be evaluated analytically; however, for the two specific cases which are most useful, satisfactory approximations can be made.

If the actual transmission of the sample is very small at exact resonance, that is, if $n'\sigma_0 > 1$, then, for values of $x$ sufficiently far from exact resonance that $T$ is appreciably different from zero, the 1 in the denominator of the exponent can be ignored compared with the $x^2$. This is so because that part of the transmission curve where the transmission is effectively zero (it matters little whether $T = e^{-10}$ or $e^{-100}$) introduces negligible contribution to the area. We can then write

$$A_E \text{ (thick)} = \frac{\Gamma}{2} \int_{-\infty}^{\infty} (1 - e^{\frac{-n'\sigma_0}{x^2}}) \, dx \tag{11.13}$$

letting $x = 1/z$

$$A_E = \frac{\Gamma}{2} \int_{-\infty}^{\infty} \frac{1}{z^2} \, dz + \frac{\Gamma}{2} \int_{-\infty}^{\infty} \frac{e^{-n'\sigma_0 z^2}}{z^2} \, dz \tag{11.14}$$

The first integral is zero; the second integral can be integrated by parts to obtain

$$A_E \text{ (thick)} = \sqrt{\pi n'\sigma_0 \Gamma^2} \quad \text{or} \quad n' \text{ (thick)} = \frac{A_E^2}{\pi\sigma_0\Gamma^2} \tag{11.15}$$

Therefore, for a "thick" sample, that is, when $n'\sigma_0 > 1$, the area between unity transmission and the actual transmission of the sample is directly proportional to the square root of the number of atoms per square centimeter of the resonant nucleus present.

In the case of a "thin" sample, that is, when $\sigma_0\Gamma \ll 1$, the exponential can be expanded in a rapidly converging series, and $A_E$ becomes

$$A_E \text{ (thin)} = \frac{\Gamma}{2} \int_{-\infty}^{\infty} \frac{n'\sigma_0}{1 + x^2} \, dx = \frac{\pi}{2} n'\sigma_0\Gamma$$

or

$$n' \text{ (thin)} = \frac{2A_E}{\pi\sigma_0\Gamma} \tag{11.16}$$

In this case the number of atoms of the isotope in the sample is directly proportional to the area.

If more detail about the sample is required, then the problem must be treated more exactly than in the simple approximations given above. In these approximations the sample was assumed to be extremely thin or extremely thick. The approximation for the thin sample can be improved by taking more terms in the expression. Thus, eight terms in the series gives to within 5% of the area for a sample as thick as $n'\sigma_0 = 8$. For intermediate values of $n'\sigma_0$ the area above a resonance dip has been evaluated by numerical integration (148), and corrections can be applied as described in section 11.6.

### 11.5. Doppler Effect

In a more rigorous treatment of this problem the "Doppler effect" (19), which has been completely neglected here must be taken into consideration. The Breit-Wigner formula as stated in eq. (6.1) applies rigorously only in the center of mass system for the collision of a neutron and a nucleus. The velocities of the capturing nuclei introduce a Doppler width $\Delta$, defined below, which is not negligible compared with the natural width of a level $\Gamma$.

If $u_x$ is the velocity of the nucleus in the direction of motion of the neutron, then $(v - u_x)$ is the relative velocity of the neutron and nucleus. The relative kinetic energy is then

$$E' - \tfrac{1}{2}m(v - u_x)^2 = E - (2mE)^{\frac{1}{2}}u_x \tag{11.17}$$

with terms in $u^2/v$ being neglected, where $E$ is the kinetic energy of the neutron in the laboratory system and $m$ is the mass of the neutron. The probability of finding a nucleus of velocity $u_x$ is given by the Maxwellian distribution function

$$N(u_x)\, du_x = \left(\frac{M}{2\pi kT}\right)^{\frac{1}{2}} e^{-\frac{M u_x^2}{2kT}}\, du_x \tag{11.18}$$

where $M$ is the mass of the nucleus, $k$ is Botzmann's constant, and $T$ is the temperature in degrees Kelvin. Thus the probability of having the relative kinetic energy $E'$ is

$$w(E')\, dE' = \pi^{-\frac{1}{2}} e^{-\frac{(E'-E)^2}{\Delta^2}}\frac{dE'}{\Delta} \tag{11.19}$$

where

$$\Delta = 2(mE_0 kT/M)^{\frac{1}{2}} \tag{11.20}$$

is the *Doppler width*, which has been mentioned previously. $E_0$ has been written instead of $E$ in the Doppler width because we are interested in this quantity only in the vicinity of the resonance. The energy which must be used in the Breit-Wigner formula is the relative energy $E'$. Thus if we designate the Breit-Wigner formula as $\sigma(E')$ the effective cross section for a neutron of energy $E$ in the laboratory system is

$$\sigma(\xi,E) = \int\sigma(E')w(E')\, dE' = \sigma_0\psi(\xi,x) \tag{11.21}$$

where

$$x = \frac{E - E_0}{\Gamma/2}, \qquad \xi = \frac{\Gamma}{\Delta}$$

and

$$\psi(\xi,x) = \frac{\xi}{2\pi^{\frac{1}{2}}}\int_{-\infty}^{\infty}\frac{e^{-\frac{\xi^2}{4}(x-y)^2}}{1+y^2}\, dy \tag{11.22}$$

where

$$y = \frac{(E' - E_r)}{\Gamma/2}$$

$\psi(\xi,x)$ is in general a complicated function of $x$ and has been calculated for many values of $x$ using large electronic computing machines (179).

This treatment applies to gaseous samples. However, Lamb (127) has shown that if the sample is a solid, these equations are valid if $(\Delta + \Gamma)$

$> 2k\theta$ where $\theta$ is the Debye temperature of the solid. If this condition is met, then it is possible to account for lattice binding by substituting for the real temperature $T$ an effective temperature $T_{eff}$ defined in Lamb's article.

A more elaborate treatment of the problem of the determination of the resonance parameter from the area over a transmisson dip and conversely the problem of determining the quantity of sample present from a knowledge of the resonance parameter and the area over a resonance dip has been given by several authors (84, 147, 148) as it is an important problem for the nuclear physicist.

### 11.6. Corrections for the "Thick" and "Thin" Approximations and Doppler Effect

The simple approximations given in section 11.4 are reasonably good even though the Doppler effect is neglected. However, for samples of

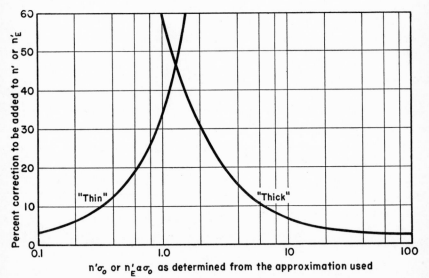

FIG. 29. Correction curves for the thick and thin approximations for the area $A_E$.

intermediate thicknesses both of them give too large a value for $A/\Gamma$. This leads to too low an estimation for the value of $n'$. By comparison with the more exact numerical solution to the problem, the error in $n'$ for the approximations can be determined (216). These values are plotted in Fig. 29. From Anderson's more Complete Calculations (7).

It can be seen from the curves that, at $n'\sigma_0 = 1.2$, the corrections for $n'$ for the two approximations are about the same (47%). However, for values of $n'\sigma_0$ of about 0.1 for thin samples and about $n'\sigma_0 = 10$ for thick samples, the deviations are only from 6 to 7%. After the value of $n'$ is determined by use of the analytical approximations, corrections can then be made from Fig. 29.

Neglecting the Doppler effect does not materially alter the determination of $n'$ from a low-energy resonance ($<5$ ev.), as the Doppler width $\Delta$ is usually small compared with the natural width $\Gamma$. Even for higher energy resonances the Doppler correction which must be applied in the

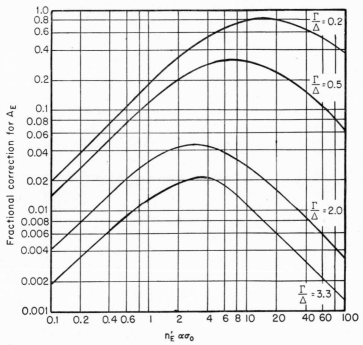

FIG. 30. Correction to the measured area $A_E$ for the Doppler effect.

determination of $n'$ from the area over a transmission dip is usually small. However, the maximum value of the cross section at the resonant energy is substantially affected by the Doppler effect. It is for this reason that a calculated value of $\sigma_0$ is given in Table VII rather than a measured value. For example for the gold resonance at 4.92 ev., which is one of the most accurately measured resonances, the maximum measured value of the cross section at exact resonance is 32,000 barns (128); whereas the calculated cross section is 37,000 barns. The correction for the resolution width of the apparatus represents only 500 barns with the Doppler width accounting for the remaining 6,500 barns.

The maximum measurable cross section with perfect resolution is the Doppler depressed cross section. The actual cross section at exact resonance $\sigma_0$ is not a measurable quantity except at a sample temperature of absolute zero. The effect of Doppler broadening is to increase the area under the resonance dip. Several curves for the fractional correction to the measured area $A_E$ are given in Fig. 30. It is this corrected area that should really be used in the "thick" and "thin" approximations to calculate the value of $n'$. However for low-energy resonances this correction can usually be neglected and since this is a correction on a correction the effect is usually not large.

### 11.7. Detectability of a Resonance

The minimum quantity that can be determined depends upon the energy at which the resonance occurs, the constants of the nuclear resonance, and the fractional abundance of the isotope responsible for the resonance, as shown by the following considerations.

Because the data taken with the modulated cyclotron neutron spectrometer are usually on the time-of-flight basis, the expression given previously for the area of the resonance dip on the energy basis can be converted to an area on a time-of-flight basis. As $dE/E = 2dt/t$, then

$$A_E \cong \frac{2E_0}{t_0} A_t \tag{11.23}$$

Therefore,

$$n'\sigma_0\Gamma = \frac{4}{\pi} \frac{E_0}{t_0} A_t \text{ for a thin sample,}$$

and

$$n'\sigma_0\Gamma^2 = \left( \frac{2E_0}{\sqrt{\pi}\, t_0} A_t \right)^2 \text{ for a thick sample} \tag{11.24}$$

where $A_E$ and $A_t$ represent the area on the energy and time-of-flight basis, respectively.

Experimentally the criterion for the detection of a resonance is not the area under the resonance dip but the change in transmission at exact resonance. It is difficult to give exact criteria for the strength and energy of the level for a specified transmission because the actual observed minimum transmission depends on the resolution width of the apparatus, the thickness of the sample, and the actual nuclear constants of the level. However, we can examine the conditions at the two limiting cases of the resolution width of the apparatus: (1) when the level is completely resolved and (2) when the resolution width is much wider than the resonance. For these cases the minimum observable number of atoms of the element per square centimeter, $n_E'$, can be estimated as follows. In the preceding discussions we have used $n'$ for the number of atoms/square centimeter of the isotope responsible for the resonance and $\sigma_0$ as its cross section at $E_0$. In the following paragraphs we shall use the number of atoms of the *element*/square centimeter, $n_E'$ and $\alpha\sigma_0$ where $\alpha$ = atom fraction of the isotope.

In the case of Cd the level has been completely resolved with $E_0$ = 0.178 ev., $\Gamma$ = 0.113 ev., and $\alpha\sigma_0$ = 7660 barns. The minimum transmission will be at the resonance energy $E_0$ when $T = e^{-n_E'\alpha\sigma_0}$. The maximum ratio of the constant transmission to the resonant transmission that can be observed is about 0.9, or $n_E'\alpha\sigma_0 \cong 0.1$, which gives $n_E'$ = 1.31 $\times$ 10$^{19}$ or 2.5 mg./cm.$^2$

For Mn, where $E_0$ = 337 ev. and $\Gamma \cong 22$ ev., with $\alpha\sigma_0\Gamma$ = 8.49 $\times$ 10$^4$, the difference in time of flight between the resonant neutron and a neutron of energy $E_0 \pm \Gamma$ corresponds to about 0.13 $\mu$sec./m. If a resolution width of 0.9 $\mu$sec./m. is used to detect this level, the observed width of the resonant dip on the time-of-flight basis will be almost completely due to the resolution width of the apparatus. In the case of Mn, if the production interval $\tau$ equals the detection interval, the observed transmission dip will be triangular in shape and have a base equal to twice the interval $\tau$. The transmission dip will be triangular in shape with a base 0.9 $\mu$sec. If we again assume that the maximum ratio of the constant transmission to the resonant transmission observable is 0.9, then the height of the triangle will be $1 - 0.9 = 0.1$. The area on the time of flight basis will thus be

$$A_t = \tfrac{1}{2} \times .9 \times .1 = 0.045 \ \mu\text{sec/meter}$$

and

$$A_E = \frac{2 \times 337}{3.94} \times 0.045 = 7.7 \text{ ev.}$$

Using the thin sample approximation

$$n_E' = \frac{2 \times 7.7 \times 10^{24}}{3.14 \times 8.49 \times 10^4}$$
$$n_E' = 5.78 \times 10^{19} \text{ or } 5.28 \text{ mg/cm}^2$$

For Mn, $\alpha\sigma_0$ = 3860; therefore,

$$n_E\alpha\sigma_0 = 3860 \times 10^{-24} \times 5.78 \times 10^{19} = 0.22$$

which means that the thin sample approximation was the proper approximation to use since $n_E'\sigma_0 < 1$.

It should be emphasized that even though the strength of the Mn level, $\alpha\sigma_0\Gamma$, is more than 100 times the strength of the Cd level, more atoms of Mn than of Cd must be present to obtain an observable effect. In the higher energy region, it is necessary to use a relatively thicker sample for determination of a resonance dip because of the effect of the poorer resolution at the higher energy.

## 11.8. Estimation of Concentration from Resonance Parameters

It was shown above that the area, $A_E$, under the curve obtained by plotting $(1 - T_r)$ against energy in electron volts could be used to calculate the number of atoms/square centimeter in two limiting cases:

$$\text{Thick sample approximation } n_E' = \frac{A_E^2}{\pi \alpha \sigma_0 \Gamma^2}$$

$$\text{Thin sample approximation } n_E' = \frac{2 A_E}{\pi \alpha \sigma_0 \Gamma}$$

Calculations are made first by means of the expression that applies best to the sample, and corrections are then made with the aid of Fig. 29. The following example will illustrate the procedure in more detail.

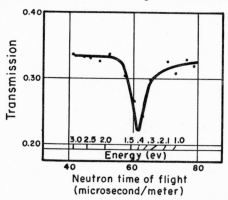

Fig. 31. Neutron-transmission curve for tin with a trace impurity of indium. Calculations show it to be about 0.02%.

In Fig. 31 the transmission curve for 45.15 g./cm.[2] of tin is shown. The dip at 1.46 ev. shows that indium is present as an impurity. The quantity present is estimated as follows. Examination of the curve shows that the constant part of the observed transmission is $T = 0.34$. The actual transmission at each point of the experimental curve is divided by 0.34 and the numbers thus obtained are subtracted from unity. This gives values of

$$\left(1 - \frac{T}{T_{\text{constant}}}\right) = (1 - T_r)$$

which are then plotted against the energy in electron volts to give the derived resonance curve. The area under this curve was found by numerical integration to be $A_E = 0.15$ ev.

Since the minimum transmission $T_r$ is a little less than 0.7, the sample is assumed to be "thin" as a first approximation. Substituting the known value of $\alpha \sigma_0 \Gamma = 3160$ for indium and the experimental value for the area $A_E$ in the thin-sample formula $n_E' = (2A_E)/(\pi a \sigma_0 \Gamma)$ gives $n_E' = 3.02 \times 10^{19}$ atoms/cm.$^2$ Reference to Fig. 29 shows that for $n_E' \sigma_0 = 3.02 \times 10^{19} \times 41,900 \times 10^{-24} = 1.27$, the correction for the approximate formula is 42%. The more precise value for $n_E'$ then becomes $4.3 \times 10^{19}$ atoms/cm.$^2$, or 8.2 mg./cm.$^2$ This corresponds to 0.018% In, with an estimated error of $\pm 0.005\%$ In. This is in reasonably good agreement with the spectographic analysis, which indicated $0.03 \pm 0.01\%$ In. With more precise transmission measurements at the indium resonance, a greater accuracy in determining the area could be achieved.

In this analysis the Doppler effect has been completely neglected. This can be taken into consideration by use of the numerical results obtained by Melkonian (147) and quoted here to show that this effect is negligible for our purposes. The Doppler width for this level is given by

$$\Delta = 2 \left( \frac{m}{M} E_0 kT \right)^{1/2} = 2 \left( \frac{1}{115} \times 1.45 \times 0.026 \right)^{1/2} \quad (11.25)$$
$$= 0.036 \text{ ev.}$$
$$\xi = \frac{\Gamma}{\Delta} = 2.1$$

The correction to the area for this case with $n_E' a \sigma_0 \sim 1$ is about 3%, which is a smaller correction than the accuracy of the area determination and can therefore justifiably be neglected.

To be determinable in small amounts by the method noted, the Breit-Wigner constants $a \sigma_0$ and $\Gamma$ should be known, and the amount of the element in the neutron beam should be such that $n_E' a \sigma_0$ is not smaller than about 0.2. Otherwise, the transmission at the resonance is too great for good measurements. For indium, this means that a foil containing about 0.9 mg./cm.$^2$ (0.0012 mm. thick) can be determined to within 5 to 10%. Similar calculations for gold with $a \sigma_0 \Gamma = 5170$, $a \sigma_0 = 37,000$ barns and $\Gamma = 0.140$ ev. show that 1.8 mg./cm.$^2$, or a thickness of 0.0009 mm., is determinable.

Application of the resonance absorption method to the specific case of the hafnium impurity in zirconium will further illustrate the procedure for a typical analysis. In the transmission dip for the 16.3 g./cm.$^2$ of zirconium shown in Fig. 27, the constant part of the observed transmission is $T = 0.496$. The observed transmission at each point is divided by 0.496, and the corrected transmission curve is then replotted. For the resonance at 69.6 $\mu$sec./m. (1.08 ev.) the area between this corrected transmission curve and unity transmission is evaluated by numerical integration and found to be $A_t = 9.5$ $\mu$sec./m. Here the area is given in terms of time of flight rather than of energy as in the previous example.

Since the minimum in the corrected transmission curve is close to zero, the thick-sample approximation is used. Substituting the known value of $\alpha\sigma_0\Gamma^2 = 26.7$ for the 1.08-ev. resonance of hafnium, and the experimental value of the area $A_t$ into the thick-sample formula, gives $n_E' = 10.3 \times 10^{20}$. The value of $\alpha\sigma_0$ for this level is 13,300 barns, and so $n_E'\alpha\sigma_0 = 13.7$, which shows that the thick-sample approximation is the one to use. The correction factor for a value of $n_E'\alpha\sigma_0 = 13.7$ is about 4%, which means that $n_E' = 10.7 \times 10^{20}$, or 0.32 g./cm.$^2$ hafnium. This corresponds to a 1.95% impurity of hafnium in the zirconium, with an estimated error of $\pm 10\%$ in the hafnium content. This is in reasonable agreement with the spectrographic analysis for the percentage of Hf. When a more precise numerical analysis of these data is made, the results can be obtained with higher accuracy. Also, direct comparison with standards of known hafnium content can be used to improve the accuracy of the determinations.

As stated previously, to be determinable to within $\pm 10\%$, $n_E'\alpha\sigma_0$ should not be smaller than about 0.2, corresponding to about 80% transmission at the resonance peak. For the 1.08-ev. resonance of hafnium there would be needed about 4.5 mg./cm.$^2$ of Hf in the beam. With high resolution, the resonance at 7.8 ev. would be more sensitive, since $\alpha\sigma_0$ is larger. Thus from Table VII, the resonance cross section $\alpha\sigma_0$ is 40,500 barns. For $n_E'\alpha\sigma_0 = 0.2$, $n_E' = 5 \times 10^{18}$ atoms of Hf/cm.$^2$, or about 1.5 mg./cm.$^2$ In the range of 0.1% hafnium in zirconium this would mean a zirconium sample about 0.25 cm. thick. The area would depend on the spectrometer or velocity selector used (1 to 2 cm.$^2$ for the Brookhaven fast chopper and 5 cm. in diameter for the Columbia pulsed cyclotron).

The sensitivity of the resonance-absorption method is illustrated in Fig. 32 by the results of E. Pilcher using the Brookhaven fast chopper. The following estimation from the known parameters of the 7.8-ev. resonance gives 0.03% Hf by weight. The area between the transmission curve and unity as measured with a planimeter is $A_t = 0.264$ $\mu$sec./m. the area on the energy basis is

$$A_E = 0.264 \times 2 \times \frac{7.8}{25.95} = 0.159 \text{ ev.}$$

With the thin-sample approximation

$$n_E' = \frac{2A_E}{\pi\alpha\sigma_0\Gamma} = \frac{2 \times 0.159}{3.14 \times 4.41 \times 10^3} \times 10^{24}$$
$$= 2.30 \times 10^{19} \text{ atoms/cm.}^2$$

From Table VII, $\alpha\sigma_0\Gamma = 4.41 \times 10^3$ for the 7.8-ev. resonance and $\Gamma = 0.109$ ev., and so

$$\alpha\sigma_0 = \frac{4.41 \times 10^3}{0.109} = 4.05 \times 10^4 \text{ barns}$$

and

$$n_E'\alpha\sigma_0 = 4.05 \times 10^4 \times 10^{-24} \times 2.30 \times 10^{19} = 0.93$$

The correction factor to the thin-sample approximation is $25\%$ from Fig. 29, which gives a corrected value of $n_E' = 2.88 \times 10^{19}$ atoms/cm.[2] The atom fraction is $(2.88 \times 10^{19})/(1.83 \times 10^{23}) = 1.57 \times 10^{-4}$, or $0.016\%$. Since the atomic weight of Zr $= 91.22$ and that of Hf $= 178.6$ the weight percentage of hafnium present is about $0.03\%$. It is estimated that about one tenth of this quantity could be detected. This shows that in favorable cases, the resonance analysis is rather sensitive.

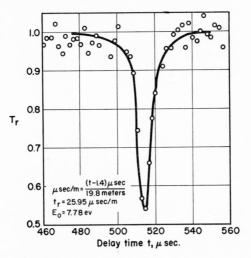

FIG. 32. Resonance-absorption curve for zirconium with a trace impurity of hafnium. This illustrates the sensitivity of the detection and determination of hafnium by use of its 7.8-ev. resonances.

### 11.9. Isotope Analysis by Resonance Absorption and Scattering

Since the resonances for an element arise from the nuclei and are therefore characteristic of the isotopes, it is obvious that any changes in isotope abundance in an element can be determined by resonance absorption and scattering measurements. If an element consists of two or more isotopes with the appropriate resonance characteristics and abundances, then it will be relatively easy to measure changes in their relative abundances. Also the atom percentage of any given isotope with the appropriate resonance characteristics can be determined by the methods of the previous sections by use of the values of $\sigma_0\Gamma$ or $\sigma_0\Gamma^2$ for the isotope rather than $\alpha\sigma_0\Gamma$ and $\alpha\sigma_0\Gamma^2$ for the element.

### 11.10. Resonance Analysis by Comparison with Standards

Analysis by resonance absorption would be simpler if the resolution of the instruments was such that the observed transmission obeyed a

Beer's type of law of experimental dependence on sample thickness. At the bottom of a narrow resonance dip where the transmission is a rapidly varying function of the neutron energy, the observed transmission is a weighted average or a range of neutron energies. The relation between $T$ at the resonance energy and the sample thickness can be calculated for a given resolution function (7, 8), triangular, for example, as shown in Fig. 33. Unfortunately the resolution functions are not always well defined; so a simple Beer's law plot of log $1/T$ vs. sample thickness

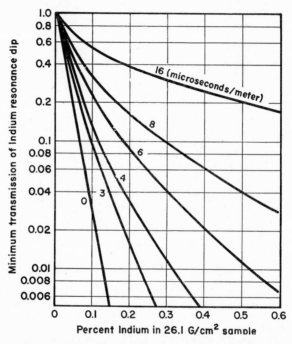

Fig. 33. Effect of resolution width on the minimum transmission of samples of tin (26.1 g./cm.²) containing different percentages of indium.

(g./cm.²) is not so useful as in measurements involving the absorption of light. The following examples will illustrate further some of the general methods of using a series of standards for resonance analysis.

Transmission curves obtained by Anderson (7, 8) for samples of tin containing different known percentages of indium are shown in Fig. 34. In plotting a working curve it is desirable to use some characteristic of the dip in the transmission curve that is not sensitive to resolution width, yet depends on the sample thickness in a manner easily determined. Three methods are illustrated for the specific case of indium in tin in the following sections.

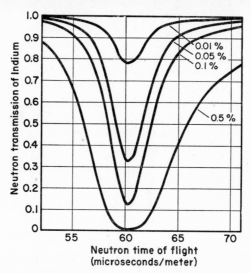

FIG. 34. Neutron-transmission curves for a series of tin samples of the same size(26.1 g./cm.²) containing different percentages of indium.

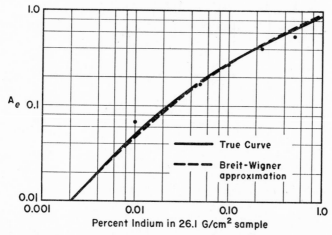

FIG. 35. The area $A_E$ (ev.) as a function of the percentage of indium, in 26.1 g./cm.² samples of tin. The "true curve" was obtained by use of the Breit-Wigner formula.

1. For each sample of known composition determine the area $A_e$ under the curve $(1 - T_r)$ vs. $E$ in electron volts between the energies $1.45 - 0.65 = 0.8$ ev. and $1.45 + 0.65 = 2.1$ ev. where $T_r = T_{exp}/T_{const}$. Plot $A_E$ vs. mg. In/cm.² to obtain a working curve. If the g./cm.² of the total sample is always the same, $A_e$ can be plotted vs. % In as shown in Fig. 35. Unknown samples can then be run in the same way and reference to the working curve will give the composition of the sample. The dotted line represents the theoretical curve calculated from the Breit-Wigner equation by

use of the known parameters for the indium resonance. In the absence of standards it can be seen that this calculated curve would be an adequate reference curve.

2. Frequently the transmission measurements are made on a time-of-flight basis rather than on an energy basis. In this case one uses the area $A_t$ under the peak of the $T_r$ or the $(1 - T_r)$, curve when plotted against the neutron time of flight $t$ between $t_1$ and $t_2$. For indium in tin, the area between $t_1 = 50$ and $t_2 = 70$ $\mu$sec./meter gave a

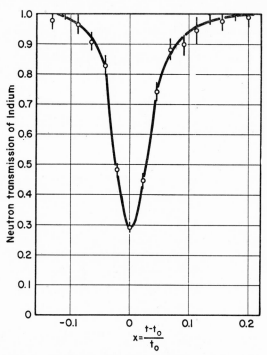

FIG. 36. Neutron-transmission curve for a sample of tin containing 13.05 mg./cm.[2] of indium.

satisfactory working curve. The area obtained by this method of plotting can be converted to the area on the energy basis by the relation

$$A_E = \left(\frac{2E_0}{t_0}\right) A_t$$

A related method that has some advantages is the area under the peak of the $T_r$ or $(1 - T_r)$ curve when plotted against $x = \dfrac{t - t_0}{t_0}$, where $t_0$ is the neutron time of flight at the resonance peak and $t$ is the neutron time of flight at which the transmission is measured. For indium in tin the limits found useful were $x_1 = -0.177$ and $x_2 = +0.255$. The area, $A_x$ for a series of standards is plotted against the mg./cm.[2] of indium or against percentage of indium for constant sample thickness. The area $A_x$ is related to the area $A_t$ by $A_t = A_x t_0$ and the area $A_E$ by $A_E = 2E_0 A_x$.

Experimental results are shown in Fig. 36 for 0.05% of indium in a tin sample with a thickness of 26.1 g./cm.[2] corresponding to a thickness for indium of 13.05

mg./cm.[2] Here the values of $T_r = T/T_{bkg}$ are plotted against $x = (t - t_0)/t$. The area $A_x$ as measured with a planimeter, by weighing, or by counting squares, is 0.059 and $A_E = 2E_0A_x = (2)(1.45)(0.059) = 0.170$ ev. Similar measurements on other samples of known composition give data for plotting a working curve of the area $A$, $A_t$, or $A_E$ vs. mg. In/cm.[2] as shown in Fig. 35.

3. The previous methods involve measurement of an area. Anderson (7, 8) found a useful empirical relation that was not sensitive to the resolution width but still depended on the sample thickness. It is

$$\phi = (1 - T_{r\,min})(\tfrac{1}{2}\ width)^{0.75}$$

where $T_{r\,min}$ is the minimum observed value of $T_r$ and the half width is the width across the curve of $T_r$ vs. $x = (t - t_0)/t_0$ at the transmission halfway between 1.00 and $T_{r\,min}$. The two quantities are measured on the best smooth curve through the experimental points. The value of $\phi$ is then calculated and plotted against the mg./cm.[2] of indium. For example, in Fig. 36 $(1 - T_{r\,min})$ is $(1 - 0.29) = 0.71$ and the half width is 0.073 units of $x$; so $\phi = (0.71)(0.073)^{0.75} = 0.0995$. This is repeated for other samples of known composition to provide a working curve of $\phi$ plotted against mg. of In/cm.[2]

The value of the exponent in the preceding equation was determined by plotting log $(1 - T_{r\,min})$ against log (half width) for the same sample with several resolution widths. A straight line was obtained with an intercept of log $\phi$ and a slope of about 0.75. Using five different sample thicknesses and running each sample at several resolution widths, the authors obtained parallel lines with slopes lying between 0.68 and 0.83. The average of these is about 0.75. These results indicated that the value of the exponent is not strongly dependent on sample thickness, and the straight line obtained demonstrated insensitiveness of the function to resolution width.

## 12. ANALYSIS BASED ON ABSORPTION IN A FLUX OF NEUTRONS

When a substance that absorbs neutrons is placed in a region where there is a flux of neutrons, the reduction in the flux can be used as a measure of the quantity of neutron-absorbing elements. Thus an element or isotope with a high-absorption cross section can be determined when in a solution or matrix of other substances of low-absorption cross section. The reduction in counting rate of a detector caused by the presence of the sample will be proportional to the quantity of the absorber and its absorption cross section. The scattering cross section of small quantities of the absorber will have only minor secondary effects.

### 12.1. Change in Flux of a Laboratory Neutron Source

The following example of the determination of boron in boron carbide with a 1-g. Ra-Be source (223) will illustrate the general method. The sample is ground to a very fine state of subdivision (less than 325 to 600 mesh) to reduce the extent of self-protection in single grains. The sample is then placed in a fixed volume of water in a soft glass or polyethylene container and stirred vigorously to keep the particles suspended as illustrated in Fig. 37. A sufficient amount of sample is used to reduce the counting rate to about one-third the rate for pure water. After the counting rate is determined to the required precision with the sample uniformly suspended, it is removed and the vessel is filled with the fixed volume of water. Next, known quantities of boron in the form of borax, boric oxide, or boron carbide of known boron content are added until the same counting rate as that with the unknown sample is obtained. It is assumed that the same quantity of boron was present in both cases since the reduction in the counting rate is the same. From this information and the weight of the sample, the percentage of boron can be calculated. It was possible, for

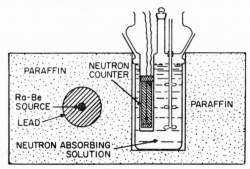

FIG. 37. Schematic diagram of an arrangement for analysis by absorption in a flux of neutrons.

example, to determine, using a 3- to 4-g. sample of boron carbide, that it contained 59.5% B.

Such determinations are somewhat easier and more precise if the sample is soluble in water, aqueous solutions of $H_2SO_4$, dilute $HNO_3$, HF (but not HCl), alcohol, benzene, acetone, or other organic solvents with low neutron-absorbing elements. It is convenient in such cases to dissolve the sample in a fixed volume of solvent, for example 50 ml., and to determine the counting rate as a function of concentration using standards. The counting rate for an unknown can then be referred to a plot of this data to determine the concentration of the absorber and from this the percentage in the sample can be calculated. With counting times of 5 to 10 min. a precision of about 1 to 2% can be attained with sufficient sample. The elements that can be determined by this method are those of high-absorption cross section (Table IV) such as certain rare earths, Cd, B, Ir, In, Rh, Hf, Au, Re, Li, Ag, and Cl. Minimum quantities ranging from 0.05 mmoles for cadmium to 3 mmoles for Cl can be determined depending on the absorption cross section of the element.

In principle it is possible to use the foregoing method in a flux of neutrons in the graphite reflector of a reactor. However, more elegant methods have been developed as described in the following sections.

### 12.2. Reactivity or "Danger-Coefficient" Method

During the development of reactors, the removal of neutron-absorbing impurities from structural materials such as graphite, aluminum, and uranium was mandatory. The presence of such impurities was "dangerous," with respect to attaining a chain reaction. Introductions of neutron-absorbing substances could easily be detected by their effect on the reactivity and power of the reactor. A method of determining these dangerous materials was devised and became known as the *danger-coefficient*, *pile-reactivity*, or simply *reactivity* method.

The general principle of the reactivity method is as follows (6). When a neutron-absorbing substance is introduced into a reactor, the reactivity and power level decreases. To keep the power level constant, the control rod must be withdrawn a certain distance. By proper calibrations of control-rod displacements with standards, a determination can be made of the quantity of an absorber in a sample.

With this method the sample is placed in a region of high flux, i.e., near the center of the reactor. The sample is spread in thin layers so as to minimize self-protection and hardening of the flux in the sample. Scattering results in a minor secondary effect unless large samples of the lighter elements are used. In this case extra moderation by the light nuclei tends to increase the reactivity. As long as standards and unknowns are measured in about the same type of matrix, corrections for these effects will not be large.

An idea of the sensitivity and quantities of materials needed can be estimated from some measurements on a boron standard (6). A total of 279 mg. of boron in layers of about 0.6 mg./sq. cm. caused a change in rod position that could be measured to 1 part in 500. The absorption cross section of boron is 755 barns, and so the total absorption-cross-sectional area of the boron was $(0.279/11.82)(6.02 \times 10^{23})(755 \times 10^{-24}) = 10.7$ sq. cm. Thus the sensitivity would be $\frac{1}{500}$ of this or about 0.02 sq. cm.; that is, $(\sigma_a \times$ number of absorber atoms$) = 0.02$ sq. cm., which for boron corresponds to $2.7 \times 10^{19}$ atoms, or about 0.5 mg. This is a rather small amount to be detectable by its effect on the operation of equipment as large as a reactor.

Although the method appears to be relatively straightforward, there are some difficulties in making the measurements. The control-rod displacement in centimeters for a given change in reactivity depends among other things upon its position in the reactor. Correction for this effect was simplified by calibrating the control rod in terms of its effect on the pile reactivity through measurements of the rate of increase in flux or power. An increase in barometric pressure lowers the reactivity of the reactor because more nitrogen is present to absorb neutrons. Similarly both temperature and humidity affect the operation of the reactor. The short-period random fluctuation in barometric pressure was apparently the factor that limited the sensitivity and precision of the method.

### 12.3. Reactor Oscillator Method

The oscillator method was devised to reduce some of the difficulties discussed in the previous section. Two different approaches have been used, one involving the over-all reactor power and the other local changes in neutron flux as the sample is oscillated in and out of the reactor or in certain regions of the reactor.

The oscillator used with the heavy-water reactor at Argonne (129) consisted of a mechanical device with a stroke of about 3 ft. that oscillated the sample in and out of the reactor through a 4-in.-diameter aluminum tube extending to the center of the reactor tank. A regular oscillation cycle was used consisting of 1 sec. going to center; 9 sec. in the center; 1 sec. to come out; 9 sec. out; etc. The amplitude of the oscillating component of the reactor flux, or power, is proportional to the absorption cross section and to the quantity of the neutron absorber in the sample. Comparison of the unknown with standards containing known quantities of a single absorber in the same base material of low absorption can be used to estimate the quantity of the absorber present.

Oscillation of a sample back and forth, close to a $B^{10}$ lined ionization chamber, produces uniform fluctuations in the ion current of the detector owing to local depressions in the neutron flux. The Oak Ridge oscillator (98, 171), which is of this type, moves the sample at the rate of 1 cycle/sec. in and out of a region of the reactor containing only graphite where the neutron-energy distribution is more nearly thermal. The oscillator can be operated while the reactor is in use for other purposes, as contrasted with the over-all power oscillator.

Since the circuits used with pile oscillators are arranged to detect only those oscillations of the signal which have the period of the mechanical motion, much of the difficulty connected with random fluctuations of the reactor power in the reactivity method is eliminated. This markedly increases the sensitivity and accuracy with which either absorption cross sections of pure substances can be determined or samples containing a single absorber in a material of low absorption can be analyzed. The oscillator is about twenty times more sensitive than the reactivity method, and so a measurable signal can be obtained if the sample contains for example 25 $\mu$g. of boron.

In using the oscillator, some of the same precautions must be observed as with the reactivity method, such as using sufficiently thin samples, correcting for scattering by using sample and standards in a similar matrix with the same scattering properties, etc.

## 13. Neutron Activation

Probably the most useful application of neutrons to analytical chemistry is trace analysis by neutron activation. This method was first used by Hevesy and Levi (92) in 1936 for the determination of dysprosium and europium. Using a 300-mc. radium-emanation–beryllium-neutron source, they compared the activity of 2.4-hr. dysprosium induced in unknown samples with that induced in known yttrium-dysprosium mixtures and were able to estimate the presence of as little as 0.1% dysprosium. Similarly, europium was determined in samples of gadolinium. These represent particularly favorable cases, but with the development of high-voltage accelerators and nuclear reactors having high neutron fluxes, the method has been applied to many other elements. Several reviews (31, 48, 90, 198, 213, 216, 217) and articles (34, 130, 158, 199) have been published on the principles and application of the method, some of which will be summarized here.

### 13.1. Principles of Neutron Activation

Most of the elements form radioactive isotopes when they are irradiated with slow neutrons. The activity induced in an isotope of an element will be determined by the number of nuclei of the isotope in the sample, the number of neutrons per second passing through the sample, the activation cross section of the isotope for the particular energy distribution of neutrons, the half-life of the radioisotope, and the time of irradiation. The quantitative relation between the activity and these factors may be derived in the following way.

When a sample containing the element to be determined is placed in a flux $f$ of neutrons, some of the nuclei will become radioactive, but at the same time these radioactive atoms will be disintegrating. There will be a steady increase in formation of radioactive atoms until the disintegration rate is equal to the rate of formation. Since the rate of formation of radioactive atoms is $f\sigma_{act}N$ and their rate of disintegration is $\lambda N^*$, the rate of growth of radioactive atoms is

$$dN^*/dt = f\sigma_{act}N - \lambda N^* \tag{13.1}$$

where $N$ is the number of nuclei of the isotope involved in the activation, $N^*$ is the number of radioactive nuclei formed from this isotope, $f$ is the neutron flux in numbers of neutrons passing through 1 sq. cm./sec., $\sigma_{act}$ is the isotopic activation cross section in square centimeters for formation of the radioactive nucleus in the particular neutron flux used, $\lambda$ is the radioactive decay constant in sec.$^{-1}$, and $t$ is the time in seconds.

The number of radioactive atoms present after irradiation for a time $t$ is obtained by integration of eq. (13.1) as follows: In the usual case the number of radioactive atoms $N^*$ is small compared to $N$ and so $N$ may be assumed to remain constant. Let $x = f\sigma_{act}N - \lambda N^*$; then differentiating with respect to time gives

$$\frac{dx}{dt} = -\frac{\lambda dN^*}{dt} \quad \text{or} \quad \frac{dN^*}{dt} = -\frac{1}{\lambda}\frac{dx}{dt} = x \tag{13.2}$$

Rearranging gives

$$\frac{dx}{x} = -\lambda \, dt \tag{13.3}$$

and on integration

$$\ln x = -\lambda t + c \quad \text{or} \quad x = ce^{-\lambda t} \tag{13.4}$$

Thus,

$$ce^{-\lambda t} = f\sigma_{act}N - \lambda N^* \tag{13.5}$$

The constant $c$ is evaluated by setting $t = 0$, at which time $N^* = 0$ and $c = f\sigma_{act}N$. Then

$$f\sigma_{act}Ne^{-\lambda t} = f\sigma_{act}N - \lambda N^* \tag{13.6}$$

or

$$\lambda N^* = f\sigma_{act}N - f\sigma_{act}Ne^{-\lambda t} \tag{13.7}$$

$$N^* = \frac{f\sigma_{act}N}{\lambda}(1 - e^{-\lambda t}) \tag{13.8}$$

The activity $A_t$ in terms of disintegrations per second from the $N^*$ atoms present after an irradiation time $t$ is $\lambda N^*$, and so

$$A = \lambda N^* = f\sigma_{act}N(1 - e^{-\lambda t}) \tag{13.9}$$

In terms of the half-life $T_{1/2}$, which is related to $\lambda$ by $\lambda = 0.693/T_{1/2}$,

$$A_t = f\sigma_{act}N(1 - e^{-\frac{0.693t}{T_{1/2}}}) \tag{13.10}$$

When the time of irradiation is very long compared to the half-life,

$$A_t = A_\infty = f\sigma_{act}N \tag{13.11}$$

This is the maximum or saturation activity. If the time of irradiation is equal to the half-life $T_{1/2}$, then

$$A_{T_{1/2}} = f\sigma_{act}N(1 - e^{-\frac{0.693t}{T_{1/2}}}) = 0.5f\sigma_{act}N \tag{13.12}$$

or one-half the activity at saturation. For a time equal to ten half-lives, the factor in parentheses of eq. (13.12) becomes 0.999 and the activity is practically the saturation activity. The term in parentheses is called the saturation factor $S$ and is plotted as a function of the number of half-lives of irradiation in Fig. 38. The expression for the activity for an irradiation of time $t$ can then be expressed as

$$A_t = f\sigma_{act}NS = A_\infty S \qquad (13.13)$$

In the foregoing expressions $\sigma_{act}$ is the isotopic activation cross section and $N$ is the number of nuclei of the particular isotope. The values listed in the $AEC$ compilation of neutron cross sections (106) are given in these terms. For chemical analyses it is more convenient to use the number of

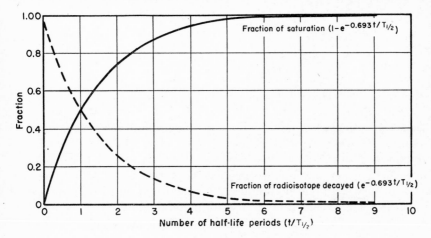

FIG. 38. Growth of activity of a radioisotope during irradiation with neutrons and decay of activity after removal from the flux.

atoms of the element $N_E$ and the atomic-activation cross sections ($\sigma_{ACT}$), which is the atom fraction $\alpha$ of the particular isotope (i.e., its abundance) times the isotopic-activation cross section. In these terms the equation for the activity of a particular radioisotope after an irradiation time $t$ then becomes

$$A_t = f\sigma_{act}\alpha N_E S = f\sigma_{ACT}N_E S = A_\infty S \qquad (13.14)$$

or

$$N_E = \frac{A_t}{f\sigma_{ACT}S} \qquad (13.15)$$

When copper, for example, is placed in a flux of neutrons both isotopes, $Cu^{63}$ (69.1%) and $Cu^{65}$ (30.9%) become radioactive, forming respectively $Cu^{64}$ (12.8$h$) and $Cu^{66}$ (5.14$m$). The isotopic activation cross section of $Cu^{63}$ for formation of 12.8-hr. $Cu^{64}$ is 3.9 ± 0.8 barns and that of $Cu^{65}$ for formation of 5.14-min. $Cu^{66}$ is $1.8 \pm 0.4$ barns. The atomic activation cross section of the element copper for formation of $Cu^{64}$ is then $\sigma_{ACT} = (0.691)(3.9) = 2.7$ barns and for formation of $Cu^{66}$ $\sigma_{ACT} = (0.309)(1.8) = 0.55$ barn.

### 13.2. Assumptions and Conditions for Application of the Activation Formula

The assumptions and approximations used in deriving the foregoing equations should be kept in mind. It was stated, for example, that the rate of formation of a radioactive nucleus was given by $f\sigma_{act}N$. This implies a constant flux and also a constant energy distribution of neutrons through the sample because the activation cross section varies with the neutron energy. The ratio of fast neutrons to thermal neutrons depends on the place in the reactor where the sample is irradiated. In regions where the cadmium ratio (p. 484) is low (p. 561), that is, in or near the lattice of a graphite-moderated reactor, the epithermal neutrons will cause appreciable resonance activation. Thus the effective activation cross section may be somewhat different here from that in the reflector where the flux has more nearly a thermal distribution.

If the listed values for thermal activation cross sections are to be used, the activation should be done in the graphite reflector or thermal column. However, the flux in the lattice is about ten times that in the graphite reflector, and so increased sensitivity is achieved. In this case the effective activation cross section for formation of a radioisotope from an element can be determined for a particular position in the reactor by means of the element of interest or, preferably, by use of standards of known concentration similar to the unknown samples. This procedure, in effect, determines $f\sigma_{act}$, which can then be used as discussed later (p. 462) for calculating the concentration in the unknown.

Alternatively, the cadmium difference can be used in most cases to correct for the resonance activation. Since a cadmium foil (0.01 in.) allows passage of practically all neutrons with energies above 0.4 ev. and absorbs practically all those with energies below this (Fig. 39)

$$(\text{activity with no Cd}) - (\text{activity with Cd}) = \text{cadmium difference}$$

or

$$\left(\begin{matrix} \text{thermal} + \text{resonance} \\ \text{activation} \end{matrix}\right) - \left(\begin{matrix} \text{resonance} \\ \text{activation} \end{matrix}\right) = \text{thermal activation}$$

The listed value of the thermal-activation cross sections can then be used. It is advisable to calibrate the flux at the same time in the same way by use of a foil as a secondary flux standard or monitor. Errors arising from fluctuations due to changes in control-rod position and other factors affecting either the total or local flux characteristics can be reduced in this manner. If the resonance absorption in the sample is near thermal energies, the cross section in the thermal region does not follow a $1/v$ response (p. 461) and the effective cross section for thermal activation must be multiplied by the factors listed in the tables. Only a few substances require such corrections. More precise calculations would require small corrections for absorption of resonance and $1/v$ neutrons by the cadmium and for the $1/v$ activation at energies higher than the cadmium cutoff. In most analytical determinations, as will be discussed later, comparison of the activity induced in the unknown sample with

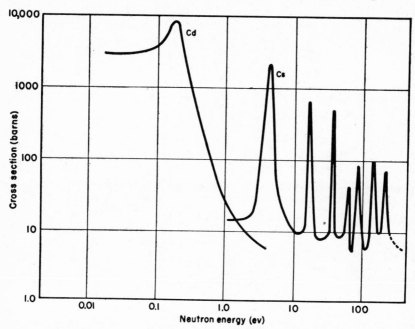

FIG. 39. Resonance-absorption curves for cadmium and cesium illustrating that irradiation with a cadmium cover results primarily in resonance activation but irradiation without the cadmium results in activation by both resonance and thermal neutrons.

standards containing known quantities of the element of interest eliminates the need for numerical values of the flux or the activation cross section.

Another complicating feature may arise in regions where the numbers of fast neutrons are high, depending on the other elements present with the one being determined. The particular radioisotope formed by the $(n,\gamma)$ reaction may also be formed from other elements by $(n,p)$ or $(n,\alpha)$ reactions. Thus, 15-hr. $Na^{24}$ can also be formed by the reaction $Mg^{24}(n,p)Na^{24}$ or $Al^{27}(n,\alpha)Na^{24}$. Although the contributions of these reactions are not large compared with the $Na^{23}(n,\gamma)Na^{24}$, the effects can be reduced by use of a region in the reflector where the numbers of fast neutrons are lower.

The sample itself may influence the flux within the sample as a result of self-protection, hardening of the beam, flux depression, or obliquity. In order to ensure that the flux of neutrons is essentially constant through the sample, relatively small and thin samples are used. If the samples are too thick, self-protection of the inner parts of the sample will result because absorption in the outer layers reduces the flux inside the sample. Also a "hardening" of the flux will result since the outer layers remove more of the slower neutrons. Because $\sigma_{act}$ varies as $1/v$, the fraction of higher energy neutrons, for which $\sigma_{act}$ is lower, increases toward the inside of the sample. This results in a lower average activation cross section and the calculated quantity would be too low. In practice, if the thickness of the sample is such that the flux is not reduced more than a fraction of a per cent in penetrating to the center of the sample, the error will be negligible. For the case of copper the number of atoms per square centimeter that reduces a beam of thermal neutrons by 1% as a result of absorption is given by $2.303 \log 1/T = n'\sigma_{abs}$ or $2.303 \log 1/0.99 = (n')(3.7 \times 10^{-24})$ from which $n' = 2.71 \times 10^{21}$ atoms/cm.$^2$ = 287 mg./cm.$^2$ or for pure copper 0.287 mm. thick. Similar values for gold with an atomic activation cross section of 98 barns are $1.025 \times 10^{20}$ atoms/cm.$^2$, 33.5 mg./cm.$^2$ or 0.0174 mm. In the isotropic flux of the reactor, the effective thickness is about twice the actual thickness. For actual analytical procedures (p. 562) one usually compares an unknown with standards in the same matrix so that some of these effects are largely canceled and the requirements are not so strict as for calculations from known constants.

In the activation equations it was further assumed that the number of target atoms $N$ did not decrease significantly during the time of the irradiation. For isotopes of very large cross section and long periods of irradiation a correction may be needed. However, in the usual case this would not be necessary, as illustrated by the irradiation of 10 mg. of copper for ten half-lives or 128 hr. in a flux of $10^{12}$ neutrons/cm.$^2$/sec. In this time the number of $Cu^{63}$ nuclei that disappear would be

$$f\sigma_{act}Nt = (10^{12})(3.9 \times 10^{-24}) \left( \frac{0.691 \times 0.010 \times 6.02 \times 10^{23}}{62.96} \right) (128 \times 3600)$$
$$= 1.19 \times 10^{14} \tag{13.16}$$

The number of $Cu^{63}$ nuclei $N$ present in the 10 mg. of copper was $6.6 \times 10^{19}$, and so the fraction of them that disappeared was $1.8 \times 10^{-6}$, or 1.8 p.p.m., by this reaction. In cases where other processes also result in the loss of the isotope, the total-absorption cross section $\sigma_{abs}$ should be used.

Another assumption in the equations is that the fraction of radioactive atoms destroyed by absorption of neutrons during irradiation is small. Instead of loss by decay alone during the irradiation, a small additional loss of radioactive atoms occurs by this effect. The effective disintegration constant (61, 181) in the flux will then be $\lambda + f\sigma_{act}^*$, and the disintegration rate at saturation will be slightly less than $f\sigma_{act}N$ as given by $f\sigma_{act}N\lambda/(\lambda + f\sigma_{act}^*)$. For cross sections of the order of 10 barns $(10 \times 10^{-24}$ cm.²) and a flux of $10^{12}$ neutrons cm.²/sec. the effect referred to here will not be significant. Sometimes, however, a new radioisotope is formed by this secondary reaction which must be considered in measurements of activity. At saturation the number of primary radioactive atoms $N^*$ is $f\sigma_{act}N/\lambda$. When these have received a saturation irradiation the number $N^{**}$ of secondary radioactive atoms is $f\sigma_{act}^*N^*/\lambda^{**}$ and the activity is $\lambda^{**}N^{**}$ or $f\sigma_{act}^*N^*$. Substitution for $N^*$ gives a saturation activity for the secondary radioisotope of

$$A^{**} = \frac{f\sigma_{act}N}{\lambda} f\sigma_{act}^* = \frac{f^2 N \sigma_{act}\sigma_{act}^* T\frac{1}{2}}{0.693}$$

If the activation cross section for formation of the secondary radioisotope is large, its activity may be an appreciable fraction of the total activity. For example, when gold ($Au^{197}$) with an activation cross section of 98 barns is irradiated, the 2.7-day $Au^{198}$ ($\beta^-$ 0.963 Mev., $\gamma$ 0.412 Mev.) is formed. Even though the number of $Au^{198}$ atoms formed is small, their high activation cross section of 35,000 barns results in the formation of 3.2-day $Au^{199}$ ($\beta^-$ 0.30, 0.25 Mev., $\gamma$ 0.159 Mev.). An appreciable fraction of the beta activity measured would be due to $Au^{199}$ (61). For a saturation irradiation of 1 mg. of gold in a flux of $1 \times 10^{12}$ neutrons/(cm.²/sec.)

$$A_{198} = f\sigma_{act}N = \frac{(10^{12})(98 \times 10^{-24})(1 \times 10^{-3})(6.02 \times 10^{23})}{197}$$

$$= 3.0 \times 10^8 \text{ disintegrations/sec.}$$

$$A_{199} = \frac{f^2 N \sigma_{act}\sigma_{act}^* T\frac{1}{2}}{0.693}$$

$$= \frac{(10^{12})^2(1 \times 10^{-3})(6.02 \times 10^{23})(98 \times 10^{-24})(35,000 \times 10^{-24})(2.38 \times 10^5)}{(197)(0.693)}$$

$$= 3.6 \times 10^6 \text{ disintegrations/sec.}$$

That is, the activity of $Au^{199}$ is about 1.2% of that for $Au^{198}$. Not many cases arise in which these effects have to be considered because the cross section of the primary radioisotope is usually much smaller than that in the illustration above.

### 13.3. Activity of Radioisotope at Time of Measurement

The equations in section 13.1 give the activity $A_{t_1}$ of a single radioactive species for an irradiation of time $t_1$. When the sample is removed from the flux, the activity of the radioisotope decays with its characteristic decay constant $\lambda$ or half-life $T_{1/2}$. If the activity is determined at a time $t_2$ after the irradiation is stopped, the disintegrations per second $A_{t_2}$ will be given by

$$A_{t_2} = A_{t_1}e^{-\lambda t_2} = A_{t_1}e^{-0.693t_2/T_{1/2}} \tag{13.17}$$

Substitution for $A_{t_1}$ from eq. (13.10) or (13.14) gives

$$A_{t_2} = f\sigma_{ACT}N_E(1 - e^{-0.693t_1/T_{1/2}})(e^{-0.693t_2T_{1/2}}) \tag{13.18}$$
$$= f\sigma_{ACT}N_ESe^{-0.693t_2/T_{1/2}} \tag{13.19}$$

The number of atoms $N_E$ in $g$ grams of an element of atomic weight $M$ is

$$N_E = 6.02 \times 10^{23} \times g/M \tag{13.20}$$

Substituting for $N_E$ and solving for $g$, gives the weight of the element in the sample as

$$g = \frac{A_{t_2}M}{6.02 \times 10^{23}f\sigma_{ACT}S(e^{-0.963t_2/T_{1/2}})} \tag{13.21}$$

and the percentage by weight is $100 \times g/W$ where $W$ is the weight of the sample. If $f$, $\sigma_{ACT}$, $S$, and $M$ are known, $g$ can be calculated once the activity $A_{t_2}$ is known.

The activity is determined not at a given time, but during an interval of time from $t_2$ at the start of the measurement to $t_3$ at the end of the measurement. During this period the sample has decayed further. The number of radioactive atoms at the beginning of the time interval is

$$N_{t_2}^* = N_{t_1}^*e^{-\lambda t_2} \tag{13.22}$$

and at the end of the time interval it is

$$N_{t_3}^* = N_{t_1}^*e^{-\lambda t_3} \tag{13.23}$$

The number of disintegrations that have occurred in the time interval $t_3 - t_2$ is then

$$(N_{t_2}^* - N_{t_3}^*) = N_{t_1}^*(e^{-\lambda t_2} - e^{-\lambda t_3}) \tag{13.24}$$

This equation can be put in the form

$$(N_{t_2}^* - N_{t_3}^*) = N_{t_1}^*e^{-\lambda t_2}(1 - e^{-\lambda(t_3-t_2)}) \tag{13.25}$$

Since $A_{t_1} = \lambda N_{t_1}^*$ or $N_{t_1}^* = A_{t_1}/\lambda$, the value of $N_{t_1}^*$ may be substituted from eq. (13.18) to give

$$(N_{t_2}^* - N_{t_3}^*) = \frac{f\sigma_{ACT}N_E}{\lambda}(1 - e^{-\lambda t_1})(e^{-\lambda t_2})(1 - e^{-\lambda(t_3-t_2)}) \tag{13.26}$$

or in terms of half-life and the saturation factor $S$,

$$(N_{t_2}^* - N_{t_3}^*) = \frac{f\sigma_{ACT}N_ES}{0.693}T_{1/2}(e^{-0.693t_2/T_{1/2}})(1 - e^{-0.693(t_3-t_2)/T_{1/2}}) \tag{13.27}$$

The weight of the element corresponding to $N_E$ is

$$g = \frac{(N_{t_2}^* - N_{t_3}^*)(M)(0.693)}{(6.02 \times 10^{23})(T_{1/2})(f\sigma_{ACT})(S)(e^{-0.693t_2/T_{1/2}})(1 - e^{-0.693(t_3-t_2)/T_{1/2}})} \tag{13.28}$$

Thus, if the number of disintegrations $(N_{t_2}{}^* - N_{t_3}{}^*)$ that occur in the time interval $(t_3 - t_2)$ can be determined by counting methods described later, the weight of the element in the sample can be calculated.

Usually the time interval during which the activity is measured is short compared to the half-life; that is $(t_3 - t_2) \ll T_{1/2}$. In this case some simplification of the equation results since the exponential eq. (13.24) can be rearranged and the exponentials expanded to give

$$(N_{t_2}{}^* - N_{t_3}{}^*) = N_{t_1}{}^* e^{-\lambda(t_2+t_3)/2} \lambda(t_3 - t_2) \tag{13.29}$$

or the average disintegrations per second for the time interval is

$$\frac{(N_{t_2}{}^* - N_{t_3}{}^*)}{(t_3 - t_2)} = \lambda N_{t_1}{}^* e^{-\lambda(t_2+t_3)/2} = A_{t_1} e^{-\lambda(t_2+t_3)/2} \tag{13.30}$$

Equation (13.19) then becomes

$$A_{t_2} = \frac{(N_{t_2}{}^* - N_{t_3}{}^*)}{(t_3 - t_2)} = f\sigma_{ACT} N_E S(e^{-0.693(t_2+t_3)/2/T_{1/2}}) \tag{13.31}$$

This equation states further that the average activity measured can be taken within the error of the approximation as the activity at the time midway between $t_2$ and $t_3$.

If the time interval $(t_3 - t_2)$ is of the order of the half-life $T_{1/2}$ or longer, the effective time corresponding to the measured activity should be weighted somewhat toward time $t_2$. The equation for the effective time can be derived as follows. Divide both sides of eq. (13.25) by $(t_3 - t_2)$ to obtain the average activity,

$$\frac{(N_{t_2}{}^* - N_{t_3}{}^*)}{(t_3 - t_2)} = \frac{N_{t_1}{}^* e^{-\lambda t_2}(1 - e^{-\lambda(t_3-t_2)})}{(t_3 - t_2)} \tag{13.32}$$

The effective time $t_{\mathrm{eff}}$ at which the actual activity is that corresponding to the measured $\dfrac{(N_{t_2}{}^* - N_{t_3}{}^*)}{(t_3 - t_2)}$ is such that

$$\frac{N_{t_2}{}^* - N_{t_3}{}^*}{(t_3 - t_2)} = \lambda N_{t_1}{}^* e^{-\lambda t_{\mathrm{eff}}} \tag{13.33}$$

Substituting in the preceding equation gives

$$\lambda N_{t_1}{}^* e^{-\lambda t_{\mathrm{eff}}} = \frac{N_{t_1}{}^* e^{-\lambda t_2}(1 - e^{-\lambda(t_3-t_2)})}{(t_3 - t_2)} \tag{13.34}$$

or

$$e^{-\lambda t_{\mathrm{eff}}} = \frac{e^{-\lambda t_2}(1 - e^{-\lambda(t_3-t_2)})}{\lambda(t_3 - t_2)} \tag{13.35}$$

Taking the logarithm of both sides yields

$$-\lambda t_{\mathrm{eff}} = -\lambda t_2 + \ln \frac{(1 - e^{-\lambda(t_3-t_2)})}{\lambda(t_3 - t_2)} \tag{13.36}$$

and

$$t_{\mathrm{eff}} = t_2 + \frac{1}{\lambda} \ln \frac{\lambda(t_3 - t_2)}{(1 - e^{-\lambda(t_3-t_2)})} \tag{13.37}$$

In terms of the half-life,

$$t_{\text{eff}} = t_2 + \frac{T_{\frac{1}{2}}}{0.693} \ln \frac{(0.693)(t_3 - t_2)}{T_{\frac{1}{2}}(1 - e^{-0.693(t_3 - t_2)T_{\frac{1}{2}}})} \qquad (13.38)$$

If, as seldom happens, the time of measurement should be long compared to the half-life, that is, if $(t_3 - t_2) \gg T_{\frac{1}{2}}$, this equation reduces to

$$t_{\text{eff}} = t_2 + \frac{T_{\frac{1}{2}}}{0.693} \ln \frac{0.693(t_3 - t_2)}{T_{\frac{1}{2}}} \qquad (13.39)$$

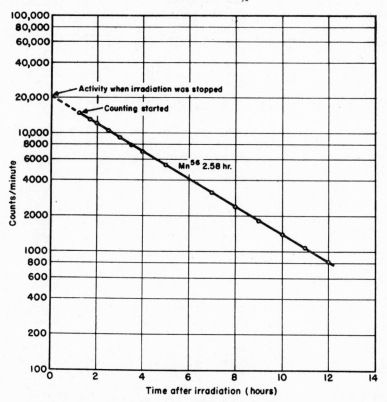

Fig. 40. Obtaining the activity of a radioisotope at the time of removal from a neutron flux by extrapolation of its semilogarithmic decay curve.

and when $(t_3 - t_2) = T_{\frac{1}{2}}$

$$t_{\text{eff}} = t_2 + \frac{T_{\frac{1}{2}}}{0.693} \ln \frac{(0.693)}{(0.5)} \qquad (13.40)$$

$$= t_2 + 0.47 T_{\frac{1}{2}}$$

Thus the effective time in this case is slightly less than that corresponding to the center of the counting period, $(t_2 + t_3)/2$.

Sometimes it is advantageous to determine the average disintegration rate $(N_{t_2}* - N_{t_3}*)/(t_3 - t_2)$ for a number of such periods of time. A plot of the log of these disintegration rates against $t_{eff}$ can then be extrapolated to the time the irradiation was stopped, as illustrated in Fig. 40. This then gives the activity at $t_1$ as

$$A_{t_1} = f\sigma_{ACT}N_E S \tag{13.41}$$

from which the weight of the element corresponding to $N_E$ is

$$g = \frac{A_{t_1}M}{6.02 \times 10^{23}f\sigma_{ACT}S} \tag{13.42}$$

For cases where the time of each measurement is small compared to the half-life, the time at the center of the counting period can be used; otherwise eq. (13.38) can be used to obtain $t_{eff}$ for the plot. The error will not be large in the usual case if the average of the times at the beginning and end of each counting period is used.

### 13.4. Disintegrations from Counts

When the equations of section 13.3 are used to make a direct calculation of the quantity of an element rather than comparison with standards (p. 562), the most uncertain part is the estimation of the disintegration

TABLE VIII

*Approximate Percentage of Efficiencies of Radioactive Detection Devices for Various Radiations*

(The efficiencies listed are the ratios of the number of events counted to the number of particles entering the detecting volume)

| | | | | Scintillation counter | |
|---|---|---|---|---|---|
| Radiation | Ionization chamber | Proportional counter | Geiger counter | Organic (anthracene) | Inorganic [NaI(Tl)] |
| $\alpha$ particle | 95 | 95 | 95 | 95 | 95 |
| $\beta$ radiation | 95 | 95 | 95 | 95 | 95 |
| $\gamma$ radiation | 1 | 1 | 1 | 10 | 25 |
| X rays* | 5 | 5 | 5 | 50 | 95 |

* Detection efficiency of X rays depends markedly on the materials of construction, filling, and size of chamber.

rate from a counting rate. The problem of doing this is markedly dependent on the nautre of the radiation and the detection device, as may be seen from Table VIII. For a Geiger-Müller counter, as an example, the counts observed in a time $t_3 - t_2$ for *one radioisotope giving a single particle or quantum radiation per disintegration* must be corrected by the following factors to obtain the number of disintegrations.

1. *Intrinsic counter efficiency* $f_E$ *for the particular radiation*. This is essentially the fraction of particles or other radiation entering the counter that gives rise to counts. It is related to the ionization probability of the particular radiation. It also includes the effect of multiple discharges resulting from inefficient quenching, etc., that tend to increase rather than to decrease the counting rate. The efficiency of most Geiger-Müller counters for $\beta$ particles is close to unity for a wide range of energies while for quantum radiations the efficiency is much smaller and energy dependent. Efficiencies for X rays range from 0.5 to 10% for special gaseous filling mixtures and appreciably lower than this for $\gamma$ rays. Scintillation counters may give efficiencies for 1 Mev. $\gamma$ rays as high as 25% for the usual size of NaI(Tl) crystals.

2. *Resolving time factor,* $f_r$. This corrects for the finite resolving time $\tau$ of the counter and circuits. It is the shortest time interval in which successive particles can produce separate counts. Significant corrections are needed for counting rates over several thousand per minute. The magnitude of the correction is determined by successive addition of small sources of known counting rates or from the deviation from exponential decay of a strongly radioactive sample of well-known half-life such as 37.5-min. $Cl^{38}$. For $n_m$ measured counts in 1 sec., the insensitive, or "dead," time is approximately $n_m\tau$ when the counting rate is not too high. More complete treatments (175) involve the random nature of disentegrations. If $n_t$ is the true number, then the number of counts lost per second is $n_t - n_m = n_t(n_m\tau)$, from which $\tau = (n - n_m)/n_t n_m$. When two sources are used to determine $\tau$, the number of counts/sec. $n_1$ and $n_2$ are first determined for the two samples separately and then with both together, $n_{12}$. If the background counting rate is $n_b$, then it can be shown (61) that

$$\tau = \frac{n_1 + n_2 - n_{12} - n_b}{n_{12}{}^2 - n_1{}^2 - n_2{}^2}$$

The value of $\tau$ is usually from 50 to 200 $\mu$sec. for the G-M counter and seldom larger than 5 $\mu$sec. for the circuits. Once $\tau$ is determined, the true counts can be calculated from the preceding equation in the form $n_t = n_m/(1 - n_m\tau)$ and the resolving time factor $f_r$ is then $n_t/n_m$. If the observed counting rate is 100/sec. (6000 c./min.) on a counter for which $\tau = 100$ $\mu$sec., $n_t = 100/(1 - 100 \times 150 \times 10^{-6}) = 100/.985$ or $n_t = 101.5$ and $f_r = 101.5/100 = 1.015$. For scintillation counters the resolving times attainable are much shorter (0.02 $\mu$sec. for anthracene to 0.25 $\mu$sec. for sodium iodide) and the electronic circuits may be the limiting factor.

3. *Absorption factor* $f_A$ *for counter window and air between the counter window and sample*. The number of particles per second that pass through an absorber of thickness $x$ is related to the number per second $n_0$ hitting a thin absorber by

$$n = n_0 e^{-\mu x} = n_0 e^{-\left(\frac{\mu}{\rho}\right)\rho x} = n_0 e^{-\left(\frac{\mu}{\rho}\right)G} \tag{13.43}$$

or

$$\ln n/n_0 = -(\mu/\rho)G \tag{13.44}$$

where $\rho$ is the density of the material, $G$ is the surface density in grams/cm.$^2$ since $(\rho \text{ g./cm.}^3)(x \text{ cm.}) = G \text{ g./cm.}^2$, and $(\mu/\rho)$ is the mass absorption coefficient. The mass absorption coefficient is practically the same for materials of low atomic number, as for example air, mica, and aluminum, and so

$$\ln n/n_0 = -(\mu/\rho)(G_w + G_{air} + G_{A1} \cdots) \tag{13.45}$$

or

$$\ln n = \ln n_0 - (\mu/\rho)(G_w + G_{air} + G_{A1} \cdots) \tag{13.46}$$

If $(\mu/\rho)$ and $G_w$ and $G_{air}$ are known, $\ln n/n_0$ can be calculated to give the value of $\ln f_A$. Usually, however, it is determined experimentally by plotting the logarithm of the counting rate, $c$, against the grams per square centimeter of absorber in the path by use of $(G_w + G_{air})$ as the first point followed by several different thicknesses of aluminum. Extrapolation of the straight line to 0 g./cm.$^2$ gives a value for $\ln c_0$. Then from the value of $\ln c$ with only the window and air in the path, $\ln c/c_0 = \ln n/n_0 = \ln f_A$, from which $f_A$ is obtained. The aluminum absorbers in the foregoing procedures should be placed close to the window to minimize scattering into the counter. Some scattering into the counter from the air occurs for $\beta$ particles, thereby tending to increase the counting rate. This effect is 1 to 2% when the sample is about 2 in. from the window. For this reason the sample should be placed as close to the window as convenient. Typical values (40, 159) for $f_A$ are 0.75 for a RaE $\beta$ source with 11 mg./cm.$^2$ of absorber (window 3 mg./cm.$^2$, air 0.5 mg./cm.$^2$, mica to absorb $\alpha$ particles 7.5 mg./cm.$^2$). For $P^{32}$ a value of $f_A = 0.98$ was obtained with 3.5 mg./cm.$^2$ of absorber (window 3.0 mg./cm.$^2$, air 0.5 mg./cm.$^2$).

4. *Back scattering factor* $f_B$ *for scattering from the material supporting the source and from the walls and housing of the counter assembly.* $\beta$ particles emitted in a direction away from the counter are scattered back into the counter causing an increase in counting rate. This effect is greater the lower the energy of the $\beta$ particle and the higher the atomic number of the scatterer as expected for Coulomb scattering. Increasing thickness up to a value of about two tenths of the range R of the $\beta$ particles increases the back-scattering factor $f_B$ to a maximum value. Saturation is reached and no further increase occurs. For energies between 0.3 and 2.5 Mev. the maximum or saturation values for $f_B$ are practically constant, ranging from 1.00 for thin (20 $\mu$g./cm.$^2$) Zapon films to 1.18 for cardboard, 1.28 for Al, 1.49 for Cu, 1.80 for Pt. Thicknesses corresponding to about 160 mg./cm.$^2$ were sufficient to obtain these saturation values for 1.72-Mev. $P^{32}$ $\beta$ particles (1 to 2 mm. cardboard, 0.6 mm. Al, 0.2 mm. Cu, or

0.1 mm. Pt). Since the range in g./cm.$^2$ of Al for the maximum-energy $\beta$ particles $E_{max}$ is given by (24) $R = 0.571 \, E_{max} - 0.161$, the saturation back-scattering thickness is approximately $0.2R$ or $(0.114 E_{max} - 0.3)$.

When the sample is deposited directly on the support material, values appreciably larger than the above may be obtained; (68) $f_B = 1.33$, for example, with Al. Scattering from the walls of Lucite shelf supports and housing is negligible but some scattering effect (about 3%) occurs when the sample is close to the bottom Lucite plate. If a lead floor or door to the counting assembly is not lined with Lucite, a 4 to 8% effect may be encountered. Because of the difficulty of mounting samples on very thin films of a plastic, reproducible results for comparative measurements are more readily obtained by using a backing thick enough for $f_B$ to be constant.

5. *Self-absorption and self-scattering factor* $f_s$ *for the effect of the mass of the source.* For very thin sources 0.1 to 0.2 mg./cm.$^2$ self-absorption and self-scattering is negligible. Thicker samples require a determination of $f_S$ by counting the same amount of radioactive material with different amounts of inert carrier or by using increasing quantities of material of the same specific activity. From a plot of the data, the factor $f_S$ = (cpm for sample)/(cpm zero thickness) can be determined for any particular sample of the same materials used in the calibration. Since both absorption and scattering are present, scattering may increase the count greater than absorption increases it for certain sample thicknesses. The absorption effect can be calculated approximately from the exponential relation

$$c = \frac{c_0}{\mu_m G} (1 - e^{-\mu_m G}) \qquad \text{or} \qquad f_S = \frac{c}{c_0} = \frac{1}{\mu_m G} (1 - e^{-\mu_m})^G$$

where $c_0$ is the counts per second for zero thickness, $c$ is the counts per second for the sample of thickness $G$ g./cm.$^2$, and $\mu_m$ is the mass-absorption coefficient $(\mu/\rho)$. If there were no absorption, the specific activity $a$ for a sample of area $A$ would be $c_0/GA$ or $c_0 = aGA$ and observed counts per second would be

$$c = \frac{aA}{\mu_m} (1 - e^{-\mu_m G}) \tag{13.47}$$

Thus for a constant area, the observed counting rate for increasing thickness $G$ of a material of uniform specific activity increases to a maximum constant value of $aA/\mu_m$ from which $c$ and $c_0$ can be evaluated for calculation of $f_S$ due to absorption. The ratio of the observed counting rates for two thick samples of the same area and material gives the ratio of their specific activities since

$$\frac{c_1}{c_2} = \frac{a_1 A/\mu_m}{a_2 A/\mu_m} = \frac{a_1}{a_2} \tag{13.48}$$

This relation is useful in the comparative methods to be discussed later.

In the case of relatively thin samples with $\mu_m G$ less than 0.1, expansion of eq. (13.47) shows that approximately

$$f_S \cong c/c_0 \cong 1 - \frac{\mu_m G}{2} \tag{13.49}$$

For such cases the absorption effect could be approximated for sample materials of low atomic number by including one-half the sample thickness in grams/square centimeter in eq. (13.46) for the absorption due to the air and counter window. These equations are only approximate because the scattering effect has been neglected. More precise corrections require the experimental determination of $f_S$ for the particular sample being measured.

6. *Geometrical factor* $f_G$ *for the percentage of solid angle about the source subtended by the sensitive volume of the counter tube*. If the sample were a point source at a distance $d$ from a counter window of radius $r$, the solid angle $\Omega$ would be

$$\Omega = 2\pi(1 - \cos \alpha) = 2\pi(1 - d/\sqrt{d^2 + r^2}) = 2\pi(1 - 1/\sqrt{1 + (r^2/d^2)}) \tag{13.50}$$

where $\alpha$ is the angle between lines to the center and edge of the window. The fraction of the total solid angle would be

$$f_G = \frac{\Omega}{4\pi} = (\tfrac{1}{2})(1 - d/\sqrt{d^2 + r^2}) \tag{13.51}$$

For an extended source this calculated value may be in error by 10% but more complete expressions are available (40) for more precise calculations. The equation is useful for calculating the effect of increased distance on counting rates when such increase is necessary to measure a source that is too active. Experiments have shown that the calculated values are in general too high, probably because the sensitive volume, the distance to the sensitive volume, or the effect of angle of entrance to the sensitive volume are not well defined.

A more reliable determination of the effective geometry factor is obtained by measurements with a source of known activity. Such a standard source can be prepared (159) and calibrated by coincidence measurements or measurements of the rate of related $\alpha$-particle emission. Alternatively a standard source can be purchased from the National Bureau of Standards. With such a source, the observed counting rate $c$ is related to the number of disintegrations per second $A_S$ by the equation

$$c = A_S f_E f_r f_A f_B f_S f_G \tag{13.52}$$

where the $f$ factors are due respectively to intrinsic efficiency and multiple pulses, resolving time, absorption and scattering in window and air, back scattering, self-absorption and self-scattering, and geometrical arrangement. The geometry factor $f_G$ and intrinsic efficiency factor $f_E$ can be combined to a corrected geometry or efficiency factor $E$ to give

$$c = A_S E f_r f_A f_B f_S \qquad (13.53)$$

or

$$E = \frac{c}{A_S f_r f_A f_B f_S} \qquad (13.54)$$

From the known activity $A_S$ of the standard source, the observed counting rate, and the other factors evaluated as described previously, the corrected efficiency can be evaluated. In a typical $\beta$-counting arrangement (40) consisting of a 2.2-cm.-diameter mica-end-window G-M counter in a Lucite sample housing, a RaE sample electrolytically deposited in an area of 1 cm.$^2$ on a 5-mil nickel plate about 1 in. in diameter was placed on a 1-mm. cardboard shelf 1.6 cm. from the counter window and 3.4 cm. from the floor. With an absorber near the window to cut out the $\alpha$ particles, the total grams per square centimeter of air, window, and absorber was 9.7 g./cm.$^2$, giving a value of $f_A = 0.87$. The back-scattering factor $f_B$ was 1.52 and the sample thickness was so small that $f_S = 1.00$. The corrected efficiency $E$ for this system was 0.074 or 7.4%.

Once $E$ is determined, it can then be used along with the other factors for a particular sample to calculate the activity of a neutron-activated radioisotope that emits, for example, a single $\beta$ particle per disintegration, as

$$A = \frac{c}{E f_r f_A f_B f_S} = \frac{c}{Y} \qquad (13.55)$$

The over-all yield factor $Y = c/A$ is the ratio between the observed counting rate and the activity in disintegrations per second for the particular sample. If successive measurements of closely similar samples of about the same size are made in the same counter assembly with the same geometrical arrangement and sample mounting, the factors $E$, $f_A$, $f_B$, and $f_S$ will be very nearly constant and can be combined to a yield factor $F$ so that

$$A = \frac{c}{F f_r} = \frac{c}{Y} \qquad (13.56)$$

Thus, for such comparative measurements, it is necessary to use only the yield factor $F$ and the resolving time factor $f_r$. For the system described above, the factor $F = (0.074)(0.87)(1.52)(1.00) = 0.098$, or about 9.8%. With a $P^{32}$ source mounted (161) on a Tygon film and placed close to a 3 mg./cm.$^2$ mica-window counter (no extra absorber needed), the factor $F$ was 20 to 30% for different counters. In general, with $\beta$ particles the yield factor for such counters is between 5 and 35%, and for $\gamma$ rays and X rays the yield factor is usually less than 1%.

The comparative method (section 13.6) in which standards of similar composition to the sample are used, the value of $F$ will be the same for the two samples and the ratio of counting rates corrected for $f_r$ will give the ratio of the activities of the standard and sample. Even for such comparative methods consideration must be given to all the factors that affect counting rates, to make certain that any differences between the standard and sample will not produce significant effects on $F$. Corrections can be made as described in this section if such differences are greater than the accuracy desired for the determination.

### 13.5. Radioisotopes with Complex Decay Schemes

Thus far we have considered only the case of a single radioisotope with a simple decay scheme. Instead of emission of a single $\beta$ particle per disintegration such as occurs with $Si^{31}$, $P^{32}$, and $Ca^{45}$, most radioisotopes have a complex decay scheme that may also involve $\beta^+$ emission, $\gamma$ emission, isomeric transitions with or without a conversion electron, and $K$ or $L$ electron capture with emission of X rays. A few typical decay schemes are illustrated in Table IX and many others are described in the literature (95). Another complication in interpreting the counting data for an element is the fact that its isotopes may form more than one radioactive species, each having different properties, as illustrated in Table IX for the case of $Cu^{64}$ and $Cu^{66}$. Fortunately, in this case $Cu^{66}$ has a short half-life; so measurements can be made on $Cu^{64}$ after $Cu^{66}$ has decayed. In many cases the radioisotope decays to a stable nucleus, but in others a daughter radioactive isotope is formed with different properties, as illustrated for the case of $Zr^{95}$. Cases of this kind will be considered again in a later section (p. 577). Again the radioisotope may be transformed during irradiation to a secondary radioisotope of the same element as discussed previously (p. 545) for gold. If it is assumed that a radioisotope of an element of interest decays to a stable rather than a daughter radioisotope and further that this element along with its radioisotope is separated chemically or otherwise from the other elements in the neutron irradiated sample, a net counting yield factor $F'$ can be estimated from a consideration of the decay scheme. Consider a radioisotope such as 12.4-hr. $K^{42}$ that decays 80% of the time with the emission of 3.58-Mev. $\beta$-particle and 20% of the time with the emission of a 2.04-Mev. $\beta^-$ particle followed by a 1.51-Mev. $\gamma$ ray. Assume that the factor $F$ has been determined for $\beta^-$ and $\gamma$ rays of these energies to be 0.21, 0.18, and 0.008 respectively; then the net counting yield $F'$ will be

$$(0.21)(0.80) + (0.20)(0.18) + (0.20)(0.008) = 0.204$$

Sometimes it is convenient to correct the counting rate for the small contribution of the $\gamma$ rays by using an absorber to remove the $\beta$ rays.

## TABLE IX

*Typical Decay Schemes (95)*

(The numbers opposite the particles are energies in Mev.)

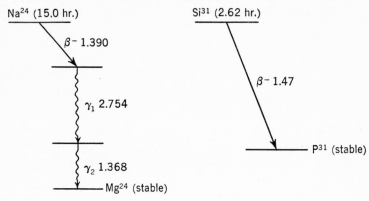

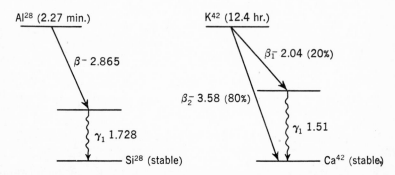

If two radioisotopes of the element are formed with markedly different half-lives, one can be allowed to decay before the other is measured. In cases where the energies of the $\beta^-$ particles are appreciably different, absorbers can be used to discriminate against one of them. Frequently the abundances, activation cross sections, or half-lives of certain isotopes are such that the resulting activity will not be significant. In this respect the time of irradiation can often be used to discriminate against the formation of certain radioisoptopes of an element. Characterization of the radiations measured by following the decay, by absorption measurements, or by use of counters other than the end-window type will aid in determining the presence of interfering activities. Some of the difficulties referred to here are minimized by the comparative method (p. 562) or by $\beta^-$ and $\gamma$-ray spectrometry using scintillation counters (p. 606).

TABLE IX. (*Continued*)

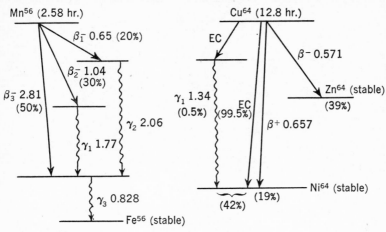

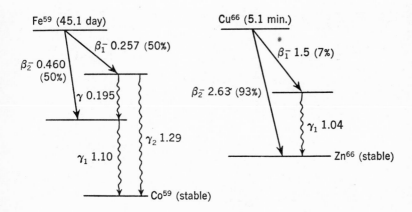

## 13.6. General Procedure for Direct or Absolute Determinations

From a careful estimate of all the terms in eq. (13.21) or (13.42), with proper consideration given to all the factors that may affect the results, the quantity of an element in a sample can be estimated without reference to standard samples. Although the accuracy of such a determination is not that obtainable by the comparative method (p. 562), it is useful in many cases of trace analysis, for example, where ±10 to 20% accuracy is adequate.

TABLE IX. (*Continued*)

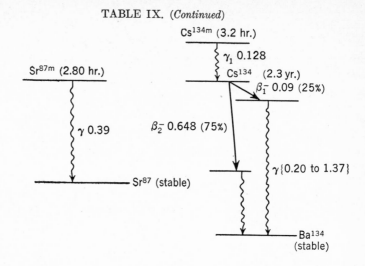

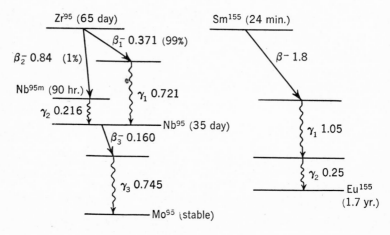

An example of the determination of manganese in aluminum described by Clark and Overman (43) and Boyd (31) will illustrate the general procedure. A small weighed piece of the aluminum was irradiated in the Oak Ridge reactor for 5 min. to make a qualitative examination of the activities formed and to obtain a rough estimate of the percentage of manganese. Resolution of the composite decay curve indicated the presence of activities due to 2.3-min. $Al^{28}$, 2.59-hr. $Mn^{56}$, and 14.8-hr. $Na^{24}$. Extrapolation of the manganese activity to the time of removal from the reactor together with rough estimates of the flux and counting yield indicated the presence of about 1% manganese. With this information a more accurate determination was made by means of a second sample.

TABLE IX. (*Continued*)

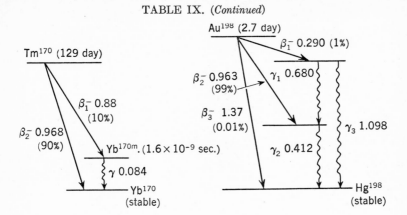

A carefully cleaned 25-mg. sample of the aluminum alloy together with a flux monitor foil were irradiated together for 5 min. in the reactor. Calculations from the activity induced in the monitor foil gave a flux of $6.4 \times 10^{11}$ neutrons/(cm.²)(sec.). After 30 min., when the strong activity due to $Al^{28}$ had decayed, the sample was dissolved and 1 mg. of manganese was added as a "carrier" to facilitate chemical separation and determination of the "chemical yield" (p. 565). The precipitated aluminum hydroxide was dissolved in 50% sodium hydroxide, and potassium cyanide was added to complex any copper present, so as to prevent contamination by radioactive $Cu^{64}$ that might be present. Several milligrams of ordinary copper could be added as a "holdback carrier" to reduce such interference further. Manganese dioxide was precipitated with hydrogen peroxide, dissolved in hydrochloric acid, and then reprecipitated and washed. Weighing of the precipitate serves to determine the chemical yield if the procedure is not quantitative. The $MnO_2$ was dissolved in a few drops of concentrated hydrochloric acid and transferred quantitatively to a 0.001-in. polystyrene film (2.6 mg./cm.²). After nearly complete evaporation, one drop of ammonium hydroxide was added to form nonhygroscopic manganese hydroxide.

The film was mounted over a 1-in. hole in a cardboard, and, after the sample was covered with a 0.001-in. polystyrene, it was placed accurately in a predetermined position under a 3.0 mg./cm.² mica-end-window Geiger-Müller counter. The corrected geometry and efficiency factor $E$ had previously been determined to be 0.0295. The observed counting rate was corrected for (a) counting losses by the factor $f_r$, (b) background, (c) counts due to $\gamma$ rays, and (d) decay from the time the irradiation was stopped to time of measurement. This rate, 140.3 counts/sec., when corrected for 88% chemical yield becomes 159.5 counts/sec.

The decay of $Mn^{56}$ (Table IX) results in 20% 0.65-Mev. $\beta^-$, 30% 1.04-Mev. $\beta^-$ and 50% 2.81-Mev. $\beta^-$ along with 2.06-, 1.77-, and 0.82-Mev. $\gamma$ rays, for which corrections were made. The factor $F = Ef_A f_S f_B$ for each type of $\beta$ spectrum is combined with its percentage to give a net yield $F'$. The factors $f_A$ for absorption in the window plus air and the factor $f_S$ for self-absorption and scattering in the sample may be combined (p. 553). Thus the net yield factor is

$$F' = (0.20)(0.0295)(0.69)(1.07) + (0.30)(0.0295)(0.77)(1.05)$$
$$+ (0.50)(0.0295)(0.96)(1.04)$$
$$= 0.0044 + 0.0070 + 0.0148 = 0.026, \text{ or } 2.6\% \tag{13.57}$$

Since the counting rate has already been corrected for counting losses by $f_r$, the activity $A$ from eq. (13.56) is $159.5/0.026 = 6140$ disintegrations/ sec. Cadmium difference measurements indicated that 5% of the activations were due to resonance activations. The disintegrations per second due to thermal activation is $(6140)(0.95) = 5830$. From this the grams of manganese in the sample can be calculated as follows:

$$G = \frac{A_{t_1} M}{6.02 \times 10^{23} f \sigma_{ACT} S} = \frac{(5830)(55)}{(6.02 \times 10^{23})(6.4 \times 10^{11})(134 \times 10^{-24})(2.24 \times 10^{-2})}$$
$$= 2.76 \times 10^{-4} g \tag{13.58}$$

and

$$\% \text{ Mn} = \frac{2.76 \times 10^{-4}}{2.5 \times 10^{-2}} \times 100 = 1.1\% \tag{13.59}$$

It can be seen from the uncertainties and the number of corrections that were necessary that the accuracy of determination may not be better than 10 to 20%. The principal uncertainties are concerned with the determination of the activity from the observed counting rate. An increase in the irradiation time would have decreased any error in the saturation factor $S$, but the total activity would have been too great for counting the manganese from the whole sample. In this case it would be necessary to take an aliquot of the final manganese solution and include this factor in the chemical yield or to use a smaller sample for the activation. Since the flux is usually determined by the activation of a suitable foil, some uncertainties arise in the determination of the activity of the foil from a counting rate, and thus the flux may not be known precisely.

Some confusion exists in the literature with respect to the value of the activation cross section, $\sigma_{ACT}$, that should be used in the calculations, partly because those who have compiled tables have not made clear their procedure in arriving at the values. In the thermal region the activation cross sections of all but a few elements vary very nearly as $1/v$. Similarly the flux monitors, such as $B^{10}F_3$ or certain foils, usually have cross sections that vary as $1/v$. The rate of formation of a radioactive nucleus in the monitor foil is

$$\text{reactions/sec.} = f \sigma_{ACT} N_E = (nv) \sigma_{ACT} N_E \tag{13.60}$$

where $n$ is the neutron density (neutrons/cubic centimeter) and $v$ is the velocity of the neutrons. Since the cross section varies as $1/v$, its value at any velocity can be given as $k/v$. Substitution in eq. (13.60) gives

$$\text{reactions/sec.} = nv\frac{k}{v}N = nkN \qquad (13.61)$$

In other words, the reactions per second or the activity induced in a $1/v$ monitor foil depends upon the neutron density rather than the flux. Since it is customary to use the neutron flux, the measured density is in effect multiplied by an arbitrary $v$ (2200 meters/sec.) to obtain a flux. This multiplication enters through use of the 2200 meters/sec. activation cross section for the monitor foil in calculating the flux. This quoted flux is slightly different from the actual flux because of changes in temperature of the graphite moderator and thus of the average velocity of the neutrons. This does not change the neutron density and consequently does not affect the activity induced in the monitor foil. An increase in temperature would increase the flux (proportional to $v$), but the cross section would decrease (proportional $1/v$) and activation would be unaffected.

In a similar way the activation of a $1/v$-type sample, like the monitor foil, is independent of $v$. The activation cross section to be used in calculations of induced activity or numbers of atoms must be the one for the same velocity as that used or implied in quoting the flux. This is practically always 2200 meters/sec., the most probable velocity of the Maxwell distribution. If instead the average velocity, which is 13% higher than the most probable velocity (p. 483), were used, the cross sections would be 13% lower and the results would be the same. It would not be correct to use a flux based on 2200 meters/sec. with an activation cross section changed from the 2200 meters/sec. value listed in the tables to one for the average velocity. If the cross section for the average velocity is to be used in the final calculation, than the cross section of the monitor foil must be changed to the average-velocity value before the flux is calculated. In both cases the results would be the same. Consequently the 2200-meters/sec. values of the activation cross section can be used for all but a few substances when the activation is carried out in the reactor shield or thermal column.

As pointed out previously (p. 542), higher intensities of thermal neutrons are available in the reactor lattice, but many epithermal neutrons are also present. These may cause resonance activation in addition to thermal or $1/v$ activation. In this case it will be necessary to correct for the resonance activation by means of a cadmium difference (p. 542) or cadmium ratio measurement. The cadmium ratio, which is the ratio of activations without cadmium to activations with a cadmium cover, varies rather widely with the position in the pile. Thus for a $1/v$ material it will be about 30 in the lattice, 3000 in the reflector, and as high as 50,000 in the thermal column. That is, in the lattice only about 3% of the activations of a $1/v$ material are caused by neutrons of energy higher than 0.4 ev. and in the reflector a negligible amount. However, for substances with strong resonances the cadmium ratio will be considerably lower. For example in a region of the Argonne heavy-water reactor where the $1/v$ cadmium ratio was 70, the values for a number of substances with resonance activations were $Mn^{55} = 35$; $Cu^{63} = 30.8$; $Br^{79} = 3.25$; $Ag^{107} = 13.35$; $Ag^{109} = 3.20$; $In^{113} = 2.68$; $Au^{197} = 2.91$. These values will vary with the $1/v$ cadmium ratio. Consequently if direct calculation of the quantity of an element in a sample is to be made by use of the thermal-activation cross section, it will be necessary to determine either the cadmium ratio or cadmium difference for the particular position of irradiation and correct for the resonance activation. This is readily accomplished by taking the cadmium difference for both the flux monitor and the sample. Fortunately the comparative method discussed in the following section obviates the necessity for such corrections and eliminates a number of the uncertainties in the absolute calculation.

### 13.7. The Comparative Method of Activation Analysis

Many of the uncertainties of absolute determination discussed in the previous sections can be reduced by comparing the activity induced in an unknown sample with that induced in standard samples of nearly the same composition. The unknown sample and the standard are irradiated under as nearly the same conditions as possible, preferably at the same time and same place in the reactor to eliminate variations in the neutron flux. Both the unknown and standards should be of about the same size and thickness so that flux depression, self-protection, hardening of the flux, and obliquity effects will be the same. If the arrangement for the irradiations are such that these effects are small under any circumstances, then error from these sources will be small in the comparative method.

After irradiation the unknown and standards are counted under as nearly identical conditions as possible. The weight of the element $x$ in the unknown is then given by

$$\frac{\text{wt. of } x \text{ in unknown}}{\text{wt. of } x \text{ in standard}} = \frac{\text{activity of } x \text{ in unknown}}{\text{activity of } x \text{ in standard}} \qquad (13.62)$$

In the usual case one standard containing roughly the same quantity of $x$ as the unknown is adequate.

It may be advantageous to activate several standards containing different amounts of the element $x$ and construct a calibration curve.

Alternatively, if the facilities are not suitable for irradiating the standards at the same time as the unknown, a boron trifluoride flux monitor or a secondary monitor foil of nearly the same neutron properties as the element of interest can be used for normalization of the flux for standards and the unknown. When the irradiations are carried out in the reflector or a thermal column where the cadmium ratio is high (p. 562), resonance activation will not be significant except for the few elements that do not follow the $1/v$ law in the thermal region. Such irradiations in other than a thermalized flux, i.e., in a reactor lattice, can be corrected for differences in resonance activation of the flux monitor foil and the standards or unknown by using a cadmium difference activation (p. 542). That is, the difference between the activation without and with cadmium (0.010 in.) gives the activation for $c$ neutrons, frequently referred to as "thermal" neutrons. Instead of a monitor foil a constant amount of a monitor material could be added to the standards for normalization prior to construction of the calibration curve of (activity of element $x$/activity of monitor) vs. (wt. of $x$). This same quantity of monitor material can then be added to the unknown samples for comparison with the calibration curve. Unless quite a number of samples are to be analyzed at different times, comparison with one or two properly chosen standards is usually sufficient for an analysis.

If the major component is not appreciably activated or if its activity decays rapidly compared with that of element $x$ and, further, if other elements present do not produce interfering activities, direct counting of the irradiated sample can sometimes give useful results. For example, when $3S$ aluminum is irradiated in a high neutron flux for 5 min., activities due to 2.3-min. $Al^{28}$, 2.59-hr. $Mn^{56}$, and 14.8-hr. $Na^{24}$ are produced (31) as illustrated in Fig. 41. After about an hour the 2.3-min. $Al^{28}$ activity has decayed to a small value. The activity of the $Mn^{56}$ can be corrected for the small contribution from $Na^{24}$. Extrapolation of the $Mn^{56}$ activity to the time that irradiation was stopped gives the activity induced in the manganese. Comparison with a standard of known manganese content under identical conditions allows a calculation of the concentration of manganese by eq. (13.62).

In general, however, the samples are not so simple as the case illustrated above and chemical separations will be necessary to remove bulk constituents and interfering radioactive elements. Both the unknown and standard are treated in identical ways, and the element of interest is finally isolated in a form suitable for counting. Aliquots are taken to give about the same counting rate for unknown and standard. The samples should be of about the same thickness and should be mounted on the same backing material and in the same place with respect to the counter.

All these precautions are taken to assure as nearly as possible the same values for the counter efficiency $f_E$, resolving time factor $f_r$, absorption factor $f_A$, back-scattering factor $f_B$, self-absorption and self-scattering factor $f_S$, and geometry factor $f_G$. The counting rates are corrected to the time that the irradiation was stopped by plotting as in Figs. 40 or 41 or by calculation by eq. (13.7). If all the factors affecting the counting rates are the same for both unknown and standard, the counting rates can be used directly in eq. (13.62) without conversion to activity because for

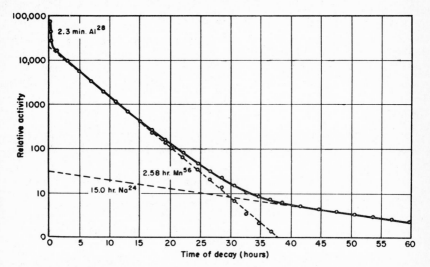

FIG. 41. Decay curve following irradiation of 3S aluminum indicates the presence of activities due to sodium and manganese in addition to the aluminum.

both the over-all yield factor $Y$ will be the same. Actually it is not necessary to extrapolate to the time that irradiation was stopped in this comparative method. Instead the two counting rates can be corrected to the same time of decay. If the half-life is long compared with the time between counting the unknown and sample, the correction for differences in time of decay can usually be neglected. Finally, to be certain of the radiochemical purity of the isolated element it is advisable to determine its half-life and its aluminum- or lead-absorption curve.

### 13.8. Chemical-Separation Problems in Activation Analysis

Up until the time a radioisotope disintegrates, its chemical behavior is the same (except for normal isotope effects due to mass differences) as that of the normal material. If an appreciable quantity of the element being determined is present, the usual analytical procedures for purification and isolation can be used, although the emphasis is on radiochemical purity, rather than on chemical purity or quantitative yields. Sometimes it is necessary to sacrifice quantitative yields for radiochemical purity, in which case means are devised for determination of the chemical yield of the procedure.

Usually neutron activation is employed for trace analysis so that the concentration of the element of interest may be much lower than one encounters in the ordinary analytical procedures. For example, if 500 mg. of a substance is irradiated to determine manganese present in about 1 p.p.m., there would be present 0.5 $\mu$g. of manganese. Assuming that a volume of 25 ml. were encountered during a procedure for separation and purification, the concentration of manganese would be $2 \times 10^{-8}$ g./ml. or $3.7 \times 10^{-7}$ molar. The concentrations of other contaminating radioisotopes may be even lower. With concentrations this low considerable difficulties may be encountered with respect to adsorption and coprecipitation as well as deposition on walls of containers, filters, or microscopic colloidal particles to form "radiocolloids." Difficulties may also be encountered with respect to precipitation because the concentration may be so low that the solubility product cannot be exceeded or the formation of supersaturated solutions may inhibit the formation of the desired precipitate. Similarly the low concentration and the effects of adsorption or complex formation must be considered in oxidation-reduction equilibria.

Many of the difficulties referred to above are circumvented by adding a small known amount (1 to 50 mg.) of the naturally occurring element after irradiation. The added material is called an "isotopic carrier" when it is the same as the element activated, but other nonisotopic carriers are sometimes used to take advantage of marked adsorption or coprecipitation to aid in the separations (61, 77). It is important that the added element be in the same oxidation state or complex as the radioactive material; otherwise it may not function as a carrier. If there is any doubt as to the form of the radioactive element, it is advisable to convert it along with the carrier to the same form, for example by alternate oxidation and reduction. The carrier serves another important function besides facilitating the separation and purification. It serves as a means of determining the chemical losses in the procedures. The ratio of the weight of the carrier added to that finally recovered is the "chemical yield" and can be used to correct the observed counting rate or activity.

The importance of radiochemical purity has been stressed. Traces of radioactive species other than the one being determined may be present. Ions of these are subject to the same problems of coprecipitation and adsorption and may contaminate the trace element being determined. Consequently it is advisable to add carriers for other activities known or assumed to be present. It is necessary to add such carriers, not only for ions to be precipitated but also for ions to be held in solution while others are precipitated. Such carriers are called "hold-back carriers." If the contaminating radioactive species is present in relatively large quantities, it may be necessary to employ the "washing-out" principle. In this the operations for removal of the radioactive contaminant are repeated several times with the addition of fresh carrier each time.

Although carriers for removal of unwanted radioactive species are usually 1 to 50 mg. of the natural element in the same chemical form, this is not always the case. Some precipitates, such as ferric hydroxide and manganese dioxide, are efficient "scavengers" and at times may be used to remove certain activities. Frequently it is possible to change the oxidation state of one substance to facilitate its separation from the element of interest. Of course, if several trace elements are being determined from a single activation, the procedures may be arranged after addition of appropriate carriers to isolate each of them from the same solution.

Since the specific procedures vary for each type of material analyzed, it will not be profitable to discuss them in detail here. Details for many separations can be found in the references given later (p. 580) to specific analyses that have been done or in more complete treatises on radio-chemical procedures (61). In general, one resorts to the usual methods of analytical separations involving precipitation, oxidation-reduction, ion-exchange, complex formation, organic precipitants, volatilization, solvent extraction, leaching, and electrochemical methods. Application of these to the problems of radiochemical separations has resulted in many rather rapid and specific separations.

For general qualitative examination the irradiated sample can be dissolved and 2 to 3 mg. of carriers for the elements suspected can be added and then each of them separated chemically and examined for radiations. As an example (35), 2 to 3 mg. each of silver, copper, arsenic, cobalt, manganese, iron, yttrium, strontium, and barium can be added to the dissolved sample and then processed by conventional "wet" chemistry to yield precipitates of $AgCl$, $CuS$, $As_2S_3$, $CoS$, $MnS$, $Fe(OH)_3$, $Y_2(C_2O_4)_3$, and $Sr_3(PO_4)_2$, $Ba_3(PO_4)_2$. Radioisotopes for which carriers were not added remain in the filtrates and except for adsorption and coprecipitation will not be detected. Each precipitate is examined radiochemically for $\beta^-$ and $\gamma$ decay, $\beta$-absorption curves, and $\gamma$ spectra with a scintillation counter. This should serve to determine the identity of the radioisotopes and thus the contaminating elements. By such a procedure, using the appropriate carriers the authors (35) were able to show that a dilute enzyme solution contained sodium, lead, rhenium, arsenic, palladium, chromium, and silicon.

Similarly standard schemes for anion separation and identification can be used to test for anion-forming elements. Frequently short cuts can be made to test for specific elements or groups of elements by employing such special techniques as volatilization in the presence of acid to test for halogens or certain sulfur compounds. With hydrochloric acid other elements may be volatilized such as antimony, selenium, or other elements that form volatile halides. Extraction, ion exchange, electrolysis, organic precipitants, oxidation-reduction, etc., can all be employed as aids in qualitative identification of the elements present. By use of $\beta$-, $\gamma$-, and X-ray spectrometry along with half-life and absorption measurements the particular radioisotope can usually be identified. Following such qualitative examinations, quantitative procedures can then be carried out with more certainty of radiochemical purity.

One important feature of activation analysis for trace elements is that after activation contamination by small quantities of the elements being determined is not of importance. One must be very careful, however, not to contaminate the sample before it is activated. Following activation the carrier is added in appreciable quantities so that further contamination by traces of the element in the reagents, etc., will not significantly add to the quantity of precipitate finally counted. In most other methods of trace analysis one must use extreme precautions throughout all the procedures to prevent contamination from any source.

### 13.9. Activation Analysis of Mixtures without Chemical Separation and Resolution of Decay Curves

Certain simple mixtures can frequently be analyzed without complete chemical isolation of each radioactive species. Separation into groups containing two or three radioactive species is sometimes sufficient; at other times, as illustrated previously (p. 563), no chemical separation is necessary. In fact, the use of recently developed methods of $\gamma$-scintillation spectrometry, to be described in a later section, make it possible to analyze certain rather complex mixtures with even fewer chemical operations.

By controlling the method of irradiation and the duration of irradiation, by counting at different times after irradiation, by resolving decay curves, by selecting the appropriate counters, or by using absorbers for the radiations, it is frequently possible to obtain useful information about the qualitative and quantitative composition of a sample from radioactive measurements alone. Almost every radioisotope differs in some respect from all others as regards its half-life, decay scheme, or the energies of its radiations. Consequently in principle it should be possible to identify each radioactive species and measure it quantitatively if instruments of sufficient selectivity and resolution were available. Practically, however, considerable interference results if counters for only one type of radiation, $\beta^-$ particles for example, are used. Besides $\beta^-$ and $\beta^+$ particles, other radiations are useful, including $\alpha$ particles, prompt $\gamma$ rays that follow other radiations in a very short time ($\sim 10^{-13}$ sec.), $\gamma$ rays from isomeric transitions, electrons from internal conversion of $\gamma$ rays, and X rays from electron capture. In addition one can sometimes take advantage of capture $\gamma$ rays emitted at the time of neutron capture; emission of protons, deuterons, $\alpha$ particles, or fission products during irradiation; and emission of photoneutrons by beryllium or deuterium in the presence of a high-energy $\gamma$ emitter. To take advantage of all these requires rather specialized techniques and counting equipment including G-M counters of various types, proportional counters, ionization chambers, scintillation counters, coincidence counters for $\beta$-$\gamma$ coincidences and X-ray–$\gamma$ coincidences, as well as $\beta$- and $\gamma$-ray spectrometers. In this section consideration will be given to the use of the usual type of G-M counter for examining mixtures of radioisotopes following a neutron activation.

The influence of varying the time of irradiation or the flux as a means of selective activation has already been discussed (p. 539). Also the application of resonance activation or thermal activation alone with cadmium as a filter has been described (p. 542) as a means of selective activation. The importance of the time of counting following an irradiation can be illustrated in the case of an activation analysis for silver in which 24.2-sec. $Ag^{110}$, 2.3-min. $Ag^{108}$, and 270-day $Ag^{110}$ are formed. Similarly, for the isotopes of rubidium, neutron activation forms 17.8-min. $Rb^{88}$ and 19.5-day $Rb^{86}$. It is not possible to separate activities due to isotopes of the same element by the usual chemical means. However, in cases such as $Rb^{88}$ and $Rb^{86}$, it is possible to follow the change in activity with time and either to correct the 17.8-min. activity for contribution from the 19.5-day activity or to wait until the 17.8-min. activity has decayed and count that due to $Rb^{86}$. Mixtures of two or three elements that form activities with half-lives differing appreciably from one another can be treated in the same way. If two activities do not differ by at least a factor of two in half-lives, it is rather difficult to resolve the decay curve accurately.

When activities of different half-lives are present, the decay curve is a composite of the exponentials for each activity. Thus, the activity $A$ of the sample is

$$A = A_1^0 e^{-\lambda_1 t} + A_2^0 e^{-\lambda_2 t} \qquad (13.63)$$

where $A_1^0$, $A_2^0$, etc., are the activities of each species at a given time (the time irradiation was stopped, for example) and $t$ is the time measured from this reference time. If the decay constants $\lambda_1$, $\lambda_2$, etc., are different, a plot of the log of the observed activity vs. time is not a straight line but curves upward from the origin as illustrated in Fig. 42. After a sufficiently long time (usually 8 to 10 half-lives) a short-lived activity contributes little to the observed activity. The last part of the curve is then due to the decay of the longest-lived activity. A straight line is drawn through these points and extrapolated back to $t = 0$. The intercept is the activity at the time that irradiation was stopped (if this was taken as $t = 0$) and the slope of the line can be used to calculate the half-life

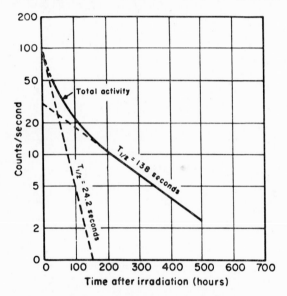

FIG. 42. Resolution of a composite decay curve.

since $-d(\ln A)/dt = \lambda$ or $-d(\log A)/dt = \lambda/2.303$ and $T_{1/2} = 0.693/\lambda$. Reference to a table of neutron-activated radioisotopes arranged in order of half-lives (66) aids in identifying the radioisotope, and the activity at $t = 0$ can be used to calculate the quantity of the element present.

The decay curve of the activity with the next shorter half-life can be obtained by subtracting from the observed activity the activity of the long-lived radioisotope as represented by its straight line. If a plot of these points is a straight line all the way to $t = 0$, radioisotopes of only two half-lives are indicated. The slope and intercept can be used as above for inferring the qualitative and quantitative composition. When a third shorter lived activity is present, the second line will curve upward near the origin. This may be resolved in the same way to obtain the half-life and activity at $t = 0$ for the third radioisotope.

It is usually not possible to resolve accurately a system of more than three components. However, even though this procedure does not give results as precise as chemical isolation of each element, it is more rapid, particularly in cases where chemical separation is difficult. For example, Boyd (31) illustrates this method for the case of impurities in a sample of rubidium carbonate. Besides the activities due to rubidium, resolution of the decay curve showed activities with half-lives of 12.8 hr. and 2.8 hr. which could be assigned to 12.4-hr. $K^{42}$ and 3.2-hr. $Cs^{134}$ or 2.8-hr. $Sr^{87}$.

More precise determination of the half-life might serve to distinguish between cesium and strontium, but the fact that the decay curve is obtained by differences involving two other decay curves makes this procedure uncertain. Radiations from both $Cs^{134}$ and $Sr^{87}$ arise from an isomeric transition in which the $\gamma$ ray causes the emission of a conversion electron from the electron system. The energy of the conversion electrons from $Cs^{134}$ are 0.127 and 0.010 Mev. with the ratio of electrons to gamma rays (conversion coefficient) greater than 1. For $Sr^{87}$ the energy is 0.388 Mev. with a conversion coefficient between 0.1 and 1. Absorption measurements for the radiations would aid in distinguishing which of the two radioisotopes were present, but it would be preferable to use a scintillation counter (p. 602) to determine the energy of the radiations. Alternatively, strontium could be separated chemically following the addition of normal strontium as a carrier.

### 13.10. Absorption Methods for Mixtures of Radioisotopes

When the half-lives of two radioisotopes are so close together that resolution of the decay curves is not possible, absorption methods may sometimes be used. The $\beta$ particles emitted from radioisotopes have energies ranging from a maximum value $E_{max}$ to zero with an average energy of about one-third $E_{max}$. This wide variation in energy rather than monoenergetic $\beta$ particles arises from the random sharing of the transition energy by the $\beta$ particle and a neutrino when a neutron changes into a proton. Conversion electrons on the other hand are more nearly homogeneous in energy since they result from transfer of the energy of a monoenergetic $\gamma$ ray to one of the electrons of the atom. Both $\alpha$ particles and $\gamma$ rays from the nucleus are also essentially monoenergetic and their absorption characteristics can be characterized more precisely (118).

Even though the $\beta$-ray spectra are complex, some useful information with respect to identification and analysis can be obtained from absorption measurements. The combined effect of the continuous spectrum and scattering in an absorber that is not too thick results in an approximately exponential law (see also p. 551) for $\beta$ particles of a given maximum energy:

$$n = n_0 e^{-\mu x} = n_0 e^{-(\mu/\rho)G} \qquad (13.64)$$

Here $n_0$ is the number of $\beta$ particles per second incident on the absorber, $n$ is the number passing through a thickness $x$ cm. or $G$ g./cm.$^2$, $\mu$ is the linear absorption coefficient, $\rho$ the density, and $\mu/\rho$ is the mass absorption coefficient. The thickness of absorber required to reduce the counting rate by one-half is the half-thickness, $x_{\frac{1}{2}} = 0.693/\mu$ or $G_{\frac{1}{2}} = 0.693/(\mu/\rho)$. These values can readily be determined by a plot of the counting rate vs. thickness of absorber on semilogarithmic paper. Only the initial part of

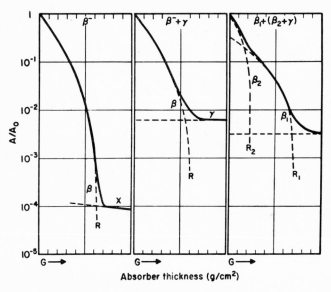

FIG. 43. Typical types of absorption curves for simple and more complex decay schemes.

such a curve approximates the foregoing equation, and even here the exact shape is influenced by the nature of the $\beta$-particle spectrum, geometrical arrangement during counting, and type of counter used. Consequently, half-thickness values are not too reliable in determining the $\beta$ energies. Instead, the range of $\beta$ particles is more frequently used.

Typical absorption curves encountered are illustrated in Fig. 43 in which the log of the ratio of the counting rate with an absorber to the counting rate without an absorber is plotted against the thickness $G$ in grams per square centimeter of aluminum. When $\gamma$ rays accompany $\beta$ emission, as is usually the case, there is a $\gamma$-ray "tail" which is about 1% of the $\beta$-counting rate. This arises because the G-M counter is only about 1 % as efficient for $\gamma$ rays as for $\beta$ rays. Energetic $\gamma$ rays are absorbed only slightly by the amount of aluminum required to stop the $\beta$ rays. Even in the case of a radioisotope such as $P^{32}$ that emits only a $\beta$ particle, there is a small "tail" resulting from X rays or *bremstrahlung* emitted as the $\beta$ particles are stopped in the absorbers. With $\beta^+$ particles annihilation radiation also contributes to the "tail." When $\beta$ particles of two different energies are present, a rapid fall is observed in the curve for the low-energy one followed by a section of the curve with a lower slope.

There is usually a sufficiently sharp difference in slope of the $\beta$ and $\gamma$ absorption curves that it is possible to estimate the point at which the $\beta$ activity is not detectable above the $\gamma$- or X-ray background. More precise estimation of the range of the $\beta$ particles can be obtained by subtraction of the tail background from the total-absorption curve, by use of a Feather comparison method (23, 120), or by use of certain analytical expressions. The range $R$ as determined by one of these methods is usually from five to ten times the thickness $G_{\frac{1}{2}}$ required to reduce the observed activity by one half. A number of curves and expressions have been published relating the maximum $\beta$ energy $E_{\max}$ to the range $R$ in aluminum (67) for energies above 0.6 Mev. Two such expressions are

$$E = 0.542E_{\max} - 0.133 \qquad (13.65)$$
$$E = 0.572E_{\max} - 0.161 \qquad (13.66)$$

For energies below about 0.6 Mev. range-energy curves should be used. The value of $E_{\max}$ as determined by these measurements serve, as an aid in identifying a radioisotope.

In making the absorption measurements one must consider a number of factors that may affect the results. For example, scattering of the $\beta$ particles either into or out of the solid angle subtended by the counter will influence the shape of the absorption curve. It is advisable to use a small solid angle (0.05) and place the absorbers near the counter window. Other factors discussed previously (p. 549) that affect counting rates should also be considered, including source thickness, back scattering, scattering from counter and sample holder, absorption in the air and counter window, etc.

A typical application of absorption methods to the activation analysis of mixtures of sodium and potassium has been discussed by Boyd (31). Neutron activation of sodium results in the formation of 14.8-hr. $Na^{24}$, which decays with the emission of $\beta$ particles of maximum energy of 1.39 Mev. followed by prompt emission of $\gamma$ rays with energies of 2.75 and 1.37 Mev. The 12.4-hr. $K^{42}$ decays with the emission of 3.58 (80%)- and 2.04 (20%)-Mev. $\beta$ particles and 1.51 (20%)-Mev. $\gamma$ rays. The half-lives are too nearly the same for resolution of the decay curves.

However, an analysis of a mixture is possible by the use of appropriate absorbers. Curves for the log of the relative activity vs. the grams per square centimeter of aluminum absorber are shown in Fig. 44. It can be seen on the one hand that the less energetic $\beta$ particles from $Na^{24}$ are practically completely absorbed by 700 g./cm.$^2$ of aluminum leaving a relatively high $\gamma$-ray tail. On the other hand, 1700 g./cm.$^2$ of aluminum are required to stop the $\beta$ particles from $K^{42}$.

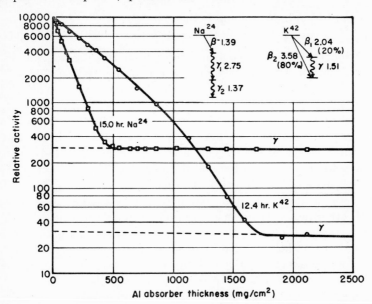

FIG. 44. Absorption curves for 15.0-hr. $Na^{24}$ which emits 1.39 Mev. $\beta$ particles followed immediately by 2.75- and 1.37-Mev. $\gamma$ rays, and for 12.4-hr. $K^{42}$ which decays 80% of the time by emission of 3.58-Mev. $\beta$ particles and 20% of the time by emission of 2.04-Mev. $\beta$ particles, followed immediately by 1.51-Mev. $\gamma$ rays.

With 1700 mg. of Al, the observed counting rate for a mixture of sodium and potassium is the sum of that due to the $\gamma$ activities of $Na^{24}$ and $K^{42}$, and with 700 mg./cm.$^2$ of Al the observed counting rate is due to the $\beta$ activity of $K^{42}$ plus the two $\gamma$ activities. Thus the difference between the measurements with 700 and 1700 mg./cm.$^2$, the latter being corrected by the factor 1.02 for the effect of the extra aluminum on the $\gamma$ rays, gives the counting rate $C_{K_\beta}$ due to the $\beta$ particles from $K^{42}$ with 700 mg./cm.$^2$ of Al. Thus

$$C_{K_\beta} = C_{700} - 1.02 C_{1700} \tag{13.67}$$

With a pure sample of a potassium salt, the ratio $R$ of the counting rates

$C_{K_\gamma}$ to $C_{K_\beta}$ can be determined. It was 0.0277 for the particular counting arrangement used by Boyd. Then

$$C_{K_\gamma} = R C_{K_\beta} = R(C_{700} - 1.02 C_{1700}) \qquad (13.68)$$

The counting rate with 1700 mg./cm.$^2$ of Al is due to the sum of the $\gamma$-counting rates from sodium and potassium:

$$C_{1700} = C_{K_\gamma} + C_{Na_\gamma}$$

The $\gamma$-counting rate for sodium is then

$$C_{Na_\gamma} = C_{1700} - C_{K_\gamma} = C_{1700} - R(C_{700} - 1.02 C_{1700}) \qquad (13.69)$$

Thus, from the observed counting rates with 700 mg./cm.$^2$ and with 1700 mg./cm.$^2$ of Al and a separate determination of $R$ with a suitable potassium salt, the counting rates due to the $\gamma$ rays of the $Na^{24}$ and the $K^{42}$ can be calculated.

These counting rates can be corrected (p. 549) by the factor for resolving time, counting efficiency, geometry, etc., to obtain the activity at the time of measurement. This activity can be corrected for decay from the end of the irradiation and the weight of K or Na in the sample can be calculated by eq. (13.42). Alternatively, a series of standards of known sodium and potassium content could be used for a calibration curve. If other radioactive species are present in the sample at the time of counting, the method is not satisfactory. A chemical separation could be made, but the method would lose some of its simplicity and rapidity.

The foregoing method is essentially one involving the measurement of $\gamma$ activity, although $\beta$ activity is also involved. The G-M counter is rather insensitive to $\gamma$ rays and the small differences in counting rates with 700 and 1700 mg./cm.$^2$ of aluminum reduces the accuracy of determination, particularly for samples containing small amounts of one element in the other. This could be improved by using scintillation-type counters since they are considerably more efficient than G-M counters for $\gamma$ rays. Gamma scintillation spectrometry is even more advantageous since, as will be described later, not only the energy of the $\gamma$ rays but the quantitative determination of the sodium and potassium in trace amounts can be made without chemical separations.

Sometimes it is desirable to determine $\gamma$- or X-ray energies either for identification of a radioisotope or for determining their decay schemes. Although this is usually done more reliably by a number of methods other than absorption (61), the latter is still useful for determining approximate energies. The attenuation of $\gamma$ rays in passing through an absorber such as lead follows the exponential law $n = n_0 e^{-(\mu/\rho)G}$ similar to eq. (13.64). When $\gamma$ rays pass through matter, they interact with the shell electrons and coulomb field of the nuclei. Although the average specific ionization caused by a $\gamma$ ray is from 0.1 to 0.01 that caused by a $\beta$ particle of the same energy, the average energy loss per ion pair formed is about the same as for $\beta$ particles, i.e. 35 ev. per ion pair in air. This ionization arises almost entirely from secondary effects of the principal interactions of $\gamma$ rays. The main processes are as follows (a) the photoelectric effect in which the $\gamma$-ray photon $h\nu$ ejects a bound electron from an atom or molecule, giving it an energy $(h\nu - E_b)$ where $E_b$ is the binding energy of the electron in its shell; (b) the Compton effect in which only part of the energy of the $\gamma$-ray photon is given to the electron (the energy of the $\gamma$ ray is reduced and its direction changed); (c) pair production in which

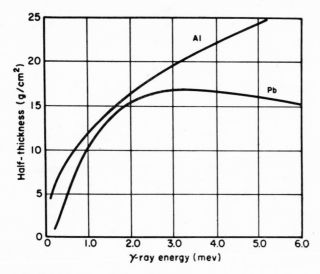

FIG. 45. Half thicknesses of Pb and Al in grams per centimeter for absorption of $\gamma$ rays as a function of $\gamma$-ray energy.

a $\gamma$ ray with an energy greater than 1.02 Mev. forms an electron-positron pair in the coulomb field of the nuclei. The positron produces ionization as it slows down, but its final fate is annihilation with the formation of two 0.51-Mev. photons. In all these processes energetic electrons are produced and these form the ion pairs referred to above.

The total-absorption coefficient $\mu/\rho$ is the sum of those for the three separate processes. Instead of $\mu/\rho$, the value of the half-thickness $G_{1/2} = 0.693/(\mu/\rho)$ is frequently tabulated or plotted as a function of the energy of the $\gamma$ rays, as shown in Fig. 45. By determining the half-thickness for the $\gamma$ rays of a radioisotope in a suitable geometrical counting arrangement, the energy of the $\gamma$ ray can be determined by reference to these curves. Ambiguities resulting from certain half-thicknesses corresponding to two different energies can be resolved by use of two absorbers. If γ rays of two different energies are present, a plot of log counting rate vs. absorber thickness can often be resolved into two straight lines. Resolution of more than two components is very difficult, and other methods must be employed.

Absorption methods may be used to distinguish X rays from γ rays, and in some cases the element from which they arise can be identified. The X rays are characteristic of the particular value of $Z$ at the time of emission. When conversion electrons are ejected from the inner shells by a γ ray from an isomeric transition, X rays are produced as the vacancy is filled. In this case they are characteristic of the radioisotope being detected with atomic number $Z$. For K capture or $\beta^+$ emission, the X rays would be characteristic of $Z - 1$, while for X rays emitted following $\beta^-$ emission they would correspond to atomic number $Z + 1$.

*Critical absorbers* are particularly useful in characterizing the X rays. Absorbers of $Z - 2$ or $Z - 3$ are usually critical for the element $Z$ and have absorption coefficients three to ten times greater than an absorber that is noncritical, $Z$ or $Z - 1$. Consequently, by using several absorbers with atomic numbers near the suspected radioisotope it is possible to infer its identity. Both critical and noncritical absorbers have about the same high transmission for γ rays that might be present. By taking the difference in counting rates for equal thickness of critical and noncritical absorbers, the X-ray activity can be estimated. Sometimes the absorption of low-energy X rays may be similar to that of β particles, but these may be distinguished by using an absorber with higher atomic number because the mass absorption coefficient for X rays increases more rapidly with $Z$.

At energies not near the absorption edge, $\mu/\rho$ varies approximately as $Z^4/AE^3$ for X rays. Between 0.1 and 2 Mev., $\mu/\rho$ for γ rays varies roughly as $Z^5/AE^2$ and above 2 Mev. as $Z^5/AE$. For particles the mass absorption coefficient varies approximately as $Z/AE$, that is as the number of electrons per unit mass. Thus, for elements other than hydrogen, $\mu/\rho$ for β particles changes only slowly with increasing $Z$. Hydrogen with $Z/A$ of 1 rather than 0.5 for carbon has an abnormally large effect on the absorption of β particles. This difference has led to a rather useful method for determining hydrogen in hydrocarbons and similar compounds.

### 13.11. Absorption of β Particles for Determination of Hydrogen

The details of the use of β-particle absorption for the determination of hydrogen have been described by Smith and Otvos (211) and by Jacobs, Lewis, and Piehl (110). Essentially the equipment consists of a 10- to 25-mc. source such as 19.9-yr. Sr[90] (0.61 Mev. β) deposited on a mica sheet with ionization chambers placed on opposite sides of the source. One beam passes through the liquid sample and the other beam passes through a reference material which may be a metal such as Invar or a standard liquid. The difference between the two ion currents can be amplified and recorded, or in one modification (111) a wedge of absorbing material is positioned with a micrometer in the sample beam until no current flows. This null position of the wedge is determined for a series of hydrocarbon samples of known hydrogen content for a calibration curve. Evaluation of the measurements also requires a knowledge of the density of the liquid. This is done by means of a specific-gravity plummet that dips into a small reservoir above the sample compartment.

Correction factors for known percentages of other elements such as nitrogen, oxygen, sulfur, chlorine, and bromine were derived empirically by use of known samples. With the $\beta$-particle absorption apparatus described above, the authors were able to determine the hydrogen content of a variety of liquids to $\pm 0.03\%$ hydrogen in 5 to 20 min. Such equipment has also been useful in the determination of the density (211) of a variety of binary mixtures to $\pm 0.0002$ g./ml. For liquids such as lubricating oils a linear relationship between density and amplifier output was obtained so that rapid determination of density might be made on such samples. Closely related to such density measurements are the well-known methods of measuring the thickness by $\beta$-particle absorption.

### 13.12. Use of Daughter Activities in Activation Analysis

A number of cases exist in which a radioisotope produced by neutron activation decays in part to a daughter which is also radioactive. At times the chemical isolation of this daughter activity may be more easily accomplished than isolating the parent activity. In this case the activity of the daughter can be used to calculate the quantity of the parent element in a sample. This requires a consideration of the growth and decay of a daughter activity during and after the irradiation (100).

During irradiation the activity of the parent $P$ with a decay constant $\lambda_P$ at a time $t_1$ is given by the usual equation

$$A_P = P\sigma_{ACT}N_E(1 - e^{-\lambda_P t_1}) \tag{13.70}$$

while the activity $A_D$ of the daughter with a decay constant of $\lambda_D$ is

$$A_D = \frac{Bf\sigma_{ACT}N_E}{\lambda_D - \lambda_P} (\lambda_D - \lambda_P - \lambda_{De} - \lambda_P t_1 + \lambda_D e^{-\lambda_D t_1}) \tag{13.71}$$

where $B$ is the fraction of the disintegration of the parent that gives rise to the radioactive daughter. After a time $t_2$ following removal from the neutron flux, the activity of the daughter is

$$A_D(t_2) = \frac{A_P \lambda_D}{\lambda_D - \lambda_P} (e^{-\lambda_P t_2} - e^{-\lambda_D t_2}) + A_D e^{-\lambda_D t_2} \tag{13.72}$$

where $A_P$ and $A_D$ are the activities given by eqs. (13.70) and (13.71). If now the daughter is separated chemically from its parent, it decays so that in time $t_3$ after such separation its activity is

$$A_D(t_3) = A_D(t_2)e^{-\lambda_D t_3} \tag{13.73}$$

Thus, by determining the activity of the daughter at time $t_3$, one can calculate the quantity of the element corresponding to the parent. However, by the use of standards and the comparative method discussed previously (p. 562) the determination is more reliable.

This method has been applied to the determination of small amounts of zirconium in nearly pure hafnium by Hudgen and Dabagian (100). The decay scheme of 65-day $Zr^{95}$ formed by neutron activation from $Zr^{94}$ (17.4% with an isotopic activation cross section of 0.08 barn) is shown in Table IX. About 99% of the disintegrations of $Zr^{95}$ goes to 35-day $Nb^{95}$ through loss of a 0.371-Mev. $\beta$ followed by a 0.721-Mev. $\gamma$. The other 1% decays to 90-hr. $Nb^{95}$ by loss of a 0.84-Mev. $\beta$. This then decays by loss of a 0.216-Mev. $\gamma$ to the 35-day $Nb^{95}$ which then decays to stable $Mo^{95}$ by loss of 0.160-Mev. $\beta$ and 0.745-Mev. $\gamma$.

An outline of the procedure is as follows: The sample of hafnium oxide (100 mg.) and several standards prepared by the addition of successive known quantities of zirconium oxide were sealed in quartz capsules for activation. After activation the samples were dissolved and 20 mg. of niobium was added as a carrier. Following chemical separation of the niobium, the ignited oxides were transferred to 1-in.-diameter tarred watch glasses and weighed to determine the chemical yields (50 to 90%). The watch glasses with the precipitates were mounted on an aluminum tray, covered with a 2.5 mg./cm.$^2$ aluminum foil, and counted in a flow-type counter. The observed counting rates were corrected for chemical yield and for growth and decay of $Nb^{95}$ after the irradiation. Contributions from both the 90-hr. and the 35-day isomers to the counting rate were considered in making this correction. When the corrected counting rates were plotted against the milligrams of zirconium added, a straight line resulted which could be extrapolated to 0 mg. of Zr added. This intercept showed that the hafnium contained 0.71% zirconium.

The advantage of using the daughter activity $Nb^{95}$ rather than the parent activity $Zr^{95}$ arises from the fact that a high activity is induced in the hafnium. The separation of zirconium from hafnium is not possible by the usual analytical procedures. The presence of nonradioactive niobium does not interfere because the short-lived 6.6-min. $Nb^{94}$ decays before the measurements are made and other niobium activities have very long half-lives.

## 13.13. Applications of Activation Analysis

The general procedures of activation analysis described in the previous sections have been applied to a rather large number of determinations in recent years. A number of these are summarized in Table X without details of the procedures or coverage of all published articles. References to *Nuclear Science Abstracts* will be given for determinations described in reports from various laboratories. The source and number of the report can be obtained from these references.

## 13.14. Sensitivity of the Activation Method

From the equations in sections 13.1 to 13.5 it can be seen that the factors contributing to the sensitivity of the neutron-activation method are neutron flux, $f$; activation cross section, $\sigma_{ACT}$; half-life, $T_{1/2}$; time of irradiation, $t_1$; and the time, $t_2$, required to prepare the sample for counting. The nature of the radiation is also important because it, as well as other factors, affects the net counting yield. The nuclear reactor gives the most intense source of neutrons, from $10^{10}$ to $10^{12}$ neutrons/(cm.$^2$)(sec.). Cyclotrons with a 100-$\mu$a. beam of 10-Mev. deuterons on a beryllium target can produce as high as $10^8$ to $10^9$ neutrons/(cm.$^2$)(sec.) at distances of from 10 to 20 cm. from the target. A 1-gram RaBe source produces about $10^7$ neutrons/sec. or a flux of about $10^4$ to $10^5$ neutrons/(cm.$^2$)(sec.) at 8 to 10 cm. Similar neutron fluxes can be obtained from other $\alpha$-n sources such as Po-Be, Po-B, or Rn-Be. Photoneutron sources such as those with 87-day Y or 60-day Sb are also useful. Low-voltage neutron generators, in which several hundred microamperes of 200-kev. deuterons bombard heavy-water ice, deuteroparaffins, or zirconium-tritium targets can produce intensities up to $10^7$ or $10^9$ neutrons/sec. and, consequently, can produce fluxes somewhat higher than the usual RaBe source. (See section 3 for a discussion of neutron sources.)

A summary of the effectiveness of the different sources in detecting elements with activation cross sections of about 10 barns is given in Table XI. These values are calculated on the basis of the neutron fluxes given and 100 counts per minute at a 25% counting yield for an element with atomic weight 100 when given a saturation exposure to the neutron flux.

The results tabulated in Table XI show that, for elements such as Mn with cross sections as high as 10 barns and with neutron fluxes as high as $10^{12}$ neutrons/(cm.$^2$)(sec.), phenomenal sensitivity may be achieved, $10^{-10}$ g. being detectable in such cases. For low neutron fluxes, however, the method is not so sensitive. Special applications may be found even here if the element in question has a reasonably high cross

TABLE X

*Applications of Neutron Activation Analysis*

| Authors | Ref. | Summary of applications |
|---|---|---|
| 1936<br>Hevesy and Levi | 92 | Neutron activation with a 300-mc. Ra-Be source was used to determine the presence of 0.1% dysprosium in yttrium and of europium in samples of gadolinium. |
| 1943<br>Aten | 12 | Hf was determined in Zr samples by short (1-min.) irradiation with slow neutrons. By use of the activity of 19-sec. Hf, the concentration of Hf in Zr could be determined to ±10% without chemical separation. Zr in Hf was also determined by means of fast neutrons with 1-hr. irradiation. After 2 hr. of waiting the Zr activity was measured and corrected for the activity of Hf. |
| Döpel and Döpel | 50 | Neutron-activation analysis was applied to the determination of Ir in Pt and Rh. Results were in agreement with spectrographic methods. The sensitivity of the method was $10^{-5}$% of Ir and thus is considerably more sensitive than usual spectrographic analysis. |
| 1947<br>Clark and Overman | 43 | Mn(0.6 p.p.m.) in precipitated aluminum hydroxide and Mn (1.25%) in 3S aluminum metal was determined by neutron activation in the Oak Ridge reactor. The general procedure for activation analysis is described. |
| Ketelle and Boyd | 122 | Rare-earth samples were activated by neutron irradiation prior to separation on ion exchange columns as means of monitoring their fractionation. Highly purified erbium, for example, was processed on a Dowex-50 column. Traces of Lu, Yb, Tm, and Na were separated from each other in passing through the column. From the activity in the fraction containing Tm, it was estimated that less than 10 p.p.m. of Tm was present in the erbium. |
| 1948<br>Overman and<br>Swarthout | 164 | P, Mn, and Ni were determined in carbonyl iron by means of the Oak Ridge reactor. |

TABLE X. (*Continued*)

| Authors | Ref. | Summary of applications |
|---|---|---|
| 1949 | | |
| Boyd | 31 | The principles and applications of activation analysis with neutrons and other particles are described in detail. Neutron activation is illustrated by the determination of Mn in aluminum, Na and K in carbonates, isotopic composition of Cu, etc. |
| Brown and Goldberg | 36 | Ga (20 to 90 p.p.m.) and Pd (2 to 6 p.p.m.) in a number of iron meteorites were determined by neutron activation. The general principles and precision of the method were discussed. Chemical procedures for radiochemical separation of Ga and Pd were devised. |
| Coon | 46 | The abundance of $He^3$ in "well" and "atmospheric" helium was measured by the $He^3(n,p)H^3$ reaction with thermal neutrons. The protons were counted during irradiation in a proportional type of counter and the background, which was less than 1%, was determined with cadmium used as a filter. The $He^3/He^4$ ratio was found to be $1.7 \times 10^{-7}$ and $13 \times 10^{-7}$ respectively in the two samples. |
| Goldberg and Brown | 69 | Re was determined in five iron meteorites by neutron activation. The average value was $0.6 \pm 0.2$ p.p.m., about 50 times greater than previous reports on the abundance of Re in nature. |
| Kohn and Tompkins | 126 | Contamination of one rare earth by another was determined by irradiation in the Oak Ridge reactor, for 1 to 5 min. for some and 16 hr. to 1 week for others. Typical analyses were 0.63% Sm in Ce; 1.18% Dy in Y; 0.023% Nd and 0.01% Ce in Pr; 0.03 to 0.3% Ce in La. |
| Macklin and Lykins | 137 | A photoneutron method for the analysis of $U^{235}$ in the range of p.p.m. in high-purity $U^{238}$ is described. |
| Muehlhause | 156 | The 19-sec. Hf activity produced by neutron irradiation was used to determine Hf in Zr. Details of the method are not given. |
| Reynolds and Bell | 178 | Results are reported for the activation analysis of Hf in Zr by use of the 45 to 55-day Hf activity. Details of the procedure are not given. |
| Tobias and Dunn | 220 | The distribution of gold in various tissues of a mouse was determined 30 days following injection of 10 $\mu$g. of Au. Each section was wetashed, then irradiated by neutrons in the |

TABLE X. (*Continued*)

| Authors | Ref. | Summary of applications |
|---|---|---|
| | | Hanford reactor. After one week the activity of the gold was determined. Concentrations from 0.005 to 4.4 $\mu$g. gold/g. of wet tissue were found in the various organs. The application of the method to other elements was discussed. |
| Smales | 198 | Review of the principles and applications of activation analysis. |
| Smales and Brown | 201 | The determination of arsenic in p.p.m. and less in germanium is considered. Methods of radiochemical separation of the arsenic are discussed. |
| Taylor and Havens | 216 | The general principles and applications of neutron interactions to chemical analysis were discussed, including resonance absorption, transmission, absorption, and activation. Examples of each were described. |

| | | |
|---|---|---|
| 1950 | | |
| Goldberg and Brown | 70 | Au and Re were determined in 300- to 500-mg. samples of meteorites after activation in the Argonne heavy-water reactor for 1 hr. Effects of self-shadowing in the sample, monitor, and standards were evaluated. Results for four different meteors in p.p.m. of Au were 0.79, 2.60, 2.84, 2.99, with a precision of $\pm 15\%$. Rhenium in two meteors was 1.5 and 2.8 p.p.m. |
| Hofstadter and McIntyre | 94 | The application of $\gamma$-ray spectrometry by means of crystals of NaI(Tl) to the assay of radioisotopes was described, including $Au^{198}$, $Na^{24}$, $Ga^{66}$, $K^{40}$, and $Co^{60}$. |
| Keynes and Lewis | 123 | Na and K were determined in nerves by irradiating them in a reactor along with standards. They were transferred to nickel dishes and counts were taken, first with a brass filter of 4.6 g./cm.$^2$ to obtain the $\gamma$ radiation from the Na and then with a filter 0.46 g./cm.$^2$ for the $K^{42}$ $\beta$ radiation. Their procedure allowed sufficient accuracy for their work without chemical separation, although potassium was separated for some of the measurements. Samples containing 0.3 $\mu$g. of Na and 3 $\mu$g. of K were analyzed without difficulty. |
| Muehlhause and Thomas | 158 | Review of the applications of nuclear reactors to chemical analysis, including neutron activation, absorption and scattering, use of resonances, photoneutrons from D and Be, counting during neutron irradiation, etc. Specific examples are given for each. (See section 13.14.) |

TABLE X. (*Continued*)

| Authors | Ref. | Summary of applications |
| --- | --- | --- |
| Picciotto | 167 | The general procedure of detection and quantitative determination of elements by neutron activation is discussed. |
| Senftle and Leavitt | 191 | Equations are given for calculating the activity produced in radioisotopes by thermal neutron irradiation. A table listing the radioisotopes produced and the activities induced in them is given. |
| Smales and Brown | 200 | Activation analysis of $GeO_2$ for As is accomplished by irradiating a 0.2- to 0.1-g. sample for 24 hr. at a flux of $10^{12}$ neutrons/(cm.²)(sec.) followed by chemical isolation of the arsenic. Interference from the $As^{77}$ arising from the $Ge^{77}$ produced during neutron activation is corrected for by use of aluminum absorbers to differentiate between the 0.8-mev. $\beta$ particles from $As^{77}$ and the 3.0-mev. $\beta$ particles from $As^{76}$; the limit of determination was about 0.2 p.p.m. of As in the Ge. |
| Winteringham | 227 | Bromides were estimated by a combined activation-exchange method. After irradiation of the unknown, the bromide is equilibrated with methyl bromide (500 mg.) in 1 ml. of aqueous acetone at 100° C. The Br is recovered from the methyl bromide as silver bromide and counted. This procedure was applied to Br in tobacco leaf. With $5 \times 10^{11}$ neutrons/(cm.²)(sec.) 0.01 $\mu$g. of Br can be determined to within a few per cent. Similar methods should be applicable to the determination of Cl and I. |
| **1951** | | |
| Albert, Caron, and Chaudron | 1 | Highly purified aluminum was shown by activation analysis to contain 4 p.p.m. of Na and 2 p.p.m. of Cu. Rare earths to the extent of 0.1 to 0.01 of these values were also present. Sm and Ho follow Cu in the chemical separations used. |
| Eicholz | 52 | The determination of Ta in ores is discussed and the influence of the presence of U is considered. |
| Daudel | 48 | Review of applications of radioactivity to analytical chemistry including activation analysis. |
| Gaudin and Pannell | 65 | A 2-curie $Sb^{124}$ gamma source was used to determine Be by the $(\gamma,n)$ reaction using 50- to 600-g. samples with concentrations ranging from 30 p.p.m. to 8% Be. The neutrons emitted were counted with $B^{10}F_3$ counters. |

TABLE X. (*Continued*)

| Authors | Ref. | Summary of applications |
|---|---|---|
| Griffon and Barband | 75 | The determination of As in hair by neutron activation for medical-legal use was discussed. The activity of As when present in a few p.p.m. can be determined along the hair and then related to the time of ingestion since the rate of the growth of the hair is known. |
| Leddicotte and Reynolds | 133 | The general method of activation analysis is described and a table of detection limits is given for elements activated in the Oak Ridge reactor. The half-life, activation cross sections, and radiations are given for the radioisotopes formed. |
| Long | 135 | A neutron-activation method is described for the determination of Ta in mixtures containing Nb, Fe, Sn, Ti, and Si. Four days after irradiation when short-lived activities had decayed, the $\gamma$ activity of 111d $Ta^{182}$ (1.13 and 1.22-mev. $\gamma$ rays) was measured and compared to standards. Accuracies of $\pm 3\%$ were achieved for mixtures containing $1\%$ or more of Ta. Interferences were discussed. |
| Picciotto | 168 | Minerals containing Li were irradiated with neutrons to produce the reaction $Li^6(n,\alpha)H^3$. The effect of the $\alpha$ and $H^3$ particles on nuclear emulsion plates was used as a sensitive determination of the presence of Li. |
| Süe | 213 | This is a rather complete review of the principles and applications of analyses with radioactive isotopes and by neutron interactions. Many applications are illustrated and references to the literature to the end of 1950 are given. |
| Taylor, Anderson, and Havens | 217 | The general principles and application of resonance absorption, transmission, absorption, and activation with examples of each are discussed. |
| **1952**<br>Atchison and Beamer | 10 | Irradiation of 1.2-g. disks of a commercial electrolytic magnesium sample in the Oak Ridge reactor at a flux of $5 \times 10^{11}$ neutrons/(cm.²)(sec.) for 4 weeks followed by chemical separation by means of carriers gave the following for the trace impurities in p.p.m.: As = 0.12; Ca = 1.3; Cr = 0.1; Cu = 8.0; P = 2.2; K = 1.4; Sr = 2.1; Samples of higher purity were also analyzed. Fe and K and Na were determined in a purified sample after irradiation |

## TABLE X. (*Continued*)

| Authors | Ref. | Summary of applications |
|---------|------|-------------------------|
| | | in the Chalk River reactor. Standards irradiated at the same time gave the following counts/(min.)/($\mu$g.) with a 2-mg./cm.$^2$ mica and window counter: As = 15,463; P = 7,095; Cu = 697; Fe = 539; K = 108; Na = 42.2; Sr = 18.7; Ca = 18.2; Cr = 5.7; S = 2.8. Sensitivities from 0.001 $\mu$g. for As to 10 $\mu$g. for S were estimated. Chemical procedures for obtaining radiochemical separation and purification are given and interferences are discussed. |
| Berlman, Lucas, and May | 17 | Neutron activation of Ag in photographic films was used to determine exposure. Agreement was found with optical density measurements for low exposures; at high exposures neutron activation was more accurate. |
| Grillot | 76 | Small quantities of Cu in luminescent materials were determined with a limit of 0.01 $\mu$g. of Cu. |
| Herr | 90 | Applications of neutron interactions to analytical determinations are reviewed. Besides neutron activation, the use of high-energy deuterons and protons is also discussed. |
| Hudgens and Cali | 99 | Sb was determined in ZrO samples in concentrations from 0.5 to 10 p.p.m. after irradiation in the Oak Ridge reactor. Methods of radiochemical purification and checking the purity were described. Sensitivity: 1 part Sb in 10$^9$. |
| Hudgens and Dabagian | 100 | Zr concentrations in the range from nearly pure Zr to as little as a few tenths p.p.m. in Hf were determined to about 1%. This was accomplished by radiochemical separation of the daughter Nb$^{95}$ activity arising from Zr$^{95}$. (See section 13.12.) |
| Hudgens and Nelson | 101 | The determination of In in a matrix of aluminum oxide or aluminum sulfate was carried out following irradiation in the Brookhaven reactor and with a 0.254-g. Ra-Be source. By means of a 20-mg. sample in the reactor the sensitivity obtained was 0.03 $\mu$g. but could be increased to 10$^{-11}$ g. With the Ra-Be source, 10 p.p.m. could be determined in a 10-g. sample. A rapid extraction procedure using isopropyl ether and 4.5 $M$ HBr was developed for separation of In. |
| Salmon | 183 | Arsenic was determined in high-purity S following irradiation in a reactor. After addition of As carrier, Ge and Se were separated by oxidative distillation with HCl and H$_2$O$_2$. Arsenic was |

TABLE X. (*Continued*)

| Authors | Ref. | Summary of applications |
|---------|------|-------------------------|
| | | then separated by distillation of AsCl₃ following the addition of HBr. Methods of preventing loss of As during dissolution of the sulfur were devised. |
| Smales | 197 | The determination of $\mu$g. amounts of U in minerals and rocks by neutron activation followed by radiochemical separation and measurement of the fission product Ba is described. Concentrations of U as low as 0.0003 % can be determined on samples smaller than 0.5 g. Chemical procedures for isolating the barium, interferences, sensitivity, and advantages of the method are discussed. |
| Smales and Pate | 203 | As was determined in GeO₂ by irradiating 300 to 600 mg. in the Harwell reactor [flux $\sim 10^{12}$ neutrons/(cm.²)(sec.)] followed by chemical separation with carrier. Standards were prepared by diluting As₂O₃ with Al₂O₃ to obtain 100 p.p.m. As. Radiometric analysis with a Geiger counter combined with aluminum absorbers gave a sensitivity of about 0.2 p.p.m. Use of an anthracene scintillation counter and suitable discriminator bias voltages allowed counting As⁷⁶ without interference from As⁷⁷ to obtain a sensitivity of 0.01 p.p.m. of As in GeO₂. |
| Smales and Pate | 204 | The application of activation analysis to the determination of As in small samples (10 ml.) of sea water is described. After irradiation in a flux of $10^{12}$ neutrons/(cm.²)(sec.) for 70 hr., the samples were allowed to stand for 24 hr. before chemical separation of the arsenic. Standards containing 1 $\mu$g./ml. were treated and counted in the same way as the unknowns. Concentrations from 1.6 to 5.0 $\mu$g. of As/liter were found in different sea-water samples. |
| Smales and Pate | 205 | The determination of arsenic in normal biological materials such as hair, nails, urine, blood, etc., by neutron activation is described. Amounts of As as small as 0.0001 $\mu$g. can be determined so that one drop of blood is sufficient for an analysis. Chemical procedures, interferences, and advantages of activation analysis are discussed. |
| 1953 Bancie-Grillot and Grillot | 15 | The determination of Cl in ZnS phosphors was accomplished by irradiation in the Châtillon |

TABLE X. (*Continued*)

| Authors | Ref. | Summary of applications |
|---|---|---|
| | | 5-kw. reactor. Cl contents from 10 to 50 $\mu$g./g. were determined to within 10% and the sensitivity was of the order of 5 $\mu$g. for a 5-g. ZnS sample. |
| Berlman | 16 | Film exposure to $\gamma$ rays was determined after development by measurement of the activity induced in the silver by neutron irradiation. The use of 270-day $Ag^{110}$ has some advantage over using 2.3-min. $Ag^{108}$ because the activity of $K^{42}$, $Na^{24}$, and $S^{35}$ can be allowed to decay before measurement. Furthermore, the $\gamma$ rays can be measured by NaI(Tl) scintillation counting with absorbers to remove $\beta$ rays. |
| Brooksbank, Leddicotte, and Mahlman | 34 | Techniques of activation analysis are discussed and specific application to a number of types of samples is described. Results of typical analyses were Mn (100 to 200 p.p.m.) in metal alloys; Co (0.01 to 2 p.p.m.) in biological materials; Sr (5 to 60 p.p.m.) in animal tissue; Ga (100 to 140 p.p.m.) in Al; V (0.7 to 1.0 p.p.m.) in crude oils; Cd (30 to 500 p.p.m.) in vinylite resins. Sensitivities for activation in a flux of $5 \times 10^{11}$ neutrons/(cm.²)(sec.) were calculated to be from 0.001 $\mu$g. for Mn to 0.6 $\mu$g. for Sr. |
| Connally and Leboeuf | 45 | The principles and applications of scintillation spectrometers to analysis of radioisotopes from fission are discussed. Although activation analysis was not of principal interest, the procedures are directly applicable. (See section 14.5.) |
| Beydon and Fisher | 20 | Oxides of Nb, Ta, and Ti in their mixtures were determined by use of radioactive tracers and by activation analysis for the Ta. |
| Delbecq, Glendenin, and Yuster | 49 | Tl was determined in KI by use of 3-year $Tl^{204}$ after irradiation in the Argonne reactor at a flux of $2 \times 10^{12}$ neutrons/(cm.²)(sec.) for 3 days. One microgram of Tl gave 670 counts/min. Accuracy: $\pm 5\%$. Sensitivity: 0.1 $\mu$g. Tl. |
| Herr | 91 | The isotopic concentration of $Li^6$ in lithium carbonate samples was determined by irradiating the samples with neutrons. The effect of the $\alpha$ and $H^3$ particles from the reaction $Li^6(n,\alpha)H^3$ on a photographic emulsion was determined photometrically. The percentages of $Li^6$ from 7.4 to 17.8 were determined with an accuracy of about $\pm 3\%$. A method for the determination of Re was also developed. |

TABLE X. (*Continued*)

| Authors | Ref. | Summary of applications |
|---|---|---|
| Kahn and Lyon | 116 | The use of scintillation spectrometry in radio-chemical analysis is discussed, including calibration and use in the assay of radioisotopes produced by neutron activation and fission. |
| Kohn | 124<br>125 | The determination of Ta in ferroniobium and niobium minerals by neutron activation without chemical separation of Nb and Ta is described. Tantalum can be determined to within ±5% by the methods used. |
| Leddicotte and Reynolds | 131 | The application of neutron activation to trace analysis in a number of types of samples was discussed, including separation methods, sensitivities, etc. Typical examples discussed are Ta in stainless steel; Mn in metals; Mn and Co in Al; Cd in vinylite resins; Na in Mg; Ga in Al; Ba in aqueous solutions; Na, K, and Cs in $Rb_2CO_3$. Other determinations considered include Mo in ores; Fe, P, S in clays, slags, and limestone; Cs, K, Na, and rare earths in fine chemicals; As, Cd, Cl, Cu, and U in organic chemicals. |
| Mayr, Bruner, and Brucer | 142 | Low boron concentrations in animals tissues were determined by use of the $B^{10}(n,\alpha)Li^7$ reaction n a flux of about $6 \times 10^3$ neutron/(cm.²)(sec.) from a Po-Be neutron source. The $\alpha$ particles were determined from their tracks in a nuclear track emulsion. |
| Meinke and Anderson | 145 | A 25-mg. Ra-Be source was used for the analysis of Rh, In, and Ag in the range of 1 to 7% in 5 to 12 min. The probable error in the assay of 1% In, for example, was 3.6%. |
| Morrison | 152 | The general applications of radiochemistry to electronic research is discussed, including the application of activation analysis to the determination of impurities transferred from graphite crucibles to germanium. Tracers were used to follow the segregation of impurities during directional cooling. |
| Phillips and Cornish | 166 | Dy was determined in "Specpure" $Ho_2O_3$ without chemical purification following neutron activation. Liquid counting gave $11.71 \pm 0.09\%$ and solid counting gave $11.66 \pm 0.16\%$ Dy in the $Ho_2O_3$. |
| Pouradier, Venet, and Chateau | 172 | Activation analysis is applied to the determination of copper in cellulose acetate films. |

TABLE X. (*Continued*)

| Authors | Ref. | Summary of applications |
|---------|------|-------------------------|
| Schmeiser and Jerchel | 185 | Phosphorus was determined on a paper electrophorogram by neutron activation. The procedure was illustrated by the determination of casein. |
| Seyfang and Smales | 193 | The determination of $U^{235}$ in uranium samples by neutron activation followed by chemical separation of the fission-product barium is described. A precision and accuracy of better than 2% was achieved for a range of concentration from 0.0006 to 82% $U^{235}$. Details of radiochemical separations, counting techniques, and other factors affecting the analyses are given. |
| Smales | 199 | The general principles of activation analysis are discussed and the physical, chemical, and nuclear limitations of the method are described. The advantages are also summarized and the applications that have been made of the method to the date of the article are listed. |

| | | |
|---------|------|-------------------------|
| 1954<br>Burril and Gale | 39 | The application of a Van de Graff neutron source to activation analysis is discussed. Tables of sensitivity based on a neutron flux of $10^9$ neutrons/(cm.$^2$)(sec.) are given along with other properties of the radioisotopes formed. |
| Faires, Johnston and Millett | 53 | This is a report on papers presented at the Second Radioisotope Conference, Oxford, England. The determination of $D_2O$ by photoneutron production with the $\gamma$ rays from $Na^{24}$ by means of $BF_3$ counters was discussed in one paper. A 1-curie $Na^{24}$ source with 25-ml. samples containing 0.1% by volume of $D_2O$ can be measured to ±2%. |
| Hall | 78 | A discussion is given on the application of neutron activation with scintillation spectrometry to the determination trace elements in biological materials. A test run was made using Fe, Zn, Co. It was concluded that Fe, Co, Zn, Na, K, and Cu should be measurable in normal biological materials and Br, Cs, Hg, and As should be detectable when present at 1 $\mu$g./cc. of material. |
| Kaplan and Wilzbach | 119 | $Li^6$ isotope was determined using the reaction $Li^6(n,\alpha)H^3$. After 2 weeks irradiation at a flux of $10^{12}$ neutrons/(cm.$^2$)(sec.) the tritium was |

TABLE X. (*Continued*)

| Authors | Ref. | Summary of applications |
|---|---|---|
| | | determined in the gas and water. A precision of 1% was obtained. Considerably shorter irradiations can be used. |
| Leddicotte and Reynolds | 132 | Trace analysis by neutron activation is discussed, with special consideration given to the determination of alkali metals. |
| Mayr | 141 | The application of nuclear emulsions to activation analysis is reviewed, and specific application to the determination of boron and iodine is described. The samples with the nuclear plates were placed 9 cm. from a Po-Be source moderated with paraffin [flux $5.35 \times 10^3$ neutrons/ $(cm.^2)(sec.)$]. The $\alpha$ tracks from the $B^{10}(n,\alpha)Li^7$ reaction were compared with standards. For iodine, the $\beta$ tracks from the $I^{128}$ produced were counted. Interferences in the determinations were discussed. |
| Meinke and Anderson | 145 | Eu-Sm and Dy-Ho mixtures were analyzed with 25-mg. Ra-Be source and comparisons were made with spectrophotometric methods. |
| Milner and Smales | 150 | Tantalum was determined in the mixed oxides of Nb and Ti, obtained from stainless steels. About 20 mg. was irradiated in the Harwell reactor for 2 hr. together with tantalum oxide standards. The $\gamma$ activity of the 111-day $Ta^{182}$ (1.11 Mev. $\gamma$) was determined with a NaI(Tl) scintillation spectrometer. Concentrations of Ta from 0.03 to 0.10% were present in the samples analyzed. |
| Osmond and Smales | 163 | A radioactivation method for the determination of oxygen in Be metal is described. It is based on the production of high-energy $H^3$ by the reaction $Li^6(n,\alpha)H^3$. These interact with oxygen to form 112-min. $F^{18}$ (0.64-Mev. $\beta^+$) by the reaction $O^{16}(H^3,n)F^{18}$. The Be metal was mixed with LiF and after activation $F^{18}$ was separated and compared with standards. The results on two samples (1.2 ± 0.1 and 0.34 ± 0.05%) were in good agreement with other methods. |
| Pauly | 165 | Activation analysis was used to determine sodium in crystallized potassium nitrate. |
| Plumb and Silverman | 169 | Na in aluminum alloys was determined in the range of 0.01 to 0.04% Na to ±1%. Consideration was given to factors influencing activation analysis, including variations in neutron flux, attenuation of the flux by the samples, and the effect of transmutation reactions other than $(n,\gamma)$, such as $(n,p)$ and $(n,\alpha)$. Concentrations of Na as low as 0.0005% were determined. |

TABLE X. (*Continued*)

| Authors | Ref. | Summary of applications |
|---|---|---|
| Stewart and Bently | 212 | Uranium was determined in sea water by fission-fragment counting during irradiation in the Argonne heavy-water reactor. Twenty milliliter of sea water is extracted with dibutylphosphoric acid in $CCl_4$. This is evaporated to dryness, ignited on a platinum counting plate, and then irradiated and counted. Pacific Ocean water, for example, was found to contain 2.49 μg./liter. |
| Szekely | 215 | Traces of Cu in Ge were determined in 0.1-g. samples by irradiation in the Brookhaven reactor for 72 hr., along with standards containing 1 p.p.m. of Cu. The irradiated samples, along with 50 mg. of carrier copper were dissolved with aqua regia and the copper was separated chemically. An end-window G-M counter was used to determine the activity. One sample, for example, was found to contain 0.8 p.p.m. of Cu, and others less than 0.001 p.p.m. The limit of detection was estimated to be $10^{-4}$ μg. of Cu. |
| 1955 Alperovitch and Miller | 3 | Activation analysis was used in searching for technetium 98 in nature. |
| Fireman and Schwarzer | 59 | $He^3$ obtained from iron meteorites was determined quantitatively by neutron activation. Its cross section for conversion to $H^3$ by the reaction $He^3(n,p)H^3$ is 5200 barns. The $H^3$ produced was transferred to a counter and its activity was determined. The gas from a 4.3-g. sample of one meteorite, for example, gave 95,000 tritium counts/min. after neutron activation. From this the number of He atoms per gram could be calculated if the neutron flux was known. Interferences from $Li^6$ and D were discussed. The results were used to calculate an $H^3$-$He^3$ age of $2.1 \times 10^9$ years for the meteorite, which corrected for cosmic-ray production of $He^3$ gave $1.5 \times 10^9$ years. |
| Foster and Gaitanis | 60 | P was determined in aluminum oxide and aluminum, in the concentration range 0.001 to 0.0001% P, to within ±5% of absolute value. Sensitivity $5 \times 10^{-7}$% P is attainable by activation in the Oak Ridge reactor. |
| Harrison and Raymond | 83 | Ba and Sr were determined in biological materials without interference from Ca. About 0.3-g. samples containing 50 μg. or less of Ba and Sr |

## TABLE X. (Continued)

| Authors | Ref. | Summary of applications |
|---|---|---|
| | | were activated for 2 hr. in the Harwell reactor. After chemical separation, the $\gamma$-ray activities of the solutions were determined with a scintillation counter. The error was estimated to be about 5% for samples containing 1 to 50 $\mu$g. of Ba and Sr. |
| James and Richards | 112 | Arsenic in silicon was determined after irradiation in the Harwell reactor and separation of the As by a distillation procedure that gave an 80 to 90% chemical yield. A 200-mg. sample with an arsenic content of 2 to 3 p.p.m. gave a counting rate of 9000 counts/min. after 3 days in the counting arrangement. They estimated the sensitivity to about 0.0003 p.p.m. on a 1-g. sample. |
| Jenkins | 113 | Samples containing from 0.0013 to 1% Th were irradiated in the Harwell reactor, and $Th^{232}$ produced 22-min $Th^{233}$. Dissolution of the sample followed by addition of carrier, precipitation of the oxalate, conversion to nitrate, chromatographic purification, and finally precipitation as hydrated thorium oxide gave a radiochemically pure sample for counting. Large excesses of potentially interfering elements did not affect the results. Details of the chemical procedures and discussions of interferences are given. |
| Lyon and Reynolds | 136 | The radioisotopes induced in reactor cooling water as it circulated through a maximum flux of $4 \times 10^{13}$ neutrons/(cm.²)(sec.) were determined by scintillation spectrometry and proportional counters. Among the activities determined in disintegrations per minute per milliliter were 7.3-sec. $N^{16}(1.8 \times 10^8)$; 2.3-min. $Al^{28}(6 \times 10^5)$; 9.5-min. $Mg^{27}(1.4 \times 10^5)$; 15.1-hr. $Na^{24}(1.2 \times 10^5)$; 12.8-hr. $Cu^{64}(2.7 \times 10^4)$; 2.6-hr. $Mn^{56}(2 \times 10^4)$; and 270-day $Ag^{110}(2.8 \times 10^3)$. |
| Mahlman and Leddicotte | 138 | U in ores, soils, and other samples was determined by use of the daughter activity 2.33-day $Np^{233}$: 25 mg. of ore was irradiated 3 hr. in the Oak Ridge graphite reactor. Soils were irradiated 62 hr. Concentration range: 0.3 to 250 $\mu$g./g. to $\pm 10$%. Sensitivity: 0.0001 $\mu$g. uranium/g. |
| Meinke | 144 | The sensitivity of activation analysis for trace elements is compared with that of emission spectrometers, flame photometers, color reactions, and amperometric methods. |

TABLE X. (*Continued*)

| Authors | Ref. | Summary of applications |
|---|---|---|
| Moljk, Drever, and Curran | 151 | The $A^{40}$ content of argon from potassium minerals was determined by neutron activation for age measurements. Argon is extracted from the mineral and irradiated for several hours in a flux of $10^{12}$ neutrons/(cm.$^2$)(sec.) The 1.5-mev. $\beta$ particles from the 1.8-hr. $K^{41}$ formed are counted in a proportional counter. Quantities of $A^{40}$ as low as 0.03 $\mu$g. can be determined by this method. The age of the mineral was $6 \times 10^7$ years. Procedures for fusion and extraction of the argon are given. |
| Morrison and Cosgrove | 153 | Determination of trace impurities in silicon by use of scintillation spectrometry without chemical separation is described. (See section 14.5.) |
| Plumb and Lewis | 170 | Errors that may arise in activation analysis are discussed. These include activity measurements, incomplete chemical separation, radiochemical purity, transmutation reactions, homogeneity of the flux, sample packaging effects, self-attenuation of the neutron flux by the sample, and standardization procedures. Some of these complications were discussed in the determination of Sb and Na. |
| Reynolds | 177 | Review of analytical radiochemistry including measurement of radioactivity, chemical techniques, activation analysis, and scintillation spectrometry. |
| Seyfang | 192 | The precision in the determination of $U^{235}$ by neutron irradiation followed by determination of the activity of the fission product Ba (193) was improved from $\pm 2\%$ to $\pm 0.44\%$. |
| Smales and Loveridge | 202 | Submicrogram quantities of Na in Li metal were estimated by neutron activation, followed by radiochemical purification by use of chemical and ion exchange methods. As little as 0.02 p.p.m. of Na in the Li could be determined. |
| Smales and Solman | 206 | Small amounts of Rb and Cs were determined in materials of geochemical interest including sea water, sea weeds, marine sediments, and coals, by activation analysis. Concentration from the sea water was accomplished with ion exchange resins, and radiochemical purification was completed by means of carriers to determine the chemical yield. Radioactive tracers of possible impurities indicated good separation. The range of concentration determined was 10 to |

TABLE X. (*Continued*)

| Authors | Ref. | Summary of applications |
|---------|------|------------------------|
| | | 0.01 μg. in 10 ml. of sea water for Rb and 50 ml. for Cs. North Atlantic sea water contained 120 μg./liter of Rb and 0.5 μg./liter of Cs. Sodium in milligram quantities was determined without chemical separation by the use of a scintillation spectrometer. |
| Smales and Wiseman | 207 | The relative abundance of Ni, Co, and Cu in deep-sea–water sediments was determined by neutron activation. Comparison with meteoritic material indicated little contribution from this source to deep sediments. |
| Upson, Connaly, and Leboeuf | 221 | Plutonium at concentrations of 50 μg./ml. was determined in the presence of fission products with 2000 times as many γ rays. A scintillation spectrometer with a 2-mm.-thick NaI(Tl) crystal was used to discriminate against higher energy γ rays and to measure the photopeak of the 100-kev. γ ray of Pu. |
| 1956 Atchison and Beamer | 11 | Cl, Br, and I were determined in microgram quantities in aqueous solutions. One milliliter was irradiated in a flux of about $2.5 \times 10^8$ neutron/(cm.²)(sec.) from a 2-Mev. Van de Graaff accelerator by use of the reaction $Be^9(d,n)B^{10}$. Br in concentrations from 3 to 13 p.p.m. was determined in polymers. F in inorganic and organic was determined in 5 to 10 min. to ±3.5%. Sensitivity: 0.5-mg. F. An apparatus for irradiating and determining activities with half-lives as short as 10 sec. is described. |
| Bopp and Sisman | 27 | The gamma activity of a number of reactor materials was measured following activation in the Oak Ridge graphite reactor for periods of from 150 to 15,000 hr. Measurements were begun 3 to 4 hr. after removal and counting was continued until the remaining activity had a half-life greater than 1 yr. Among the materials tested were iron alloys, nickel alloys, stainless steels, aluminum alloys, concrete, graphite, Be, Cd, Cu, Pb, Nb, Ti, Th, Fe-W, Zr. A high-pressure ionization chamber was used for the measurements. |
| Geiger and Plumb | 66 | The radioisotopes produced by neutron activation are arranged in order of their half-lives. |

TABLE X. (*Continued*)

| Authors | Ref. | Summary of application |
|---|---|---|
| Hummel and Smales | 109 | Sr was determined in sea water by irradiating 1 to 2 ml. along with a standard for 5 to 10 min. After addition of carrier, the Sr was made radiochemically pure and counted. In addition to activation analysis, the Sr was determined by isotope dilution by use of radioactive Sr[89] and by stable isotope dilution. |
| Morrison and Cosgrove | 154 | The determination of trace impurities in germanium was accomplished with a minimum of chemical separations with scintillation spectrometry. (See section 14.5.) |

*Summary of References to Articles Describing Determinations by Neutron Activity*

| Element | References | Element | References | Element | References |
|---|---|---|---|---|---|
| A | 151 | Fe | 10, 78, 131, 153 | P | 10, 60, 131, 164, 185 |
| Ag | 16, 17, 91, 145 | Ga | 34, 36, 94, 131 | | |
| Al | 158 | Ge | 154 | Pb | 35 |
| As | 10, 35, 75, 78, 112, 131, 138, 153, 154, 200, 201, 203, 204, 205 | H(D) | 53 | Pd | 35, 36 |
| | | He[3] | 46, 59 | Pu | 221 |
| | | Hf | 12, 156, 178 | Rb | 206 |
| | | Hg | 78 | Re | 35, 60, 70, 91 |
| Au | 70, 94, 220 | Ho | 1 | Rh | 145 |
| B | 141, 142 | I | 11, 141 | S | 10, 131 |
| Ba | 83, 131 | In | 101, 145 | Sb | 99, 170 |
| Be | 65 | Ir | 50 | Si | 35 |
| Br | 11, 78, 227 | K | 10, 31, 78, 94, 123, 131, 153 | Sm | 1, 126 |
| Ca | 10 | | | Sr | 10, 34, 83, 109 |
| Cd | 34, 131 | Li | 119, 168, 223a | Ta | 20, 52, 124, 135, 150, 153 |
| Ce | 126 | Lu | 122 | | |
| Cl | 11, 15, 131 | Mn | 31, 34, 43, 131, 158, 164 | Tc | 3 |
| Co | 34, 78, 94, 131, 207 | | | Th | 113 |
| | | Mo | 131 | Tl | 49 |
| Cr | 10, 35, 153, 206 | Na | 1, 31, 35, 78, 94, 122, 123, 131, 153, 154, 165, 169, 170, 202, 206 | Tm | 122 |
| Cs | 31, 78, 131 | | | U | 131, 137, 138, 192, 193, 197, 212 |
| Cu | 1, 10, 31, 76, 78, 131, 153, 154, 158, 172, 207, 215 | | | V | 34 |
| | | | | W | 153 |
| | | Nb | 158 | Yb | 122 |
| Dy | 92, 126, 145, 166 | Nd | 126 | Zn | 78, 153, 154 |
| Eu | 92, 145 | Ni | 164, 207 | Zr | 12, 100 |
| F | 11 | O | 163 | | |

section such as In, Sm, Eu, Dy, Ho, Lu, Re, Ir, and Mn, or for others if high sensitivity is not required. This may be true for example, for certain alloys or ores.

Leddicotte and Reynolds (35, 133) have tabulated the sensitivities of most of the elements that can be determined conveniently by activation in a reactor. They list the micrograms of an element that produces 40 disintegrations/sec. after an irradiation to saturation or 1 month in a flux of $5 \times 10^{11}$ neutrons/(cm.$^2$)(sec.). These are summarized in Table XII in groups according to ranges of sensitivity and half-life. Special methods for rapid handling are required for those radioisotopes with half-lives shorter than about 1 min. and complications from secondary radio-isotopes (p. 545) may arise from long irradiations.

TABLE XI

*Sensitivities Using Different Neutron Sources*

| Neutron source | Usable neutron flux $[n/(cm.^2)(sec.)]$ | Approximate weight to give 100 counts/ min. (g.) $\sigma_{ac} = 10$ barns |
|---|---|---|
| Reactor | $10^{10}$ to $10^{12}$ | $1 \times 10^{-8}$ to $1 \times 10^{-10}$ |
| Cyclotron | $10^8$ to $10^9$ | $1 \times 10^{-6}$ to $1 \times 10^{-7}$ |
| Low-voltage D-D neutron generator | $10^5$ to $10^6$ | $1 \times 10^{-3}$ to $1 \times 10^{-4}$ |
| 1-gm. RaBe | $10^4$ to $10^5$ | $1 \times 10^{-2}$ to $1 \times 10^{-3}$ |
| 1-curie SbBe 60-day half-life | $10^3$ to $10^4$ | $1 \times 10^{-1}$ to $1 \times 10^{-2}$ |
| 1-curie PoBe 140-day half-life | $10^3$ to $10^4$ | $1 \times 10^{-1}$ to $1 \times 10^{-2}$ |

Meinke (144) has compared the sensitivities in Table XI with those obtainable in the Oak Ridge reactor with a flux of $1 \times 10^{13}$ and with the sensitivities by emission spectroscopy, flame photometry, color reactions of organic reagents, and amperometric methods.

Muehlhause and Thomas (158) have used a somewhat different method of estimating sensitivities. The activity induced in an element according to eq. (13.13) after a saturation irradiation is $A = f\sigma_{ACT}NE$ and the counts observed per second will be determined by this and the net yield factor $Y$ so that $C = Yf\sigma_{ACT}NE$. They take the limit of detection to be a counting rate equal to the background rate and calculate the number of atoms of an element corresponding to this as a measure of the sensitivity. By this method the sensitivity will depend upon the type of counter used. Typical cases are considered in which a G-M counter and an ionization chamber are used for $\beta$ particles from 2.27-min. $Al^{28}$; a no-window ionization chamber for conversion electrons from 6.6-min. $Nb^{94}$; a G-M counter with a magnet for $\beta^+$ from 12.8-hr. $Cu^{64}$; a scintillation counter with an absorber for $\gamma$ rays from aluminum; a scintilla-

## TABLE XII
### Sensitivities and Characteristics of Radioisotopes for Activation Analysis*

0.0001 to 0.001 μg.

| Radio-isotope | Half-life | $\sigma_{ACT}$ atomic (barns) | Decay modes, radiations, and energies |
|---|---|---|---|
| In$^{116}$ | 13 sec. | 50 | $\beta^-$ 3.29; $\gamma$ none |
| Ag$^{110}$ | 24.2 sec. | 54 | $\beta^-$ 2.24 (60%), 2.82 (40%); $\gamma$ 0.66, 0.94, others |
| Rh$^{104}$ | 44 sec. | 140 | $\beta^-$ 2.6; $\gamma$ 0.552 |
| In$^{116m}$ | 54.1 min. | 139 | $\beta^-$ 1.00 (51%), 0.87 (28%), 0.60 (20%); $\gamma$ 0.137 to 2.09 |
| Dy$^{165}$ | 139 min. | <282 | $\beta^-$ 1.25, 0.88, 0.3; $\gamma$ 0.094, 0.36, 0.76, 1.0 |
| Mn$^{56}$ | 2.58 hr. | 13.4 | $\beta^-$ 2.81, 1.04, 0.65; $\gamma$ 0.828, 1.77, 2.06 |
| Lu$^{176m}$ | 3.7 hr. | 34 | $\beta^-$ 1.1, 1.2; $\gamma$ 0.089 |
| Eu$^{152}$ | 9.2 hr. | 668 | $\beta^-$ 1.88; $EC$; $\gamma$ 0.122, 0.344, others |
| Re$^{188}$ | 18.0 hr. | 47 | $\beta^-$ 2.07; $\gamma$ 0.15, 0.48, 0.64, 0.94, 1.43 |
| Ir$^{194}$ | 19.0 hr. | 80 | $\beta^-$ 2.24, 1.90, 0.98; $\gamma$ 0.33, others 0.29 to 2.05 |
| Ho$^{166}$ | 27.3 hr. | 60 | $\beta^-$ 1.76, 1.84; $\gamma$ 0.080, others |
| Sm$^{153}$ | 47 hr. | 37 | $\beta^-$ 0.69, 0.62, 0.80; $\gamma$ 0.069, 0.103, 0.548 |
| Re$^{186}$ | 3.8 days | 37 | $\beta^-$ (95%); 1.07 (80%), 0.93 (20%); $EC$ 5%; $\gamma$ 0.137, others |
| Lu$^{177}$ | 6.8 days | 104 | $\beta^-$ 0.495 (65%), 0.37 (17%), 0.17 (18%); $\gamma$ 0.112, 0.206, others |
| Ir$^{192}$ | 74 days | 270 | $\beta^-$ 0.66, others; $EC$; $\gamma$ 0.316, 0.296, 0.308, 0.468, others |

0.002–0.01 μg.

| Radio-isotope | Half-life | $\sigma_{ACT}$ atomic (barns) | Decay modes, radiations, and energies |
|---|---|---|---|
| Ag$^{108}$ | 2.3 min. | 23 | $EC$ (1.5%); $\beta^-$ (98.5%) 1.77; $\beta^+$; $\gamma$ 0.45, 0.66 |
| V$^{52}$ | 3.8 min. | 4.5 | $\beta^-$ 2.5; $\gamma$ 1.4 |
| Br$^{80}$ | 18 min. | 4.3 | $EC$ (5%); $\beta^+$ (3%) 0.87; $\beta^-$ (92%) 2.04, 1.42; $\gamma$ 0.62 |
| Th$^{233}$ | 23.3 min. | 7.7 | $\beta^-$ 1.23; $\gamma$ |
| U$^{239}$ | 23.5 min. | 2.8 | $\beta^-$ 1.21; $\gamma$ 0.073 |
| Sm$^{155}$ | 24 min. | 1.2 | $\beta^-$ 1.8; $\gamma$ 1.05, 0.25 |
| I$^{128}$ | 25 min. | 5.5 | $EC + \beta^+$ (5%); $\beta^-$ (95%) 2.02; $\gamma$ 0.428 (7%) |
| Cu$^{64}$ | 12.8 hr. | 2.7 | $EC$ (42%); $\beta^+$ (19%) 0.657; $\beta^-$ (39%) 0.571; $\gamma$ |
| Pd$^{109}$ | 13.6 hr. | 3.2 | $\beta^-$ 0.961; $\gamma$ (with Ag$^{109m}$) 0.087 |
| Ga$^{72}$ | 14.2 hr. | 1.4 | $\beta^-$ 3.15 (9%), 2.52 (8%), 1.5 (11%), 0.9 (32%), 0.6 (40%); $\gamma$ 2.508, 2.491, 0.84, others |
| Na$^{24}$ | 15.0 hr. | 0.60 | $\beta^-$ 1.390; $\gamma$ 1.368, 2.754 |
| Pr$^{142}$ | 19.2 hr. | 10 | $\beta^-$ 2.15 (96%), 0.64 (4%); $\gamma$ 0.135, 1.59 |
| W$^{187}$ | 24 hr. | 9.7 | $\beta^-$ 1.33 (30%), 0.63 (70%); $\gamma$ 0.072, 0.134, 0.479, 0.686, others |
| As$^{76}$ | 27 hr. | 4.2 | $\beta^-$ 2.98, 2.40, 1.76; $\beta^+$ 0.1%; $\gamma$ 0.55, 0.64, 1.20 |
| Br$^{82}$ | 35.9 hr. | 1.7 | $\beta^-$ 0.465; $\gamma$ 0.547, 0.692, 0.823, 1.312, others |

## TABLE XII. (Continued)

### 0.002 to 0.01 μg. (Continued)

| Radio-isotope | Half-life | $\sigma_{ACT}$ atomic (barns) | Decay modes, radiations, and energies |
|---|---|---|---|
| La$^{140}$ | 40 hr. | 8.4 | $\beta^-$ 1.32 (70%), 1.67 (20%), 2.26 (10%), others; $\gamma$ 2.50, 1.60, 0.82, 0.490, 0.335, others |
| Y$^{90}$ | 63 hr. | 1.2 | $\beta^-$ 2.18; $\gamma$ none |
| Au$^{198}$ | 2.7 days | 96 | $\beta^-$ 0.963 (99%), 0.290 (1%), 1.37 (0.01%); $\gamma$ 0.4118, 0.680, others |
| Sb$^{122}$ | 2.8 days | 3.9 | $\beta^-$ 1.40, 2.00, 0.72; $\gamma$ 0.566, others 0.95 to 1.9 |
| Yb$^{175}$ | 4.21 days | 19 | $\beta^-$ 0.50, 0.1; $\gamma$ 0.138, 0.259, 0.283, 0.396, others |
| Tb$^{160}$ | 73 days | >22 | $\beta^-$ 0.860 (43%), 0.521 (41%), 0.396 (16%); $\gamma$ 1.27, 0.962, 0.876, others |
| Sc$^{46}$ | 85 days | 12 | $\beta^-$ 0.357; $\gamma$ 0.89, 1.12 |
| Ta$^{182}$ | 111 days | 19 | $\beta^-$ 0.510; $\gamma$ 0.0334 to 1.454, others |
| Tm$^{170}$ | 129 days | 130 | $\beta^-$ 0.968 (76%), 0.884 (24%); $\gamma$ 0.084 |

### 0.02 to 0.10 μg

| | | | |
|---|---|---|---|
| In$^{114}$ | 72 sec. | 0.085 | $EC$ >3%; $\beta^+$ 0.01%; $\beta^-$ (<97%) 1.98; $\gamma$ |
| Al$^{28}$ | 2.27 min. | 0.21 | $\beta^-$ 2.865; $\gamma$ 1.782 |
| Gd$^{161}$ | 3.6 min. | 0.18 | $\beta^-$ 1.6; $\gamma$ 0.102, 0.316, 0.360 |
| Tl$^{206}$ | 4.2 min. | 0.07 | $\beta^-$ 1.51; $\gamma$ none |
| Cu$^{66}$ | 5.14 min. | 0.6 | $\beta^-$ 2.63 (91%), 1.5 (9%); $\gamma$ 1.044 |
| Hg$^{205}$ | 5.5 min. | 0.03 | $\beta^-$ 1.8; $\gamma$ none |
| Se$^{81}$ | 17 min. | 0.25 | $\beta^-$ 1.38; $\gamma$ none |
| Rb$^{88}$ | 17.8 min. | 0.03 | $\beta^-$ 5.30 (78%), 3.6 (13%), 2.5 (9%); $\gamma$ 2.8, 1.86, 0.90 |
| Ga$^{70}$ | 20.2 min. | 0.84 | $\beta^-$ 1.65; $\gamma$ |
| Pd$^{111}$ | 22 min. | 0.04 | $\beta^-$ 2.13; $\gamma$ 0.38, 0.56, 0.65, 0.73 |
| Te$^{131}$ | 25 min. | 0.08 | $\beta^-$ 2.0 (55%), 1.4 (45%); $\gamma$ 0.16, 0.7 |
| Se$^{83}$ | 25 min. | 0.37 | $\beta^-$ 1.5; $\gamma$ 0.95, 0.18 |
| Pt$^{199}$ | 31 min. | 0.28 | $\beta^-$ 1.8 |
| Cl$^{38}$ | 37.5 min. | 0.14 | $\beta^-$ 4.81 (53%), 2.77 (16%), 1.11 (31%); $\gamma$ 2.15, 1.60 |
| Zn$^{69}$ | 52 min. | 0.19 | $\beta^-$ 0.897 |
| Te$^{129}$ | 72 min. | 0.04 | $\beta^-$ 1.8; $\gamma$ 0.3, 0.8 |
| Ge$^{75}$ | 82 min. | 0.17 | $\beta^-$ 1.14 (85%), 0.88 (15%); $\gamma$ 0.265, 0.418, 0.63, others |
| Ba$^{139}$ | 85 min. | 0.36 | $\beta^-$ 2.38, 2.23, 0.82; $\gamma$ 0.163, 1.43 |
| Nd$^{149}$ | 1.8 hr. | 0.21 | $\beta^-$ 1.5, 1.1, 0.95; $\gamma$ 0.030, 0.424, 0.538, 0.650, others |
| Yb$^{177}$ | 1.8 hr. | 0.7 | $\beta^-$ 1.3; $\gamma$ 0.150 |
| A$^{41}$ | 1.82 hr. | 0.5 | $\beta^-$ 1.245; $\gamma$ 1.37 |

## TABLE XII. (*Continued*)

### 0.02 to 0.10 μg. (*Continued*)

| Radio-isotope | Half-life | $\sigma_{ACT}$ atomic (barns) | Decay modes, radiations, and energies |
|---|---|---|---|
| $Ni^{65}$ | 2.57 hr. | 0.03 | $\beta^-$ 2.10 (57%), 1.01 (14%), 0.60 (29%); $\gamma$ 1.49, 1.12, 0.37 |
| $Kr^{85m}$ | 4.4 hr. | 0.06 | $\beta^-$ 0.855 (77%); $IT$ (23%) $\gamma$ 0.305; $\gamma$ 0.150 |
| $Ru^{105}$ | 4.5 hr. | 0.13 | $\beta^-$ 1.150; $\gamma$ 0.726 |
| $Er^{171}$ | 7.5 hr. | 1.3 | $\beta^-$ 1.49 (6%), 1.05 (72%), 0.67 (22%); $\gamma$ 0.113, 0.118, 0.308, 0.420, others |
| $Te^{127}$ | 9.3 hr. | 0.15 | $\beta^-$ 0.7; $\gamma$ none |
| $K^{42}$ | 12.4 hr. | 0.07 | $\beta^-$ 3.58 (75%), 2.04 (25%); $\gamma$ 1.51 |
| $Pt^{197}$ | 18 hr. | 0.03 | $\beta^-$ 0.670; $\gamma$ 0.077, 0.191 |
| $Gd^{159}$ | 18 hr. | 1.0 | $\beta^-$ 0.9, 1.1; $\gamma$ 0.058, 0.36 |
| $Os^{193}$ | 31 hr. | 0.66 | $\beta^-$ 1.10; $\gamma$ (with $Ir^{193m}$) 0.066 |
| $Ce^{143}$ | 34 hr. | 0.11 | $\beta^-$ 1.09, 1.39, 0.71; $\gamma$ 0.290, 0.356, 0.660, 0.720, others |
| $Cd^{115}$ | 53 hr. | 0.32 | $\beta^-$ 1.11 (58%), 0.58 (42%); $\gamma$ 0.360, 0.500, 0.525 |
| $Mo^{99}$ | 67 hr. | 0.03 | $\beta^-$ 1.23 (80%), 0.45 (20%); $\gamma$ 0.04, 0.181, 0.741, 0.780, others |
| $Xe^{133}$ | 5.3 days | 0.05 | $\beta^-$ 0.347; $\gamma$ 0.081 |
| $Er^{169}$ | 9.4 days | 0.54 | $\beta^-$ 0.33; $\gamma$ none |
| $Nd^{147}$ | 11.3 days | 0.31 | $\beta^-$ 0.83 (60%), 0.60 (15%), 0.38 (25%); $\gamma$ 0.092, 0.53, 0.32, others |
| $P^{32}$ | 14.3 days | 0.23 | $\beta^-$ 1.701; $\gamma$ none |
| $Os^{191}$ | 16.0 days | 2.1 | $\beta^-$ 0.143; $\gamma$ 0.042, 0.129 |
| $Rb^{86}$ | 19.5 days | 0.52 | $\beta^-$ 1.82 (80%), 0.72 (20%); $\gamma$ 1.08 |
| $Ce^{141}$ | 32 days | 0.27 | $\beta^-$ 0.581 (33%), 0.442 (67%); $\gamma$ 0.145 |
| $Ru^{103}$ | 41 days | 0.37 | $\beta^-$ 0.22 (99%), 0.698 (1%); $\gamma$ 0.498 |
| $Cd^{115m}$ | 43 days | 0.4 | $\beta^-$ 1.61 (98%), 0.7 (2%); $\gamma$ 0.46, 0.50, 0.96, 1.28 |
| $Hf^{181}$ | 46 days | 3.5 | $\beta^-$ 0.408; $\gamma$ 0.133, 0.136, 0.344, 0.481, 0.611 |
| $Hg^{203}$ | 47 days | 1.1 | $\beta^-$ 0.208; $\gamma$ 0.279 |
| $Sb^{124}$ | 60 days | 1.1 | $\beta^-$ 0.61, 2.31, 0.23; $\gamma$ 0.603, 1.71, 2.11 |
| $W^{185}$ | >73 days | 0.6 | $\beta^-$ 0.428; $\gamma$ 1.34 |
| $Ag^{110m}$ | 270 days | 1.4 | $\beta^-$ 0.087 (58%), 0.530 (35%), 2.12 (3%), 2.86 (3%), others; $\gamma$ 0.116, 0.656, 0.885, 1.516, others |
| $Sn^{121m}$ | >400 days | 0.33 | $\beta^-$ 0.383; $\gamma$ none |
| $Cs^{134}$ | 2.3 yr. | 26 | $\beta^-$ 0.65 (75%), 0.09 (25%); $\gamma$ 0.20, 0.561, 1.37, others |
| $Co^{60}$ | 5.28 yr. | 20 | $\beta^-$ 0.306; $\gamma$ 1.173, 1.332 |

### 0.20 to 10 μg.

| | | | |
|---|---|---|---|
| $F^{20}$ | 11 sec. | 0.009 | $\beta^-$ 5.41; $\gamma$ 1.63 |
| $Ne^{23}$ | 40 sec. | 0.0032 | $\beta^-$ 4.21 (93%), 1.18 (7%); $\gamma$ 3 |

## TABLE. XII. (Continued)

### 0.20 to 10 μg. (Continued)

| Radio-isotope | Half-life | $\sigma_{ACT}$ atomic (barns) | Decay modes, radiations, and energies |
|---|---|---|---|
| $Ge^{77m}$ | 57 sec. | 0.002 | $\beta^-$ (50%) 2.9, 2.7; $IT$ (50%) $\gamma$ 0.159; $\gamma$ 0.215 |
| $Se^{83m}$ | 67 sec. | 0.005 | $\beta^-$ 3.4 |
| $Sb^{124m_1}$ | 1.3 min. | 0.013 | $\beta^-$ 3.2; $IT$ $\gamma$ 0.012 |
| $Cr^{55}$ | 3.6 in. | 0.009 | $\beta^-$ 2.8 |
| $Xe^{137}$ | 3.9 min. | 0.013 | $\beta^-$ 4 |
| $Ti^{51}$ | 5.8 min. | 0.0075 | $\beta^-$ 1.9 (70%), 2.2 (30%); $\gamma$ 0.32 |
| $Ca^{49}$ | 8.5 min. | 0.0012 | $\beta^-$ 2.7; $\gamma$ |
| $Mg^{27}$ | 9.5 min. | 0.0056 | $\beta^-$ 1.75, 1.59; $\gamma$ 1.02, .084 |
| $Sn^{125}$ | 10 min. | 0.012 | $\beta^-$ 2.04, 1.17, 0.5; $\gamma$ 0.326, others |
| $Mo^{101}$ | 14.3 min. | 0.019 | $\beta^-$ 1.2, 2.2; $\gamma$ 0.191, 0.960 |
| $Ta^{182m}$ | 16.4 min. | 0.030 | $\beta^-$ 0.6 (5%); $IT$ (95%) $\gamma$ 0.180 |
| $Sb^{124m_2}$ | 21 min. | 0.013 | $\beta^-$; $IT$ $\gamma$ 0.018 |
| $Sn^{123}$ | 40 min. | 0.007 | $\beta^-$ 1.26; $\gamma$ 1.53 |
| $Kr^{87}$ | 77 min. | 0.010 | $\beta^-$ 3.63 (75%), 1.27 (25%); $\gamma$ 0.41, 1.89, 2.3 |
| $Si^{31}$ | 2.62 hr. | 0.0034 | $\beta^-$ 1.47; $\gamma$ |
| $Xe^{135}$ | 9.13 hr. | 0.021 | $\beta^-$ 0.91; $\gamma$ 0.250 |
| $Ge^{77}$ | 12 hr. | 0.0153 | $\beta^-$ 2.20 (42%), 1.38 (35%), 0.71 (23%); $\gamma$ 0.042, 0.213, 0.418, 0.564, 1.75, others |
| $Sn^{121}$ | 27.5 hr. | 0.0462 | $\beta^-$ 0.383; $\gamma$ none |
| $Bi^{210}$ | 5 days | 0.019 | $\beta^-$ 1.17; $\gamma$ none; $\alpha$ |
| $Fe^{59}$ | 46 days | 0.0028 | $\beta^-$ 0.460 (50%), 0.27 (50%); $\gamma$ 1.10, 1.29 |
| $Sr^{89}$ | 53 days | 0.004 | $\beta^-$ 1.463; $\gamma$ none |
| $Zr^{95}$ | 65 days | 0.0174 | $\beta^-$ 0.364, 0.396; $\gamma$ 0.754, 0.722 |
| $S^{35}$ | 87 days | 0.011 | $\beta^-$ 0.167; $\gamma$ none |
| $Ca^{45}$ | 152 days | 0.013 | $\beta^-$ 0.254; $\gamma$ none |
| $Tl^{204}$ | 2.7 yr. | 2.36 | $\beta^-$ 0.765 (98%); $EC$ 2%; $\gamma$ none |
| $Cd^{113m}$ | 5.1 yr. | 0.007 | $\beta^-$ 0.57 |
| $Kr^{85}$ | 9.4 yr. | 0.034 | $\beta^-$ 0.666, 0.054 |

* The grouping of the elements in each sensitivity range is based on the tables published by Leddicotte and Reynolds (133), Brooksbank, Leddicotte, and Strain (35), and Meinke (144). Sensitivities of elements not listed by these authors were estimated from the atomic-activation cross section, $\sigma_{act}$.

Half-life values were taken from the neutron-cross-section compilation (106) and from the table by Geiger and Plunb (66). The atomic-activation cross section for formation of the radioisotope listed was calculated from the isotopic-activation cross section (106) and the natural abundance of the isotope ($\sigma_{ACT} = \sigma_{act} \times$ atom fraction of isotope).

Decay schemes and radiations of the radioactive isotope were taken from Friedlander and Kennedy (61), and Hollander, Perlman and Seaborg (95). Reference to these and to the current Nuclear Data Cards (160) or the summaries in Nuclear Science Abstracts (162) should be consulted for more detailed information. Besides the usual notation $\beta^-$, $\beta^+$, and $\gamma$ for the irradiations, $IT$ refers to isomeric transition, $EC$ to electron capture, and $m$ with the mass number of the isotope to a metastable state. The $Q$ values and the magnitude of the internal-conversion coefficients for gamma transitions to conversion electrons are not indicated.

counter with critical absorbers for X rays; and a neutron counter to detect photoneutrons produced by the $\gamma$ rays from a neutron-activated sample containing aluminum or manganese. A useful summary is given by the authors in which the elements are listed according to the type of radiation and counter that can be used for the detection of their neutron-activated radioisotopes.

It can be concluded that neutron activation, when properly used, is a very sensitive method for a large number of elements. Depending upon the properties of the particular radioisotope and methods of measurement, accuracies between 1 and 10% can readily be achieved by the comparative method. For samples containing a number of elements to be determined, the necessity of chemical separations and high radioactive purity for use with a G-M counter may require more time than other methods of trace analysis. However, its greater sensitivity in many cases make it applicable where other methods fail. Recent developments in the use of scintillation spectrometers eliminate the necessity of chemical separations in some cases and reduce the chemical separations needed in others. These methods are described in the following sections.

## 14. ACTIVATION ANALYSIS BY MEANS OF SCINTILLATION SPECTROMETRY

After a sample is irradiated in a neutron flux, the activity of the trace elements of interest must be determined. If several trace elements are present, the use of G-M counters or ionization chamber as described in section 13 will usually require chemical separations, some of which may be time consuming. With the development of $\gamma$- and $\beta$-scintillation spectrometers, the need of chemical separations is reduced and in some cases they are not necessary at all. This simplifies activation analysis, but interferences of another type may be present. In the previous methods chemical similarity presented problems of radiochemical purity. Although the energies of the $\gamma$ rays from a particular radioisotope are characteristic, interference in scintillation spectrometry can result when two radioisotopes have $\gamma$ rays with energies so nearly the same that the instrument does not resolve them. Combining the scintillation spectrometer measurements with half-life determinations, maximum $\beta$ energies, and limited chemical separations will usually resolve such interferences.

Scintillation spectrometry identifies not only the element but also the particular radioisotope. Thus the method has applications beyond neutron-activation analysis. It has been used rather effectively, for example, in the study of decay schemes (114, 196) and analysis for fission products (45). The general principles and applications of scintillation spectrometry have been discussed by a number of authors (114, 115, 143, 196). They will be reviewed briefly in the following sections.

## 14.1. Principles of Scintillation Counters

A number of inorganic crystals as well as organic crystals or their solutions in solvents and plastics have been found to have rather desirable characteristics for detecting radiations, particularly $\gamma$ rays (21, 94, 214). Their fast response and rapid recovery time, along with their efficiency and a pulse height proportional to energy, have made them more useful than G-M counters for the determination of $\gamma$-emitting radioisotopes. Inorganic halides, including NaI(Tl), KI(Tl), CsI(Tl), LiI(Tl), LiI(Eu), CaI$_2$(Tl), CsF, and such crystals as CaWO$_4$ and CdWO$_4$ have properties suitable for detection of radiations, although their decay period (from 0.25 to 2 $\mu$sec.) is somewhat longer than for organic crystals. Among the organic crystals commonly used are naphthalene, anthracene *trans*-stilbene, *p*-terphenyl, phenanthrene, dibenzyl, and diphenylacetylene with decay periods of 2 to 30 $\times$ 10$^{-9}$ sec. Liquid scintillators consisting of *p*-terphenyl in xylene or toluene (176) or similar solutions of diphenyl-oxazole plus diphenylhexatriene (89, 222) find numerous applications. Similarly terphenyl and tetraphenyl butadiene in a plastic such as polystyrene have desirable characteristics (186, 214) and are easily handled. Some of the most commonly used phosphors are NaI(Tl-activated) for $\gamma$ rays, anthracene for $\beta$ particles, ZnS(Ag-activated) for $\alpha$ particles, LiI(Eu) for neutrons.

When an ionizing particle or photon passes into or through one of the posphors, it loses energy, resulting in excitation and ionization of the atoms or molecules in the crystal. As the excited electrons fall back into their lower states, fluorescent light of characteristic lines or bands [about 4000 Å. for NaI(Tl)] are emitted with a period of the order of 10$^{-8}$ sec. Some of the energy is transferred to the lattice and is dissipated as heat. In certain types of crystals there is a delayed emission of the light owing to trapping of electrons at crystal imperfections, impurities, or on activators. If the lifetime of such electrons is sufficiently short (less than 10$^{-5}$ or 10$^{-6}$ sec.), useful light flashes or scintillations will still result. However, in certain crystals the delay may range from this to years; in others it will be released only on suitable thermal or optical activation. Delayed emission of this type is called *phosphorescence* or *thermal luminescence*. Only those crystals that have short decay periods are useful for scintillation counters. A further important requirement is that they be transparent to their own radiations. Frequently in solution scintillators the addition of a second component to the solvent serves as a wave-length shifter to aid in greater transparency to the fluorescent light. The light flashes produced in a crystal are reflected onto the photocathode of a multiplier tube as illustrated in Fig. 46. The pulses from the photomultiplier tube are amplified, selected according to pulse height, and counted in the usual type of scaling circuits or count-rate meters.

The nature of the scintillation process is rather complicated and not completely understood, but the general aspects by which radiations lose energy in traversing matter has been rather thoroughly investigated. Some of the processes that occur when $\gamma$ rays, for example, pass through a solid, such as NaI, were discussed in a previous section (13.9). These are the photoelectric effect, which produces electrons of an energy equal to the energy of the original $\gamma$ ray less the binding energy of the electrons;

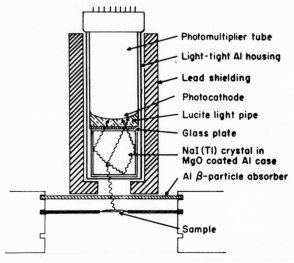

Photomultiplier tube

Light-tight Al housing

Lead shielding

Photocathode

Lucite light pipe

Glass plate

NaI (Tl) crystal in MgO coated Al case

Al $\beta$-particle absorber

Sample

FIG. 46. Schematic diagram of scintillation-crystal and photomultiplier-tube arrangement for scintillation counting.

the Compton effect, in which only part of the energy of the $\gamma$ ray is imparted to an electron; $\beta^+$ and $\beta^-$ pair production for $\gamma$ rays with energies greater than 1.02 Mev. For organic crystals with elements of low atomic number the principal interaction is through the Compton effect giving rise to continuum of electron energies up to the Compton edge about 0.25 Mev. below the $\gamma$ ray energy. However, with crystals of higher atomic number the photoelectric effect and pair production become appreciable, resulting in electrons of well-defined energy. Added to the light flash from the electrons of the photoelectric effect is that corresponding to the energy required to overcome the binding of the electrons in the K or L shell. The X rays emitted when these shells are refilled are absorbed or produce Auger-electron emission. Thus the pulse from the photoelectric effect corresponds to the full energy of the $\gamma$ ray.

All the foregoing processes result in energetic electrons that cause the excitation and ionization of the atoms and molecules in the crystal. For a crystal such as NaI, which contains elements of reasonably high atomic number, an appreciable fraction of the energy of a γ ray will be converted to light, from 10 to 100 ev. being expended per photon produced. The wave length of the light from NaI(Tl) is about 4100 Å., corresponding to about 3.0 ev., which for 100 ev. per photon corresponds to an energy efficiency of about 3%. Modern photomultiplier tubes are sufficiently sensitive that one photoelectron results from about ten photons of the proper wavelength reaching the photosensitive surface. This means that at least one photoelectron is obtained from the photosensitive surface for roughly 1000 ev. of energy lost in the crystal.

At room temperature some 5000 electrons/sec. are emitted by the photosensitive cathode of the photomultiplier tube, giving rise to a background. However, if the bias is set at six "average electrons," only about 1/sec. will be observed (114, 155). When 100 kev. is expended in the crystal, some 100 photoelectrons will be produced. With 10 dynodes the amplification will be about $10^5$, giving $10^7$ electrons, or 1.6 μμcoulombs. In a properly designed circuit, about 10-mv. signal will result, which can be further amplified in a linear pulse amplifier. Thus, if the crystal is large enough (1 to 2 in. in each dimension), practically all the energy of a 100-kev. γ ray will be lost in the crystal, giving a total pulse height well above background. Consequently, practically every γ ray entering the crystal will lead to a count and the intrinsic efficiency will be nearly 100%. This can be corrected for geometry, absorption, scattering, etc. (p. 549) to obtain the over-all efficiency for direct counting. When the energy of the γ ray is as high as 1 Mev. not all its energy or the energy of the secondary electrons arising from the various processes will be absorbed in the usual size crystals. The intrinsic efficiency may then be only about 20 to 30%. Only with rather large crystals or with large volumes of solutions or plastics can total absorption of the high-energy γ rays be achieved. At any rate, when the bias is set high enough to cut out most of the pulses due to the noise of the photomultiplier, high efficiencies for γ rays compared with G-M counters are obtained with the usual size crystals. Similarly, relatively high intrinsic efficiencies are also obtained for β particles. Thus scintillation counters can be used in the place of G-M counters for determination of the activity of radioisotopes produced by neutron activation as described in section 13. The high efficiency of NaI(Tl) scintillation counters for γ rays also makes it possible to use absorbers of aluminum or beryllium for the β particles and count only the γ activity.

A number of techniques for counting samples of low specific activity have been described, as, for example, the counting of β activity of solids by Bluh and Tereniuk (25) and solutions by Wagner and Guin (222). The last two authors have compared the efficiencies of counting $\gamma$ rays with NaI(Tl) in a well-type counter, dip counter, and end-on counter. For the well-type counter, a $1\frac{3}{4}$-in. diameter by 2-in. high crystal with a $\frac{3}{4}$-in. diameter by $1\frac{1}{2}$-in. deep hole was used with a DuMont 6292 photomultiplier. When the instrument was shielded with 7 cm. of lead around the counter and 6 cm. above the crystal, the background count was 200 c./min. The same size crystal properly canned in aluminum and attached to the tube, was used for a dip counter as well as an end-on counter. Using 5-ml. samples of $W^{181}$ (0.057 Mev. $\gamma$), $Cr^{51}$ (0.32 Mev. $\gamma$) and $Zn^{65}$ (1.1 Mev. $\gamma$) in the well-type counter, the authors found the efficiencies for these gamma energies to be respectively 0.84, 0.62, and 0.30. Concentrations of $\gamma$ emitters could be determined in solutions as low in specific activity as 10 to 20 $\gamma$/(min.)(ml.) depending on the energy of the $\gamma$ rays. End-on counters using 50 ml. of solution in a volumetric flash gave minimum determinable specific activities from 3 to 10 $\gamma$/(min.)(ml.) and the dip counter in 150 to 2500 ml. of solution gave from 2 to 0.2 $\gamma$/(min.)(ml.). This is some 40 times lower than the usual $\beta$ counting with a G-M counter. For $\beta$ emitters such as $H^3$ and $C^{14}$ Wagner and Guin used a liquid scintillation counter in which the radioactive sample (a hydrocarbon) was dissolved. For a 10-g. sample of hydrocarbon dissolved in 50 ml. of the liquid scintillator, 10 disintegrations/(min.)(g.) for $C^{14}$ could be counted to $\pm 10\%$ accuracy in 30 min. with an over-all efficiency of 50%. Because only small samples can be used in the usual types of (a) windowless flow counters (0.15 g. as hydrocarbon or 0.011 g. as $BaCO_3$), (b) an internal gas counter (0.019 g. as $CO_2$), or (c) an ionization chamber (0.25 g. as $CO_2$), the minimum detectable specific activities considering background and other factors were respectively (a) 1480 and 16,200, (b) 1600, and (c) 660 disintegrations/(min.)(g.). For $H^3$ in hydrocarbons the minimum detectable specific activity with a liquid scintillator was 64 disintegrations/(min.)(g.) with 2% over-all efficiency. When the hydrocarbon was burned to water, 0.74 g. was dissolved in a liquid scintillator consisting of 60 ml. of $\frac{2}{3}$ toluene-$\frac{1}{3}$ ethanol with 4 g. of diphenyloxazole and 15 mg. diphenylhexatriene/liter. The background was 200 counts/min. and the minimum detectable specific activity of $H^3$ was 2,580 disintegrations/(min.)(g.) of water.

The foregoing examples show the relatively high sensitivity of scintillation counting for cases where rather large volumes of low specific-activity material are being measured. For example, 0.2$\gamma$ ray/(min.)(ml.) corresponds to 1 $\mu$curie ($3.7 \times 10^4$ disintegrations/sec.) dispersed in about 11 tons of solution. In the usual case of activation analysis the specific activity is sufficiently high that small solid samples can be employed in the usual fashion, although at times it may be advantageous to count the solutions obtained in chemical separations.

An important advantage of NaI(Tl) scintillation counters over G-M counters besides their efficiency is the fact that from about 50 kev. to 3 Mev. the pulse height for γ rays is closely proportional to the γ-ray energy. This makes it possible to discriminate against the lower energy γ rays and count only those of higher energy. However, one of the most important aspects of such counters is their use in scintillation spectrometry (94).

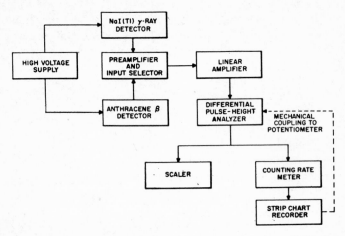

Fig. 47. Block diagram showing the essential units of a scintillation spectrometer.

### 14.2. Scintillation Spectrometers

A block diagram of a typical scintillation spectrometer (45) is given in Fig. 47. For γ rays a crystal of NaI(Tl) $1\frac{1}{2}$ in. in diameter and $\frac{1}{2}$ to 2 in. thick is covered with a MgO reflector, hermetically sealed in an aluminum container and optically coupled to a photomultiplier tube such as RCA 5819 or DuMont 6292 as illustrated in Fig. 47. The pulses from the tube pass through a condenser and resistor to a cathode follower preamplifier which couples the signal into a linear amplifier. It is advantageous to have a second photomultiplier equipped with an anthracene crystal 1 to $1\frac{1}{2}$ in. in diameter and about $\frac{1}{2}$ in. thick for a β detector. This crystal can be cemented to one end of a Lucite cylinder, which in turn is cemented to the photomultiplier tube for transmitting the scintillations. The end of the crystal is covered with a 0.2-mg./cm.$^2$ foil as a β-particle window and the other surfaces are wrapped with 0.2-mil aluminum foil as a reflector. The whole assembly is then mounted inside a light tight housing with shielding to cut down the background. A switch is used to select either the γ or the β detector.

The linear amplifier feeds a single-channel differential pulse-height analyzer which accepts only those pulses from the linear amplifier that fall within a narrow range of voltages. This is called the "window," "channel width," "acceptance slit," or "slit width" and may be adjusted between, for example, 1 and 5 volts. By rotation of the potentiometer of the pulse-height analyzer, the acceptance slit can be made to scan the region from 0 to 100 volts either manually in steps for use with the scaler or continuously through a mechanical connection from the strip chart recorder of the count-rate meter. The speed of the automatic scan can be adjusted so that the acceptance slit covers the full range every 30 min. The gain adjustment of the linear amplifier can be set in steps so that the maximum pulse height is 100 volts for γ rays of 0.5, 1, 2, 3, or 4 Mev. By means of radioactive sources of known γ-ray energies such as $Cs^{137}$ (0.66 Mev.) and $Co^{60}$ (1.17 and 1.33 Mev.), the pulse-height dial for the different gain settings can be calibrated in terms of γ-ray energy. The count-rate meter and recorder can be omitted for most analytical problems, although they facilitate the analysis. Multichannel pulse-height analyzers are also available commercially. With these the counting rates are recorded on registers for 10 to 100 or more channels simultaneously. Other instruments such as the photographic gray-wedge analyzer also have important applications in pulse height analysis.

A typical γ-ray scan with the spectrometer is shown in Fig. 48. The recoil electrons from the photoelectric effect produce the peaked response known as the *photopeak* in the pulse-height scan. Electrons from the Compton effect range in energy from that of the γ ray to zero. A rather sharp rise in the response begins at the wing of the photopeak, giving rise to the Compton background or continuum. Those γ rays that lose only a small part of their energy by Compton scattering may lose the remainder by the photoelectric effect, thus contributing to the photopeak. A small peak may appear above the Compton continuum at 1.02 Mev. below the photopeak as a result of pair production. At higher energies the pair peak will increase and a small one due to the annihilation radiation may appear. The pair peak will always be absent for γ rays with energies below 1.02 Mev. The small peaks in the response at the lower energies arise from 180° scattering and back scattering from the walls surrounding the crystal. At very low pulse heights the noise from the photomultiplier is counted. The larger the crystal, the greater the chance of total absorption of the γ-ray energy and the larger will be the photopeak. At times, however, it may be desirable to use a thin crystal to discriminate against the higher energy $\gamma$ rays when a radioisotope with low energy $\gamma$ rays is determined in a mixture (221).

The pulses giving rise to the photopeak have pulse heights proportional to the original $\gamma$-ray energy, and the area under the peak is related to the number of $\gamma$ rays/min. interacting with the crystal. The area under the photopeak expressed in counts per minute is approximately $A = \Sigma r \Delta E$ where $r$ is the counts per minute per slit width and $\Delta E$ is the increment in energy corresponding to the slit width. This area may also be approximated from the equation $A = 1.07 \rho r_{(max)}$, where $r_{(max)}$ is the maximum

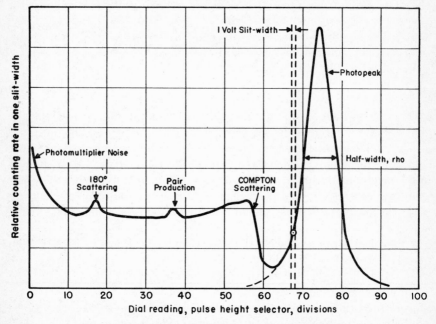

FIG. 48. Schematic representation of a $\gamma$-ray spectrum.

photopeak height in counts per minute and $\rho$ is the width at half maximum in units of slit width. The factor 1.07 arises from the fact that the shape of the photopeak is Gaussian and approximates a normal curve of error (45).

In order to convert the counts per minute under the photopeak to an activity in disintegration per minute, it is necessary to calibrate the particular spectrometer with radioisotopes of known activity and $\gamma$-ray energies in a way similar to that described previously for G-M counters. Thus, the photopeak counting yield will be $Y_p = $ (counts per minute under photopeak)/($\gamma$ rays per minute from the known source). Connally and Leboeuf (45) found the yield to vary with the $\gamma$ energy from 1% for

$Cs^{137}$ (0.66 Mev.) to 2.5% for $Au^{198}$ (0.4 Mev.) in their spectrometer and geometrical arrangement. Kahn and Lyon determined the photopeak yield for a number of radioisotopes with energies varying from 30 kev. to 2.76 Mev. They used a crystal of NaI(Tl) $1\frac{1}{2}$ in. in diameter, 1 in. thick, with a 5819 photomultiplier tube, and mounted the sample 2.45 cm. from the crystal on a 1-in. diameter watch glass. For γ-ray energies from 2.76 to 1.2 Mev. the photopeak yield increased from 0.15 to 0.5%; for energies from 1.2 to 0.5 Mev. the yield increased from 0.5 to 1.5%; and for 0.5 Mev. to 30 kev. the yield increased rapidly from 1.5 to 10%.

Once a calibration for energy and for the photopeak yield has been made for the spectrometer, the identity and the activity of a particular radioisotope can be determined in a sample that has been irradiated in a neutron flux. From the activity the quantity of the radioisotope can be calculated as described in section 13. Of course, such calibrations will not be necessary when the comparative method is used. In this the quantitative estimation is accomplished by measuring the areas under the photopeaks and comparing them with the areas under photopeaks obtained from standards of known concentration.

In certain repetitive measurements it is possible to adjust the pulse discriminators so that the acceptance slit is large enough to cover the full width of the photopeak. If the Compton background from peaks of higher energy is essentially constant from sample to sample, an empirical working curve of counting rate vs. concentration can be constructed. Counting rates for other samples can then be referred to this curve for the concentration of the element. In favorable cases rather rapid radiochemical assays for a particular radioisotope can be made by such methods.

### 14.3. Measurement of β-Particle Energies with the Scintillation Spectrometer

By using the anthracene crystal in place of the sodium iodide, the β-energy spectra can be measured by scanning with the acceptance slit. Calibration with β particles of known energy has shown that the pulse height is linear with energy from 0.125 to 3.2 Mev. (96). This can be extended to lower energies (114) by drilling a conical hole in the crystal so that the β particles entering it are not likely to be scattered back out of the crystal.

The particular spectrometer used is calibrated with β emitters of known energy. Then the counting rate for each setting of the acceptance slit is plotted vs. the pulse height or energy setting. Such a plot for a simple β emitter approaches a straight line toward the higher energies. Extrapolation of the straight-line portion to zero counting rate gives the maximum energy of the β spectrum to within ±10%. More precise values can be obtained with a Kurie plot (114). If two or three $\beta$ emitters are present whose energies are sufficiently different, the observed curve may be resolved to straight-line sections and the maximum energy of each obtained.

### 14.4. Scintillation Spectrometry for Mixtures of Radioisotopes

The qualitative identification of a particular radioisotope is based on the observation that the pulse height at which the photopeak occurs varies nearly linearly with the $\gamma$-ray energy from 25 kev. to 3 Mev. Thus the photopeak energy can identify the radioisotope or limit it to a few possibilities. A typical $\gamma$-ray scan for a mixture of radioisotopes is shown in Fig. 49. Interference arises when the principal energies of the $\gamma$-emitting radioisotopes do not differ by more than the half width $\rho$ of the spectrometer. For the spectrometer described above, the half width for $Cs^{137}$ (0.66 Mev.) was 0.093 Mev., or 14%. The half width varies as the square root of the $\gamma$ energy, and so for the instrument used

$$\rho = k \sqrt{E} = 0.114 \sqrt{E}$$

A smaller crystal gave a resolution of 9%, but at the expense of a greater ratio of Compton continuum to photopeak and lower photopeak yield for the higher energies.

In cases where the principal $\gamma$-ray energies of two radioisotopes are unresolved, their identity can sometimes be determined from a $\beta$-particle scan to determine their maximum energy. Also the changes with time may be used for half-life determinations associated with the photpeaks and $\beta$ spectra. It is seldom that two radioisotopes have decay constants, $\gamma$, and $\beta$ energies so close that they cannot be identified by these methods. Difficulties can be encountered when a radioisotope with a low energy $\gamma$ ray is in a mixture with others of higher $\gamma$ energy. Also, if high-energy $\beta$ particles are present, the thickness of Al or Be required to absorb them will reduce the intensity of the $\gamma$ rays reaching the crystal. A thinner crystal can be used to discriminate against those radioisotopes with the higher $\gamma$ energies (221). In difficult cases a simple chemical separation will be of assistance in resolving interferences.

A quantitative analysis can be accomplished for certain favorable mixtures of radioisotopes without chemical separation. If the activity of any one of the radioisotopes in the mixture is less than about 10% of the total gamma activity, the accuracy of the determination may be low and a chemical separation will be needed. With suitable mixtures, results within 1 to 5% can be obtained.

The quantitative estimation of the radioisotopes from a $\gamma$-ray scan such as illustrated in Fig. 49 requires the determination of the photopeak area due to the principal $\gamma$ rays of each radioisotope. Contributions from the Compton continuum, pair peaks, minor photopeaks, and background of each higher energy photopeak must be subtracted for the lower energy peaks. This is done by first determining the area of the highest energy photopeak. From a previous scan of this radioisotope alone a normalized curve with the principal photopeak height equal to 1 can be constructed. The ratio of the photopeak height to the heights due to the other effects at any energy setting can then be read from this curve and tabulated if desired. With the height of the highest energy photopeak known, the height due to the other effects can be calculated and subtracted from that of the next lower photopeak. This is continued for each of the photopeaks.

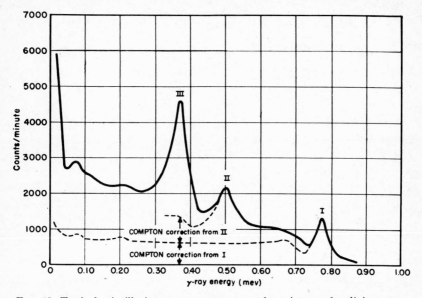

Fig. 49. Typical scintillation-spectrometer scan of a mixture of radioisotopes.

When all the net peak heights have been determined, the half width $\rho$ of each is measured and the areas are calculated as previously described.

Once the areas are known, the disintegration rate can be calculated from the calibrations of photopeak yield vs. energy. These disintegration rates, combined with flux measurements, activation cross sections, decay-scheme data, and half-life, can be used for calculation of the quantity of the element by the absolute method previously described. More frequently, however, the comparative method is used in which the areas of the photopeaks are compared with the areas from samples of known concentration treated in the same way. This procedure results in a more precise determination than the direct or absolute calculations from calibrations.

### 14.5. Analytical Applications of Scintillation Spectrometry

The use of scintillation counters and spectrometers for studying decay schemes and measurement of $\gamma$ and $\beta$ energies for problems in nuclear physics and chemistry has been reviewed by a number of authors (63, 93, 94, 114, 115, 117). Connally and Leboeuf have applied $\gamma$ and $\beta$ scintillation spectrometry to the determination of mixtures of three radionuclides, $Nd^{95}$, $Ru-Rh^{106}$, and $I^{131}$. They also applied the method to a number of pairs of radionuclides having similar $\gamma$ energies to test the resolution of the scintillation spectrometer. In cases where the resolution was not sufficient, most of the pairs could be resolved by measuring the $\beta$ energies with a $\beta$-scintillation spectrometer.

Kahn and Lyon (116) described the calibration of scintillation spectrometer for radiochemical analysis and applied it to the following: identification of fission products $Cs^{137}$, $Rh^{106}$, $Ce^{144}$ in waste solutions and air filters; following traces of radioactive elements in analytical procedures such as traces of Co carried with a nickel dimethyl-glyoxime precipitate; detection of $Sr^{85}$ impurity in $Ca^{45}$ amounting to 0.01% of the total activity; detection of $Ba^{140}$ in small amounts in $Sr^{89}$ solutions; and identification of $Sn^{113}$ and $Sb^{115}$ in the presence of each other.

Upson, Connally, and Leboeuf (221) have employed scintillation spectrometry for the determination of the low-energy gamma emitters in fission-product mixtures. Special consideration was given to the determination of $Pu^{239}$ from its 100-kev. $\gamma$ ray by use of a thin crystal of NaI(Tl) to discriminate against the higher $\gamma$ energies of the fission products. Miller (149) has described a similar method for the determination of $U^{235}$ from its 0.2-Mev. $\gamma$-ray photopeak.

The foregoing applications of scintillation spectrometry to analysis do not directly involve neutron-activation analysis, but the methods are essentially the same. An interesting example of the application of $\gamma$ scintillation spectrometry to activation analysis is the determination of trace impurities in transitor silicon by Morrison and Cosgrove (153). This represents a particularly favorable case because the activity induced in the major component does not interfere and the analysis could be done without chemical separations. During irradiation in a neutron flux 2.6-hr. $Si^{31}$ is formed and decays by $\beta$ emission to stable $P^{31}$, but during the irradiation this forms 14-day $P^{32}$ that also decays by $\beta$ emission to stable $S^{23}$. Since no $\gamma$ rays are emitted, the $\beta$ rays from both these radioisotopes can be absorbed in aluminum without significantly affecting the $\gamma$ rays from the impurities.

Samples from 0.05 to 1 g. together with the standards were sealed in separate quartz ampules and irradiated in the Brookhaven reactor for

3 days with a flux of approximately $3.4 \times 10^{12}$ neutrons/(cm.$^2$)(sec.). After irradiation, the surface of the samples was washed with a solution of KOH and $H_2O_2$ to remove any surface contamination. The samples were crushed and mounted in aluminum planchets of 0.74 g./cm.$^2$ thickness to absorb the 1.47-Mev. $\beta$ particles from $Si^{31}$. The standards were dissolved and suitable aliquots were evaporated for comparison with the silicon sample.

A scintillation spectrometer similar to that described in section 14.2 was used with a crystal of NaI(Tl) $1\frac{1}{2}$ in. in diameter by $\frac{1}{2}$ in. thick attached to a DuMont 6292 photomultiplier tube. The energy scale was calibrated with $Co^{60}$ and $Sb^{125}$ for qualitative identification. Quantitative estimation was accomplished by measuring the areas under the photopeaks and comparing them to the areas of the photopeaks obtained from the standards. Only those radioisotopes with half-lives greater than 2 hr. were determined because 4 hr. was required to bring the samples from the reactor to the laboratory and to prepare them for counting. This time would be much shorter if the counting were done at the reactor laboratories. Most radioisotopes with half-lives greater than 200 days would not be sufficiently activated by a 3-hr. irradiation. However, if the concentration or cross sections of an element is high enough, it may be detected even though its half-life does not fall within 2 hr. to 200 days.

The radioisotopes found and the $\gamma$ energy used for the measurements in one sample of silicon were 14-hr. $Zn^{69}$ (0.44 Mev.); 25-hr. $As^{76}$ (0.55 Mev.); 24-hr. $W^{187}$ (0.69 Mev.); 44-day $Fe^{59}$ (1.09 Mev.); 14.8-hr. $Na^{24}$ (1.36 Mev.); 12.4-hr. $K^{42}$ (1.52 Mev.). A quantitative evaluation for the elements gave the following percentages: $Zn = 2.2 \times 10^{-2}$; $As = 1.8 \times 10^{-4}$; $W = 5.5 \times 10^{-5}$; $Fe = 2.0 \times 10^{-3}$; $Na = 8.5 \times 10^{-6}$; $K = 8.5 \times 10^{-5}$. Another purer sample gave only $As = 2.0 \times 10^{-3}\%$ and $Ta = 8.3 \times 10^{-4}\%$. The accuracy and reproducibility obtainable were evaluated by analyzing National Bureau of Standards aluminum alloy 86-C for copper and chromium. After irradiation the samples were dissolved and aliquots containing 10.8 $\mu$g. of Cu and 2.54 $\mu$g. of Cr were counted. The percentages calculated from the activation analysis were $8.01 \pm 0.11$ for Cu and $0.029 \pm 0.0004$ compared to $7.92 \pm 0.03$ and $0.029 \pm 0.003$ reported by the National Bureau of Standards. Similar methods are applicable to many other substances although not always without some chemical separation. Sensitivities from 0.001 to 1 $\mu$g. for many of the elements are obtainable. (See Table XII.)

A similar study of the trace impurities in transistor germanium has been reported by the same authors (154). Irradiation of germanium with neutrons results in the formation of $Ge^{71}$, $Ge^{75}$, and $Ge^{77}$ as well as $As^{77}$ by secondary activation. The $\gamma$ rays from these radioisotopes of germanium interfere with the measurement of the $\gamma$-emitting impurities. Consequently it was necessary to separate the germanium. This was done by dissolving the sample and adding 25 mg. of Cu as a hold-back carrier for nonvolatile impurities and 25 mg. of As as carrier for the arsenic impurity. Distillation under oxidizing conditions with hydrochloric and nitric acid removed the germanium as $GeCl_4$. Following this separation, the addition of HBr reduced $As^{+5}$ to $As^{+3}$, which was then distilled as $AsCl_3$ into another receiver containing water. After removal of the Ge and As, the solution in the distilling flask was evaporated to dryness and the $\gamma$-emitting trace elements were determined without further chemical separation by use of the scintillation spectrometer. One sample of germanium dioxide, for example, was found to contain $1.5 \times 10^{-4}\%$ As, $3.9 \times 10^{-5}\%$ Na, $1.6 \times 10^{-6}\%$ Cu, and $1.4 \times 10^{-3}\%$ Zn.

These applications of scintillation spectrometry to activation analysis illustrate one of its important advantages, namely rapid analysis with a minimum of chemical separation. Although it will not supplant the usual methods of activation analysis described in section 13, scintillation spectrometry will find many important applications.

### 14.6. Other Applications of Scintillation Counters and Spectrometers to Neutron Interactions

The use of scintillation counters for detecting the prompt $\gamma$ rays emitted during resonance absorption has already been mentioned (p. 447). Resonance absorptions measured in this way can be used for the determination of a resonance absorber by comparison of the response with samples of known composition. Since prompt $\gamma$ rays are emitted in most cases of neutron absorption, their measurement during irradiation of a sample with neutrons can form the basis of an analysis. Such methods may be particularly useful for a number of the lighter elements that have no low-energy resonances or form radioisotopes of short half-life. There is also the possibility of dissolving a neutron-absorbing element in a liquid scintillator, in which case not only $(n,\gamma)$ but $(n,p)$ or $(n,\alpha)$ reactions may give responses suitable for analytical purposes. Similarly, a solid sample may be suspended in liquid scintillators for such measurements.

The principal difficulty with the application of scintillation counters to such measurements is that they are sensitive to the $\gamma$-ray background that usually accompanies neutrons fluxes or beams. Some neutron sources such as one of Po-Be have low $\gamma$-ray intensities, and shielding is possible. In other cases special shielding and geometrical arrangements would be required. A crystal spectrometer can be used to deflect a neutron beam so that it would be possible to do the measurements at a distance from the direct beam coming from a reactor. With time of flight arrangements using pulsed or chopped beams, the response of neutrons arriving after the $\gamma$ rays and fast neutrons can be measured.

Besides measuring $\gamma$ rays that result from absorption of neutrons, scintillation counters are useful in measuring the intensity of neutron beams themselves. One of the most promising scintillators for such purposes is LiI activated with tin or europium (184), particularly if the lithium is enriched in $Li^6$. Muehlhause (157) has described a number of neutron detection techniques involving scintillation counters. These include the use of trimethyl boron in a liquid scintillator, cadmium plates suspended in a liquid scintillator, and ZnS(Ag) fused with $B_2O_3$. Improvements in neutron detecting devices for the various energy ranges will increase the possible uses of neutron interactions for analytical problems.

Scintillation counting has been applied to isotope analysis of lithium, boron, and uranium. For example, Wänke and Monse (223a) used a 100 millicurie Ra-Be neutron source surrounded with paraffin and counted particles from the following reactions:

$Li^6(n,\alpha)$ $H^3$; 2.8 Mev. $H^3$, range in air = 6 cm.; 2.18 Mev. $\alpha$, range in air = 1.1 cm
$B^{10}(n,\alpha)$ $Li^{7*}$; 2.57 Mev.; 1.6 Mev. $\alpha$, range in air = 0.8 cm.
$U^{235}(n,f)$; 160 Mev.

The thermal neutron cross sections of the natural elements for these reactions are respectively 71, 755, and 7.68 barns or 945, 4010, and 687 for the isotopes. A photomultiplier tube with a zinc sulfide screen was used to count the particles emitted during neutron irradiation.

With a 3 cm.$^2$ layer of LiF, 2 mg./cm.$^2$ thick, about 300 pulses per minute were obtained for natural lithium and 8 per minute for a sample depleted from 7.52 to 0.2% $Li^6$. The background count was reduced to 1 to 2% by the proper setting of the discriminator of the measuring circuits. For natural boron 135 pulses per minute with a background count of about 16% was obtained, while for natural uranium the number of pulses were 6 per minute with no background pulses. Thus, scintillation during irradiation with neutrons provides a relatively rapid method for the determination of changes in abundance of these isotopes. By proper discrimination against the smaller light pulses, low backgrounds can be achieved.

## 15. NEUTRON DIFFRACTION

The general aspects of neutron diffraction were discussed briefly in section 5.3. Space is not available to discuss this topic adequately here. Neutron diffraction is now a large and rather important application of neutron interactions. It has been particularly valuable in such areas as the following: position of light atoms in crystals with heavy atoms;

structure of alloys involving elements of nearly the same mass; investigations of paramagnetic, ferromagnetic, and ferrimagnetic properties; studies of order-disorder, free and hindered rotation, liquid structure, vitreous state, gaseous state, lattice distortion effects in cold-working of metals, small angle scattering, lattice vibrations, etc. The application of neutron diffraction to these and other problems has been described in detail in a number of books and reviews (13, 41, 85, 102, 194). Although these techniques have not been applied directly to chemical analyses, they are very important in many problems in chemistry, particularly in the chemistry of the solid state.

## REFERENCES

1. Albert, P., Caron, M., and Chaudron, G., *Compt. rend.* **233**, 1108 (1951).
2. Almqvist, E., *Can. J. Research* **28A**, 433 (1950).
3. Alperovitch, E., and Miller, J. M., *Nucleonics* **13**, No. 1, 68 (1955).
4. Alvarez, L. W., *Phys. Rev.* **54**, 609 (1938).
5. Anderson, H. L., Nuclear Science Series, Preliminary Report No. 3. National Research Council, Washington, D.C., 1948.
6. Anderson, H. L., Fermi, E., Wattenberg, A., Weil, G. L., and Zinn, W. H., *Phys. Rev.* **72**, 16 (1947).
7. Anderson, R. H., Dissertation, Columbia University, 1954.
8. Anderson, R. H., Taylor, T. I., and Havens, W. W., Jr., AEC Report CUD-91, 1951.
9. Arley, N., *Kgl. Danske Videnskab. Selskab Mat. fys. Medd.* **16**, 1 (1938).
10. Atchison, G. L., and Beamer, W. H., *Anal. Chem.* **24**, 1812 (1952).
11. Atchison, G. L., and Beamer, W. H., *Anal. Chem.* **28**, 237 (1956).
12. Aten, A. H. W., Jr., *Ned. Tijdschr Natuurk.* **10**, 257 (1943).
13. Bacon, G. E., Neutron Diffraction. Oxford, U. P., New York, 1955.
14. Baker, C. P., and Bacher, R. F., *Phys. Rev.* **59**, 332 (1941).
15. Bancie-Grillot, M., Grillot, E., *Compt. rend.* **237**, 171 (1953).
16. Berlman, I. B., *Nucleonics* **11**, No. 2, 70 (1953).
17. Berlman, I. B., Lucas, H. F., and May, H. A., *Nuclear Sci. Abstr.* **6**, 5734 (1952).
18. Bethe, H. A., and Bacher, R. F., *Revs. Mod. Phys.* **8**, 83 (1936); **9**, 69 (1937); Livingston, M. S., and Bethe, H. A., *ibid.* **9**, 245 (1937).
19. Bethe, H. A., and Placzek, G., *Phys. Rev.* **51**, 462 (1937); Bethe, H. A., *Revs. Mod. Phys.* **9**, 140 (1937).
20. Beydon, J., and Fisher, C., *Anal. Chim. Acta* **8**, 538 (1953).
21. Birks, J. B., "Scintillation Counters." McGraw-Hill, New York, 1953.
22. Blatt, J. M., and Weisskopf, V. F., "Theoretical Nuclear Physics." Wiley, New York, 1952.
23. Bleuler, E., and Goldsmith, G. J., "Experimental Nucleonics." Reinhart, New York, 1952.
24. Bleuler, E., and Zünti, W., *Helv. Phys. Acta* **19**, 137 (1946).
25. Blüh, O., and Terentruk, F., *Nucleonics* **10**, No. 9, 48 (1952).
26. Bohr, N., *Nature* **137**, 344, 352 (1936).
27. Bopp, C. D., and Sisman, O., *Nucleonics* **14**, No. 1, 46 (1956).
28. Borst, L. B., *Ann. Revs. Nuclear Sci.* **5**, 179 (1955).

29. Borst, L. B., and Sailor, V. L., *Rev. Sci. Inst.* **24**, 141 (1953).
30. Borst, L. B., Ulrich, A. J., Osborne, C. L., and Hasbrouck, B., *Phys. Rev.* **70**, 108 (1946).
31. Boyd, G. E., *Anal. Chem.* **21**, 335 (1949).
32. Briet, G., and Wigner, E. P., *Phys. Rev.* **49**, 117 (1947).
33. Brill, T., and Lichtenberger, H., *Phys. Rev.* **72**, 585 (1947).
34. Brooksbank, W. A., and Leddicotte, G. W., and Mahlman, H. A., *J. Phys. Chem.* **57**, 815 (1953).
35. Brooksbank, W. A., Jr., Leddicotte, G. W., and Strain, J. E., Nuclear Engieering and Science Conference, Reprint 308. American Institute of Chemical Engineers, New York, 1955.
36. Brown, H. S., and Goldberg, E. D., *Science* **109**, 347 (1949).
37. Burger, L. L., and Rainwater, L. J., A.E.C. Declassified Document AECD. 2138 (1948).
38. Burgy, M. T., Ringo, G. R., and Hughes, D. J., *Phys. Rev.* **84**, 1160 (1951).
39. Burril, E. A., and Gale, A. J., Pamphlet. High Voltage Engineering Corp., Cambridge, Mass., May 1954.
40. Burtt, B. J., *Nucleonics* **5**, No. 2, 28 (1949).
41. Cassels, J. M., *Prog. Nuclear Phys.* **1**, 185 (1950).
42. Chadwick, J., *Proc. Roy Soc.* **A136**, 692 (1932); **A142**, 1 (1933).
43. Clark, H. M., and Overman, R. T., AEC Report MDDC-1329 (1947).
44. Cockcroft, J. D., Duckworth, J. C., and Merrison, E. R., *Nature* **163**, 869 (1949).
45. Connally, R. E., and Leboeuf, M. B., *Anal. Chem.* **25**, 1095 (1953).
46. Coon, J. H., *Phys. Rev.* **75**, 1355 (1949).
47. Dash, J. G., and Sommers, H. J., Jr., *Rev. Sci. Instr.* **24**, 91 (1952).
48. Daudel, P., *Anal. Chim. Acta* **5**, 426 (1951).
49. Delbecq, C. J., Glendenin, L. E., and Yuster, P. H., *Anal. Chem.* **25**, 350 (1953).
50. Döpel, D., and Döpel, K., *Physik Z.* **44**, 261 (1943).
51. Dunning, J. R., Pegram, G. B., Fink, G. A., and Mitchell, D. P., *Phys. Rev.* **48**, 704 (1935).
52. Eicholz, G. G., *Nuclear Sci. Abstr.* **6**, 1541 (1952).
53. Faires, R. A., Johnston, J. E., and Millett, R. J., *Nucleonics* **12**, No. 10, 48 (1954).
54. Fermi, E., "Nuclear Physics." U. of Chicago Press, Chicago, 1950.
55. Fermi, E., *Ricerca Sci.* **7**, 13 (1936).
56. Fermi, E., Marshall, J., and Marshall, L., *Phys. Rev.* **72**, 193 (1947).
57. Fermi, E., Sturm, W. J., and Sachs, R. G., *Phys. Rev.* **71**, 589 (1947).
58. Fertel, G. E. F., Gibbs, D. F., Moon, P. B., Thomson, G. P., and Wynn-Williams, C. E., *Proc. Roy. Soc.* **175**, 316 (1940).
59. Fireman, E. L., and Schwarzer, D., Brookhaven National Laboratories, Report August 18, 1955.
60. Foster, L. M., and Gaitanis, C. D., *Anal. Chem.* **27**, 1342 (1955).
61. Friedlander, G., and Kennedy, J. W., "Nuclear and Radiochemistry." Wiley, New York, 1955.
62. Gaerttner, E. R., Yeater, M. L., and Albert, R. D., Report KAPL 1084, General Electric Co. (1954); Gaerttner, E. R., Yeater, M. L., and McRoberts, W. J., Report KAPL 1108, General Electric (1954).
63. Garlick, G. F. J., *Progr. Nuclear Phys.* Vol. 2, 51 (1952).
64. Garth, R. C., Hughes, D. J., and Levin, J. S., *Phys. Rev.* **87**, 222 (1952).
65. Gaudin, A. M., and Pannell, J. H., *Anal. Chem.* **23**, 1261 (1951).

66. Geiger, R. C., and Plumb, R. C., *Nucleonics* **14**, No. 2, 30 (1956).
67. Glendenin, L. E., *Nucleonics* **2**, No. 1, 12 (1948).
68. Glendenin, L. E., and Solomon, A. K., *Science* **112**, 623 (1950).
69. Goldberg, E. D., and Brown, H. S., *Phys. Rev.* **76**, 1260 (1949).
70. Goldberg, E. D., and Brown, H. S., *Anal. Chem.* **22**, 308 (1950).
71. Goldsmith, H. H., and Rasetti, F., *Phys. Rev.* **50**, 328 (1936).
72. Gould, F. T., Taylor, T. I., and Havens, W. W., Jr., *Phys. Rev.* **100**, 1248A (1955).
73. Gould, F. T., Taylor, T. I., and Havens, W. W., Jr., *Bull. Am. Phys. Soc.* **1** (II), 69 (1956); also unpublished work.
74. Gould, F. T., Taylor, T. I., and Havens, W. W., Jr., unpublished work.
75. Griffon, H., and Barband, J., *Compt. rend.* **232**, 1455 (1951).
76. Grillot, E., *Compt. rend.* **234** (18), 1755 (1952).
77. Hahn, O., "Applied Radiochemistry," Cornell U. P., Ithaca, 1936.
78. Hall, T. A., *Nucleonics* **12**, No. 3, 34 (1954).
79. Halliday, D., "Introductory Nuclear Physics." Wiley, New York, 1955.
80. Halpern, O., and Johnson, M. H., *Phys. Rev.* **51**, 992 (1937); **52**, 52 (1937).
81. Hanson, A. O., Taschek, R. F., and Williams, J. H., *Revs. Mod. Phys.* **21**, 635 (1949).
82. Hanstein, H. B., *Phys. Rev.* **59**, 489 (1941).
83. Harrison, G. E., and Raymond, W. H. A., *J. Nuclear Energy* **1**, 290 (1955).
84. Harvey, J. A., Hughes, D. J., Carter, R. S., and Pilcher, D. E., *Phys. Rev.* **99**, 10 (1955).
85. Hastings, J. M., and Corliss, L. M., *in* "Physical Methods of Organic Chemistry," (A. Weissberger, ed.), 2nd ed., Vol. 1, Part III. Interscience, New York, 1954.
86. Havens, W. W., Jr., "Proceedings of the International Conference on Peaceful Uses of Atomic Energy," Vol. 4, p. 74. United Nations, New York, 1956.
87. Havens, W. W., Jr., and Rainwater, L. J., *Phys. Rev.* **83**, 1123 (1951).
88. Haworth, L. J., Manley, J. H., and Luebke, E. A., *Rev. Sci. Instr.* **12**, 591 (1941).
89. Hayes, F. N., *Nucleonics* **11**, No. 3, 27 (1954).
90. Herr, W., *Angew. Chem.* **64**, 679 (1952).
91. Herr, W., *Z. Naturforsch.* **8a**, 305 (1953); Herr, W., and Merz, E. A., *Z. Naturforsch.* **10A**, 613 (1955).
92. Hevesy, G., and Levi, H., *Kgl. Danske Videnskab. Selskab Math. fys. Medd.* **14**, 5 (1936); **15**, 11 (1938).
93. Hofstader, R., *Nucleonics* **4**, No. 4, 2 (1949); **4**, No. 5, 29 (1949); *Phys. Rev.* **75**, 796 (1949).
94. Hofstader, R., and McIntyre, J. A., *Nucleonics* **7**, No. 3, 32 (1950).
95. Hollander, J. M., Perlman, I., and Seaborg, G. T., *Revs. Mod. Phys.* **25**, 469 (1953).
96. Hopkins, J. I., *Rev. Sci. Instr.* **22**, 29 (1951).
97. Holt, N., Rustad, B. M., and Gould F. T., *Bull. Am. Phys. Soc.* **1** (II), 69 (1956); Holt, N., in press.
98. Hoover, J. I., Jordon, W. H., Mook, C. D., Pardue, L. A., Strong, J. D., Pomerance, H., and Wollan, E. O., *Phys. Rev.* **74**, 864 (1948).
99. Hudgens, J. E., Jr., and Cali, P. J., *Anal. Chem.* **24**, 171 (1952).
100. Hudgens, J. E., Jr., and Dabagian, H. J., *Nucleonics* **10**, No. 5, 25 (1952).
101. Hudgens, J. E., Jr., and Nelson, L. C., *Anal. Chem.* **24**, 1472 (1952).
102. Hughes, D. J., "Neutron Optics." Interscience, New York, 1954.
103. Hughes, D. J., "Pile Neutron Research." Addison-Wesley, Cambridge, Mass., 1953.

104. Hughes, D. J., Burgy, M. T., and Ringo, G. R., *Phys. Rev.* **77,** 291 (1950).
105. Hughes, D. J., Garth, R. C., and Eggler, C., *Phys. Rev.* **83,** 234 (1951).
106. Hughes, D. J., and Harvey, J. A., Brookhaven National Laboratories, Report BNL 325. U.S. Government Printing Office, Washington, D.C.
107. Hughes, D. J., Spatz, W. D. B., and Goldstein, N., *Phys. Rev.* **75,** 1781 (1949).
108. Hummel, V., and Hamermesh, B., *Phys. Rev.* **82,** 67 (1951).
109. Hummel, M. W., and Smales, A. A., *Analyst* **81,** 111 (1956).
110. Jacobs, R. B., Lewis, L. G., and Piehl, F. J., *Anal. Chem.* **28,** 324 (1956).
111. Jacobs, R. B., Lewis, L. G., and Piehl, F. J., *Anal. Chem.* **28,** 324 (1956).
112. James, J. A., and Richards, D. H., *Nature* **175,** 769 (1955).
113. Jenkins, E. N., *Analyst* **80,** 301 (1955).
114. Jordan, W. H., *Ann. Revs. Nuclear Sci.* **1,** 207 (1952).
115. Jordan, W. H., and Bell, P. R., *Nucleonics* **5,** No. 4, 30 (1949).
116. Kahn, B., and Lyon, W. S., *Nucleonics* **11,** No. 11, 61 (1953).
117. Kallmann, H., *Natur u. Tech.* July, 1947.
118. Kaplan, I., "Nuclear Physics," Addison-Wesley, Cambridge, Mass., 1955.
119. Kaplan, L., and Wilzbach, K. E., *Anal. Chem.* **26,** 1797 (1954).
120. Katz, L., Penfold, A. S., Moody, H. J., Haslam, R. N., and Johns, H. E., *Phys. Rev.* **77,** 289 (1950).
121. Kennard, E. H., "Kinetic Theory of Gases," Chapter II. McGraw-Hill, New York, 1938.
122. Ketelle, B. H., and Boyd, G. E., *J. Am. Chem. Soc.* **69,** 2800 (1947).
123. Keynes, R. D., and Lewis, P. R., *Nature* **165,** 809 (1950).
124. Kohn, A., *Chimie & industrie* **71,** 69 (1954).
125. Kohn, A., *Compt. rend.* **236,** 1419 (1953).
126. Kohn, H. W., and Tompkins, E. R., *Nuclear Sci. Abstr.* **4,** 2651 (1950).
127. Lamb, W. E., Jr., *Phys. Rev.* **55,** 190 (1939).
128. Landon, H. H., and Sailor, V. L., *Phys. Rev.* **93,** 1030 (1954).
129. Langsdorf, A., *Phys. Rev.* **74,** 1217 (1948).
130. Leddicotte, G. W., and Reynolds, S. A., *Bull. Am. Soc. Testing Materials* No. **188,** 29 (1953).
131. Leddicotte, G. W., and Reynolds, S. A., *Nuclear Sci. Abstr.* **7,** 1611 (1953).
132. Leddicotte, G. W., and Reynolds, S. A., *Nuclear Sci. Abstr.* **8,** 1527 (1954).
133. Leddicotte, G. W., and Reynolds, S. A., *Nucleonics* **8,** No. 3, 62 (1951).
134. Lichtenberger, H. V., Nobles, R. G., Monk, G. D., Kubitschek, H., and Dancoff, S. M., *Phys. Rev.* **72,** 164 (1947).
135. Long, J. V. P., *Analyst* **76,** 644 (1951).
136. Lyon, W. S., and Reynolds, S. A., *Nucleonics* **13,** No. 10, 60 (1955).
137. Macklin, R. L., and Lykins, J. H., *Nuclear Sci. Abstr.* **5,** 1941 (1951).
138. Mahlman, H. A., and Leddicotte, G. W., *Anal. Chem.* **27,** 823 (1955).
139. Manley, J. H., Haworth, L. J., and Luebke, E. A., *Phys. Rev.* **61,** 152 (1942); *Rev. Sci. Instr.* **12,** 587 (1941).
140. Marshall, J., AEC Declassified Document MDDC 78.
141. Mayr, G., *Nucleonics* **12,** No. 5, 58 (1954).
142. Mayr, G., Bruner, H. D., and Brucer, M., *Nucleonics* **11,** No. 10, 21 (1953).
143. Meinke, W. W., *Anal. Chem.* **28,** 745 (1956).
144. Meinke, W. W., *Science* **121,** 177 (1955).
145. Meinke, W. W., and Anderson, R. E., *Anal. Chem.* **25,** 907 (1953).
146. Melkonian, E., *Phys. Rev.* **76,** 1750 (1949).
147. Melkonian, E., "Proceedings of the International Conference on Peaceful Uses of Atomic Energy," Vol. 4, p. 340. United Nations, New York, 1956.

148. Melkonian, E., Havens, W. W., Jr., and Rainwater, L. J., *Phys. Rev.* **92**, 702 (1953).
149. Miller, D. G., AEC Report H. W. 39969 (Oct. 7, 1955).
150. Milner, G. W. C., and Smales, A. A., *Analyst* **79**, 425 (1954).
151. Moljk, A., Drever, R. W. P., and Curran, S. C., *Nucleonics* **13**, No. 2, 44 (1955).
152. Morrison, G. H., *Nucleonics* **11**, No. 1, 28 (1953).
153. Morrison, G. H., and Cosgrove, J. F., *Anal. Chem.* **27**, 810 (1955).
154. Morrison, G. H., and Cosgrove, J. F., *Anal. Chem.* **28**, 320 (1956).
155. Morton, G. A., *R.C.A. Rev.* **10**, 525 (1949).
156. Muehlhause, C. O., *Anal. Chem.* **21**, 1214 (1949).
157. Muehlhause, C. O., *Nucleonics* **14**, No. 4, 38 (1956).
158. Muehlhause, C. O., and Thomas, G. E., *Nucleonics* **7**, No. 1, 9 (1950).
159. National Research Council, *Nuclear Sci. Ser.* Preliminary Report No. 8, Oct. 1950.
160. National Research Council, Nuclear Data Cards, Washington, D.C.
161. Novey, T., Nuclear Science Series, Preliminary Report No. 8, National Research Council, p. 16. Washington, D.C., 1950.
162. Nuclear Science Abstracts, New Nuclear Data, Yearly Accumulations, AEC Technical Information Service, Oak Ridge, Tennessee.
163. Osmond, R. G., and Smales, A. A., *Anal. Chim. Acta* **10**, 117 (1954).
164. Overman, R. T., and Swarthout, J. A., AEC Report AECD 2245 (August 31, 1948).
165. Pauly, J., *Compt. rend.* **238**, 80 (1954).
166. Phillips, G., and Cornish, F. W., *Nuclear Sci. Abstr.* **8**, 1524 (1954).
167. Picciotto, E., *Rev. circle. sci. univ. libre Bruxelles* **1**, 20 (1950).
168. Picciotto, E., *Compt. rend* **232**, 855 (1951).
169. Plumb, R. C., and Silverman, R. H., *Nucleonics* **12**, No. 12, 29 (1954).
170. Plumb, R. C., and Lewis, J. E., *Nucleonics* **13**, No. 8, 42 (1955).
171. Pomerance, H., *Phys. Rev.* **83**, 641 (1951).
172. Pouradin, J., Venet, A. M., and Chateau, H., *Chim. Anal.* **35**, 125 (1953).
173. Rainwater, L. J., and Havens, W. W., Jr., *Phys. Rev.* **70**, 136 (1946).
174. Rainwater, L. J., Havens, W. W., Jr., Wu, C. S., and Dunning, J. R., *Phys. Rev.* **71**, 65 (1947).
175. Rainwater, L. J., and Wu, C. S., *Nucleonics* **1**, No. 2, 60 (1947).
176. Reynolds, G. T., Harrison, F. B., and Salvani, G., *Phys. Rev.* **78**, 488 (1950).
177. Reynolds, R. A., *Record Chem. Progr. Kresge* **16**, 99 (1955).
178. Reynolds, S. A., and Bell, G. C., *Anal. Chem.* **21**, 1214 (1949).
179. Rose, M. E., Miranker, W., Leak, P., Rosenthal, L., and Hendrickson, J. K., Report WAPD-SR-506, Westinghouse Atomic Power Division, October, 1954, Vols. I and II.
180. Ringo, G. R., unpublished Argonne Results (1949) from reference 103.
181. Rubinson, W. J., *Chem. Phys.* **17**, 542 (1949).
182. Ruderman, I., Havens, W. W., Jr., Taylor, T. I., and Rainwater, L. J., *Phys. Rev.* **75**, 895 (1949); Ruderman, I., *ibid.* **76**, 1572 (1949).
183. Salmon, L., *Nuclear Sci. Abstr.* **7**, 520 (1953).
184. Schenck, J., *Nature* **171**, 518 (1953).
185. Schmeiser, K., and Jerchel, D., *Angew. Chem.* **65**, 490 (1953).
186. Schorr, M., and Torney, F., *Phys. Rev.* **80**, 474 (1950).
187. Schultz, H. L., and Wadey, W. G., *Rev. Sci. Instr.* **22**, 383 (1951).
188. Segre, E., ed., "Experimental Nuclear Physics," Vol. II, Part VII. Wiley, New York, 1953.

189. Selove, W., *Phys. Rev.* **76**, 187 (1949).
190. Selove, W., *Phys. Rev.* **84**, 869 (1951); *Rev. Sci. Instr.* **23**, 350 (1952).
191. Senftle, F. E., and Leavitt, W. Z., *Nucleonics* **6**, No. 5, 54 (1950).
192. Seyfang, A. P., *Analyst* **80**, 74 (1955).
193. Seyfang, A. P., and Smales, A. A., *Analyst* **78**, 395 (1953).
194. Shull, C. G., and Wilkinson, M. K., *Revs. Mod. Phys.* **25**, 100 (1953).
195. Seidel, F., Hughes, D. J., Palevsky, H., Levin, J., Kato, W., and Sjöstrand, N. J., *Phys. Rev.* **95**, 476 (1954).
196. Siegbahn, K., ed., "Beta- and Gamma-Ray Spectroscopy." Interscience, New York, 1955.
197. Smales, A. A., *Analyst* **77**, 152 (1952).
198. Smales, A. A., *Ann. Reports on Progr. Chem. Soc. London* **46**, 285 (1949).
199. Smales, A. A., *Atomics* **4** (3), 55 (1953).
200. Smales, A. A., and Brown, L. O., *Chemistry & Industry*, p. 441 (1950).
201. Smales, A. A., and Brown, L. O., *Nuclear Sci. Abstr.* **4**, 3404 (1950).
202. Smales, A. A., and Loveridge, B. A., *Anal. Chim. Acta* **13**, 566 (1955).
203. Smales, A. A., and Pate, B. D., *Anal. Chem.* **24**, 717 (1952).
204. Smales, A. A., and Pate, B. D., *Analyst* **77**, 188 (1952).
205. Smales, A. A., and Pate, B. D., *Analyst* **77**, 196 (1952).
206. Smales, A. A., and Salmon, L., *Analyst* **80**, 37 (1955).
207. Smales, A. A., and Wiseman, J. D. H., *Nature* **175**, 464 (1955).
208. Smith, E. C., Gibbons, J. H., Good, W. M., Neiler, J. H., and Banta, H. E., *Bull. Am. Phys. Soc.* **1**, (II), 71 (1956).
209. Smith, R. R., Dissertation, Columbia University, 1953.
210. Smith, R. R., Taylor, T. I., and Havens, W. W., Jr. *Phys. Rev.* **88**, 163 (1952); Smith, R. R., Dissertation, Columbia University, 1953.
211. Smith, V. N., and Otvos, J. W., *Anal. Chem.* **26**, 359 (1954).
212. Stewart, D. C., and Bently, W. C., *Science* **120**, 50 (1954).
213. Süe, M. P., *Bull. soc. chim. France*, D9 (1951).
214. Swank, R. K., *Ann. Revs. Nuclear Sci.* **4**, 111 (1954).
215. Szekely, G., *Anal. Chem.* **26**, 1500 (1954).
216. Taylor, T. I., and Havens, W. W., Jr., *Nucleonics* **5**, No. 6, 4, 1949; **6**, No. 2, 66 (1950); **6**, No. 4, 54 (1950); *Science* **114**, 341 (1951).
217. Taylor, T. I., Anderson, R. H., and Havens, W. W., Jr., *Science* **114**, 341 (1951).
218. Taylor, T. I., Smith, R. R., and Havens, W. W., Jr., *Science* **102**, 789 (1954).
219. Tittle, C. W., *Nucleonics* **8**, No. 6, 5 (1951); **9**, No. 1, 60 (1951).
220. Tobias, C. A., and Dunn, R. W., *Science* **109**, 109 (1949).
221. Upson, U. L., Connally, R. E., and Lebouef, M. B., *Nucleonics* **13**, No. 4, 39 (1955).
222. Wagner, C. D., and Guinn, V. P., *Nucleonics* **13**, No. 10, 56 (1955).
223. Walker, R., AEC Report MDDC-362 (1946).
223a. Wänke, H., and Monse, E. U., *Z. Naturforsch.* **10a**, 667 (1955).
224. Wattenberg, A., *Phys. Rev.* **71**, 497 (1947); Nuclear Science Series, Preliminary Report No. 6. National Research Council, Washington, D.C., 1949.
225. Way, K., *et al. Nat. Bur. Standards Circ.* **No. 499** (1950).
226. Wiblin, E. R., "Proceedings of the International Conference on Peaceful Uses of Atomic Energy," Vol. 4, p. 35. United Nations, New York, 1956.
227. Winteringham, F. P. W., *Analyst* **75**, 627 (1950).
228. Wollan, E. O., and Shull, C. G., *Nucleonics* **3**, No. 1, 8 (1948); **3**, No. 2, 17 (1948).
229. Zinn, W. H., *Phys. Rev.* **70**, 102 (1946); **71** 752 (1947).

# Author Index

Numbers in parentheses are reference numbers and are included to assist in locating references when the authors' names are not mentioned in the text. Numbers in italics indicate the page on which the reference is listed.

## A

Adams, R. N., 100(13), *104*
Adams, T. J., 82(8), *104*
Adler, I., 397(1), *398*
Agar, H. D., 37, 60(111), *68*
Albert, P., 583, 595(1), *616*
Albert, R. D., 473(62), *617*
Alder, B. J., 353(94), *381*
Aldrich, T., 72(59), *105*
Alkemade, C. T. J., 230(126), 231(2), 233(126), 240(2, 126), 246(126), 253(126), 254(126), 262(1), 262(126), 267(126), 268(126), 269(126), 270 (126), *276*, *279*
Almqvist, E., 472(2), *616*
Alperovitch, E., 591, 595(3), *616*
Alpert, D., 147(1), *181*
Alsberg, C. L., 203(10), *216*
Alvarez, L. W., 470(4), *616*
Ambrose, D., 10, *27*
Amend, G., 35(106), 55(106), *68*
Anderson, H. L., 452(5), 537(6), *616*
Anderson, K., 115(12), 118, 126(2), 130(20), *133*
Anderson, R. E., 588, 590, 595(145), *619*
Anderson, R. H., 532, 535, 539(217), 584, *616*, *621*
Anderson, W. A., 354(1, 2), 358(1), *379*
Andrew, E. R., 305(4), 308(4), 309(4), 315(5), 331(4), 336(4), 338(4), 339(4), 343(4), 344(3), *379*
Aqvist, S., 57(40), *66*
Arditti, R., 124, 126(3), *133*
Arley, N., 465(9), *616*
Arnold, J. T., 350(6), 353(7), 354(1, 2, 7), 358(1), 367(7), *379*
Arrhenius, S., 30(1), *65*
Ashton, G. C., 62(38), *66*

Ashworth, F., 138(2), 153, 171, *181*
Atchison, G. L., 584, 594, 595(10, 11), *616*
Aten, A. H. W., Jr., 580, 595(12), *616*
Attoe, O. J., 254(121), 270(121), 272(121), 275(5, 121), *276*, *279*
Axelrod, J. N., 397(1), *398*

## B

Baas, G., 136(50), 153(50), *182*
Bacher, R. F., 460(18), 464(18), 470(14), 484(18), *616*
Bacon, G. E., 458(13), 616(13), *616*
Bader, A. L., 364(8), *379*
Bahadur, K., 176(49c), 177(49c), *182*
Bailey, J. R., 444, *445*
Baily, E. D., 200(1), *216*
Baker, C. P., 470(14), *616*
Bancie-Grillot, M., 586, 595(15), *616*
Banerjee, M. K., 322(9), *379*
Banta, H. E., 472(208), *621*
Baptist, V. H., 50(14), *66*
Barband, J., 584, 595(75), *618*
Barker, G. C., 83, 84(1), *104*
Barnes, G., 143(2a), *181*
Barnes, R. B., 221, 223(7, 18), 225(6), 227(6), 229(6), 230(18), 232(6, 18), 239(6), 246(7), 249(6, 18), 250, 252 (18), 254(6, 18), 258(6, 18), 262(6, 18), 265(6, 18), 266(18), 268(6), 271 (18), 273(7), *276*, *277*
Barnett, A. J. G., 60(1a), *65*
Barnett, J. E., 60(2), *65*
Barnett, P. R., 202(3, 7), *216*
Barschel, R. P., 231(31), 262(31), 263(31), *277*
Batchelor, T. M., 221(97), 249(97), 250(97), 255(97), 262(97), 263(97), 266(97), 273(97), *279*

623

## Subject Index

### A

Accelerators in neutron spectroscopy, 470

Acetate ion separation by electrochromatography, 63

Acetylenes, separation by gas chromatography, 22

Acids, generation by coulometry, 100

Activated carbon as adsorbent in gas chromatography, 14

Activation analysis, chemical separation problems, 564
comparative method, 562
sensitivity, 579

Adenosine diphosphate separation by electrochromatography, 59

Adenosine monophosphate separation by electrochromatography, 58

Adenosine triphosphate separation by electrochromatography, 59

Adsorption in electrochromatography, 34
isotherms from displacement gas chromatography, 26
monitoring by high frequency analysis, 121

Agar carrier in electrochromatography, 30, 35

Alanine in electrochromatography, 52, 53

Albumin separation by electrochromatography, 30

Alcohols, separation by gas chromatography, 9

Alkaline earths, analysis by flame photometry, 273

Alkaloid separation by electrochromatography, 62

Alloys, determination by fluorescent X-ray analysis, 394

Aluminum radiation quenching, 263
separation by electrochromatography, 63

Amanitins, separation by electrochromatography, 53

Amines, separation by gas chromatography, 8, 9, 14, 17

Amino acids, determination by retention analysis, 50
separation by electrochromatography, 30, 35, 51

Aminobutyric acid in electrochromatography, 52

Ammonia, isotopic analysis by microwave spectroscopy, 292

Amperometric titration, 94

Amyl alcohol detection by gas chromatography, 11

Amylase separation by electrochromatography, 55

Analytical distillation, 401
high temperature distillation, 428
low temperature distillation, 419
theory, 406

Anion effect on flame emission, 265

Anodic stripping, 103

Argentimetric titration in high frequency analysis, 130

Arginine in electrochromatography, 52

Aromatics, determination by high frequency analysis, 131
separation by gas chromatography, 8

Asbestos fiber support in electrochromatography, 35

Aspartic acid in electrochromatography, 52, 53

Atomizers, discharge type, 237
reflux, 242
total consumption, 240

Azeotrope, 409

### B

Back scattering in activation analysis, 551

Barn, definition, 455

Barium separation by electrochromatography, 30

Barium suppression of radiation, 263

# PHYSICAL METHODS IN CHEMICAL ANALYSIS

## VOLUME III